THERMOANALYTICAL
METHODS OF
INVESTIGATION

THERMOANALYTICAL METHODS OF INVESTIGATION

By Paul D. Garn

DEPARTMENT OF CHEMISTRY
THE UNIVERSITY OF AKRON
AKRON, OHIO

1965

ACADEMIC PRESS   New York · London

ACADEMIC PRESS INC.
111 Fifth Avenue, New York, New York 10003

United Kingdom Edition published by
ACADEMIC PRESS INC. (LONDON) LTD.
Berkeley Square House, London W.1

LIBRARY OF CONGRESS CATALOG CARD NUMBER: 65-18426

PRINTED IN THE UNITED STATES OF AMERICA

Preface

Although the art of differential thermal analysis has reached a maturity that warrants a detailed and critical examination of the experimental methods used, the current literature still reveals a lack of knowledge of such basic considerations as heat transfer and atmospheric effects.

This monograph provides extensive discussions of the important parameters used in differential thermal analysis, thermogravimetric analysis, and related fields. It is designed principally for the research worker who finds, or has reason to believe, that one or more of the thermoanalytical techniques may prove useful to him. Furthermore, it will be of great aid to those who have to purchase an instrument and are not familiar with its many advantages and disadvantages. Finally, for the specialist in the techniques of thermal analysis, it provides a comprehensive discussion of design features which will enable him to construct an instrument suitable for his purposes.

The many variables affecting the course of a change in state, and hence the appearance of the thermogram, are considered. Examples from the literature are cited to demonstrate the merits or demerits of particular methods. These range from the rather prosaic effects of dilution or heating rate to the disordering effects of radioactive decay. A few examples are cited only to illustrate the range of applicability of the techniques.

Most of the parameters are discussed stressing particularly the relation to differential thermal analysis, but nearly all of them will affect thermogravimetric analysis, electrical resistance, dilatometric, or other measurements since they affect the course of the thermally induced process.

The general topic of thermoanalytical investigations is truly interdisciplinary, being useful in the earth sciences of geology, mineralogy, and oceanography; the natural sciences, notably metallurgy, chemistry, and ceramics; biological sciences such as botany and agronomy; and in chemical and food processing, and medical and forensic technology.

This work is concerned with the behavior of the sample material and the effects of the treatment to which it is subjected. The type of apparatus used will influence the behavior of the sample because of its direct effect on the treatment of the sample, thus discussions of types of apparatus are necessary. Since the commercial apparatus of today may not be available even a year from now, an aggregation of photographs of apparatuses is not offered; in fact, specific descriptions are avoided. If, for example, one of the features claimed for an apparatus is the small sample needed, the advantages and disadvantages of small samples can easily be reviewed. Hence the discussion is pertinent to the particular advantage claimed for the apparatus.

This monograph was written almost entirely while I was employed at the Bell Telephone Laboratories, Murray Hill, New Jersey. The concentration on techniques rather than on data of immediate and commercial interest would not have been possible at many industrial laboratories. The library, drafting shop, and stenographic services provided so liberally by the Bell Telephone Laboratories brought the preparation of this monograph within the realm of possibility to a working chemist.

For the background training and experience which made this work possible, I am indebted to the late Dr. William M. MacNevin, my preceptor at The Ohio State University, and to Dr. Wilfred E. Campbell, formerly of Bell Telephone Laboratories. For their helpful discussions and reviews of substantial parts of the manuscript I am grateful to Drs. Ralph Hansen and Patrick Gallagher, both of Bell Telephone Laboratories, and to Mr. Emlyn Rowland, then of Leeds and Northrup Co. For his major contribution in criticizing the entire manuscript, I am especially thankful to Dr. Robert Bohon of 3M Company. Because of his careful examination of this book, many passages that were clear to me are now also clear to the reader; he also caught errors of omission and transcription. I should also like to thank, for their helpful discussions, Drs. John Lundberg and John McChesney of Bell Telephone Laboratories and Dr. H. James Harwood of The University of Akron.

To Polly, my beloved wife, and to our children, Michael and David, I am grateful for their patience with my almost continual absence, evenings and weekends, for a couple of years.

Akron, Ohio
October, 1965

PAUL D. GARN

Contents

Chapter I

Changes in State on Heating

Chapter II

Differential Thermal Analysis

Chapter III

Operational Parameters

Chapter IV

Apparatus for Differential Thermal Analysis

Chapter V

Evaluation of Differential Thermal Analysis Curves

Chapter VI

Kinetics

Chapter VII

Atmosphere Control

Chapter VIII

Special Techniques

Chapter IX

Thermogravimetric Analysis

Chapter X

Thermogravimetric Apparatus

Chapter XI

Simultaneous Measurements

Chapter XVI

Miscellaneous Apparatus and Information

Chapter XVII

Apparatus Design

Appendix I

Appendix II

Calibration Data

Appendix III

Acknowledgments

The author is deeply grateful to Bell Telephone Laboratories, Incorporated for releasing the previously unpublished data contained herein and for providing him with drafting, stenographic, and library services during the preparation of most of this book.

The author acknowledges with thanks the use of published data from a number of journals and other publications. He is grateful to the following publishers and commercial or scientific organizations for permission to use the listed figures:

American Ceramic Society (*Journal* and *Bulletin*)—II-6, 7, 9, 16; III-3, 11, 17, 18; IV-11; V-4, 5, 7, 8; VI-4, 5, 6, 7, 8, 9; VII-4, 18; VIII-11, 12, 13, 29; X-6; XI-10; XII-4, 10, 11, 12, 17;
American Journal of Science—III-4, 5, 6; IV-8.
American Mineralogist—I-9; II-14, 15, 19, 20, 21, 22; III-25, 27; IV-5, 6, 7, 18; V-9, 12, 15; VII-3, 9; XIII-5, 8.
Analytica Chimica Acta—I-7; VI-15.
Analytical Chemistry—II-23; III-7, 10, 15, 19, 20, 21; IV-2, 10, 12, 13, 21, 22, 23, 24, 28, 29, 30, 31; V-19, 20, 21, 22; VI-10, 11, 12, 13; VII-1, 2, 5, 13, 16, 28; VIII-17, 18, 19, 25, 26, 30, 31, 32; IX-1, 2, 4, 8, 9, 10, 11, 14; X-2, 3, 5, 7, 12, 13, 14, 15; XI-1, 11, 12, 13, 14, 15, 16; XII-7, 8; XIII-3, 4, 16, 17, 19; XIV-2, 3, 4, 5, 11, 12, 13, 14, 15, 18, 19, 20, 21, 22, 23, 24; XVI-3; XVII-4.
Berichte der Deutschen Keramischen Gesellschaft—VIII-23, 24.
Brennstoff-Chemie—XI-9.
Bulletin Societé Chimie de France—VII-8, 9, 10.
Bulletin Societé Française Ceramique—X-19, 20.
Bulletin Societé Minéralogie et Cristallographie Française—XI-5, 6, 7.
Canadian Journal of Chemistry—X-9, 10, 16, 17; XIII-12, 18.
Clay Mineralogy—V-3.
Economic Geology—XV-6.
Fuel—VIII-14, 16.
Geologie e Mijnbouw—IV-19; V-16, 17.
Journal of Applied Chemistry—III-30.
Journal of Applied Polymer Science—II-18; V-23, 24; XII-5, 6; XV-7.
Journal of Chemical Education—X-11.

Journal of Inorganic and Nuclear Chemistry—XI-2.
Journal of Less-Common Metals—IV-33.
Journal of Pharmaceutical Science—I-11; XII-13.
Journal of Polymer Science—XIII-2, 13.
Journal of Scientific Instruments—X-8; XII-2; XVI-5.
Journal of the American Chemical Society—VI-1, 2; XIII-6, 7.
Leeds and Northrup Co.—XVI-1.
Materials Research Standard—VII-25, 26.
Microchemical Journal—VIII-1.
Mineralogical Society (London)—II-24.
Nature—IX-5, 6; XIII-14, 15.
Physics and Chemistry of Glasses—II-25, 26; III-26.
Reviews of Scientific Instruments—VII-20; X-4; XII-14, 15, 16; XVII-6, 7.
Schaevitz Engineering Co.—XVI-7, 8.
Talanta—IX-3; XIV-6, 7, 8, 9, 10.
Textile Research Journal—XIII-1.
Transactions of the British Ceramic Society—IV-20, VI-3.
Transactions of the Metals Society, AIME—I-8.
Wiley (Interscience)—VIII-2, 3, 4, 5, 6, 7.

CHAPTER I

Changes in State on Heating

1.1. Introduction

An appropriate beginning for a monograph of this nature is an explanation of the need for it—a justification of its existence. The work deals mainly with differential thermal analysis and thermogravimetric analysis, since these are the most popular techniques. These are the best known and the most used and yet they have developed almost independently and certainly unsystematically. There have been reportorial works in differential thermal analysis and an array of data from thermogravimetric analysis. The need for this book stems from the inability of users of orthodox techniques in either field to obtain data that can be generally related unequivocally to the data obtained with the same material but using a different apparatus, or to obtain data by differential thermal analysis which can be generally related unequivocally to thermogravimetric data obtained even by the same person on the same material.

In 1952, MacKenzie and Farquharson (M6) reported some results of differential thermal analysis studies of standard mineral specimens by a number of observers—with no attempt to control the type of apparatus used by each. The results are disturbing. Curves obtained by MacKenzie on the standard minerals are shown in Fig. I-1. Since clay mineralogists

1

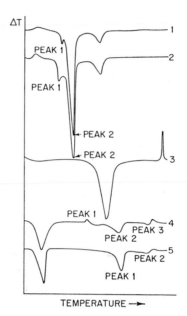

Fɪɢ. I-1. Thermograms for the *standard* minerals reported by MacKenzie and
Farquharson (M6). The minerals are: 1, bauxite; 2, bayerite; 3, kaolinite; 4, Mis-
sissippi bentonite; and 5, Wyoming bentonite.

Specimens of each material were sent to each participant in the study.

generally use peak temperatures as comparison points MacKenzie and
Farquharson showed the results in this manner. They found that for the
same peak various observers reported temperatures varying by as much
as 100°C!

Fɪɢ. I-2. Distribution of peak temperatures as reported by MacKenzie and Farquharson (M6). The classes of apparatus having sufficient members to warrant group-
ing are:

	A	B	C	D	E	F
Type of Specimen Holder:	Metal	Metal	Metal	Ceramic	Ceramic	Metal
Position of Temperature Thermocouple:	Inert	Specimen Holder	Inert	Inert	Various	Various
Sample weight (gm)	<1.0	<0.5	0.5–15	<1.0	—	—
Heating rate (°C/minute)	9–10	11–14	14–16	9–11	—	—

The range of data is related to the type of apparatus by the shading.

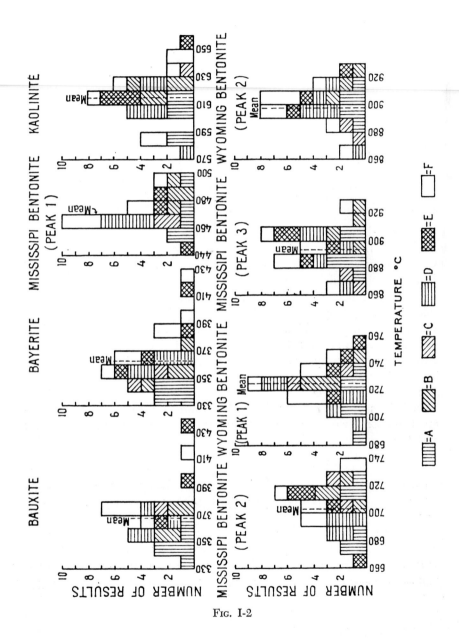

Fig. I-2

The uncorrected peak temperatures are shown for some common classes of apparatus in Fig. I-2. Bauxite (peak 2) not only yielded a 100°C range for all types of apparatus but even for the same general type yielded differences of 30–50°C not occasionally but routinely. This latter statement ignores the wider variations in the catch-all classes E and F. Even when (Fig. I-3) the data were corrected to yield the temperature of the sample rather than the block or inert material, the scatter was still serious indeed.

These results are not unusual. Kissinger (K29) examined the effect of heating rate—and, to a lesser degree, sample dimensions—on peak temperature and found variations of the same (100°C) magnitude. Webb and Heystek (W11) assembled a considerable array of thermal data on carbonates and offer a number of curves for chalybite (naturally occurring ferrous carbonate) as shown in Fig. I-4. Data of this kind will lead naturally and invariably to controversy among the various workers—each of whom can get, for a single mineral on his own apparatus, very reproducible curves which bear little resemblance to the equally reproducible curves obtained by someone else on *his* apparatus.

There must necessarily be an explanation for the divergent results which find their ways into the literature. Specimens do not customarily behave according to whim. Under the same thermodynamic conditions specimens of the same material can be expected to do the same things at the same temperature whether the measured variable is temperature, time, weight, length, electrical conductivity, thermal conductivity, or even color.

Deviations in any measured variable from time to time or from observer to observer or disagreement among the various measured variables must then be a result of the measuring technique. A principal objective of this book is to explore the reasons for the lack of agreement that does exist and provide some clarification. Another objective is to provide basic instruction in the principal tools common to thermal analysis and in the techniques of the principal methods of thermal analysis.

The literature appearing in the various scientific journals has been consulted and is cited freely to show the development of the art. Some technical literature is not reasonably accessible to the author and some available reports may have been overlooked. In addition, the author has deliberately omitted mere compilations of curves without interpretation and those reports which are obviously of no significance. The technical literature contains a liberal portion of data which may now be evaluated or reinterpreted in light of current knowledge. Since the errors were most frequently the result of inadequate knowledge of the atmosphere effect, a clear understanding of Chapter VII is essential.

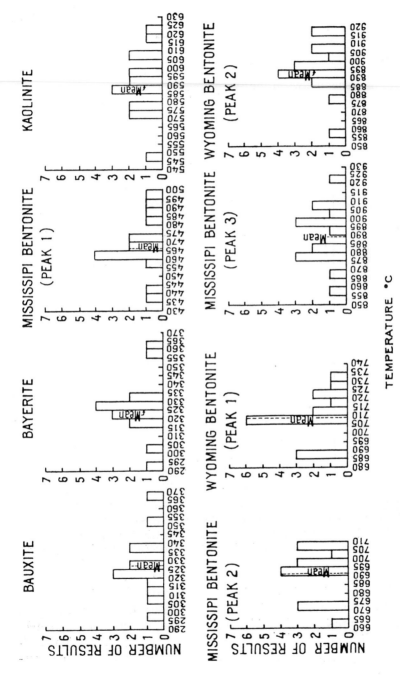

Fig. I-3. Distribution of data (5°C intervals) of *corrected peak temperatures* (M6).

If the several apparatus were equivalent the deviations would approach the error in temperature measurement, ca. 2–5°C.

1.2. Scope

The field of thermal analysis may be considered to comprise the following fields, as described:

(1) Differential thermal analysis—the measured variable is the temperature difference between the sample and a contiguous reference material, generally, as they are heated or cooled. Any change in state which takes place fairly rapidly can be detected. It is closely related to calorimetry.

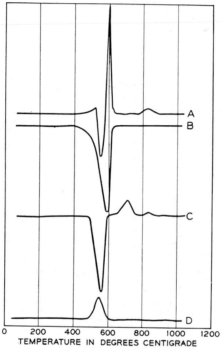

Fɪɢ. I-4. Thermograms of chalybite: A, in open sample holder; B, in nitrogen atmosphere; C, in sample holder with loosely fitting cover; D, fine-grained chalybite, loosely packed without cover. From Webb and Heystek (W11).

The same mineral will show grossly different thermograms depending on its surroundings.

(2) Thermogravimetric analysis—the measured variable is the change in weight of the sample as it is heated, cooled, or programmed through some temperature interval. Oxidation, reduction, dehydration, decomposition, volatilization, drying, reaction with the atmosphere, reaction yielding a volatile product, and similar occurrences are amenable to observation.

(3) Dilatometry—the measured variable is the size of the specimen, frequently as measured along a chosen axis but sometimes as measured by volume change. Generally, the information desired is gained directly, but the results also disclose phase changes.

(4) Microscopy—the observed variable may be the color, shape, optical rotation, or index of refraction of the sample. Changes occur from the same phenomena that may be detected by differential thermal analysis.

(5) X-ray diffraction—the measured variable is the intensity of a reflection. The quantity determined from the angles of the diffraction peaks is the crystal lattice spacing. Disappearance of the peak implies disappearance of the associated crystal structure.

(6) Calorimetry—the quantity measured may be the temperature of the sample or temperature change of its surroundings. The same effects as in differential thermal analysis are observable. Heats of reaction, heat capacities, and heats of transition can be measured with greater accuracy than in differential thermal analysis.

(7) Conductivity—the measured variable is the electrical resistance or some function of the resistance. The data yield a measure of the order of the sample, e.g., the degree of perfection of crystalline materials. The imperfections may be due to impurities as well as crystal defects.

(8) Effluence analysis—the measured variable may be the thermal conductivity, density, or volume of the gas given off while the sample is heated. Qualitative analysis of the decomposition products is an aid in interpreting or identifying the reaction taking place.

(9) Differential calorimetry—the measured variable is the temperature difference between the sample and the furnace. Occurrences detectable by differential thermal analysis can be detected by differential calorimetry.

The list could be continued by additions such as dielectric properties, in which the measured quantity will itself be of interest, or thermoelectric emf or magnetic properties, in which the data might be used principally for detection of a change.

The first two subjects will be covered in considerable detail; the remaining topics will be treated quite briefly as they relate to nonequilibrium thermal analysis, even though some are extensive fields in their own right. Note that these properties or occurrences are characteristic of the state of combination, i.e., the compound, rather than the elemental species comprising the compound.

1.3. Phenomena Detectable by Thermal Analysis

The several types of changes of state commonly observed by differential and other kinds of thermal analysis necessarily involve heat, whether or not this heat provides the means of detection and/or measurement of the change. Consider first the nondestructive changes in state.

Any material has a free energy content $F = H - TS$ where H is the heat content, T is the absolute temperature, and S is the entropy. Any system will tend to reach whichever of the possible states has the least free energy at the temperature of the system; hence, if a material is in a given crystalline structure and it is taken to a temperature at which another structure has a lower free energy, it will tend to change to the more stable structure. This transformation may be very slow (e.g., aragonite $\rightarrow$ calcite) but the tendency to transform is real. Consider a material heated from room temperature up to T_f as indicated in Fig. I-5.

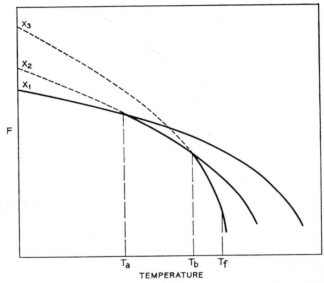

Fig. I-5. Representation of the free energies of three states of a material as functions of the temperature.

The thermodynamically stable state is that with the least free energy. Any other state will tend to change to the stable form.

The free energy of the stable state at room temperature changes with temperature indefinitely along the curve X_1. Let us consider, though, that there is another possible arrangement of the atoms of our sample and that the free energy of this arrangement follows the curve X_2. At T_a the two structures have the same free energy and can coexist but at higher temperatures the second structure has a lower free energy and is consequently more stable and the first structure will tend to disappear as the atoms or ions rearrange to form the second. This appearance of a more stable crystal structure may occur several times as the sample is heated, as at T_b, or the more stable state need not be another crystalline phase. The more stable state may be the liquid or vapor in which cases the material will tend to melt, boil, or sublime.

Generally, these reactions are rapid and a given state will not exist in detectable amounts outside the temperature limits prescribed. (Exceptions will be treated later.) The temperatures of coexistence of phases are variously transition, melting, boiling, or sublimation points.

These points of equal free energy are decidedly not without heat effects. The equality of F_{X_1} and F_{X_2} does not imply equality of H_{X_1} and H_{X_2} or S_{X_1} and S_{X_2}. These quantities normally change by measurable amounts. The change in H is of principal concern. This ΔH, $H_{X_2} - H_{X_1}$, is the measured or detected quantity in several techniques in thermal analysis.

Figure I-6 shows a reasonably typical variation of H with tempera-

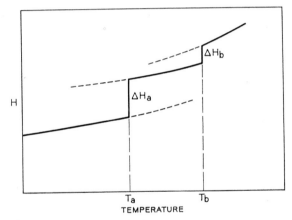

Fɪɢ. I-6. Representation of heat content vs temperature for a material undergoing two changes of state.

The heat content of any single form of a material increases continuously with temperature. At T_a or T_b additional heat must be supplied to change the material to the other form.

ture. This might be, for example, chemical reaction at a and melting at b; except for the relative values of ΔH_a and ΔH_b it might be a crystalline phase transformation and melting; it might be a simple melting and boiling. No matter, each involves a quantity of heat being added to the system at (ideally) a constant temperature and the occurrence can be detected and generally measured. Heats of solution and second-order phase transformations can also be measured and detected.

A change in weight may result from boiling, sublimation, dehydration, decomposition, combustion, oxidation, absorption, desorption, and perhaps a few other occurrences. Let us ignore the first two ordinary volatilizations as trivial cases. The latter two are special problems beyond the normal scope of thermal analysis; they are generally measured isothermally. Some of the apparatus and techniques are applicable.

The observations of weight changes immediately distinguish changes in (condensed) state from the occurrence listed above but this is a collateral use. The principal value of weight measurements is in the relative accuracy of the numbers obtained. It is not a good means of independent determination of the temperature of those occurrences, but is of immense value in determining what is occurring. Weight gain or loss (Fig. I-7) is directly related to the quantity of material reacting.

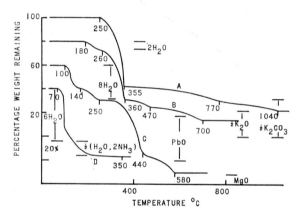

Fɪɢ. I-7. Thermal decomposition curves of metal diliturates and of magnesium ammonium phosphate hexahydrate: A, Potassium diliturate, 373.8 mg heated at 300°C/hour; B, Magnesium diliturate octahydrate, 109.5 mg heated at 65°C/hour; C, Lead diliturate dihydrate, 37.6 mg heated at 150°C/hour; D, Magnesium ammonium phosphate hexahydrate, 106.8 mg heated at 65°C/hour. From Berlin and Robinson (B47).

The several weight losses can be measured and these quantities related to the specific occurrences.

The measuring of dimensional changes on heating is of considerable significance in metallurgy, ceramics, physics, and glass-making. In those fields, the information desired is that which is determined, namely, how much does a given material expand (or contract) in a given direction when heated to a given temperature. A complete treatment of the subject is obviously beyond the scope of this book. The technique is treated herein as a means of gathering the information obtainable from anomalies or discontinuities in thermal expansion, e.g., detection of phase changes or sintering or determination of the state of oxidation or densification.

In the normal course of heating a solid crystalline material, the increasing thermal energy brings about lattice vibrations of increasing amplitude. In an isotropic crystal or in random assemblies of crystals the material expands. In single crystals of low symmetry the increasing amplitude of vibrations may be so directed that while the whole crystal grows in size it may actually contract along one axis. In any case, the expansion along the various axes of an anisotropic crystal can (like other properties) vary according to the direction of observation. Along with the ordinary expansion discontinuous changes in dimensions occur at phase transitions (see above). These discontinuous changes may be used to detect changes of state (Fig. I-8).

The changes in dimensions may be detected or determined by means other than direct measurement of the length or breadth of a specimen. Electron, or more commonly, X-ray diffraction techniques determine the geometric relationship of the nuclei within the crystal; hence, variation

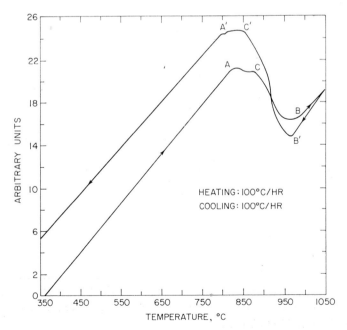

FIG. I-8. Thermal expansion of zirconium. From Intrater (I3).
The change in state ca. 850°C brings about a change in dimensions.

of the interplanar spacing may be used to measure the expansion along a given axis. Obviously, the disappearance or appearance of a reflection may be used to detect a discontinuous change in state, i.e., phase change, decomposition, etc. (Fig. I-9).

Most nonmetallic crystalline materials are poor conductors of electricity—their valence bands are filled and there is only an occasional electron in a conduction band. During a phase transformation, the transitory disorder in the crystal leads to nondiscrete energy levels and

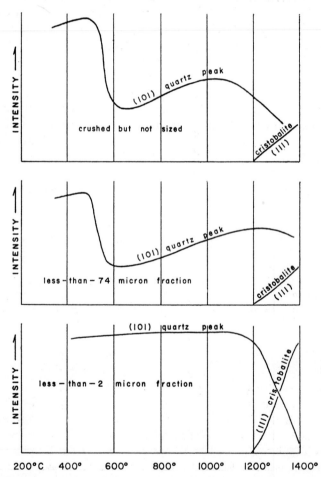

Fig. I-9. Intensity of quartz (101) X-ray diffraction peak as a function of temperature. From Wahl *et al.* (W2).

The change in arrangement of the nuclei changes the intensity of a given reflection, hence detecting the appearance or disappearance of a phase.

a diminished energy gap between valence bands and the lowest-lying conduction levels. While this disorder exists, the electrical conductivity of the specimen may be several orders of magnitude higher than for either of the ordered states (Fig. I-10).

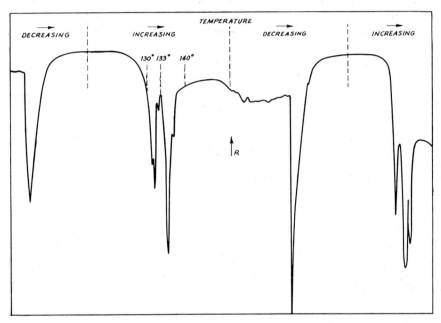

FIG. I-10. Electrical resistance variation with temperature in silver iodide. From Garn and Flaschen (G10).

As the specimen undergoes a transformation the electrical resistance decreases sharply.

Optical properties are easily observed at low temperatures. If the material is well-ordered and large enough so that single particles may be observed directly or microscopically, any discontinuous change may be observed quite without regard to the energy involved (Fig. I-11). Organic materials are especially good subjects since fair-sized molecules may find several ways to crystallize at various temperatures and a phase transformation may be little more than an unkinking of a carbon chain.

Analysis of the gaseous products of a reaction or decomposition will yield rather specific information concerning the nature of the reaction. The specific reaction can often be deduced from the temperature and the presence—or absence—of a particular product. Quantitative data may be obtained (see Chapter XIV).

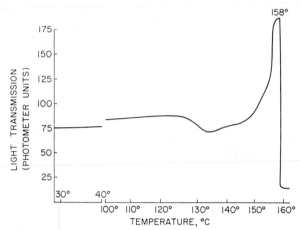

Fig. I-11. Transmission of polarized light as a function of temperature. From Reese *et al.* (R11).

A change in state will change the degree of rotation of the polarized light.

1.4. Dielectric Constant

The dielectric properties will vary as a result of decomposition or phase changes (Fig. I-12). Changes in symmetry due to a crystallographic transformation, possibly but not necessarily induced by a decomposition, may bring about a change in the rotational freedom of the molecule or ion so as to change the dielectric constant.

1.5. Thermoelectric Emf

The discontinuities in thermoelectric potentials with temperature may be used for the study of metals or alloys.

1.6. Magnetic Properties

Magnetic susceptibilities will change discontinuously for some materials for some changes of state and hence may be used to detect these changes.

1.7. Summary

Nearly any property of a material may be used to detect a change in state, but some are better than others. Several types of measurement will yield information of direct interest, e.g., dilatometry. If the purpose of the experiment is only to detect changes rather than to measure properties, any type of measurement suitable for the material can be used. Differential thermal analysis is most used because it is experimentally convenient and the occurrence of changes of state are quite apparent from the record. The interpretation is quite another matter.

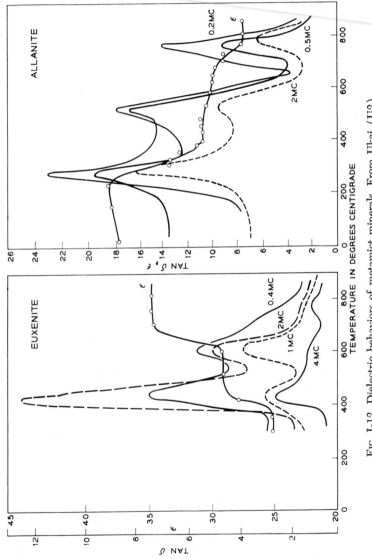

Fig. I-12. Dielectric behaviors of metamict minerals. From Ukai (U2).

The change in structure is reflected in a change of dielectric constant, ε, and in dissipation factor, tan δ.

CHAPTER II

Differential Thermal Analysis

2.1. Description

Differential thermal analysis is a technique by which thermal effects are measured, usually as the sample is heated or cooled. It is of use or assistance in quantitative and semiquantitative analysis. The basic technique is simple and straightforward; it is related, of course, to calorimetry.

Consider first an adiabatic calorimeter to which heat is being added at an essentially constant rate (Fig. II-1). The temperature of the calorimeter will increase also at an essentially constant rate. Now let us insert in the calorimeter a sample which undergoes a reaction requiring the absorption of heat. This time, as the calorimeter is heated, the temperature varies in a slightly different manner because of the heat capacity of the specimen; nevertheless the temperature increases in an approximately linear manner until the temperature of the reaction is reached (Fig. II-2). Since the sample is at a temperature at which it *can* undergo reaction, it *will* undergo reaction and a portion of the heat that otherwise would have raised the temperature of the calorimeter is instead absorbed by the sample without change of temperature. When the necessary heat, dictated by the nature of the material and the size of the sample, has been supplied, the additional heat again raises the temperature of the calorimeter. This additional quantity of heat that must be added without changing the temperature of the samples is specifically the heat of reaction and may be, of course, the heat of fusion, decomposition, or transition depending upon the nature of the reaction taking place.

The temperatures measured in calorimetry are often high and the quantities of interest are frequently the differences between large numbers. This type of measurement is inherently subject to error, since the uncertainties in the two separate temperature readings may approach the

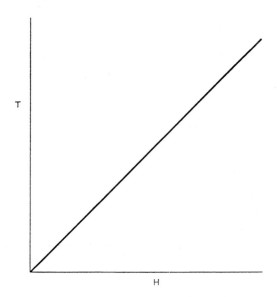

Fɪɢ. II-1. Temperature as a function of heat input for a calorimeter without a specimen.

As heat is added to the isolated system the temperature of the system rises approximately linearly.

same magnitude as the desired difference. This temperature that is measured, however, is basically a difference itself. It is most generally the difference between the furnace or calorimeter temperature and an ice bath temperature as measured with a thermocouple junction in the furnace opposing a reference junction immersed in an ice bath. Let us now take the reference junction out of the ice bath and put it in a second (empty) calorimeter and heat the two of them simultaneously. We have now a nearly zero signal since the temperature difference is small. Under ideal conditions the displacement is due only to the heat capacity of the sample. Now as the sample reaches the reaction temperature the sample begins to lag behind the reference material because a portion of the heat supply is required to carry out the reaction (Fig. II-3). When the reaction is complete a new, nearly constant signal is obtained. (This is the essence of differential calorimetry.) Subsequent reactions may be detected in a similar manner. Now, however, the magnitude of the signal imposes a possible limitation on the sensitivity of the method. So let us move the reference junction into the same calorimeter or furnace and

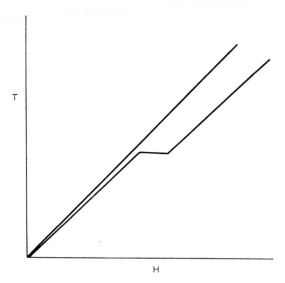

Fɪɢ. II-2. Temperature as a function of heat input for a calorimeter with a specimen.

The calorimeter temperature rises a bit more slowly because the specimen must be heated too. When the transformation temperature is reached an additional quantity of heat must be added to change the specimen to the new form.

permit heat to flow between the sample and reference thermocouples, but not too freely. In this case (Fig. II-4) as the sample is heated there is a very slight deviation of the signal from zero until the reaction temperature is reached. The reaction goes on as before and a temperature signal is obtained, but now, with the possibility of exchange of heat with the reference region, heat flows from the reference region to the sample region and the temperature of the sample again approaches that of the reference region. The subsequent reaction is detected in essentially the same manner. Now we are in position to use highly sensitive measurements since the temperature difference will return to near zero after the

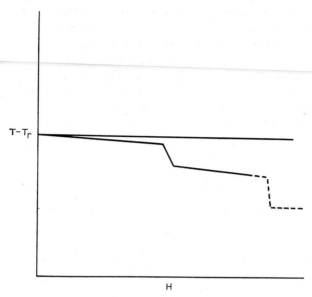

Fɪɢ. II-3. Temperature as a function of heat input for a calorimeter with a moving reference temperature.
Relatively small temperature differences need to be measured.

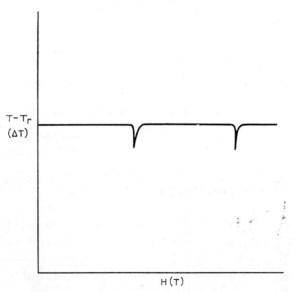

Fɪɢ. II-4. Differential thermal analysis.
By permitting a temperature difference to decay the system is ready to detect a subsequent thermal effect with a high degree of sensitivity.

completion of each reaction, so that detection of a subsequent reaction is not inhibited or prevented.

If, now, we call $T_r - T$, ΔT, and plot this function against the temperature rather than heat input, and if we put the sample thermocouple into the specimen and the reference thermocouple in a rather similar specimen of inert material, we have the essential ingredients of differential thermal analysis. We can, in fact, put the sample and the reference materials in a single block as in Fig. II-5 so that exchange of heat can be quite rapid. Chapter IV shows a variety of methods of containing the sample.

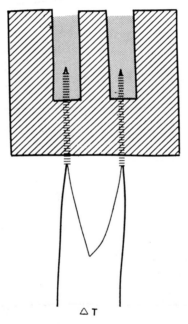

ΔT

Fig. II-5. Typical sample block showing placement and connection of thermocouples.

The thermocouples are connected in opposition, i.e., the temperature difference, ΔT, is measured between two like wires.

Differential thermal analysis, then, is generally performed by heating a sample and a reference material in rather close contiguity—permitting moderately free exchange of heat—and measuring the temperature difference between them. Here ends the resemblance between the apparatus used by the various observers.

Evaluation or use of data reported by other workers is difficult because of the many effects which can influence the peak height, temperature, or shape. Identification of a material by comparing temperatures derived from an experimental curve with temperatures cited in the literature would be foolhardy. MacKenzie (M4) and co-workers have compiled a punched-card index of differential thermal analysis data in which the two principal peaks of materials are listed as reported by each worker. The forty-four reports cited for kaolinite cover a range of 540–660°C for the dehydroxylation and 995–1060°C for the exotherm. Still another report (K31) gives 665°C as the peak temperature—at a heating rate of 20°C/minute. Similarly, the thirty-one reports (M4) on dolomite have a 740–820°C range for the dolomite decomposition and 830–1010°C for the subsequent calcite decomposition. It is quite apparent that, in the present state of the art, any use of data obtained by another observer must be done with considerable caution.

Before discussing the several operational parameters, an understanding of some rather basic topics is needed. The apparent simplicity of the technique leads the uninformed to assume that satisfactory data may be obtained, for example, by sticking a pair of thermocouples into a specimen and a reference and lighting a fire under them. The inevitable result of such work will be data which are not interpretable or relatable to other data, hence a subjective consequence—conviction by the user and others who see the data that the technique has no value.

First of all, we must be aware of the occurrences in a specimen being heated. This requires a nodding acquaintance with the heat-flow equation

$$\nabla^2 T = \frac{\rho c}{k} \frac{\partial T}{\partial t}$$

where the operator ∇ refers to the derivative with respect to the co-ordinate system chosen. In the case of unidirectional flow, the equation is simply

$$\frac{\partial^2 T}{\partial x^2} = \frac{\rho c}{k} \frac{\partial T}{\partial t}$$

where x is the distance from the reference point, ρ is the density, c is the heat capacity, k is the thermal conductivity, and $\partial T/\partial t$ is the rate of heating. The terms ρ, c, and k are often combined in a single term, a, the thermal diffusivity:

$$a = \frac{k}{\rho c}.$$

The various forms of the heat-flow equation apply to a homogeneous system; at a boundary of any sort there is a discontinuity beyond which another expression must be applied—with the appropriate new values of ρ c, or k. Boundaries will exist, for example, between the heater and furnace tube, between furnace tube and block, between block and specimen, and even between the parts of the specimen that have and have not undergone the thermal reaction being studied.

2.2. Sample Size and Geometry

Most users of differential thermal analysis agree that a proper shape for a sample is a cylinder heated, as symmetrically as possible, from the outside. The uniform approach of heat to the center permits the highest convenient symmetry and hence little disturbance of the peak shape due to irregularities of heat flow. Other shapes have been used (see Chapter III); many occasions will arise on which the cylinder may be impractical (see Chapter VIII).

There is a natural tendency among users of differential thermal analysis to attempt to work with smaller and smaller samples. This urge is obviously laudable (but see below); not only is the utility of the technique extended but also the errors inherent in the use of large samples are avoided or diminished.

The major problem in the use of large sample holders is the finite time required for an advancing temperature front to permeate the sample. Recall now that as a small particle is heated to a temperature at which it will undergo a phase transformation the increase in temperature will be continuous until the transition temperature is reached. The sample remains at that temperature while absorbing sufficient heat to undergo the transformation and then, and only then, it will pass heat onward to a particle further from the heat source. We may picture then a cross section of a cylinder containing a sample undergoing a phase transformation. A thermocouple is placed at the center of the cylinder. Hence at the time that the material at the edge of the sample begins its transformation, flow of heat to the center diminishes sharply. Since the reference thermocouple is continuing its increase in temperature a difference signal is immediately obtained. The rate of advance of the transition temperature front is governed by the rate of supply of heat to the sample and by the thermal diffusivity of the new phase. In any case a finite time is required A thin cylinder will require a shorter time for the reaction (Fig. III-16) to go to completion and, hence, the thermal deflection will occupy a shorter interval of temperature and consequently will be less likely to interfere with the detection of subsequent transformations or reactions. More than enough compensation for the diminished initial signal can be gained by electronic amplification.

The use of small specimens must be undertaken judiciously; however, the question immediately arises: is the sample representative of the whole? The present author has described techniques for the use of milligram quantities of samples, but he has also encountered irreproducibility (see Chapter VIII) for the reason cited. The use of small samples just for the sake of using small samples is nonsense; each problem ought to be considered separately and the technique chosen according to the needs of the problem.

2.3. The Behavior of a Specimen Undergoing a Transformation

Any specimen whose temperature is being raised by application of heat to the outside cannot possibly be at a uniform temperature; this should be obvious. Less obvious is the manner in which the temperature changes within the specimen as it undergoes a transition. Smyth's (S36) treatment, although a few simplifying assumptions were required, is the best treatment of which the present author is aware. The major criticism is the assumption that the density, specific heat, and thermal conductivity all remained constant.

Smyth chose to consider a pair of infinite slabs with the sample between. The distance from side to center could be subdivided mathematically into a number of slabs such that if the boundary conditions were known the temperature of each slab could be easily calculated. The progress of the reaction inward could then be followed.

Let us now restrict our discussion to the simplest system and later expand it to include some description of decompositions and such. We will concern ourselves with a reversible crystallographic phase transformation which is reasonably rapid, i.e., any typical transition. For such a system, the temperature uniquely describes the phase present except at precisely the transition temperature. Any particle at a temperature lower than this transition temperature will necessarily have the lower-temperature structure, while any above will equally certainly be in the high-temperature form. Let us now heat a specimen—along with a reference material—from below to above the transition temperature and let us form the materials in slabs heated from both sides so that we can use Smyth's figures. The reference material will assume some temperature gradient which will vary slowly with changes in thermal diffusivity so that the temperature of the center lags behind that of the wall (Fig. II-6a) by a nearly constant amount.

The specimen under observation must behave differently in the region of the transition or we would see no differential temperature. As the wall exceeds—slightly—the transition temperature the sample in contact with the wall transforms and then is able to continue to pass on heat to succeeding layers (Fig. II-6b). The high-temperature form will set up a

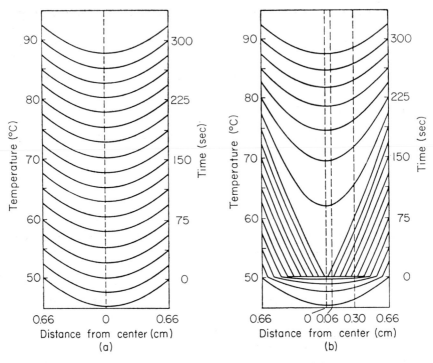

Distance from center (cm)
(a)

Distance from center (cm)
(b)

Fig. II-6a. Temperature distributions in the reference material at intervals of 18.75 sec. (S36).

The gradient at any point in the reference will assume a nearly constant value depending on the heating rate, the geometry, and the thermal diffusivity of the material.

Fig. II-6b. Temperature distributions in the test material at intervals of 18.75 sec. *There is a discontinuity in thermal gradient at the reaction front.*

(Note that the temperature gradient is not constant. For any short temperature range during steady temperature rise

$$\frac{\partial^2 T}{\partial x^2} = \text{constant}.$$

This is apparent from the obvious need for each segment to pass inward enough heat to supply *all* segments between it and the center. The amount of heat passed on is proportional to the temperature difference so a linearly varying temperature difference will give, under the conditions stated, a uniform change of temperature for each segment, i.e., a steady state.)

rather different gradient than that in the low-temperature form both because of a change in diffusivity and—more important—because of the
need to transport an additional quantity of heat. Assuming uniform conditions over the slab, a more-or-less discrete interface will move inward
from the surface toward the center. The transforming material acts as a
heat sink during the moment of transformation, but this sink is—in effect
—of infinite thinness so that the infinite heat capacity at the transition
temperature is reflected as a discontinuity in the temperature gradient
(Fig. II-7). The discontinuity is, of course, at the transition temperature.
The gradient in the high temperature form must obviously be higher than
in the low; it is the change in this latter gradient that is of particular
interest.

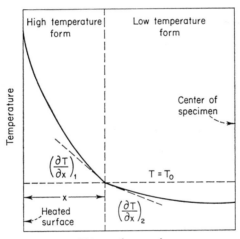

Fig. II-7. Temperature gradients close to boundary between low- and high-
temperature forms. From Smyth (S36).
*The reaction front appears as a moving boundary between the low- and high-
temperature forms.*

In effect, the center of the slab has seen, at a distance, a constantly
rising temperature which has caused a similar but delayed rise in its own
temperature.

At the start of the transition the center no longer sees the rising temperature but a constant temperature front advancing toward it from the
wall (Fig. II-8). The events outside this front influence the center only
by their influence on the movement of the front.

The temperature difference between the center and the front becomes smaller as time passes and because the movement of the front is slowed by its need to carry out the transformation the gradient inside the front can become very small. Eventually, the reaction front reaches the center, i.e., the center reaches the transition temperature, and this center is suddenly exposed to the relatively high temperature gradient. Since this temperature gradient is higher than that in the reference, the center be-

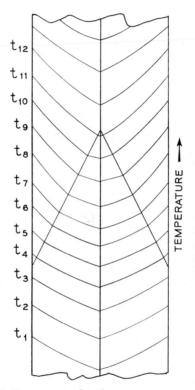

Fɪɢ. II-8. Temperature distribution at successive times.

The actual form of advance of the front at transition temperature, T, will probably not be linear. The relative diffusivities of the two forms will determine the shape.

gins to gain in temperature more rapidly than the center of the reference, decreasing the temperature lag. This event is, of course, the peak in the differential temperature. The return to a new steady state will be governed by the thermal diffusivity of the high-temperature form.

Now let us consider—qualitatively—the effect of geometry, the specific question being to what degree the discussion above pertains to the more common cylindrical sample cavity. The same general arguments hold, of course; the specimen will still experience a movement of a reaction front inward—this time from all directions perpendicular to the front.

The form of the operator is different, the expression now being

$$\frac{\partial^2 T}{\partial r^2} + \frac{1}{r}\frac{\partial T}{\partial r} = \text{constant}$$

with the same assumptions as before. Qualitatively, this means that near the center the heat is supplied noticeably faster than in the case of the slab, but this is rather obvious from inspection anyway. The result is a sharper peak; the general form will vary somewhat depending on the thermal diffusivities of the two forms.

The behavior of a material undergoing decomposition will be complicated by the transitory presence of reaction products; this will be discussed at greater length in Chapter VII.

The flow of a gas through the specimen will affect the appearance of the peak because it supplies a second heat transfer mechanism acting perpendicular to the conductive flow of heat. The influence of the gas flow will be highly dependent on (1) the sample material because of its thermal conductivity, heat capacity, density, and surface characteristics; (2) the particle size because of the area of contact between particles and the surface area available for heat exchange with the gas; (3) the flow rate because of the greater or lesser heat that the gas may bring or carry away; (4) the temperature because of the changing importance of conduction and radiation with temperature; and (5) the nature of the gas because of differences in heat capacity and thermal conductivity.

For many samples, the total effect is going to be small and will decrease with increasing temperature, but the user of dynamic atmospheres must be aware of the possibility of a significant error in unfavorable cases.

2.4. The Shape of the Differential Temperature Peak

Smyth's (S36) calculations also permitted description of the shape of the differential peak and the effect of the manner of plotting. [The reader must bear in mind that assumptions have been made (p. 23) to permit these computations.] For his slab specimens he obtains the plots of Fig. II-9a, b and c. Considering now the effect of the cylindrical heat flow the form can be modified somewhat. In essence, the first two plots are ΔT vs time and the third is ΔT vs temperature, so the first two are the same curve with a displacement equal to the temperature drop in the reference.

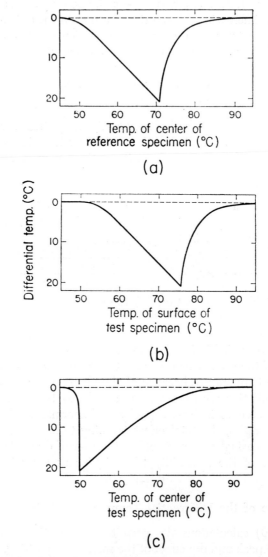

Fig. II-9. Calculated plots for a slab heated from both sides. (a) Differential temperature plotted against the temperature at the center of the reference material. (b) Differential temperature plotted against the surface temperature of the test or the reference sample. (c) Differential temperature plotted against the temperature at the center of the test specimen. From Smyth (S36).

These plots are based on assumed equalities of k, ρ, *and* c *for both low- and high-temperature forms.*

Note that there is no reason to expect a differential thermal analysis peak to be symmetrical; the conditions after the peak temperature is reached are quite different from the initial conditions. The latter part of the curve is a period of temperature equalization; its shape will depend on the thermal diffusivity of the high-temperature form of the material.

The curves are somewhat exaggerated. The difference signal is shown as increasing linearly with time (Fig. II-9a and b) during most of the approach to the peak. This is definitely not the general case in cylindrical cavities. He shows also a rapid approach by the center of the specimen (Fig. II-9c and Fig. II-6b) to the transition temperature and, apparently, a constant temperature for a couple of minutes while the transition goes to completion. This is unrealistic; the heat required to bring the center to the transition temperature must flow under the influence of a temperature gradient, implying that the temperature must be changing continually. While some part of the specimen is in the low-temperature form, the center can reach the transition temperature only asymptotically.

Experimentally, the peaks look like those of Figs. II-10 and II-11. The specimen was cycled automatically for several hours, giving the multiple

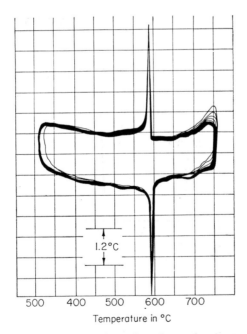

1.2°C

500   400   500   600   700

Temperature in °C

Fig. II-10. Repetitive differential thermal analysis of potassium sulfate in Type 310 stainless steel block; heating rate, 8°C/minute.
Both the peaks and the programming are highly reproducible.

trace shown in Fig. II-10. A time-based record was obtained simultaneously; the peaks in Fig. II-11 are a pair of these. Note in Fig. II-11 that there is no straight-line portion of the curve as the transition progresses; there is curvature at all points. The nearly straight portion has been used from time to time in empirical estimations of transition temperature, but no basis on which to expect a straight-line portion exists. After the peak the return to a base line is rapid because it is now limited only by the thermal diffusivity of the high-temperature form.

Figure II-10 contains ten cycles. The peak heights were determined from the time-based record of which Fig. II-11 is a portion. The base was

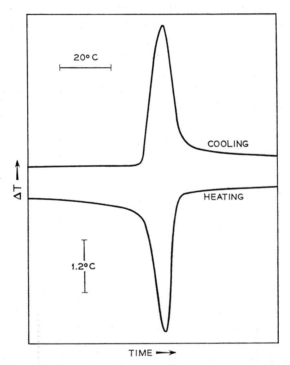

Fig. II-11. Differential thermal analysis curve for the potassium sulfate transition. *The differential temperature is plotted against time.*

chosen arbitrarily as the point of rapid departure from (on cooling) and approach to (on heating) the steady state. The peak height and the average and median deviations on heating were 2.70 inches, 0.022 inch, and 0.025 inch, respectively. Similarly, the cooling peak height and average and median deviations were 2.67 inches, 0.014 inch, and 0.015 inch, respectively. The root mean square deviations were, on heating, 0.030 and, on cooling, 0.022 inch, respectively. The root mean square deviations then are 1.1% on heating and 0.8% on cooling.

Exact matching of the heating and cooling peaks even on ideally reversible phase transformations would be rare. The differences in thermal properties between the high- and low-temperature forms are ordinarily great enough to cause noticeable differences. Consider the case in which there is a sizable increase in thermal diffusivity in the high-temperature form. On heating, the movement of the reaction front is aided by the existence of the high-diffusivity material between the front and the surface and the return to the base line is quick. On cooling the specimen, as the reaction front moves inward, it leaves behind it an increased barrier to flow of heat, so that the heat of transformation serves to delay the cooling of the inner regions. The return to the base line is also slowed because the heat must be lost by and through this lower-diffusivity material.

The plot in Fig. II-10 shows not only the reproducibility possible with good control equipment but also the significant points of measurement. Note that the peaks on heating and on cooling are at essentially the same temperature. Allowing for a small amount of supercooling, this is the proper result. The center is the hottest point during cooling, so its temperature depends on the rate at which heat is lost from the sample to the block and from the block to its environment.

The steady state that is set up is interrupted when the edge of the specimen reaches the transition temperature. As the transition front moves inward, the cooling of the center is slowed because the heat of transition must be carried away to permit the front to move. The slow approach of the center to the transition temperature results in a relatively steep indication on a ΔT vs T_{sample} plot. Actually, the peak temperature is the temperature at which the transition front has reached the center and is hence the transition temperature. The fact that the heating and cooling peaks do not agree may be attributed to the tendency of many materials to superheat or supercool. Potassium perchlorate appears to superheat rather more than most materials (Fig. II-12). The sharp departure from the base line on heating and the large displacement of the cooling—relative to the heating—curve indicate this. Heat conduction along the thermocouple may lead to a displacement, but this should be about the same on heating or cooling.

The reader must remember that the description thus far has been limited to phase transformations. The complicating features of decompositions will modify the appearance of the thermogram somewhat for reasons which will be pointed out after discussion of the atmosphere effect (Chapter VII).

2.5. Exothermal Reactions

Reversible phase changes are always endothermal; this must follow from the Mass Action Law, for if a reaction tended to give off heat as the material was heated, it would tend to raise the temperature of the substance and accelerate the reaction, and similarly the material on cooling would—at the start of the transformation—take up heat and again accelerate the change. The two phases could not coexist. It follows from this consideration that any phase change which gives off heat as the specimen is heated must be irreversible. There are several conditions which permit these exothermal effects.

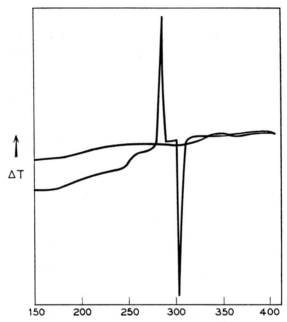

Fig. II-12. Differential thermal analysis curves for the potassium perchlorate transition. The differential temperature is plotted against the specimen temperature.
The lack of overlapping superheating and/or supercooling.

Chemical reaction is an obvious source of heat. Oxidations will ordinarily yield an exothermal peak; the special case of combustion invariably will.

Crystalline rearrangements are a common cause of exothermal effects; the prerequisite for such an event is the formation, by some means, of an unstable phase. The origin of the unstable phase will influence the thermal behavior so the ordinary causes must be examined; the thermal behavior will depend most on whether the unstable phase occurred by an act upon the specimen by an outside agency or by the customary behavior of the material.

In the former classification will fall quenching or distorting of the specimen; these two quite different acts have the same general effect. If a specimen is heated to such a temperature that a new phase is formed—one which is not stable at ordinary temperatures—and the specimen is chilled quickly, e.g., by dropping it in liquid nitrogen, it may not transform completely to the low-temperature form because the transformation proceeds slowly enough that the mobility of the ions drops essentially to zero before they can move to their proper location. The high-temperature form is "frozen-in"; it may persist indefinitely at room temperature.

Consider now the heat content plots in Fig. II-13 and bear in mind that (Fig. I-5) the free energy of this frozen-in phase is higher than that of the low-temperature form so the tendency to transform is always present. If the specimen is now heated, the probability of reversion to the lower state becomes greater because of the added vibrational energy. When the temperature becomes high enough, the ions are sufficiently mobile to regain the low-temperature form. As they drop into their

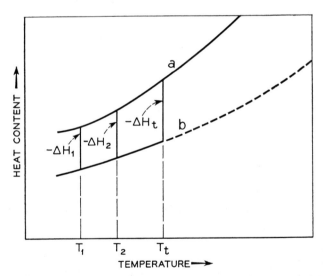

Fig. II-13. Heat content vs temperature for a material having a crystallographic phase transition.

If the material in the high-temperature form a is cooled rapidly far below the transition temperature, T_t, it may retain the a structure. If it is now heated it may give up its surplus energy below T_t and revert to the stable form b. The energy released will vary with the temperature at which the event occurs.

proper places, the excess energy must be given up in the form of heat; the amount of this heat will depend on the temperature at which the reversion takes place. Reversion at T_1 of Fig. II-13 would yield a heat effect of ΔH_1 while if the specimen remained in the high-temperature form until T_2 the heat effect would increase to ΔH_2. (In the general case, the heat capacities of the higher-temperature species are greater so $d\Delta H/dT$ is positive.) If, by some chance, the material did nothing prior to the transformation temperature, there would be no heat effect because the transformation would no longer be needed.

Note that a very thoroughly quenched specimen ought to persist in the high-temperature form to greater temperatures than a less well-quenched specimen because it has a regular structure; imperfections (see below) would tend to cause earlier reversion. Variations in quenching will cause variations in both temperature and magnitude of the thermal effect.

Any treatment of the specimen which distorts the lattice markedly may also produce exothermal effects (see Chapter III). The resulting structure will not have the long-range regularity of a well-quenched specimen; in fact, a fairly continuous variation from the ordered interior to the greatly distorted or even amorphous surface ought to occur. This high-energy condition, like the quenched state, can persist until the vibrational movement is enough to permit reversion to the ordered lattice. Since the reversion will tend to heat the specimen locally, the commencement of reversion may heat the next most disordered neighbors enough so that they in turn drop back, giving up their energy to the next, etc. The reversion could in this case appear as a well-defined exotherm. One may also postulate, however, a condition in which small region after small region gives up energy without inducing any reversion by neighbors. The observed effect in this latter case would be an apparent decrease in the heat capacity of the entire specimen. An example is brannerite.

Brannerite is a multiple oxide of titanium and uranium of rather variable composition. Apparently, during the time since its formation, the internal bombardment due to its own radioactive decay has rendered it amorphous—at least to the limits of detection by X-ray diffraction. A result of this occurrence is that various specimens of the mineral show different thermal effects and the thermal effects of most interest are exothermal (Fig. II-14); the additional energy taken up during the destruction of the original lattice is released as the various ions again fall into an ordered arrangement. Variations of these exothermal effects have been related by Kulp, Volchok, and Holland (K47) to the age of the mineral.

Adler and Puig (A1) showed that if specimens of brannerite from Cordoba, Spain, were heated at 550°C for varying periods the first exothermic reaction diminishes (Fig. II-15) while the second peak increases.

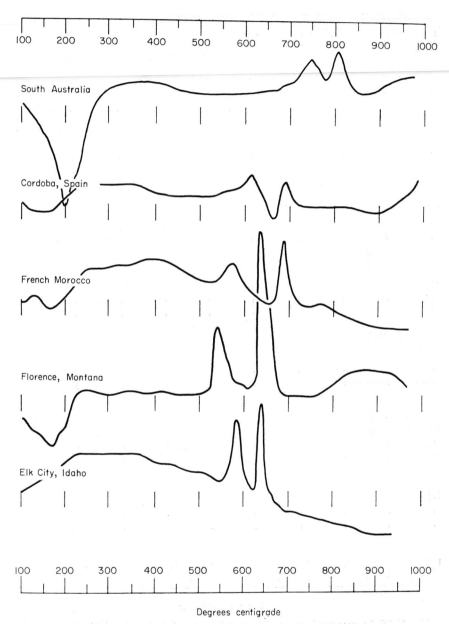

FIG. II-14. Thermal curves of brannerite. From Adler and Puig (A1).
The variable appearance of thermograms of the mineral is due partly to its varia-
ble composition but partly also to its history.

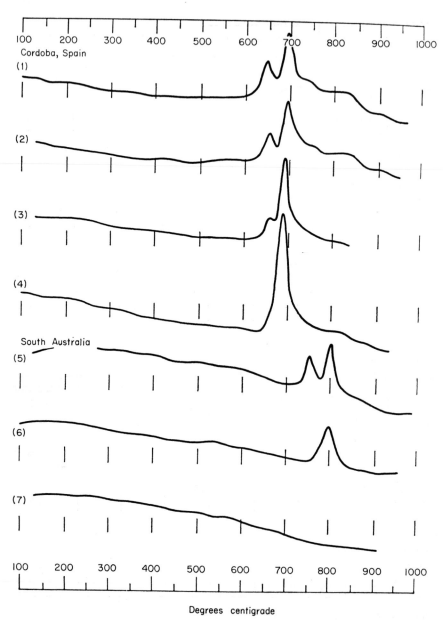

FIG. II-15. Progressive heating of brannerites: (1) 3 hours at 550°C; (2) 5 hours at 550°C; (3) 7 hours at 550°C; (4) 9 hours at 550°C; (5) 1 hour at 685°C; (6) 3 hours at 705°C; (7) 6 hours at 770°C. From Adler and Puig (A1). *The annealing permits reordering of the lattice.*

After 9 hours heating at 550°C, the first peak appears only as a barely discernible shoulder on the second peak. Adler and Puig pointed out that the area under this last peak was greater than the combined area under the two peaks for the untreated material. They attributed this increased area after the heat treatment to absorption of thermal energy from the furnace. This is, of course, a rather improbable event; the heating would tend to enable movement toward a *more* rather than a *less* stable state. A more likely explanation can be found by observing the shifting base line.

In the run on the unheated specimen there is a continual exothermic tendency. This may be only ordinary base line drift but it may also be principally—or at least substantially—reversion to a stable crystal structure. The appearance of peaks at reproducible temperatures implies the existence of metastable states. The two metastable states in the brannerite from Cordoba are clearly, even though not greatly, separated. The rather deep "valley" between them, ca 660°C, implies only that there are not many highly energetic particles or regions in the second (more stable) of the two metastable states. The heating at 550°C permits movement enough to allow the higher-energy state regions to drop to the lower-energy state as shown not only by the enhancement of the second peak at the expense of the first but also by the gradual shifting of the first peak to higher temperatures as the material gains in stability. The increase in area of the single peak over the sum of the two peaks is due not to any absorption of energy from the furnace but to the consolidation of the high-energy states into a fairly narrow energy band. The base line shift because of the annealing process not only increases the population of this band but also shifts the reference line giving a further increase in area.

Similarly, the heating at progressively higher temperatures (curves 5, 6, and 7 of Fig. II-15) moves the first peak to a somewhat higher temperature, then destroys it—with some gain by the second peak. Heating for several hours on a temperature (770°C) corresponding to a point on the return slope of the first peak in an unheated specimen completely removes the second peak because the ions can move around enough to revert to the ordered arrangement.

Quenching and distortion will have one important common characteristic: irreproducibility. Stable states are obviously more easily produced and repeated than unstable states; the apparently exact reproduction of a given state of quenching should be difficult and in most cases fortuitous. (Quenching of very sluggish systems, e.g., polymer melts, is very probably an exception to this last statement.)

The last major group of exothermal reactions comprises those reversions which occur as a part of the ordinary behavior of the specimen. In a number of cases, a reaction occurs such that it leaves a metastable product which sooner or later reverts to a stable form. Two well-known examples are the kaolin minerals and basic magnesium carbonate.

The kaolin minerals undergo two reactions in particular which distinguish them and which are used for identification: a dehydroxylation in the 500–700°C range and an exothermal rearrangement ca. 1000°C. The dehydroxylation of kaolinite yields a product generally referred to as *meta*-kaolinite; the structure and nature of it have been the subject of considerable discussion. Whatever the nature of this intermediate, it rearranges ca. 1000°C to mullite or γ-alumina plus cristobalite—possibly depending on the specimen, possibly on the experimental conditions during and after the dehydroxylation.

Similarly, the dehydroxylation-dehydration of basic magnesium carbonate apparently leaves the material with the original lattice even after several of the constituent particles have gone out of it. This is unstable, of course, so it soon collapses to the magnesium carbonate–magnesium oxide structure. In carbon dioxide atmospheres the collapse is a multistep process.

The outstanding feature of exothermal reactions of this last type is the reproducibility of the effect. Under ordinary experimentation, the initial reaction produces a repeatable intermediate state, so this intermediate state collapses or reacts at a repeatable temperature. These exothermal reactions can properly be used as part of an identification.

2.6. Second-Order Transitions

Second-order transitions involve a discontinuous change in heat capacity. Occurrence of such a transition during a differential thermal analysis run will result in a change in direction which, with small samples, will be discernibly angular.

The over-all shape of the thermal effect will depend on the type of material. Second-order transitions in inorganic materials such as Curie points involve an increase in heat capacity (or specific heat) followed by a sudden decrease (Fig. II-16). This bears a moderate resemblance to ordinary first-order transitions and the peaks will vary in appearance from being just small (because of no true heat of transition) peaks (Fig. II-17) down to mere discontinuities in the base line.

In contrast, polymeric materials will ordinarily show an increase (Fig. II-18) in specific heat at the glass transition temperature as motion of chain segments becomes possible.

Since there is no mechanism for additional absorption up to the time of the transition temperature, the appearance of the thermogram will be quite different from that of an inorganic specimen. If the angle is not

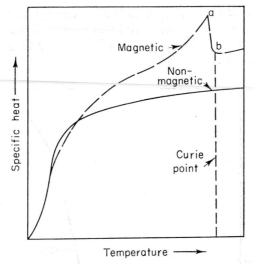

FIG. II-16. Specific heat for a magnetic and a nonmagnetic material. From Blum *et al.* (B57).

The heat capacity increases just prior to the Curie point but since no phase change occurs there is no ΔH of transition. The heat capacity simply drops off suddenly.

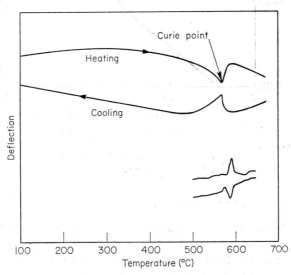

FIG. II-17. Differential thermal analysis curves of (upper) Blum *et al.* (B57) and (lower) Garn (G6).

The present author obtained the lower peaks using the sample holder of Fig. IV-15b.

well-defined and if the heating rate is high enough to obtain a sizable deflection the thermal effect observed will appear almost sigmoidal, but tending to return toward some value of ΔT lower than the peak (see Chapter V, Sec. 5.6).

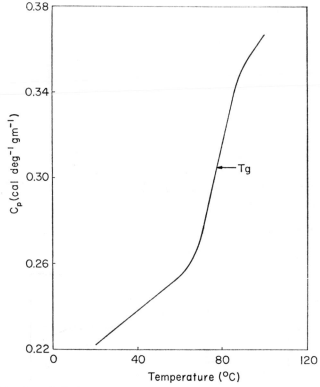

Fɪɢ. II-18. Specific heat vs temperature for a polymer about the glass transition. From Strella (S65).

For polymers, the specific heat increases at the glass transition because another mode of absorption of energy becomes possible.

2.7. Measurement of Temperature

At present, temperature measurement can be done sufficiently accurately by thermocouples and recording potentiometers. The accuracy will be dependent on the type of measuring system as described in Chapter XVII. Linearity—or approximate linearity—of recorder response to temperature requires considerable effort. The quantity usually recorded is the thermal emf, the nonlinearity of which varies considerably from one combination to another (see Fig. XVI-1). Thermocouples become contaminated and most other systems use comparison measurements so occasional calibration is worthwhile.

If the experimenter is not measuring the sample temperature directly —or indirectly by measuring the reference temperature—the system should be calibrated. The calibration will provide a measure of the temperature lag in the system or, more specifically, a measure of the temperature difference between the sample and the point of measurement. This calibration will be necessary for unusual experimental techniques which the investigator may concoct for use in special problems.

More sensitive determinations can be made by use of thermistors, but for most purposes at present such a high degree of sensitivity is not needed.

The ingenious work of Barshad (B9) is principally of historical importance now but the technique of temperature calibration will be of occasional interest and we shall have reason to examine some of his conclusions. Barshad contrived a temperature scale by using small quantities of known materials in the sample or reference wells to give a number of thermal effects (Fig. II-19) which then served as temperature indices. This procedure eliminated need for temperature-measuring apparatus, resulting in a comparatively economical apparatus. (The technique of differential thermal analysis has been developed to a level such that one would now use Barshad's procedure only for instruction or as a shift.)

The inclusion of these several materials is not necessarily a very serious handicap considering that only a few milligrams are used while his sample can hold well over ½ gm. of alumina. By including two or three of these salts (Fig. II-20), Barshad suggests, the operator may obtain a temperature scale if he has any justification for assuming that the heating rate is essentially linear. If the variation in the rate of heating is small, a few more points would help establish the scale.

In addition, Barshad devised a way to check the sensitivity of his differential thermocouple, galvanometer, and optical system at the temperature range of any reaction. He added a portion of a temperature indicator to some of the sample and placed this around the thermocouple (with undiluted sample above and below it). In the reference well he placed small quantities of other temperature indicators to bracket the peak as closely as possible. Since the first temperature indicator was chosen to give a thermal effect as near as possible to the maximum deflection of the sample peak, a rather large deflection already existed when this indicator showed its effect (Fig. II-20). By interpolation, the operator could determine the reference temperature at the time the indicator in the sample went through its change and, knowing the temperature at which the change took place for that indicator, he could ascertain the temperature difference, relate this to the magnitude of the deflection, and calculate the sensitivity. This was particularly necessary for any quantitative work because galvanometers are current-drawing instruments. For potentiometer recorders, this procedure would be less important. A major objection to the general technique is that it yields curves as given in Fig. II-20, where most of the effects are from the added materials. We can assume that Barshad also ran specimens with few or no indicators.

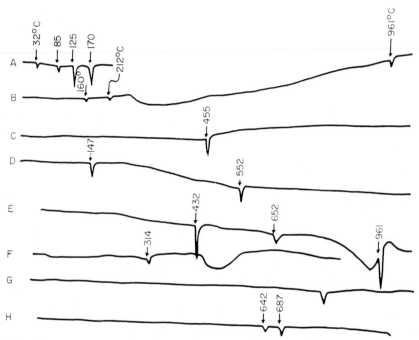

Fig. II-19. Differential thermal analyses curves of salts useful for temperature calibration. From Barshad (B9). The salts are: A, 10 mg NH_4NO_3; B, 3 mg $AgNO_3$; C, 2 mg AgCl; D, 15 mg AgI; E, 20 mg Ag_2SO_4; F, 2 mg $NaNO_3$; G, 2 mg NaCl; H, 3 mg Na_2MoO_4.

The salts were dispersed in 10 mg of Al_2O_3 and centered around the thermocouple. As many salts as the operator felt were needed could be incorporated into the reference.

Barshad's work showing the effect of distance from the thermocouple on the area of the peak has greater significance than has been noted. The rapid decrease (Table II-1) of the measured thermal effect of kaolin and the striking variation in the curves for ammonium nitrate (Fig. II-21) show that only the material near the thermocouple has a worthwhile effect on the thermocouple. The rest is of no value and need not exist.

Ergo, huge samples are of no merit; smaller samples will produce nearly the same effect. Note that 2–15 mg of temperature indicator is generally enough to give a sizable thermal effect. Let us confine the conclusion, however, to the phase transformations; other factors enter into decomposition reactions.

Note that the exothermic reaction shows a quite different peak height vs position relation from that of the phase changes. The rush of hot gases

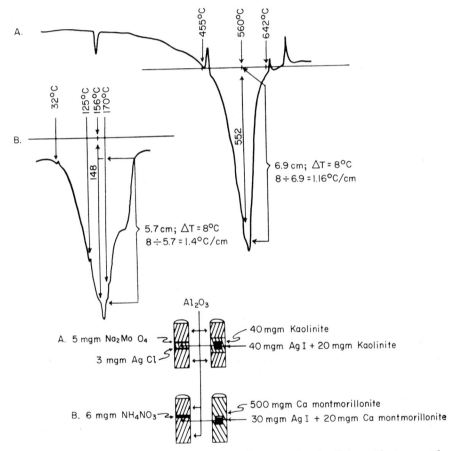

Fig. II-20. DTA curves of a Ca-montmorillonite and a kaolinite with impressed temperature reference points suitable for measuring the sensitivity of the DTA apparatus. The silver iodide peaks at 552°C in A and 148°C in B occur at reference temperatures of 560° and 156°C, respectively. The 8°C lag in each case gives a measure of the sensitivity of the recording system at that temperature. From Barshad (B9).

The variation is due to nonlinearity of thermal emf.

from the bottom past the thermocouple can be expected to show a noticeable thermal effect while a similar reaction at the top will push the hot gases into the surrounding atmosphere. Note further that the phase changes, unlike the decomposition, show a somewhat greater effect at the top. This is due to lack of symmetry; the material at the bottom is in contact with the metal block and can gain heat quickly while the material at the top has a corresponding exposure to the atmosphere. Since it cannot gain heat quickly the temperature will lag more and the deflection will be greater. Let us confine the conclusion, again, to the phase transformations.

TABLE II-1

PEAK AREA OF THE ENDOTHERMIC BREAK IN THE DIFFERENTIAL THERMAL ANALYSIS CURVES OF 50 MG OF KAOLINITE DISPERSED IN AN INCREASING VOLUME AND CENTERED AROUND THE THERMOCOUPLE

Volume of sample (cm³)	Peak area (cm²)
0.040	4.06
0.130	3.02
0.220	2.55
0.310	2.23
0.400	1.94
0.490	1.62

2.8. Effect of Dilution with an Inert Material

Specimens are often diluted with aluminum oxide or other inert material. In some cases, this dilution is to avoid such a high-temperature difference signal that it cannot be kept on the scale of the recording system; another reason is to try to match heat-transfer characteristics of specimen and reference, a third reason is to obtain a series of specimens of varying concentrations to enable quantitative estimation of the active material in another specimen. So long as the effect examined is a change in state rather than a decomposition the effect of dilution should be only the diminution of the peak area and height. The temperature of the change should be unaffected by dilution.

One hazard that can be avoided by dilution is sintering. Some powdered materials will shrink on heating to such a degree that the specimen must pull away from the sample holder. The heat-transfer changes and the base line will ordinarily shift.

If the purpose is to match heat-transfer characteristics substantial dilutions are required. If the material used as reference is used to dilute the sample, the effect of small additions is a diminution of both heat effect and base line signals so there is no gain. As the effect of dilution is nonlinear, the sample eventually assumes very nearly the same heat-transfer characteristics as the reference; since the signal from the heat effect is attenuated linearly, a gain in signal-to-noise ratio is achieved. Electronic amplification can restore the differential temperature peak to a readable level and with a lesser base line displacement.

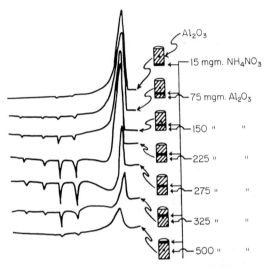

Fig. II-21. DTA curves of 15 mg of NH$_4$NO$_3$ placed at different positions with respect to the thermocouples. From Barshad (B9).

The maximum response is obtained when the thermocouple is in contact with the active material.

Dilution—as a technique for smoothing base lines—must be used with considerable caution, otherwise the experimenter will have difficulty reconciling his data to others. Again it is matter of diffusion of atmospheres in and out during decompositions, oxidations, and such. Compare the several curves of Fig. II-22 and compare these to Fig. I-4. At the low concentrations, the over-all reaction

$$2FeCO_3 + \tfrac{1}{2}O_2 \rightarrow Fe_2O_3 + 2CO_2$$

can proceed almost without hindrance because the diluting particles create additional diffusion paths for gases without a corresponding need for said gases. The oxygen can diffuse in rapidly enough to sustain the highly energetic oxidation. As the siderite concentration is increased the

nitrogen and freshly released carbon dioxide fill the open regions enough
to slow the oxidation briefly (curve H). At one-third siderite (curve G),
the carbonate decomposition, needing no gas supply, is proceeding
rapidly enough to balance the heat effect of the oxidation. As the concentration of siderite is increased, the ratio of inert-to-active material
decreases so the effect of diffusion is quite pronounced.

The over-all effect, then, is a change in shape of the curve so great
that there is no discernible relation between the more dilute and the
undiluted specimens.

We may conclude from this that samples which decompose may show
—upon dilution—a marked change of shape of their differential thermal
analysis peaks under static atmosphere conditions. Dynamic atmos-

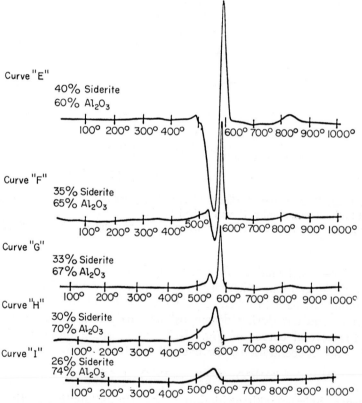

Fig. II-22. Differential thermal analyses of diluted specimens of siderite. From
Rowland and Jonas (R33).

*The shape of the "peak" changes markedly because of the changing access of
oxygen.*

pheres will maintain an essentially fixed concentration of each component about each particle so dilution should present no untoward results.

Barrall and Rogers (B7) show (Fig. II-23) that liquid diluents can be useful with solid specimens. In essence, the liquid surrounding the particles represses dehydration because the gaseous layer on the surface approaches the equivalent of an atmosphere of water vapor (see Chapter VII). When the water vapor pressure exceeds atmospheric, the decomposition proceeds. On Carborundum, the escape of water vapor permits a less sharp decomposition. Barrall and Rogers (B7) also pointed out that solubility of the specimen in the liquid diluent would depress the melting point, but this is to be expected.

The reason that dilution is effective in matching heat-transfer characteristics is that the surface properties, rather than bulk properties, present the greater resistance to flow of heat. Consider an aggregation of

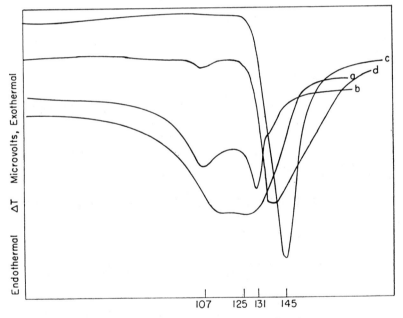

System Temperature, Degrees Centigrade

Fig. II-23. Differential thermograms of copper acetate and copper sulfate at a heating rate of 15°C per minute and a ΔT sensitivity of 200 μv per 3 inches. (a) Copper sulfate diluted to 6.5% with Carborundum; (b) Copper sulfate diluted to 20% with Nujol; (c) Copper acetate diluted to 20% with Nujol; (d) Copper acetate diluted to 6.9% with Carborundum. From Barrall and Rogers (B8).

The Nujol traps and retains the water until the vapor pressure approaches the ambient pressure.

particles of sample material, s, and of diluent, D, with the understanding that the diluent is the same material as the reference. The addition of a small portion of D to a specimen comprised previously only of s has little effect on the heat-transfer characteristics of the specimen because the great majority of contacts are still between particles of s.

As greater numbers of D replace s, the s–s contacts diminish, being replaced by s–D, contacts. In the region of predominance of s–D contacts the conduction of heat will be limited to something approximating the conductance of particles of the poorer conductor. At either end of the range, i.e., high s–s or D–D contacts, the conduction would approach that of particles of the pure material. The diluents generally used are not good conductors (in aggregations of particles); for this reason they are effective in the middle range. It is only necessary to diminish the s–s contacts to a relatively small fraction to approach fairly close to the heat conductance of the pure diluent and hence the reference.

2.9. Pretreatment of Specimens

Like most other questions in thermal analysis the preparation of a specimen for differential thermal analysis must be considered separately for each specimen or group of specimens. Some authors have found it expedient to premelt specimens to erase any effects of thermal history; others are interested specifically in this same thermal history. The experimentor may wish to compare a number of specimens "as received" and possibly again in some standard initial state.

In general, the decision will depend on the use to which the data will be put. If the study is of the intrinsic properties of pure material, pretreatment to eliminate effects of impurities and history would be proper; if the study is of the effect of some condition or act or if processing decisions depend on some details of the raw material, pretreatment is, in diagnostic jargon, contraindicated.

Some pretreatment to eliminate a material or to bring the specimen to the chosen standard initial state may be useful. The most frequently used pretreatments for eliminating interferences are acid-leaching to remove carbonates and hydrogen peroxide treatment to remove organic matter. The present author has used the acid-leaching (G12) but has no experience with the latter. Beech and Holdridge (B22), however, show an example (Fig. II-24) of the effect of such a treatment. Several clays have substantial amounts of organic matter because of the conditions of formation; ball clays are among them. Oxidation of the organic matter during differential thermal analysis in air or even degradation in nitrogen will throw considerable doubt on any data inferred from thermal effects below ca. 700°C so the pretreatment is imperative. The peroxidetrated clay shows thermal effects easily identified as typical of kandites.

Other kinds of clays are subject to variation of the loosely held water according to source and recent history. The variations cause substantial differences in the low-temperature portion of the thermogram; this in turn gives rise to doubt of identity of specimens. MacKenzie and Farquharson (M6) recommended a standard treatment for clays to bring them to a reproducible state of hydration. The clays are equilibrated over a saturated solution of magnesium nitrate.

The importance of knowing the starting material in solid-state reactions is shown rather clearly by some data of Wilburn and Thomasson

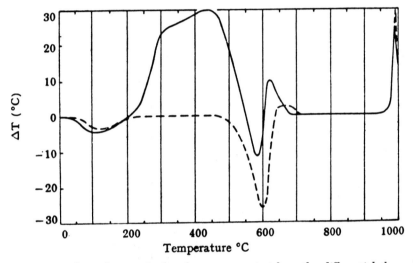

Fig. II-24. Effect of removal of carbonaceous material on the differential thermal curve of a black ball clay: ———, original clay; - - - -, clay after removal of carbonaceous matter. From Beech and Holdridge (B22).

The oxidation of the organic matter could easily obscure a reaction. Note that the peak ca. 600°C is shifted downward in the original clay due to dilution of the atmosphere.

(W34) shown in Figs. II-25 and II-26. These authors were studying reactions of glass-making materials. The silica types used, both better than 99% pure, were Loch Aline sand for the coarser grain sizes and Welsh silica flour for the finer. They found that these reacted quite differently with calcium carbonate (Fig. II-25).

The possibility that particle size difference was the reason for the differences in reactions—particularly C as compared to A or B in Fig. II-25—was checked by Wilburn and Thomasson by reacting calcium carbonate with similar grain size ranges of each type of silica. They ground some Loch Aline sand to pass 200 and 300 BSS and compared the reactions of 200–300 BSS and 300–350 BSS Loch Aline sand with those of Welsh silica flour of the same size ranges (Fig. II-26). While there are minor differences between the two fractions of either silica, the two silicas react quite differently from each other; in fact, the Loch Aline sand tends to form more calcium orthosilicate while the Welsh silica flour favors the formation of calcium metasilicate.

The use and description of specially prepared materials is commendable. From time to time research workers in thermal analysis, as well as in other fields, have taken elaborate precautions to assure themselves of

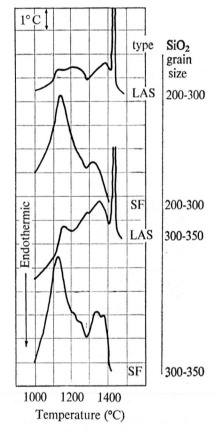

Fig. II-25. Differential thermal analyses of $3SiO_2$–$2CaCO_3$ mixtures with different types of silica and various grain sizes. $CaCO_3$ to pass 300 BSS. From Wilburn and Thomasson (W34).

The possibility existed that the particle size influenced the mode of reaction.

nearly perfect samples or sample materials. A question arises: "How can a procedure be checked by another observer without a similar preparation of sample materials?" Kissinger, McMurdie, and Simpson (K31) are to be commended for their approach:

"Reagent grade $MnCO_3$ and $FeCO_3$ were used in this study. Each of these compounds was also made in this laboratory by hydrothermal methods, care being taken to insure purity of the product. Since the materials prepared in this way did not differ significantly from the reagent grade material, the more readily available reagent grade was used."

The experimentor reporting extensive or elaborate preparative procedures should, like Kissinger *et al.*, also verify the need for them.

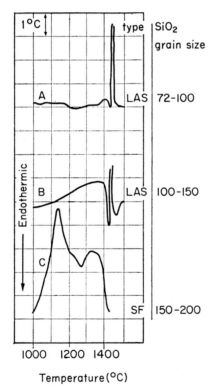

Fig. II-26. Differential thermal analyses of $3SiO_2$–$2CaCO_3$ mixtures with different types of silica and various grain sizes. $CaCO_3$ to pass 300 BSS. From Wilburn and Thomasson (W34).

The behavior is dependent on the history rather than the particle size of the specimen.

2.10. Summary

Differential thermal analysis comprises the heating and/or cooling of a specimen and reference and measuring the difference in temperature between them. Sample sizes can range over several orders of magnitude and should be chosen to suit the problem. Cylindrical specimens are most often used but other shapes can be used. The shape of the peak will depend on sample size and shape.

Exothermal reactions may occur either because of sample treatment or because of the nature of the sample itself.

Temperature calibration should be done occasionally on all systems and always on new experimental apparatus.

Dilution or pretreatment can have drastic effects on the shape of the peak.

CHAPTER III

Operational Parameters

3.1. Introduction

The major work of P. L. Arens, *A Study on the Differential Thermal Analysis of Clays and Clay Minerals* (A12), comprises an exceedingly thorough examination of differential thermal analysis empirically and to a limited degree theoretically. Because of the significance of this work, his conclusions are reviewed and the points he raised are examined in the following sections. (The relative unavailability of the work led to extensive repetition in the following paragraphs.)

Arens suggests a number of experimental factors affecting the shape of differential thermal analysis curves:

(*a*) rate of temperature rise of the furnace;
(*b*) nature of the sample holder;
(*c*) depth and radius of the sample holes in the holder;
(*d*) the measurement sites of both furnace and differential temperatures;
(*e*) nature and proportions of the thermocouples;
(*f*) the nature of the inert substance;
(*g*) the tightness of packing of the clay and inert substance in the holes;
(*h*) the effect of covering the sample holes; and
(*i*) the composition of the furnace atmosphere.

Since Arens is principally interested in clay minerals, he looks for additional factors:

(*j*) the particle size of the clay minerals present;
(*k*) the degree of crystallization;
(*l*) the cations absorbed; and
(*m*) the presence of admixtures in the clay.

He further points out that the recorded results are determined primarily by items *a, c, d, g, h, i, j,* and *k.*

He concludes regarding the effect of rate of temperature rise:

(1) There exists a systematic difference between the reactions accompanied by a loss in weight and those not accompanied by it.
(2) Types of reaction accompanied by a loss of weight are strongly influenced by the heating rate; with increasing heating rate the peak temperatures increase, as do also the peak height and peak area. But the peak range, measured as the time of reaction, decreases.
(3) If the furnace temperature is measured in the clay sample, those types of reactions in which there is no loss in weight are not affected as regards peak temperature, but are affected as regards peak height, range and area.
(4) From the results of experiments with varying heating rate, all other factors being kept constant, it is possible to compute empirically the reaction temperatures for zero rates of heating (static dehydration, etc.). These "asymptotic" reaction temperatures are of importance for correlating DTA with dehydration studies.

From his experiment with varying types of sample holders he concludes:

(1) Nickel blocks yield DTA curves with relatively flat endothermal and sharp exothermal reactions.
(2) Ceramic blocks yield curves with sharp endothermal and relatively flat exothermal reactions.
(3) All types of reactions undergo influences of the sample holder, irrespective of whether the reactions are accompanied by loss of material or not.
(4) No noticeable peak shifting is observed.

From a number of runs Arens concludes:

(1) The depth and radius of sample holes greatly affected the appearance of thermal reactions accompanied by changes in weight, as regards peak temperature, peak height, and total duration of reaction.

(2) Reactions not accompanied by changes in weight are not affected as regards peak temperature, and only slightly as regards peak height.

(3) It is possible to mask or to enhance reactions, by varying the depth and radius of the sample holes.

From his other experiments and without special examination of the effect of placement of the differential thermocouple junctions, he offers these conclusions:

(1) Deep placement of the differential thermocouple junctions in the samples yield DTA curves with relatively strong endothermic reactions in the low-temperature range and flat endothermic reactions in the high ranges.

(2) Exothermic reactions (in the high-temperature range) are recorded the best with deep placement of the differential thermocouple.

(3) For most reactions the thermocouple should be inserted in the samples without protective cover.

(4) Thermocouples fixed in the sample holders are a great advantage as regards reproducibility of data.

He summarizes the effect of the inert substance as follows:

(1) The inert material should have thermal characteristics (specific heat, heat conductivity, thermal diffusivity) as closely equal as possible to those of the clay. This requirement is never fully realizable, because the thermal characteristics of clay undergo rather sudden changes accompanying the reactions.

(2) If the furnace temperature is measured in the inert substance, an apparent peak shift is observed, the amount of which is increased with increasing radius of sample holder and increasing heating rates. This holds for all types of reactions.

(3) It is recommended that furnace temperature be measured in the clay sample.

(4) The use of calcined clay, of the same sample as is to be investigated, as inert material has no fundamental advantages over the use of calcined alumina, provided particle size distribution of the latter is not different from the clay.

Similarly, he concludes:

(1) Differences in density of packing are the most common causes of deviations from straight zero lines in temperature ranges where no reactions occur.

(2) Hard packing, considered the easiest to reproduce, is recommended for most cases, to obtain recordings with pronounced reactions and with straight zero lines.

(3) Loose packing gives rise to faint reactions, the effect lying in the same direction for all types of reaction, except probably the oxidation reaction.

Since the covering or not of the sample hole and the influence of the composition of the furnace atmosphere are so closely related, his conclusions on these two points are offered as a single unit:

(1) Covering the sample holes exerts considerable influence upon the appearance of reactions when there is a change in weight of the reactant (Fig. III-1).

(2) Reactions accompanied by loss in weight (dehydration, loss of CO_2) may be enhanced by covering while a peak shifting upwards occurs.

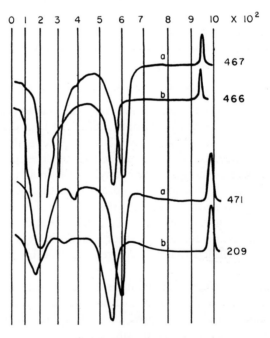

a. Sample hole covered
b. Sample hole uncovered

Fig. III-1. Thermograms of halloysite (466, 467) and of indianaite (209, 471) with covered and uncovered sample holes. From Arens (A12).

The restriction of decomposition product gases affects the temperature of decomposition.

(3) Reactions accompanied by gain in weight (oxidation) may be fully inhibited by the covering or may not be well-defined.

(4) Though covering may aid in certain cases to obtain straight zero lines, it should be avoided for general prospecting purposes.

(5) The composition of the atmosphere affects considerably the initiation and course of reactions accompanied by changes in weight.

(6) The initiation and course of dehydration reactions are influenced by the partial vapor pressure of water. The decomposition reactions of carbonates are influenced by the partial vapor pressure of CO_2 and the oxidation reactions are influenced by the partial vapor pressure of O_2 in the furnace atmosphere.

3.2. Rate of Temperature Rise

Whether or not the rate of temperature rise has a significant effect on the peak temperature depends not only on the nature of the sample but also on the manner of containing the specimen. If the sample undergoes only a change in state, the nature of the sample holder is immaterial, except for heat-transfer problems. The effect of a change of heating rate will be small in such cases and any effect will be related principally to heat-transfer considerations. Arens (A12) used heating rates of 6, 12, 18, and 21°C per minute on quartz and found no noticeable shift of transition temperature. Even the exothermic effect in kaolin was little affected.

The reactions involving loss in weight show a quite different behavior. Peak shifts of 75° are reported for kaolinite and all the weight loss reactions behave in the same manner [Kissinger (K29) found even greater shifting; see Chapter VII].

These peak shifts with temperature are quite normal and easily explained (see Chapter VII); the gases that are given off tend to inhibit further decompositions. These gases will diffuse out of the sample chamber, but this need for effusion means that the concentration of the gas will be time-dependent.

The higher the heating rate, the less gas will diffuse out before the reaction becomes very rapid. The fact that the initially released gas does not have time to diffuse out means that the concentration of gas can increase to some particular level with less total decomposition.

Assume—purely arbitrarily—that at the peak temperature at some heating rate the average partial pressure of water vapor in the vicinity of the last particles of a hydrate to decompose is one-third of an atmosphere. This heating rate is slow enough to permit fairly good interchange of gases between sample holder and furnace. If we hurry the reaction along on a run at a higher heating rate, this one-third of an atmosphere partial pressure will be reached with less than complete decomposition for two reasons. The time interval between the start of decomposition and the achievement of this partial pressure has not allowed the same amount of effusion, and the presence of the water vapor in higher concentration has repressed the decomposition. Yet at this same pressure of water vapor our sample should be at the peak temperature of the first experiment. Since we still have undecomposed material, the peak temperature in this second run must obviously be higher than that in the first.

A greater problem than mere peak shifting is the possibility of different degrees of peak shifting; i.e., differential thermal analysis peaks of a single specimen may be shifted unequally in such a manner that one of them is obscured. A prime example is the series of thermograms of gypsum (Fig. III-2) obtained by Dilaktorskii and Arkhangel 'skaja

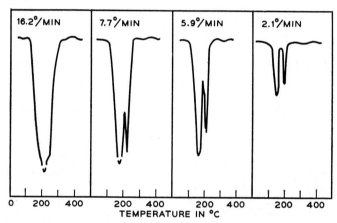

Fig. III-2. Effect of heating rate on the dehydration of gypsum. From Dilaktorskii and Arkhangel 'skaja (D11a).

Very high heating rates may completely mask a thermal effect.

(D11a). At very high heating rates the second peak is nearly covered by the first. We may reasonably assume that the rapid heating produces water vapor so rapidly that it cannot diffuse away from the specimen nearly so fast as it is supplied (see Chapter VII). By the time the center of the specimen has reached the first decomposition temperature under the extant atmosphere conditions—ca. one atmosphere of water vapor—the outside of the specimen, in contact with the wall, is already warm enough to start the second decomposition. This decomposition will go quite rapidly since no atmosphere change will impede it; the first and second reaction peaks are consequently very close together.

As the heating rate is lowered the temperature difference across the sample becomes lower, not only because thermal diffusion can transfer heat and hence can keep the specimen nearer thermal equilibrium but also because diffusion of water vapor out of the specimen diminishes the temperature required for this decomposition. At a quite low heating rate the first reaction is essentially complete before the second begins.

Not merely the separation of reactions but the general appearance of thermal effects can be affected by the heating rate. During the heating of ferrous carbonate (Fig. III-3), for example, the higher rate of heating causes evolution of carbon dioxide rapidly enough to slow the diffusion of oxygen back into the specimen holder. This causes a broadening and flattening of the oxidation exotherm so that the oxidation is not complete until the specimen is more than 50°C hotter than at the slower rate. Atmosphere effects are discussed in Chapter VII.

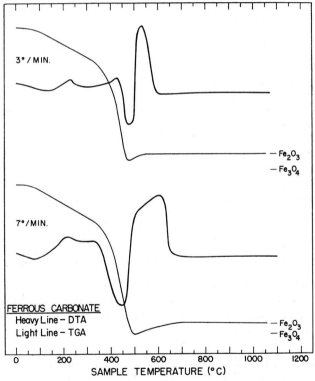

Fɪɢ. III-3. Differential thermal analysis-thermogravimetric analysis patterns of FeCO₃ at 3° and 7°C per minute. From Kissinger *et al.* (K31).

Different rates of heating may cause substantial alteration of the appearance of the thermogram.

As early as 1923, Houldsworth and Cobb (H25) reported the influence of the rate of temperature rise on the reaction ranges of kaolinite; i.e., at high-temperature-rise velocities the dehydration reaction is delayed over 100°C above the "equilibrium" temperature. There are several factors involved in the shift in temperature and in the increase in area of the peak that accompanies the increase in temperature. At low heating rates the decomposition product of kaolinite, that is, water vapor, can diffuse out into the atmosphere readily and the partial pressure of water is never high. The entire decomposition may then be carried out without the partial pressure even approaching one atmosphere.

Accounting for the peak area is rather more difficult. The difficulty arises principally from the need to offer a mechanism or hypothesis that will explain the increased area with increasing rate of temperature rise for kaolinite as well as for the inversion of quartz [cf. Arens (A12)]. While there is no shift in temperature for the quartz inversion the rate of change of peak area with heating rate is approximately the same as for the decomposition of kaolinite. Consequently, the change of heat of reaction with the temperature cannot be cited to explain this change in area.

The probable cause of the increasing area with the higher heating rates is again the problem of heat transfer. A differential signal exists because the heat is being used for a process other than increasing the temperature, but this other process cannot continue indefinitely because the quantity of sample is limited. This differential signal is dependent on—among other things—the amount of material reacting at any given time; this in turn depends on the rate at which heat is supplied. The given amount of material will require a given number of extra calories to carry out the process so the rate of supply of extra heat integrated over the time this extra heat is supplied ought to be directly proportional to the quantity of material. The error lies in failure to detect the heat and the failure is due to the technique. The ease of heat transfer which makes differential thermal analysis useful in detecting reactions imposes a hardship in measuring the amount of heat.

In essence, the low rates of heating allow heat to diffuse in or out of the specimen in a manner only slightly affected by the reaction. With differential temperatures of a few tenths of a degree the flow in both specimen and reference are still nearly the same. Now let the heating rate be increased, say, three times. A steeper gradient within the specimen and reference will be set up and a steady state ensues in which the differential temperature is again zero or nearly so.

As the transition temperature front with its additional heat requirement moves inward, the wall continues to rise steadily in temperature, but as the center approaches the transition, its heating rate tends to decrease because it sees, essentially, a constant temperature front moving inward from the wall and shielding the center from the higher gradient between this front and the wall. There is, consequentially, a volume— substantial at first but constantly diminishing—which is influenced only secondarily by the temperature of the wall. This is the reason not only for the larger differential temperature but also, because the transport of heat is dependent on time as well as temperature, for the greater $\int \Delta T \ dt$. The hot wall simply cannot supply heat at the rate required by the heat capacity of the specimen until it has also supplied that necessary to carry out the transition.

An optimum heating rate cannot often be determined immediately or *a priori* so a generally useful heating rate is used routinely or for initial examination. Most apparatus are designed to permit several rates. The most common heating rate is 10°C/minute. It is the rate used most often by the present author (see Chapter XVII) and is the one recom- mended to the International Geological Congress (M6). For quantita- tive work a constant heating rate is recommended (see Chapter V).

Discussion of the effects of rate of heating must include the work of Keith and Tuttle (K14) who used rates on the order of 0.5°C per min- ute in their study of quartz. For lack of temperature-recording tech- niques that are really suitable for the purpose, they selected a pair of materials having crystallographic phase changes closely above and below the quartz inversion and obtained the inversion temperatures by inter- polation as shown in Fig. III-4. Note that it is only necessary for their needs that the cooling—or heating—be nondiscontinuous through the range between the cryolite and potassium sulfate inversions; it can be nonlinear so long as it is always reproducibly nonlinear.

With this slow heating rate Keith and Tuttle were able to study varia- tions in quartz. Not only were they able to recognize variations within a single quartz deposit as in Fig. III-5, but even differences within a crystal as in Fig. III-6. We may reasonably conclude that low heating rates are usable and necessary for detecting differences in close-lying inver- sion temperatures.

3.3. Influence of the Sample Holder

The means of supporting the sample and providing for temperature measurement has been the subject of abundant controversy. Let us re- call the description of differential thermal analysis in Chapter II and consider specifically the step from differential calorimetry to differential thermal analysis. We permitted heat to flow between the sample and the reference materials in order that the difference signal might return to zero, thus enabling detection of a number of successive reactions. The passage of heat between the sample and the reference specimens necessarily reduces the temperature difference and, therefore, the signal available for detection and measurement. The use of differential thermal analysis is a sacrifice of total sensitivity to gain another kind of sensitivity —sensitivity to any thermal effect almost independent of previous occurrences. We must examine, then, the consequences of the extreme cases of well-separated specimens as in differential calorimetry and of rather intimately connected specimens as in a high-conductivity differential thermal analysis sample block.

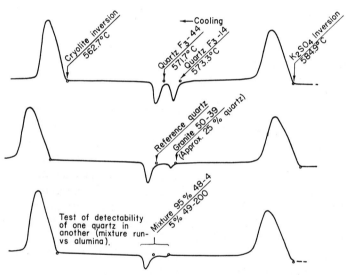

FIG. III-4. Chart records illustrating thermal curves for inversion on cooling (rising-temperature records are similar). From Keith and Tuttle (K14).

The inversion break temperature is taken as the beginning of the heat effect, defined as the intersection of a line drawn through the first straight portion of the thermal curve with the base line.

Considerable evidence has been presented to show that sample holders in the form of isolated cups have greater sensitivity than blocks. The present author (G12) has done his part in continuing the discussion, concluding that isolated cups will provide a gain in sensitivity but that the sample vessel must be thick enough to provide temperature homogeneity around the sample.

The author has since concluded that to rely on one type of sample holder for all types of samples would be to risk failure in studying half or more of the samples that have needed examination; the author has,

in fact, had to develop nearly a dozen ways to hold particular specimens. Let us examine the effect of the sample holder on a simple phase
transformation (Fig. III-7). The thermal effect is quite sharply defined
in the block, A, and in the thicker-walled cups, B and C. The return
to the base line is rapid in A because the specimen diameter is small
and the total magnitude of the specimen does not matter greatly. B and
C are more spread out because the system is approaching more closely
differential calorimetry; in these cases, and in D and E, the entire specimen has to be warmed up so the transfer of heat to and throughout the
sample will take a greater time. The ratios of the total heights to the
half-widths of the deflections are about 25, 23, 39, 11, and 14 for

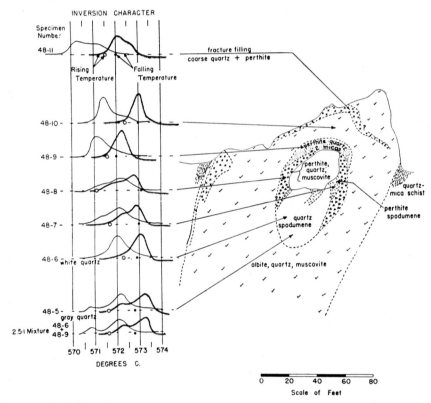

Fig. III-5. Quartz inversion results of Keith and Tuttle (K14) on samples from
the Helen Beryl Mine pegmatite, Custer County, South Dakota, shown in relation
to a vertical section after M. H. Staatz and J. J. Norton of the U. S. Geological Survey.

*At least four different types of quartz can be recognized and each sample shows
evidence of containing more than one type of quartz.*

A, B, C, D, and E, respectively. The apparent reason for the relatively low peak heights for D and E is the relatively poor conduction around the sample holder itself; this would result in a nonuniform temperature at the edge of the specimen and hence a nonsymmetrical thermal gradient. This nonsymmetrical thermal gradient would mean, in turn, that some portion of the material in the immediate vicinity of the thermocouple would, during steady heating, be at some higher temperature than another corresponding portion. When this warmer region begins to transform—before the other—the usual heat flux from that direction is diminished and the center of the sample begins to lag in temperature; i.e., the endotherm begins. The endothermic reaction will progress at different rates in different directions and hence will occur over a greater time interval and the center will not be the last region to reach the transition temperature (Fig. III-8). This will appear also as a greater

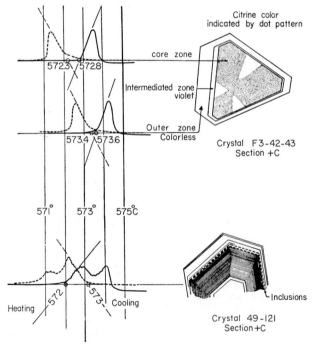

Fig. III-6. Character of the heat effect obtained on two zoned single crystals. Crystal F3–42–43 was separated into two fractions as illustrated and the inversion of each fraction is shown (solid lines = thermal effect on heating, dashed lines = thermal effect on cooling). From Keith and Tuttle (K14).

The very low heating rate permits clear distinction of materials transforming at temperatures only a degree apart.

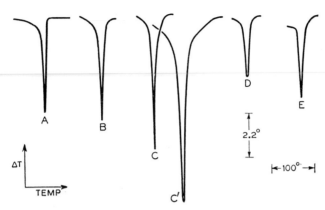

FIG. III-7. Thermograms of 170 mg of potassium sulfate in various specimen holders. The sample size was determined by the capacity of the block. A, Platinum block
cavities 5×10 mm. B, Platinum cups, 0.6-mm wall, 6–8 mm ID $\times$ 10 mm.
Aluminum oxide, ca. 110 mg, mixed in with 170 mg specimen to fill cup. Cups supported in firebrick block. C, Same specimen as B, but cups supported on wire loops.
D, Quartz cups, 1-mm wall, ca. 6 mm ID $\times$ 10 mm. Aluminum oxide, ca. 20 mg,
mixed with specimen to fill cup. Cups supported on wire loops. E, Platinum cups
fabricated from 0.06-mm sheet, same specimen as B and C. Cups supported on wire
loops.

*The relative broadness of D and E suggests the need for good thermal conductivity
around the specimen.*

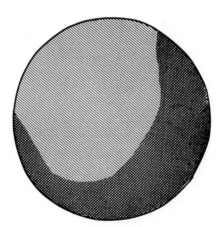

FIG. III-8. Representation of an unsymmetrically heated specimen. The progress
of the high-temperature form (crosshatched area) will leave material untransformed
(diagonal lines) when the center reaches the transition temperature.

*Transfer of heat around the specimen should be more rapid than transfer of heat
into the specimen.*

temperature interval so the endotherm is spread out to a greater degree than in the case of the thicker specimen holders (see Chapter II).

The transfer of heat from the edge of the sample container into the sample has been treated by Speil (S40), Vold (V10), Arens (A12), Vold and Vold (V11), Sewell and Honeybourne (S19a), Smythe (S36), and Allison (A4). There is, however, an almost equally significant problem of transferring the heat from the furnace winding to the sample surface. In considering this problem let us assume only at this time that the sample and reference material are in symmetric locations within a cylindrical vertical furnace. Now let us consider a common case of a ceramic tube with the heater winding on the outside heating a sample block inside the tube. There is customarily no direct mechanical contact between the furnace tube and the sample block.

The question now arises concerning the choice of materials for the sample block. The question of block vs cup will be considered separately. Even the casual observer will realize immediately that a metallic block provides greater temperature homogeneity within the block than does a ceramic or other nonmetallic block. The relative mass of metallic and ceramic blocks will be discussed later. The immediate question of the relative efficiency of moving the heat to the sample entails consideration of thermal conductivity, heat capacity, and thermal emissivity. At lower temperatures the heat-transfer coefficients of the two types of block and furnace wall to air must be considered as well as the thermal conductivity of air or other vapor. At the temperatures at which radiation is the principal method by which heat is conveyed, the relative emissivity of the two materials is of major importance. Polished metallic strips have emissivities ranging from less than 0.1 near room temperature to the order of 0.23 at 1000°C. From the equation for rate of interchange of heat between bodies A and B

$$Q_{ab} = \frac{\sigma(t_a^4 - t_b^4)}{(1/\epsilon_a) + (1/\epsilon_b) - 1}$$

where Q_{ab} is the rate of heat flow from A to B, σ is the Stefan-Boltzman constant, t_a and t_b are the temperatures of surfaces of A and B, respectively, and ϵ_a and ϵ_b are the thermal emissivities of these surfaces. If one takes the emissivity of the ceramic furnace tube as being essentially one, the equation is then readily converted to

$$Q_{ab} = \sigma \epsilon'_b(t_a^4 - t_b^4)$$

and the heat exchange is essentially a function of the emissivity of the block material. Obviously thermal energy can be transported from heater winding to block much more rapidly if the block is a ceramic rather than a polished metal. Since the total heat capacities of, say, nickel, platinum, and alumina are never the same for a sample block of a given size, the relative merits of these types of sample blocks must be considered with special regard to the heat-transfer characteristic, bearing in mind at all times that completely free flow of heat is not necessarily desirable.

Arens (A12), from a rather limited number of runs, concluded that ceramic blocks gave sharp endothermic reactions while nickel block gave sharp exothermic reactions (Fig. III-9). His evidence is too scanty to draw conclusions of this type. An equally valid conclusion from the evidence at hand is that ceramic blocks are more sensitive in the lower-temperature regions than nickel blocks but that nickel blocks are more sensitive at higher temperatures. Below red heat, the relatively low heat

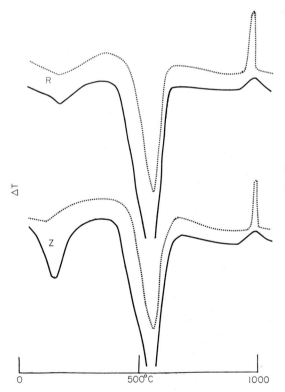

Fig. III-9. Thermograms of kaolinite from, R, Renau, and Z, Zettlitz, in nickel (• • • • •) and in ceramic (———) blocks. From Arens (A12).
The relative sensitivities of the blocks vary with temperature.

conductivity of alumina results in a comparative thermal isolation of the sample and reference, all other conditions being equal. As the temperature is increased and radiation takes a greater part in the transfer of heat, the relatively high emissivity of alumina compared to nickel permits transfer of heat quite readily from the blocks to the sample. At such temperatures nickel tends to play the same part as did the alumina at the lower temperatures; that is, the poor transfer of heat from sample to sample block or vice versa permits a sharper indication of a reaction. This explanation should apply to low thermal conductivity ceramics. The present state of ceramic art permits use of high-density formulations of some fairly conductive ceramics.

The thermal conductivity of high-density alumina is roughly the same as many of the high-temperature alloys but still only about one-quarter that of commercially pure nickel or ca. one-tenth that of aluminum. Competing with the effect of the thermal conductivity is the effect of the thermal emissivity. A third property influences the transfer of heat: the interfacial or surface characteristics of the block.

The emissivity determines, to a very great extent, how much heat is transferred from one body to another. Bear in mind that high emissivity also implies ready absorption of energy. If a ceramic and a nickel surface were each exposed to a hot surface under identical conditions the surface of the ceramic would heat faster. If a nickel and a ceramic *body* were similarly exposed the interior temperature of each body would depend on the thermal conductivity as well as the emissivity. While the outside of the ceramic body may be heating up quite rapidly the relatively high diffusivity of the nickel might well permit the center of the latter body to heat more rapidly at first.

The effect of interfacial layer characteristics is often severe. These layers take two forms—solid oxide or corrosion layers and the static gas which adheres to any surface. The oxide layer can—and often will—be the major resistance to the flow of heat; a metal block whose heat must traverse an oxide layer may—under steady-state heating—have a negligible temperature gradient. The static gas layer is of somewhat less importance because it is present on all materials and partly because it influences only the heat transfer by conduction (including convection).

To evaluate the relative heat-transfer characteristics, the present author heated a pair of geometrically identical sample holders (Fig. III-10), one of nickel and the other of high-density alumina, and measured the temperature difference between their centers. The sample holders were set on ¼″ (nominal) alumina two-hole rods and calcined alumina powder was put in each and pressed tight. A vertical furnace was put in place and power supplied from a motor-driven autotransformer. The immediate response (Fig. III-11) was a more rapid heating of the alumina holder. The thermocouple at its center showed a continually increasing lead until the Curie temperature of nickel was reached. The sharp change in thermal conductivity (Fig. III-12) permits the nickel-enclosed sample to heat more rapidly until the differential temperature approaches (and slightly exceeds) zero ca. 900°C.

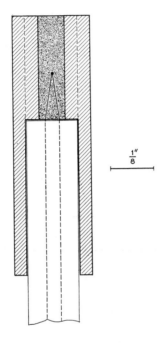

Fig. III-10. Cross sectional view of trial sample holders of nickel and alumina. From Garn (G9).

The alumina sample holder comprised a (nominal) ¼ OD tube cemented into a longer ¼ ID tube; the nickel holder was machined to the same dimensions.

The sample holders were interchanged in a second run to avoid any errors due to accidental misalignment. There was no difference in shape and the difference in magnitude was negligible.

The thermal conductivity of the nickel is, through the whole temperature range, substantially larger than that of alumina, yet the alumina transmits heat to the specimen faster at the lower temperatures. It is frequently as easy to test the myths and misconceptions as it is to try to justify them.

3.4. Design of the Sample Block

The depth and radius of the sample wells are quite naturally a part of the total design of the sample block. The designs are extremely varied; sample cavities and blocks are not necessarily round. The design is partly dependent on the means of support. In the horizontal furnace supports can be devised for a wide range of shapes with equal ease because the specimens are not symmetric about the furnace axis anyway. In the vertical furnace a cylindrical block is virtually the only shape used. Arens (A12) used several shapes in his studies (Fig. III-13) and other authors have contributed other structures.

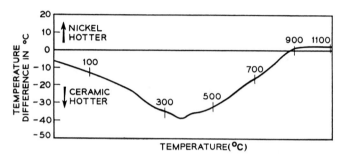

Fɪɢ. III-11. Temperature differential between alumina- and nickel-enclosed samples vs temperature of one of the samples. From Garn (G9).

The alumina transmits heat more readily than the nickel over most of the range. The nonlinearity of heating rate is typical of motor-driven autotransformers.

The thin-walled arrangements pose a special problem, particularly when the individual chambers are in contact. One assumption generally made in the use of a block is that the temperature gradient within the block is virtually zero. This is an essential prerequisite for symmetric heating of the specimens. A narrow wall between sample and reference specimens can hardly be at the same temperature as the portions more directly exposed to the hot furnace wall, but if the sample wells are reasonably spaced the metal cross section will be sufficient to maintain a fair approximation to uniformity. If the wells are separated to such a degree that they are near the edge of the block a rather similar problem exists but this time the narrow portion of the metal is a source (relative to the specimens) of heat. The degree of asymmetry of heating will be heavily dependent now on the rate of transfer of heat to the block—as well as on the conductivity within the block. Both of these quantities change with temperature. A reasonable guide is to maintain a thickness of metal at least equal to the well diameter all around each cavity.

The block will be supported, generally, by an insulating material, not to keep heat from it but to avoid what would amount to a distortion of the temperature distribution in the block. For vertical furnaces, such as the present author generally uses, the block may be supported on the ceramic tubes that carry the thermocouple wires, in the manner of Fold-vari-Vogl and Kliburszky (F11) (Fig. III-14). The present author uses stepped holes rather than stepped ceramic tubes to position the block. In

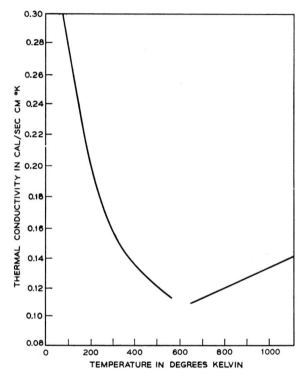

Fig. III-12. Thermal conductivity of nickel as a function of temperature. From Goldsmith *et al.* (G27).
The change at the Curie temperature is quite pronounced.

horizontal furnaces the present author has used both alumina and fire-brick to support blocks such as that in Fig. III-15. Stone (S51) supported his sample block directly on the metal gas-flow tubes.

Assuming some given heating rate, a large cavity will have a large temperature drop from side to center. This implies that by the time the center reaches a given temperature the side is at a substantially higher temperature. Since a temperature effect will have its beginning at the

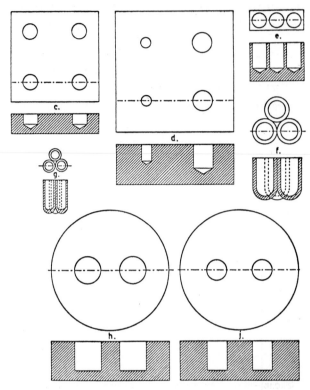

FIG. III-13. Top and cross sectional views of some of the blocks tested by Arens (A12).

The variety of blocks gives a wide range of ease of transfer of heat.

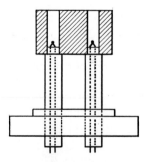

FIG. III-14. Sample block supported by thermocouple tubes (F11).

By minor changes in design a dynamic atmosphere can also flow through the supporting tubes.

time the wall reaches the reaction temperature and its ending when the *center* reaches the reaction temperature, the effect will be spread out in time.

We may also conclude (Fig. III-16) that a smaller-diameter specimen will have a lower drop and the peak will be over a narrower time range. The relative smallness of the peak need not be a great disadvantage since electrical amplification can be used; on the contrary, the small differences from the block temperature will mean a low drift of the base line because the temperature drop from block to center of sample or reference cannot be large and hence their difference cannot be large.

Data by de Jong (J9) tend to show, from sets 2, 5, and 6 of Fig. III-17, that depth of placement of the thermocouple has only a minor effect on

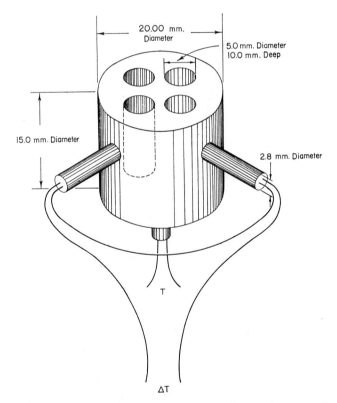

Fig. III-15. Sample block showing method of introducing thermocouples for furnace temperature, T, and differential temperature, ΔT. From Garn and Flaschen (G12).

The four holes permit interpolation of temperatures in the manner of Keith and Tuttle (K14).

peak area in full, covered sample cavities. The conclusion is not firmly based on these data because the thermocouple bead is relatively close to the bottom in each case; Barshad's work cited in Chapter II showed the end effect quite clearly.

The various widths of set A show an increasing thermal isolation of the thermocouple because of the relatively low thermal diffusivity of the specimen. This larger area is not necessarily a desirable attribute (see Chapter II). The fourth set in Fig. III-17 shows the diminution of the peak area due to a lesser quantity of specimen in the immediate vicinity of the thermocouple.

The general case may be stated quite simply: the longer and narrower the sample cavity the greater will be the effect of the atmosphere gen-

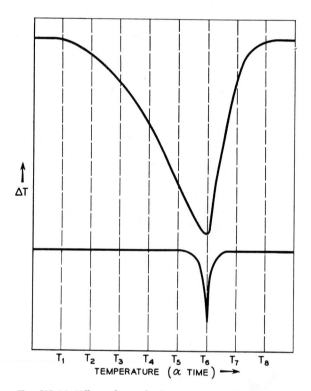

Fɪɢ. III-16. Effect of sample diameter on width of peaks.

A material which reacts at a temperature T_6 will appear to begin reacting at a much lower temperature (when ΔT is plotted against the temperature at the center) because the outside of the specimen is already at T_6. The lower edge-to-center temperature difference in the smaller specimen yields peaks of lesser magnitude but better definition.

erated by the sample itself and the less the effect of the composition of the ambient gas. The data in Fig. III-17 show that the effect reaches a virtual limit.

There should be no magic number expressing the length-to-depth ratio; in fact there will be occasions for most observers to use shallow as well as deep sample cavities (see Chapter VII). The actual dimensions should be selected, then, on the basis of experimental convenience and conformity with other parts of the apparatus. Bear in mind that in a dynamic atmosphere (see Chapter VII) or in a vacuum the length of the cavity is immaterial so long as it is the sample temperature rather

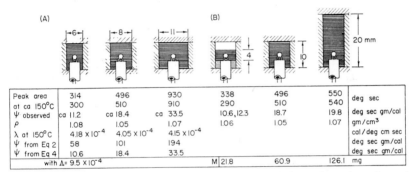

Peak area	314	496	930	338	496	550	deg sec
at ca 150°C	300	510	910	290	510	540	deg sec
ψ observed	ca 11.2	ca 18.4	ca 33.5	10.6,12.3	18.7	19.8	deg sec gm/cal
ρ	1.08	1.05	1.07	1.06	1.05	1.07	gm/cm³
λ at 150°C	4.18×10^{-4}	4.05×10^{-4}	4.15×10^{-4}				cal/deg cm sec
ψ from Eq 2	58	101	194				deg sec gm/cal
ψ from Eq 4	10.6	18.4	33.5				deg sec gm/cal
with Λ= 9.5×10^{-4}				M 21.8	60.9	126.1	mg

FIG. III-17. Test results for $CuSO_4 \cdot 5H_2O$ diluted with $\alpha\text{-}Al_2O_3$ (weight ratio, 1 : 7). (A) Samples of different diameter and equal height and (B) samples of different height and equal diameter. From de Jong (J9).

The considerable change in depth of thermocouples in the last two examples yields only a slight change in the peak area, but this is partly because the thermocouple bead is the same distance from the bottom in each case.

than that of the flowing or evolved gas that is measured. In other words, one cannot pass a gas through a thin layer of specimen and hope to have a good measure of the specimen temperature. The dynamic gas should pass through a sufficient thickness of specimen that thermal equilibrium is approached quite closely.

In a nondynamic atmosphere and with samples of rather substantial size, i.e., more than a few millimeters in diameter, the user may wish a cavity with a length-to-width ratio of two or more so that the heat supply comes principally from the sides. This is not particularly important for detection but those who wish to make calculations from data obtained using a block have enough other troubles. (See Chapter V.)

3.5. Placement of Thermocouples

The manner of recording T and ΔT and controlling (programming) T will depend greatly on the apparatus available, but a few simple considerations must be borne in mind; variations can be made successfully, but the consequences must be understood.

Since knowledge of the behavior of the specimen as its temperature is changed is the object of the study, the best temperature to measure and record is that of said specimen. If the thermocouple junction is placed in the center of a cylindrical specimen and an endothermic reaction is observed the thermocouple is at the place where the reaction last occurs. When the center finally reacts, the lag behind the reference is at its greatest and hence the peak of the endotherm is the reaction temperature. When practical, then, the temperature of any sizable specimen should be recorded from the center of the sample.

The maximum sensitivity and sharpness of reactions will certainly be obtained by maximum thermal and atmospheric isolation of the detecting thermocouple junction so that the surrounding material—whether sample or inert—will exert the maximum effect on the temperature of the thermocouple bead. No implication that this is necessary nor the best arrangement is implied. The present author has repeatedly—and successfully—used thermocouples with protective cover (Fig. VIII-5) at the edge of a sample. Under these conditions, however, very small samples were used. Arens' conclusions on the effect of placement of thermocouples were apparently based on curves in which the atmosphere effect overshadowed the geometric.

If the experimenter needs to control from the recording thermocouple, as did the present author for some years, two quite usable locations were available: the block, if one is used, or the reference specimen. In the latter case, the transition or decomposition temperature may be found easily by adding or subtracting the difference temperature; the control thermocouple is rather isolated from the heater, causing thermal lag, so especially good control apparatus is required.

Recording and controlling the block temperature would permit better control but at the price of some uncertainty in the actual specimen temperature. We can assume—with some reservations—that we know the temperature of the interface between block and specimen but the drop to the interior of the specimen is not known; there is also no convenient and continuous method for determining the drop. Said temperature drop will vary from specimen to specimen and from temperature to temperature and the variation will be discontinuous at thermal effects. For simple phase transitions no great problem exists; the beginning of the deflection is the reaction temperature. For decompositions the temperature of the center of the specimen will be of greater interest and a two-step measurement will be of use.

If the temperature drop in the reference material is known as a function of temperature for the heating rate used, this value and the differential temperature may be added to the block temperature to obtain the specimen temperature. This temperature drop will vary with both material and heating rate. In small-diameter cavities the errors become less and possibly negligible. The differential signal is diminishing too, but the discontinuities at reaction temperatures can still be detected easily even at small thicknesses of specimen material.

> Note that control of the specimen temperature is decidedly impractical for ordinary differential thermal analysis. The temperature-control device would lose control at the very time when smoothness of control was most needed. At the start of, for example, a simple endothermic phase change the control device will receive a sudden call for more heat. Assuming a typical separation of heat source from a sample a few intermediate layers must be heated more rapidly before the effect is felt by the specimen. In the meantime, the specimen temperature is lagging still further behind the programmed temperature, so the demand for heat continues to increase. By the time the reaction is complete, the surroundings are overheated and the temperature will rise at a rate greater than the programmed rate. The sensing thermocouple will cease to call for heat and the furnace input will be cut back sharply. When the programmed temperature again catches up there will be another demand because the specimen temperature is rising only slowly or may even by falling. How soon the control system can return to the program will depend very much on the type of control system and the care used in its adjustment, but in any case the apparatus will be off control for some time after the start of the reaction. During this time, it is incapable of dependable and reproducible detection of additional thermal effects and thereby has lost a significant part of the usefulness of differential thermal analysis.

The detection of this one thermal effect would not be inhibited but the shape of the deflection would likely be more than usually dependent on particle size, packing, etc.

The general problem of placement of the control thermocouple is discussed in Chapter XV.

Improper positioning of sample and reference thermocouples within the specimens will result in a diminution or deformation of the differential signal. Ordinarily this will be quite undesirable, although there are conceivable uses for deliberately nonsymmetric arrangements. In general, the aim is to obtain the maximum and best-defined signal available under the experimental conditions. This position will—in most systems—be at the center of symmetry or at the point corresponding as nearly as possible to it.

> Understand, however, that the goal here is the maximum information. The application of the general principles to specific problems will sometimes be experimentally unfeasible. Good, usable data can be obtained with other arrangements. See also Cole and Rowland's (C20) observations on the effect of placement of the thermocouple wires.

In the usual cylinder the best thermocouple location is along the axis as would be expected; in Smyth's (S36) slab arrangement a central plane is the most isolated position. Smyth's calculations of the effect of thermocouple position provide a convenient starting point, and we can extend his conclusions qualitatively to the cylindrical cavity. Fig. III-18a and b show time-based plots, but these can be related easily to a temperature-based curve; let us first examine the events against a time base.

Let us note that the temperature differences generally encountered in differential thermal analysis are often quite small. A phase change involving a temperature differential of 2°C can be detected quite routinely. Yet on a range of 1000°C, this 2°C corresponds approximately to the dead zone of a good controller (L3a). This means that small deflec-

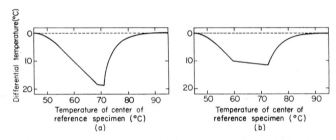

Fig. III-18. Effect of having the thermocouple displaced (a) 0.06 cm and (b) 0.30 cm from the center of the test specimen. From Smyth (S36).

The discontinuity occurs as the reaction front passes the thermocouple (see also Fig. III-8).

tions will have only a slight influence on the control system. This magnitude of signal is obtained with small samples undergoing crystallographic phase transitions; meltings, decompositions, and phase transitions in large samples will often produce a signal in excess of this. These larger signals will invariably influence the programming of the temperature because of the transitory lag (or lead) of the temperature compared to the programmed rate.

In short, if the thermal effects are small in magnitude the program control signal can be taken from a point in or near the sample—without serious upset of the program. Unless the differential signal is already known to be small the wiser course is to program from some other point. The user of this technique *must* use small samples.

As the transition proceeds, the temperature of a point not at the center will lag further and further behind the reference temperature as previously discussed. As the transition front reaches this point, the temperature at the point is no longer affected directly by the high "heat capacity" at the front. The temperature is now dependent on the new thermal diffusivity and the temperature difference between the wall and the now-receding front. A discontinuity is the natural result. The temperature rises more swiftly so that the differential temperature does not increase at the same rate as before. Whether or not the differential temperature will increase or decrease slightly will depend on the relative diffusivities of the two forms. The point will not, however, begin a rapid climb to a zero differential temperature because the unreacted material still behaves as a heat sink. The differential temperature may decrease somewhat, but only when the transformation is complete does the final return to the base line begin. The time that the point spends in the high-temperature form before the transition is complete is directly related to the displacement from the center and hence the flattened region in Fig. III-18 is greater with the larger displacement.

The general form of the plot is applicable to the cylindrical sample holder but the two-dimensional flow of heat (instead of unidirectional) will tend generally to smooth any changes. The converging flow of heat tends to diminish the difference in temperature so that the curve features will be somewhat less sharply defined. Thermocouple assymmetry, then, like assymmetric heating (Fig. III-8), will yield a less sharp peak; the degree of rounding will vary with the amount of assymmetry.

Barrall and Rogers (B7) examined the relation of heating rate and thermocouple location to the measured peak temperature. Their furnace arrangement is shown in Fig. IV-10. Note that heat transfer to the specimens is deliberately very poor. Under such conditions, a rapid heating rate will cause an apparent upward shift (Fig. III-19) of the peak temperature. The material does not actually remain in the solid state to higher temperatures as suggested by Fig. III-19 but rather the lag between block and thermocouple has increased substantially as the heating rate increased. Locating the measuring thermocouple in the specimen provides a reproducible peak temperature for the simple reason that the measurement is made where the measured event is occurring. So long as the thermocouple is at the center and the process is rapid the maximum signal occurs when the material around the thermocouple bead reaches the reaction temperature.

The use of a second thermocouple within the sample or reference for measuring the total temperature is fairly common. Since this not only disturbs the symmetry of heating but provides another path for heat leakage, compensation is applied in the form of a dummy thermocouple in the reference or sample. When the recording circuit is a potentiometric device requiring no current at balance, no further problems are encountered (see Chapter XV). With most multirange recorders—and particularly X-Y recorders—a new problem arises.

Most general purpose adjustable-range recorders use a voltage divider in their input circuit. This requires a current flow even when no change is being recorded. This in turn requires that work be drawn from the furnace. If the temperature is being recorded from the sample or reference, an unbalance is created. The unbalance arises because the work

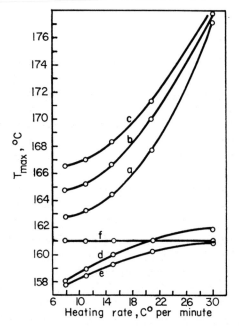

Fig. III-19. Peak temperature of (diluted) salicylic acid melting as measured in the block (a,b,c), the reference (d,e), and the sample (f). Curves a, d, and f refer to the same sample weight. From Barrall and Rogers (B7).

Variations in thermal lag at the several locations will be dependent on heating rate; the actual melting point will not.

drawn as electrical energy must be supplied as thermal energy, decreasing the temperature of the thermocouple itself and its immediate surroundings. This unbalance will be accentuated if the temperature is being recorded from one junction of the differential thermocouple. The solution in either is to draw an equal amount of work from the other thermocouple. This is done by putting a resistive load across the other thermocouple to match the recorder input. This maneuver requires sup-

ply of a little extra heat, but this will not normally be of any consequence unless one is attempting to describe the curve mathematically
(see Chapter V).

3.6. Influence of the Nature and Proportions of the Thermocouples

The present author reports, in another chapter, work in which metal
shields over the thermocouples were used routinely. In other works, thermocouple wires as small as 0.003 inch and as large as 0.030 inch have
been used. There is no significant qualitative effect. A systematic evaluation of quantitative effects was not made, except to note that there is a
considerable loss of sensitivity with shielded thermocouples and particularly a sluggish response with shielded thermocouples with ungrounded
junctions.

Vassallo and Harden (V3) report (Fig. III-20) that change from 40- to
28-gage thermocouple wire resulted in a 15% diminution in peak height,

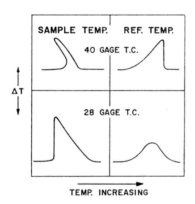

FIG. III-20. Character of boiling endotherms using sample and reference temperature measurement. From Vassallo and Harden (V3).
The curve at the upper left is typical for specimens that superheat.

but this is a change from 0.08 mm to 0.32 mm diameter wire in tubes
that are only 1.5 to 2.0 mm in diameter. The larger thermocouple wires
occupy a significant cross section of the sample tube.

Since the thermocouple must be heated (or cooled) to deliver the
proper indication there must be some deleterious effects with unduly
large thermocouples because of the heat capacity and thermal conductivities of the wires. Some authors (see Chapter V) have found it necessary to take the thermal properties of the thermocouple wires into
account, but this will generally be unnecessary.

3.7. Choice of Inert Substance

Under steady heating conditions with no reaction, the observed temperature difference depends both on the ease of heat transfer within the reference or inert material (thermal conductivity) and on the amount of heat necessary to raise the temperature of the material (heat capacity). The quantities of interest are the density, specific heat, thermal conductivity, and particle size. The first three of these are related in a term called the thermal diffusivity, a, which is defined by

$$a = \frac{\lambda}{\rho c}$$

where λ is the thermal conductivity, ρ is the density, and c is the specific heat.

Arens derives an expression for the steady-state temperature difference,

$$\Delta T = \frac{1}{4} \frac{dT}{dt} r^2 \left(\frac{1}{a'} - \frac{1}{a} \right)$$

where dT/dt is the heating rate, r is the radius of the cavity, and a' and a are the thermal diffusivities of the sample and reference, respectively.

But while the density and thermal conductivity are generally known for solids in large sizes, the effective density and the effective thermal conductivity will depend on particle size and packing. Smith (S34) relates the thermal conductivity of a powder to the volume fractions of air and solid. He gives

$$\lambda = \lambda_a P_a + \lambda_s P_s$$

where P_a and P_s are the volume fractions of air and the powdered substance. For ordinary purposes the contribution of air can be neglected but even the packing must be carefully controlled as part of any effort to obtain a zero base line.

The underlying problem in achieving a low ΔT and hence a nearly zero base line is that of matching the thermal diffusivity of the reference (or inert) material to that of the specimen. The problem in achieving also a zero base line drift is that of matching the thermal diffusivity of the inert material to that of the specimen at *all* temperatures in the range studied. Note, from the expression (see above) for the steady-state temperature difference, that the difference is a direct function of the heating rate; i.e., at higher heating rates the drift will be larger. With a single reference material, this matching is obviously not possible for more than a few fortuitously chosen specimens. Some base line deviation and indeed some drift is to be expected unless the observer has made a special effort to match the reference to the specimen. In the absence of such precautions, a base line of nearly zero and which does not drift is prima-facie evidence of a low-sensitivity apparatus.

It is for this same reason that one need not be perturbed when a base line is not the same before and after a reaction. Even in crystalline rearrangements but especially in decompositions the thermal conductivity and the specific heat of the product will differ from that of its initial form; in decompositions, too, the density must change. Attaining the same thermal diffusivity after the reaction as before the reaction would be strange indeed. This is one of the effects which frustrate attempts to derive exact expressions for quantitative differential thermal analysis.

The dilution of materials may also result in apparent changes because of sorption of the material and/or decomposition products. Barrall and Rogers (B7) have shown (Fig. III-21) the sorption of water and alcohols

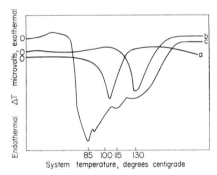

Fig. III-21. Differential thermograms of vapors sorbed on glass beads and alumina at a heating rate of 7.9°C per minute and a ΔT sensitivity of 200 μv per 3 inches. a, Water sorbed on 0.029-mm glass beads. b, Water sorbed on calcined alumina. c, Methanol, ethanol, and water sorbed on calcined alumina. From Barrall and Rogers (B7).

Affinity of the "inert" material for vapors may lead to data that is difficult to interpret.

on their calcined alumina diluent. If a sample material contained some adsorbed water, an undiluted specimen might well lose this water in the 60–100°C range without any very noticeable effect. In a specimen diluted with calcined alumina, evolved water would be immediately absorbed by the alumina and not lost again until the specimen was substantially over 100°C as in Fig. III-21. The comparatively rapid release then might provide a spurious peak which could impel the observer to seek the material in the specimen which gives a peak at, e.g.,

127°C. On the other hand, if water initially adsorbed on the sample material could be reliably adsorbed by the diluent and later desorbed over a narrow temperature range to give a well-defined peak, a useful and convenient method for detection of—specifically—adsorbed water might result.

The present author generally uses calcined alumina as diluent or inert material but has used other materials for special problems. Magnesium oxide, powdered fused quartz, manganese magnesium ferrite, and even powdered silicon have been useful, as well as organic materials for organic problems. The author has no particular procedure to recommend in selecting an inert material except to try substances as like the sample as possible. When a special problem requires a special reference material, it is selected quite empirically. Fortunately, the problem does not arise often. A drifting base line does not discompose the author unless there is some chance that an effect might be missed, but this would require a very rapid drift. Of course, if one were trying to measure the peak area anything more than a very small drift could not be tolerated; the operator must choose his reference material to suit the particular problem. Of prime importance, the base line drift—or shift—must be reproducible. So long as the deviation is reproducible it will be, or at least can be, compensated for in calibration. The resulting error will be relatively small.

Careful matching of the inert material to the sample material, in those cases in which it might be successful, is seldom profitable except in those cases in which a larger number of samples are to be run and compared with one another.

3.8. Effect of Packing

The tightness of packing affects the thermogram in two ways: in all cases it affects the transfer of heat from the wall of the sample cavity to the thermocouple junction, but in decompositions it also affects the diffusion of gases in or out. Let us consider the effects in that order.

In the absence of any forced passage of gas or a need to modify diffusion, forced passage of tight packing is generally preferable; not only does it decrease the thermal gradient by increasing the thermal conductivity (see above discussion on choice of inert material) but it is more reproducible. Kissinger (K29), on the other hand, was able to get reproducible packing by treating the specimens uniformly—tapping the side of the sample vessel to compact the specimen. To a limited degree, packing differences may be used to alter the diffusivity and thereby help to match reference to sample, but this can only be recommended as a shift. Arens (A12) found rather severe differences (Fig. III-22) on thermograms of quartz and kaolinite. Unduly loose packing of the specimen yields the effect of a long-drawn-out endotherm because the lower thermal conductivity produces a larger temperature lag.

The effect of packing on decompositions will depend on the conditions of atmosphere accessibility (see Chapter VII). If one is using a closed-chamber sample holder the packing should be tight simply to delay any appreciable reaction as long as possible.

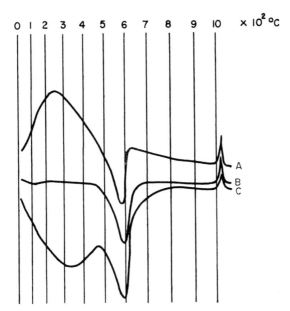

FIG. III-22. The influence of tightness of packing on differential thermal analysis records: A, tightly packed kaolinite, loosely packed reference; B, kaolinite and reference tightly packed; and C, loosely packed kaolinite and tightly packed reference. From Arens (A12).

The tighter packing provides better heat conduction and leads to base line displacement if the packing is poorly matched.

In a static atmosphere with a comparatively thin specimen (see Chapter VII) the sample needs to be compacted only slightly. This is necessarily a compromise between the very loose packing which would inhibit diffusion less and the tighter packing which facilitates heat transfer.

A dynamic atmosphere has its own special problem. Since "diffusion" occurs under the influence of a gaseous pressure gradient, the packing may be relatively tight; the flow will be controlled, in part, by the pressure drop across the specimen. A very firmly packed specimen might possibly have a sufficient pressure difference across it to affect the reaction temperature but this is rather unlikely. The firm packing does permit better heat exchange between solid and gas as well as between particles. A dynamic atmosphere differential thermal analysis sample, then, should be packed firmly unless there is reason to believe that there is a deleterious effect on the particular system under study. In short, the degree of packing is a matter of convenience. The present author is generally concerned with the nature of the reaction rather than the magnitude of the heat effect, so only moderate reproducibility of packing is sufficient; the specimen is usually pressed down with a rod (or drill bit) held fairly firmly between thumb and two fingers.

If the peak height or area is to be measured and compared to another, somewhat more attention to reproducibility is needed. Whether Kissinger's (K29) technique is sufficient or whether the material must be compacted with considerable force will probably depend on the material involved. The present author is not prepared to offer a generally applicable opinion; the experimenter is constrained to assure himself that he can obtain reproducible curves.

Note, however, that reproducible packing is not necessarily good packing; the reproducible packing should still be firm enough to permit reasonable heat flow. While Kissinger's technique is, from the present author's experience, generally suitable for clays and many inorganic powders, it would not be suitable, for example, for some of the hydrated carbonates of magnesium. These might be compacted only 20% by tapping but an additional 50% by pressing. The data are experimental but only approximate.

3.9. The Effect of Covering Sample Holes

Covering the sample holes has an effect ascribed by some to the elimination of direct radiation from the furnace wall into the specimen. While this radiation or lack thereof may have some small effect, the change in results is principally an atmosphere effect (see Chapter VII). The cover inhibits, to some degree, the diffusion and escape of gaseous reaction products or ingress of reacting gases. Arens (A12) reported specifically on the effect of covering the sample holes on thermograms of two clay minerals (Fig. III-1). Note that there is no shift of the exothermic reactions.

The present author has found that simply loosely covering the sample holder is not adequate. It will cause a shift of temperatures, of course, in reversible or oxidation reactions, but the peak shifting is not so great as in a closed-chamber sample holder because the vapor pressure of the reaction product gas does not reach the ambient pressure. This shows *per se* that there is diffusion both ways and the ambient atmosphere can enter the sample hole. This raises the possibility—or indeed the probability—that the atmosphere within will not be reproducible temperature by temperature from run to run and hence the peak temperatures will similarly be less reproducible than they ought to be. Differences in particle size might cause sufficient difference in reaction rates that the exchange of gases has a significant effect. Bear in mind that the equilibrium vapor pressure expression says nothing about rate of decomposition.

Consider two specimens of clay, identical except for particle size. Since we can assume that under a given set of temperature and partial pressure conditions the rate of diffusion of the gaseous decomposition product within the particle affects the rate of decomposition, we can also assume, for convenience, that our smaller particles are of such a small size that diffusion within the entire solid particle occurs instantly. We shall further assume for the purpose of this discussion that the larger particles are of such size that diffusion within the particle takes a measurable time. Now let us heat these two specimens in lightly covered sample holes allowing a small exchange of gases and also in a closed-chamber sample holder allowing—in effect—gases to escape but not enter.

As the specimens are heated, the finer particles will tend to decompose first in either sample holder but the increase of the partial pressure prevents complete decomposition immediately. Since we have both a rising temperature and a tendency to dilute by ingress of the ambient atmosphere the reaction in the lightly covered sample hole continues at an ever-increasing rate until the material is exhausted. The increase in rate of decomposition is partially vitiated by the increase in gaseous diffusion rate with temperature. Under the same conditions, the larger particles will begin to decompose in much the same manner, but as soon as the decomposition has progressed a few layers deep, it can no longer maintain equilibrium as could the smaller particles. The progress of the decomposition now depends more and more on the increase of the reaction rate with temperature, but it is obviously not at equilibrium with the atmosphere within the sample hole. Since the reaction rate increases exponentially with temperature there will finally be a rapid decomposition of the remainder of the specimen; in order to achieve such a rate, the temperature has probably reached the point corresponding to an equilibrium vapor pressure equal to the ambient atmosphere. Compare this set of events with those in the closed-chamber sample holder.

As stated above, the smaller particles will tend to react first simply because it is the nature of small particles to react more readily than large (surface imperfections, i.e., unsatisfied valences such as at corners, occur more frequently on small particles than on large, other parameters being equal), but the surface of the larger particles does not lag far behind. Since only enough of either specimen to satisfy the equilibrium vapor pressure requirement will decompose, not much really happens. Very little of the material needs to decompose to keep the partial pressure increasing properly, so the problems arising from slow diffusion in the solid particles will probably not be of any concern. The temperature meanwhile is increasing to that corresponding to equilibrium at the ambient pressure. As the temperature increases, the reaction rate increases and so does the diffusion rate within the particles, even though the net reaction is inconsequential. By the time the partial pressure within the chamber exceeds the ambient pressure and gas begins to leave rapidly, the total rate of decomposition of the large particles is fairly rapid and the decomposition will be complete not much later than that of the finer particles. Depending on the identity of the material and the particle sizes, the peak shift may be so small as to be imperceptible. It will almost certainly be negligible.

The relative ease of diffusion into the covered hole raises the possibility of reaction with the atmosphere but at a rate that may be so low as to leave some doubt (from the thermogram alone) that a reaction even occurred. An oxidation, for example, may well begin at the usual temperature, but the limited supply of oxygen limits the rate so that it is spread out over a wider temperature range than in an uncovered hole. Note, however, that if the ambient atmosphere were pure oxygen rather than air the consumption of oxygen would draw in an equal volume of oxygen and the reaction would go on because a steady (actually an increasing) supply is available. In air, on the other hand, as a volume of oxygen is used less than one-fifth of this volume is brought in as direct replacement. Any further supply must be supplied by diffusion (see also Chapter VII).

The present author uses a long thin cylindrical diffusion path instead of a cover as a barrier, but even a 3-inch path no more than 0.003 inch thick and ¼ inch in diameter does not completely prevent oxidation. The edges of the hemispherical sample (Fig. III-23) sometimes show signs of oxidation with appropriate samples; nevertheless there may be striking differences in the nature of the reactions.

3.10. The Influence of the Composition of the Furnace Atmosphere

The advantages of using a known atmosphere are covered extensively in other parts of this book. The discussion here will be limited to the effects of ambient air. Even in static heating dehydration experiments Nutting (N16) found "In the lower range of temperature, weight curves vary with the humidity, an effect which vanishes above about 160°C." Since a material will have no tendency to lose weight until its vapor pressure exceeds the ambient partial pressure (Chapter VII), a crystalline hydrate that may be stable up to a given temperature on a very damp day will decompose at a lower temperature on a dry day. Arens (A12) gives a range of 30–40°C for kaolinite.

Similarly, the decomposition temperatures of carbonates—as measured in ambient air—may well vary from laboratory to laboratory, being generally higher for laboratories in cities or associated with manufacturing plants, ranging from 300 to 600 ppm (C11a). The magnitude of the temperature shift will depend on the extant relative concentrations of carbon dioxide and, of course, the heat and temperature of decomposition of the particular carbonate.

3.11. The Particle Size of Clay Minerals

Arens (p. 55) also discusses the particle size of the clay, reporting the work of Kelly and co-workers, Perkins, Speil, and Kulp and Kerr. These workers all report that the grinding of clays results in a decreased intensity of reaction (see Chapter II). This decreased intensity of reaction is

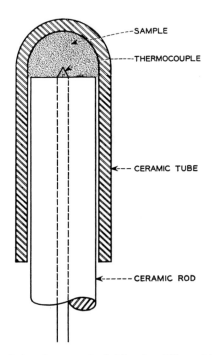

FIG. III-23. Closed-chamber sample holder for differential thermal analysis. *The long diffusion path inhibits but does not completely prevent exchange of gases.*

related to the crystallinity effect also discussed by Arens. The effect of the grinding is to raise the surface energy of the clay or other material such that a portion of the material will react at a considerably lower temperature. The surface energies of the various particles should follow some statistical relation and a continuous breakdown of particles would occur from this lower temperature of initiation up to the original temperature of reaction.

3.12. The Nature of the Clay Minerals Present

The fact that the thermogram depends for its appearance on the nature of the material present is naturally of basic importance in differential thermal analysis; we are concerned here with the effect of one material on the thermogram of another. Arens (A12, p. 52) refers to the work of Agafonoff (A2), Orcel (O6), and Caillère and Hénin (C2), showing peak shifting as a consequence of mixing. Caillère and Hénin compared the effect to the lowering of melting points of mixed systems. Arens disagrees, pointing out, "the reaction temperatures are not systematically lowered in DTA, but sometimes increase by the presence of admixtures. There exists consequently a fundamental difference between the two phenomena." The present author agrees. This effect generally should be traceable to the evolution of dissimilar gases in the case of lowering the reaction temperatures or similar gases in the case of raising the reaction temperature. In the case of the dissimilar gases, the formation and movement of either gas is necessarily going to sweep out the other gas, thereby lowering the partial pressure of the second gas. If the reactions occur simultaneously, each gas acts strongly to reduce the partial pressure of the other, and in turn its own partial pressure is being held to a lower value than would otherwise occur. The raising of a reaction temperature can occur in those cases in which a reaction has already occurred such that the interstices are at least partially filled with the product gas. This rather substantial increase in the partial pressure of this gas raises the reaction temperature for the subsequent decomposition (see Chapter VII).

An example of the effect of an earlier reaction is in the work of Webb and Heystek (W11) who show that (Fig. III-24) dehydration of magnesium hydroxide delays the decomposition peak of calcium hydroxide ca. 50°C higher than in the absence of magnesium hydroxide even though the first dehydration is essentially over by the time the calcium hydroxide peak would otherwise begin. The cause is simply the high concentration of water vapor left behind among the particles. The calcium hydroxide is diluted to 10% in each case but the alumina dilution has air rather than water vapor to displace so the reaction occurs at a relatively low temperature. The peak temperature is lower than in pure calcium hydroxide (ca. 585°C) because of the dilution effect; i.e., the ease of diffusion is about ten times greater per unit of water vapor or hydrate so the vapor pressure is less likely to approach ambient pressure and the hydrate can decompose at a lower temperature than with a pure sample.

Diffusion of water vapor out of the sample matrix is as important in the magnesium hydroxide dilution as raising the temperature; the dehydration peak is still lower than that of pure calcium hydroxide, show-ing that even with the high initial concentration the water partial pressure does not maintain the value reached during decomposition of pure calcium hydroxide.

3.13. Comparison of Records Obtained with Different Equipment

Arens obtained a "general equation" for the comparison of reaction temperatures in curves obtained with different DTA equipment:

$$\hat{T} = T_{observed} - \tfrac{1}{4} r^2 C \left(1/fa - 1/f'a'\right) - Q \log T/4.571\, b(b - \log p),$$

in which $\hat{T}'$ is the asymptotic reaction temperature in degrees Centigrade or Kelvin; $T_{observed}$ is the experimentally obtained initial or peak reaction temperature; r is the sample cavity radius in centimeters; C is the heating rate in degrees Centigrade per second; f and f' are dimensionless constants; a and a' are the thermal diffusivities of the sample and reference materials, respectively, in square centimeters per second; Q is the heat of reaction in calories per mole; p is the appropri-

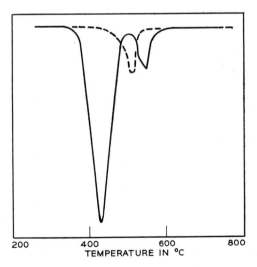

200   400   600   800
TEMPERATURE IN °C

Fig. III-24. Thermograms of calcium hydroxide diluted with: _____, magnesium hydroxide; - - -, alumina. From Webb and Heystek (W11).

The prior decomposition of the magnesium hydroxide leaves behind an atmosphere greatly enriched with water vapor; this vapor raises the decomposition temperature of the calcium hydroxide. A rather abrupt beginning of the record decomposition should be expected.

ate pressure in millimeters of mercury; and b represents the variation in the heat of reaction with temperature.

In his comparisons, Arens used the ambient partial pressure of the appropriate gas when using the initial observed temperature and assumes $p = 760$ mm of mercury when using the peak observed temperature. The first assumption is reasonable only in those cases in which no reaction has occurred prior to the one under examination; for if a reaction has occurred which involves evolution of a gas, the composition of the vapors within the sample has been modified. Diffusion of gases into and out of the sample is a reasonably rapid process; nevertheless, a substantial modification of the atmosphere composition may remain for many minutes and consequently 100 or more degrees. The second assumption is clearly incorrect. In conventional sample holders, i.e., sample blocks or cups with top openings of the same order of magnitude as the depth, the partial pressure of the product gas does not reach one atmosphere. If the pressure did equal one atmosphere at the peak, the reaction would show no effect of covering the sample holes and yet Arens shows from his own work the effect of covering sample holes for two clays, halloysite and indianaite. His plots show clearly a difference on the order of 50°C in the peak temperature for the 600°C peak.

Arens proves the applicability of this equation by a substitution of some data obtained from runs using kaolinite from Zettlitz, and obtains the numerical values $\hat{T} = 480 - 9 - 57 = 414°C$. He cites an expected value of $\hat{T}$ of $420 \pm 10°C$. (The above data were for the initial temperatures of the deflection.) He then inserted the appropriate data for the peak observed temperature leading to the equation $\hat{T} = 590 - 9 - 162 = 419°C$. This appears to be a good agreement until one realizes that the temperature of initiation is suspect. Arens' data from Zettlitz kaolinite shows clearly that there is a reaction between 100 and 200°C and, since this reaction probably is a dehydration, $\log p$ is almost certainly too low and consequently the largest correction value is likewise too low; hence the apparent agreement is unrealistic.

Arens also relates this general equation to qualitative analysis by showing that when an asymptotic reaction temperature could be calculated the material causing the deflection could be determined. He cites a clay as an example, finding a $\hat{T}$ of 598°C and in Table 10, p. 86, he cites the $\hat{T}$ for calcite as 610°C. It is appropriate to examine the definition of T' on p. 78: "We define T' as the absolute temperature at which the reaction starts and finishes in a time approaching infinite, under a heating rate $C = 0$ and under a vapor pressure of the volatile component approaching 0." This temperature is necessarily one at which the vapor pressure cannot be measured. Hence, if a vapor pressure can be measured this asymptotic reaction temperature value is incorrect. Let us look first at calcite and its cited asymptotic reaction temperature of 610°C. Smyth and Adams (S35) found a dissociation pressure of ca 2 mm Hg in this temperature range. Similarly for kaolinite and its suggested asymptotic reaction temperature of 420°, there is present a sizable concentration of water vapor contributed partly by the ambient atmosphere and partly by the reaction. [Nutting (N16) reports an initiation temperature in the order of 380°C.]

The values cited by the comparison of data by different observers show only a moderate agreement and hence could fit other expressions for the asymptotic reaction temperature equally well. Because of the considerable uncertainty in the values which must be used, there is sufficient error in this expression and its use so that its validity is questionable. On the other hand, its invalidity is also not proved. The lack of any really suitable method for comparison of results from apparatus to apparatus points up the necessity for obtaining differential thermal analysis curves under known thermodynamic conditions.

Nonetheless, if Arens' work had been more generally known—and used —by others active in the field, the art of differential thermal analysis would have advanced more rapidly than it has. It would still remain an art, however, for while Arens observed well and reached generally well-founded conclusions of a qualitative nature, his approach to a quantitative treatment of differential thermal analysis was not soundly based.

Arens (A12) assumed that if two substances or objects, not necessarily alike, are heated in the same furnace at the same rate, each will be supplied with the same number of calories. This means that at a constant heating rate $dT/dt =$ constant; so also is $dQ/dt =$ constant. MacKenzie and Farmer (M5) pointed out two such cases, the first in Arens opening assumptions on theoretical considerations (cf. Chapter IV of ref. A12). Arens, ignoring for the moment the thermal conductivity, set down the expressions, for the inert sample,

$$c_1 = \frac{Q}{m_1(T_2 - T_1)}$$

and for the clay sample,

$$c_2 = \frac{Q}{m_2(T_2' - T_1)}$$

where c_1 and c_2 are the heat capacities and m_1 and m_2 the masses. He then stated "Q is equal for both samples in one and the same furnace." With this assumption he concludes that one can obtain a straight base (or zero) line when $c_1m_1 = c_2m_2$, which conclusion has been quoted and acted upon by later workers. Obviously, since (T_2-T_1) must equal (T'_2-T_1), the equality must be

$$\frac{Q_1}{m_1 c_1} = \frac{Q_2}{m_2 c_2}$$

and therefore the condition necessary for a straight zero line is simply that, if one sample has a higher $m \times c$ than the other, more heat must be supplied to it, but see Chapter II.

Similarly, MacKenzie and Farmer call attention to the time-of-reaction equation

$$t = \frac{qm}{(c_1 m_1 + c_2 m_2 + \ldots)} \cdot \frac{1}{C}$$

where q is the number of calories needed to raise the temperature from the initial temperature, T_i, to the final temperature, T_f, at heating rate C. This equation is not valid; MacKenzie and Farmer attribute its non-applicability to the assumption that the quantity $T_f - T_i$ is independent of heating rate; the present author suspects that it is a recurrence of the uniform addition of heat assumption. In his discussion of nickel and ceramic sample blocks Arens states "the heat supplied per unit of time (dQ/dT) is the same in one furnace for all types of blocks. . ." (see Sec. 3.3).

MacKenzie and Farmer also disagreed with Arens' derivation of an expression for the area under an endothermic peak, part of which is the heat flow into the sample. Arens describes this as

$$\int_0^t \Delta T_2 \, dt \text{ (heat supply)} = \frac{Q m_1}{c_1 m_1 + c_2 m_2 + \ldots} \int_0^t \frac{1}{2} \, dt$$

which is the integration of a straight line; i.e., the flow of heat into the sample is constant during the course of the reaction.

MacKenzie and Farmer raised objections to Arens "asymptotic reaction temperature" which he calculates from

$$T_{\text{observed}} - \hat{T} = \frac{Q}{4.571(b - \log p)} - \frac{Q}{4.571 \, b}$$

where $b = \Sigma v \cdot 1.75 \log T + \Sigma v \epsilon + \log 760$,
  Q = heat of reaction,
  p = partial pressure of gaseous product in mm Hg,
  $\hat{T}$ = the asymptotic reaction temperature,
  v = number of moles of gas formed, and
  ϵ = conventional chemical constant.

The term "log 760" arises from Arens' assuming that (1) the maximum rate of reaction occurs at the peak temperature and (2) the partial pressure of the reaction product is then equal to the ambient pressure. MacKenzie and Farmer take exception to the first and the present author to both of these statements. The assumption of most rapid reaction at the peak temperature is at variance with practically all other observers. The peak temperature occurs—in an endothermal reaction—at the *time* when the point of measurement lags in temperature most behind the reference or furnace temperature. This is obviously true from the manner of measurement. In a cylindrical sample reacting uniformly about the axis, this ought to be at the time the material at the axis reacts, but since the reaction front or surface is shrinking it is hardly likely that the maximum rate of reaction is reached at that time. The present author believes that the temperature of maximum rate of reaction cannot be identified from a differential thermal analysis peak. It should depend not only on the geometry of the sample but also on the relative thermal diffusivities before and after the reaction, the heat of reaction, the ease of diffusion of the gas evolved and the ambient gas, and very decidedly on the heating rate (see Chapter V for other opinions).

The second assumption is only a poor approximation. One of the major reasons for variation of peak temperature with heating rate is the variation of the atmosphere within the sample. A slow heating rate permits interchange of product with ambient gas rapidly enough to avoid a really great enrichment; an extremely high heating rate will enable the product gas to sweep out nearly all the ambient gas; intermediate heating rates will yield an intermediate condition. This peak temperature will even vary with depth of placement of the thermocouple, because the ambient atmosphere partial pressure will be quite pronounced near the top of the sample well.

3.14. Effect of Particle Size and Grinding

A naturally formed surface of a mineral particle can be presumed to be fairly stable, otherwise it would have reverted to a stable state before reaching the thermal analysis laboratory. Recently formed surfaces are quite a different problem. The added surface activity of ground or milled samples is demonstrated strikingly by the Schaller and Vlisidis' (S8) report that powdered siderite had spontaneously oxidized at ambient temperatures. The ferrous iron content, reported as FeO, decreased from 59.42 to 6.23% in 29 years and to 0.74% in 43 years. Chunks of siderite do not oxidize in a similar time. Similarly, freshly formed surfaces can be expected to react at lower temperatures or more vigorously in thermal analysis studies, as (Fig. III-25) do the asbestos specimens described by Martinez (M19).

Even among naturally formed particles one may reasonably expect to find differences in reactivity depending especially on particle size. Let us consider the effect of subdivision of a cube, but let us first recall that a particle is unlikely to be equally reactive all over its surface. Corners or other discontinuities will tend to react before a smooth surface. Even different crystal faces will differ in reactivity.

Assume for the moment that we have a cube of some material and that it is a perfect single crystal of unit length. It has, of course, eight cor-

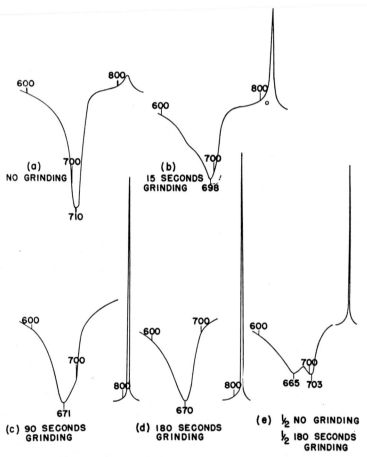

Fig. III-25. Differential thermal analyses of chrysolite asbestos samples ground in Wig-L-Bug for varying lengths of time. From Martinez (M19).

The short-term grinding has produced a substantial change in the thermal effects.

ners, twelve edges with a total length of twelve units, and six faces with a total area of six square units. Let us now subdivide this crystal into perfect single crystals one-tenth unit on the side. These thousand crystals have eight thousand corners, twelve thousand edges with a total length of twelve hundred units, and six thousand faces with a total area of sixty square units. The less reactive portions of the surface increase slowly compared to the much more reactive corners and edges. Continue the subdivision and again the more reactive portions multiply rapidly so that a gram or a cubic centimeter of a material may have a wide range of "active regions," depending on the particle size. The reactivity can then be expected to vary inversely with the particle size.

These differences in reactivity are unimportant for most materials at room temperature. (If the reactivity were substantial, some process would have occurred to relieve this driving force.) If the particles are heated, though, this hitherto negligible difference in reactivity can become important. As the sample approaches a temperature at which even a plane surface will react the discontinuities, whether corners, edges, or cracks, will naturally tend to react first—hence finer particles tend to react to a greater extent at a given temperature.

It is not necessary to postulate cubes; any geometry leads to the same general conclusion: assuming that natural materials are the same in reactive behavior except for particle size, the smaller particles will be more reactive (Fig. III-26) because as the surface area is increased so are the unsaturated valences, especially at discontinuities whether they are corners, edges, cracks, lattice defects, or just plane surface.

The artificial diminution of particle size by grinding yields more striking results than does separation of naturally occurring particles. The naturally occurring particles have had time for degeneration of the surface irregularities which lead to increased reactivity. Corners and edges are rounded, cracks become cleavages, and the new edges become curves. Even impurities may disappear from the surface perhaps by leaching; the particle may be covered by materials adsorbed on the surface. Contrast this condition with freshly formed surfaces.

A newly formed surface has a degree of disorder greatly dependent on the method of formation of the surface: precipitation cannot be expected to form the same type of surfaces as grinding, so even specimens of a small particle size range may show considerably different thermal effects. The newly formed surfaces from either grinding or precipitation will not have had much opportunity to react in any way to destroy the active regions, so there should be a marked difference between these and well-aged surfaces. Let us examine some data showing these various effects.

Kulp, Kent, and Kerr (K42) crushed a sample of Santa Fe calcite and sieved the powder to separate various size fractions. Their data (Fig. III-27) show only a slight reduction in reaction temperature in four size fractions down to 200 mesh. They extended the range of study to smaller particles by grinding some of the finest fraction to pass the 200-mesh screen. Now an effect appears more clearly, the reaction begins at a distinctly lower temperature, and at 900°C the deflection is greater than for the next larger size, yet the temperature range of the reaction is well above that of either the deep sea sedimentary calcite or the freshly precipitated calcium carbonate.

We can safely assume that crushing a sample—as Kulp, Kent, and Kerr did—will cause cleavage along reasonably well-defined crystal directions so that, while new faces are formed, reactivity of the particle is not increased very much. Grinding of 120–200 mesh particles to pass 200

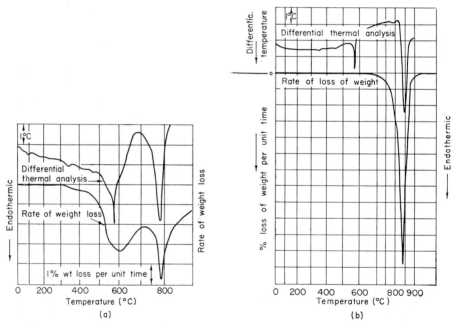

(a)   (b)

Fɪɢ. III-26. Differential thermal analysis and rate of loss of weight against temperature for 85 mole parts SiO_2–15 mole parts Na_2CO_3 mixture: (a) both grain sizes below 300 BSS; and (b) both materials between 72 and 100 BSS. From Thomasson and Wilburn (T7a).

The higher reactivity of the smaller particles is reflected in the substantial reaction below 700°C in (a). The lowered final reaction temperature in (a) is due to the formation of a eutectic between the sodium carbonate and the silicate formed by the early reaction.

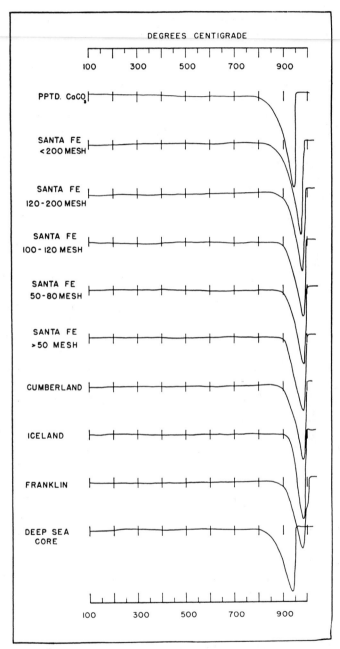

FIG. III-27. DTA curves of various specimens of calcite and of various particle sizes for the Santa Fe–Iceland spar. From Kulp *et al.* (K42).

The precipitated calcium carbonate and that from the deep sea core have relatively high reactivity.

mesh does not constitute a major operation but the initiation and completion of the decomposition both occur at lower temperatures; this is due partially to decrease of particle size and partly to distortion of the lattice which we shall consider further below. The passage of a particle through a 200-mesh sieve implies only that two perpendicular directions can be defined such that at no point in the particle does the width along either of these exceed 74 μ. The third dimension is unspecified; acicular particles have some reasonably substantial probability of getting through. We know from this that the particles which get through the sieve can still have an average cross section of 74 μ or more. We can surely assume that the average size is at least 50 μ. Newly precipitated crystals can be expected to have imperfectly formed faces and edges and usually a small particle size. Sedimentary carbonate ought to be small (sedimentary clays are in the order of 5 μ) but the surfaces should be uniform. Whether the effect is due to particle size alone or surface imperfections as well as particle size, the decomposition temperature range of these calcium carbonates is lower than that of a lightly ground specimen.

When particles are subjected to more vigorous treatment more striking results than a mere shift in temperature may be obtained. Dry grinding, usually done by ball milling, is a repeated abrasion of the particle under the impact of the falling balls. Strains are built up in the surface layers so that they will tend to undergo reaction more readily because of the high-energy state.

McLaughlin (M28) showed the change in reaction temperatures for dickite, a clay mineral related to kaolin. The curves are shown in Fig. III-28. He started with the 2–20 μ fraction (nearly all the material was in this range) and ground it in a mechanical mortar and pestle. The dry-ground samples show an immediate drop in reaction temperature of a portion of the material (curve 2), with some remaining apparently unchanged. After 6 hr no trace of the original material remains and the total 500–700°C dehydration peak has lost much of its magnitude.

The simultaneous appearance of an endothermic peak in the 100–300°C range indicates prior water adsorption but, more important, the great spread of this water loss is evidence that the water is held by a range of bonding strength. These forces arise from the high energy of the distorted surface; the localized heating and the shearing forces resulting from each impact leave their mark in the form of a greatly disturbed surface layer. McLaughlin reports that X-ray diffraction lines began to disappear after 2 hours dry grinding and noticeable changes in the lattice dimensions occurred, particularly an increase along the Z axis. Other spacing showed both increases and decreases. The high surface energy is most strikingly demonstrated by the enhanced exothermic reaction shown by the dry-ground specimens ca. 980°C. Now that a temperature is reached at which another form is more stable the individual ions can move around and rearrange to the new crystal structure. The additional energy from the lattice distortion on the surface is now readily lost and appears as increased heat of reaction.

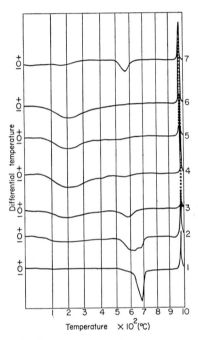

FIG. III-28. Differential thermal curves for dickites: 1, unground material; 2, ground 2 hours; 3, ground 6 hours; 4, ground 15 hours; 5, ground 24 hours; 6, ground 140 hours; 7, ground wet 60 hours. From McLaughlin (M28).
The wet grinding (curve 7) has relatively little disruptive effect on the crystallinity.

In contrast to all this, the specimen ground wet for 60 hours shows a slight broad low-temperature endotherm, a broadening and lowering (by ca. 120°C) of the normal dehydration, and a quite normal exotherm at 980°C. The lowering of the temperature appears to be the ordinary particle size effect; the broadening is probably due to a great increase in particle size range. McLaughlin points out that "the material ground wet 60 hours lies intermediate in size between 2 hours and 6 hours dry grinding" and concludes that "very long periods of wet grinding would be needed to reach the equilibrium which is apparently obtained after

15 hours dry grinding." The present author disagrees. The effect of 60 hours wet grinding can probably not be achieved by 2–6 hours of dry grinding nor will the effect of 15 hours of dry grinding be duplicated by a couple of months of wet grinding.

Wet grinding in moderation brings about some changes in reactivity but frequently, at least, these changes are in the direction of enhanced peaks. Caillère and Hénin (C2a) have shown (Fig. III-29) that chlorite minerals show better definition of peaks after wet grinding and a general simplification of the thermogram. The lowering of temperatures by grinding is probably due simply to the relative ease of escape of the water from the smaller particles. In a controlled-atmosphere experiment (using water vapor), the peaks would presumably begin at the same temperature in both samples, but the peaks for the ground sample would be extremely sharp compared to those of the unground material.

A large portion of the distortion of the surface of the dry-ground par-

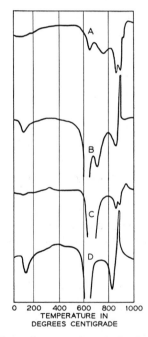

0   200   400   600   800   1000
TEMPERATURE IN
DEGREES CENTIGRADE

Fɪɢ. III-29. Differential thermal curves for: A, leuchten bergite, Beramy, Madagascar, -60 mesh; B, same mineral particles $<2 \mu$ esd.; C, clinochlore, Besafotra, Madagascar, -60 mesh; D, same mineral, particles $<2 \mu$ esd. From Caillère and Hénin (C2a).

The exothermic peaks in B and D have shifted enough to obscure any evidence for the second part of the double endothermic peaks in A and C.

ticles is due to the local heating resulting from the impact and shearing. The wet-ground specimen does not show distortion to nearly the same degree simply because each impact, each scrape, and each abrasion is fluid-cooled. Any significant tendency to heat a portion of a surface would bring about vaporization of a little of the grinding fluid in contact with the surface so that the areas that reached temperatures much above the boiling point would be rare indeed.

The effect of particle size, then, is related to the method of producing the particle size. Wet grinding—not necessarily wet with water—should produce much less of a surface distortion than dry grinding. The effect of dry grinding is to produce a high-energy surface—probably quite useful in preparing materials for reaction—which cannot be depended on to show thermal effects closely like those of the original material. Dempster and Ritchie (D10), for example, dry-ground quartz enough to form a surface layer (M3) thick enough, apparently, to insulate the interior and prevent detection of the low-energy α-β transition at 573°C. The coating formed was probably similar to fused quartz, i.e., amorphous and with little tendency to crystallize. Since the α-β transition represents little movement as well as little energy, even repeated passage through the transition would not likely crystallize much of the amorphous layer. The added layer through which heat must pass and the irregularity of that layer could easily cause diffuseness of the peak sufficient to render its existence uncertain.

Whether or not the means of dry grinding has a great influence on the nature of the surfaces produced has not—to the present author's knowledge—been established. Some inferences may be drawn by comparing the McLaughlin work discussed above with that reported by Gregg *et al.* (G42). These latter authors studied kaolinite rather than dickite but these minerals are very similar—at least from a nonmineralogist's viewpoint. Gregg, Parker, and Stephens milled a china clay (95% kaolinite with some mica, tourmaline, feldspar, and quartz) in a pebble mill at 25 rpm for 1000 hours, taking samples at intervals for measurement of specific surface, apparent density in carbon tetrachloride, bulk density *in vacuo*, particle size distribution, and base exchange capacity. In addition specimens were studied by X-ray diffraction, dissolution in hydrochloric acid, and thermogravimetry.

In general, the particles decreased in size but eventually began to agglomerate so that the specific surface and the base exchange capacity passed through a maximum about midway through the grinding period. Of special interest are the weight-loss curves. Figure III-30 shows the rate of weight loss as a function of temperature, Δ_W/Δ_T vs T. Compare the curves for 576 hours to that for 2 hours in Fig. III-26.

The inference from the limited data would be that ball (or pebble) milling—like wet grinding—is much slower than mortar-and-pestle grinding. This may be true, but there is at least a high probability that the results differ in kind as well as in degree. Recall that McLaughlin found changes in spacing but still a recognizable X-ray diffraction pattern in specimens ground dry for 140 hours. On the other hand, Gregg *et al.* report that the X-ray diffraction lines "become progressively broader and weaker against a darkening background until, at 1000 hours, no pattern

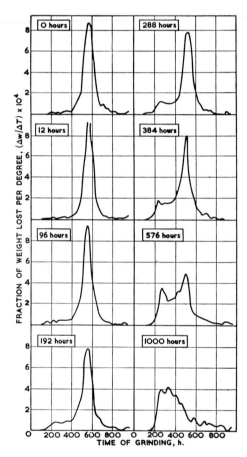

Fɪɢ. III-30. Grinding of kaolin. The thermogravimetric analysis of the ground samples. In each graph the fractional loss of weight per degree is plotted against the temperature of the furnace. The time of grinding is marked on each sample. From Gregg *et al.* (G42).

Only after ca. 20 days milling does the kaolin peak at 600°C diminish greatly.

could be identified." Even mild-acid treatment restored the pattern of kaolinite only up to the 576-hour sample.

Just how different the two treatments ought to be is rather hard to judge. The falling of a ball or pebble results in a fairly reproducible impact but how this impact is distributed among the particles on which the ball falls will probably vary along with the particle size and shape. We may easily infer, nevertheless, that a given impact will cause a range of effect from a high tendency to fracture the particles directly in line with the impact to a greater tendency to shear the particles to the side of the line of impact, but of course the force diminishes with the cosine of the angle. A mechanically driven mortar and pestle will have principally a shearing action. Note here that a manually operated mortar and pestle will have a range of behavior from crushing to shearing depending on the operator and the sample. This effect would likely be highly irreproducible if it were measurable. Fortunately the reduction of particle size to the 100-mesh range will not often produce noticeable surface effects. Few experimenters will go to finer size ranges manually.

The conclusion to be reached is that, if the particle size of a specimen must be reduced, even the method used must be chosen with consideration of possible effects. This applies especially to the very fine sizes. As we reduce the particle size of a material by some given method, at some point the effects of surface irregularities will become noticeable against the behavior of the bulk material. As the size reduction continues this surface layer becomes a greater portion of the whole particle and will determine the behavior of the particle to a greater and greater extent. The sample sizes at which the surface effect appears or predominates can be expected to vary not only with the manner of particle size reduction but also from material to material.

3.15. Summary

The values of the several parameters must be chosen to suit the problem. A high rate of heating will offer more sensitivity for detection at a risk of loss of resolution. Depending on the type of apparatus, peak shifting may or may not occur with a change in heating rate.

The material chosen for the sample block will depend on the temperature range. Ceramic materials are available with thermal conductivities as good as commonly used high-temperature alloys and with superior surface heat-transfer properties.

For changes in condensed states, the design of the sample block can introduce small aberrations due to assymmetry of heating of the sample. For decompositions or reactions producing or using a gas pronounced changes will appear with different designs arising from differences in accessibility to the atmosphere. The nature of the change will depend on the atmosphere and the material.

Thermocouples are generally placed as near as possible to the center of symmetry to obtain the maximum signal. Other arrangements are usable but the form of the differential signal will be different. The size of the thermocouple will have a relatively small effect unless the wire— or shield—is large enough to conduct appreciable heat to or from the sample.

The inert substance ought to be chosen to match the total heat-transfer characteristics of the material being studied, but these characteristics often change drastically upon occurrence of some thermal event. An empirically chosen reference material (such as calcined aluminum oxide) is often used. The sample may also be diluted to a point at which the thermal properties of the diluent obscure those of the sample; the diluent is used also as the reference material.

The particle size and often the means of obtaining the particle size will influence the peak shapes. On very fine particles the surface characteristics obtained by grinding may predominate.

CHAPTER IV

Apparatus for Differential Thermal Analysis

4.1. Introduction

For many reasons, most workers in the field of differential thermal analysis have constructed their own apparatus. The principal reason has been the usually well-founded conviction that no apparatus with which he was familiar would give him the particular information he needed. We may assume that the new features introduced in a particular apparatus were usually of some benefit in the type of study for which it was designed. To extrapolate this assumption to conclude that any particular innovation is of general utility would be rash. The discussion of apparatus following relates to specific types and includes in many cases the present author's evaluation.

Some discussion of principles pertaining especially to differential thermal analysis is included. More general topics are explained or described in Chapters XIV–XVI. Special types of sample holders are described in this chapter even though some properties or characteristics of sample holders in general are discussed in Chapters II, III, and V.

107

Except to illustrate a particular feature, the extant commercially available apparatus are not discussed in detail. A description would become obsolete almost during the printing time for a book not only because of additions but also because of changes. We will be concerned herein with principles by which to judge the suitability of an apparatus. A list of suppliers is offered in Appendix I.

4.2. Furnace Orientation

Whether a horizontal or a vertical furnace should be used will depend mostly on individual preferences; both have advantages. Horizontal furnaces can generally be constructed for greater ease of manipulation; a track allowing rather accurate positioning can be easily supported on a bench top, making the sample support easily accessible to the operator. Vertical furnaces of some contemporary designs will have the sample position at or above eye level when set on a standard bench. If the heating element with insulation is heavy and/or bulky it matters little for a horizontal furnace but the support mechanism becomes a rather important consideration in vertical furnaces. The heater support mechanism must move to expose or enclose the sample support without change in orientation except along the straight-line extension of the furnace tube axis and without appreciable vibration or other disturbance such as flexing of the support. The ordinary relay rack is not strong enough. The lighter and smaller furnaces currently available alleviate most of the support problem so the relative merits of the two systems can be examined with somewhat less regard for mechanical considerations.

A horizontal tube furnace generally comprises a resistance wire or ribbon wound on the exterior of a ceramic tube and with insulation outside of this winding (Fig. IV-1). The horizontal furnace [patterned after that of W. Coffeen (C18)] used by the author for several years is shown in Fig. IV-2. It moved on a ball slide fastened to a steel mounting plate; this steel plate was set on a benchtop. Since all parts are fixed in relation to the mounting plate and the mounting plate was under no strain, devising a sample support could be done easily with the assurance that clearances would be maintained when the furnace was moved into operating position—subject, of course, to heating effects.

The horizontal furnace will have, if wound uniformly, a temperature gradient along the axis or any line parallel to the axis whose magnitude will depend greatly on the length/width ratio. After the high gradient at the ends, the temperature (under steady-state heating) will increase toward the center not because the heater winding is any hotter or the insulation is any better but because the center cannot radiate heat to appreciably cooler surfaces. It is obvious from this consideration that a long, narrow tube-and-winding will have a low gradient in the middle region. Since long tubes are often impractical, ways of conserving heat or otherwise decreasing the gradient are used. One practical solution is the supplying of additional heat to the ends of the windings (see Chapter XVII). In addition, the ends of the tube are insulated inside as well as practicable. In Fig. IV-2, the detail 19 is a firebrick plug extending approximately 2 inches into the heated region. Like most users of horizontal furnaces the author then assumed that the central portion of the

Fig. IV-1. Helical winding on insulating tube.
The winding is cemented into place with a material having high thermal conductivity to equalize the temperature.

furnace was, for all practical purposes, uniform. One may question rather seriously whether the uniformity of temperature is maintained under high heating rates. The need to heat the end plugs introduces the problem of convection currents because these plugs are insulators and not easily heated. Likely as not the principal source of heat for warming the plug surface (at least below 600–700°C) is convection. In the absence of such precautions a very favorable condition for the occurrence of a sizable convection current is set up: a vertical wall substantially cooler than the gas inside and a heat source at the bottom. If the inside of the tube is comparatively empty a current will probably become established. The presence of the heat source around the sides of the tube ought to result in turbulence but will probably not stop the flow.

The construction of a vertical tube furnace poses somewhat different problems from those associated with horizontal furnaces. Most problems are connected with the greater opportunity for convection because there will generally be a greater height of open volume heated along the edges. Note, too, that a vertical cylinder with heated walls can permit a continuous smooth flow of gas up the walls and down the center while the flow in the same cylinder in a horizontal position will become turbulent before an appreciable velocity is reached. A uniform temperature zone is much easier to achieve, then, in a horizontal than in a vertical furnace; it is essential therefore that the advantages of the vertical arrangement be examined carefully and critically.

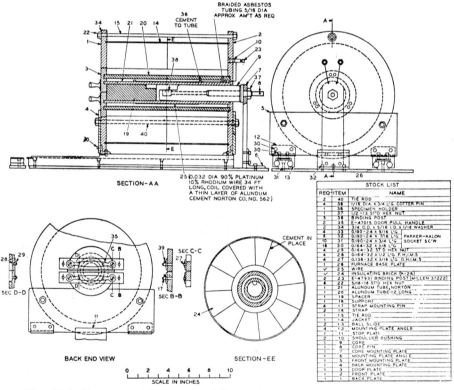

Fɪɢ. IV-2. Conventional furnace for differential thermal analysis. From Garn and Flaschen (G12).

The horizontal furnace is moved into place around the sample block. Double-wound ends provided a low-temperature gradient in the center of the furnace (see Chapter XVII).

A vertical furnace has the significant advantage that specimens, liquid or solid, may be placed symmetrically about the axis; this permits uniform exposure to heating at all temperatures. A vertical thermal gradient is necessarily going to exist and this gradient is almost certain to be larger than that in a horizontal furnace. This is no real cause for alarm, however, because under the same heating conditions the temperature variation at any point should be reproducible (but see below). So long as the sample is at a reproducible height and the temperature is being measured either at the sample or at the same height no significant errors should occur.

The use of a vertical furnace requires some caution. An open-end tube or one in which a cold region exists above the hot zone can lead to rather striking convection currents. The author discovered with some dismay that the earlier vertical furnaces wound for him were subject to a temperature oscillation that might persist for 100–300°C. The oscillation was not a "hunting" of the control apparatus since—once started—it continued even if the furnace power was turned off for a short time. The author eventually deduced that surges of gas were set up because of the unfavorable temperature gradient (see Fig. IV-3).

This unfavorable temperature gradient occurred for two reasons, insufficient insulation at the top and termination of the windings ½ inch from the top of the tube. The top of the furnace chamber may be 50°C or more cooler than the region within the windings. Since the author began winding his furnaces himself the temperature gradient in the top 2½ inches is generally on the order of 20°C; no evidence of surges of air have been seen. This was accomplished by extending the winding of the furnace to the top of the tube. Note that the temperature-inversion problem did not occur in the furnace shown in Fig. IV-2 even when it was mounted vertically; this is presumably because the plug (detail 19) which was above the sample was inserted well within the windings and consequently was quite well heated. Further, there was only a small open region between the sample and this plug.

These surges of gas are probably of little importance when the thermocouple is hidden deep in a block with a nondynamic atmosphere; the cool gas has to encounter many hot surfaces before reaching the thermocouple bead. However, in dynamic-atmosphere operation in the Lodding-Hammell (L10) manner one must examine the origin and possible effects of these surges. The author can only speculate on this extension of the surge phenomenon because the short-term cooling one might expect is highly irreproducible. Consider, though, a furnace in which windings are terminated noticeably short of the end of the tube (Fig. IV-4b). At very high flow rates of gas there is probably sufficient turbulence in the top of the chamber to force a reasonable mixing. At some poorly defined flow rate—probably heavily dependent on temperature and composition—the turbulence is insufficient to prevent significant cooling at the very top of the chamber. At still lower flow rates the gas rising beside the block from the lower part of the chamber can flow across the upper surface of the block and through the sample and reference

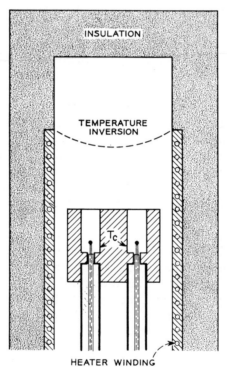

Fig. IV-3. Cross section of top end of early model of vertical furnace.
The cold end caused oscillation of temperature as the inversion broke down and re-established itself.

without appreciable disturbance of the temperature distribution in the upper chamber; this is the potentially most troublesome situation. We have now a condition in which a general flow of gas produces no stirring so the gas in the top of the furnace may cool. The gas in the region of the winding is heated but, with no driving force to assure continual mixing, a temperature inversion is established—a sort of micro Los Angeles. This unstable condition is unlikely to persist for a considerable time so after a little while the cooler gas drops down the middle of the tube as far as the block, warm gas replaces the cooler gas, the cool gas—mixed somewhat with warm gas—flows down through sample and reference and hence is disposed of, and now the temperature-inversion cycle may begin again.

The time of the breakdown of the temperature inversion concerns us here. The cool gas entering the sample or reference cavity will tend to cool rather than heat the specimen and will cause a spurious signal of short duration. The problem is compounded if one is controlling (programming) from either the sample or reference thermocouple for

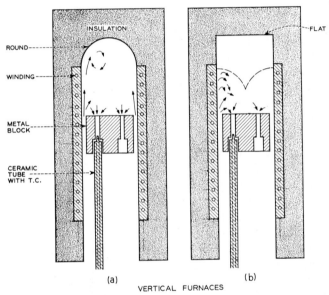

(a)   (b)

VERTICAL FURNACES

Fig. IV-4. Cross sections of furnaces showing dynamic gas flow.
Round ends and higher windings prevent establishment of significant temperature inversions.

the cooling—or cessation of heating—will bring about an increase of power input (see Chapter XVI). Proof or disproof of these speculations is not easily acquired; the curves obtained by the author show deviations in accord with the events described. When one is working with a high-sensitivity system in which the total heat capacity is small the gas surges are large enough to ruin the experiment. The surges do not occur with a properly wound furnace.

The fact that thermal gradients will exist must be accepted; the problem becomes a dual one of decreasing the gradient so far as practical and then decreasing the effect of that which remains by careful arrange-

ment of the parts. The most important source of trouble is the top end
of the furnace hot zone. In uncontrolled atmosphere furnaces and in
some controlled atmosphere furnaces there is no serious problem; one
simply inserts a firebrick plug into the heated zone far enough so that
it is well-heated. In closed-end tubes—such as the present author generally uses—no such easy way out exists.

Small vertical temperature gradients are of little importance except
insofar as they affect gas flow. A pair of specimens at the same level
and symmetrically placed with respect to the axis of the furnace tube
will still reach the same temperature; the gradient should be small to
compensate for errors in locating. The author has repeatedly put
< 10-mg samples in small tubes placed over the ends of shielded ther-
mocouples and obtained good thermograms with a low base line drift.

Further, a block will equalize the temperature within itself quite
well even if the top and bottom edges are adjacent to furnace wall sections several degrees different in temperature. Conduction within the
block—except at quite high temperatures—transfers heat more rapidly
than from furnace wall to block.

In horizontal furnaces a common technique used to provide a uniform
temperature zone is to wind the ends closer than the center (Fig.
XVI-1). This technique is worthless in vertical furnaces because of the
existence of the thermal gradients. Consider especially the closer winding at the top. Gases flowing up the wall become very hot just below a
cool surface. The temperature inversion discussed earlier can become
serious indeed. Table IV-1 shows data for just such a furnace, with the
winding of 1 inch of 16 turns/inch, 3 inches of 10 turns/inch, and 1 inch
of 16 turns/inch ending about ⅝ inch from the top of the tube. A variable autotransformer was set successively at a series of convenient points
and the furnace allowed to reach a steady state as indicated by the

TABLE IV-1

TEMPERATURE INVERSION IN TOP OF CLOSED-END TUBES
AT SOME ARBITRARILY CHOSEN TEMPERATURE

	Single-wound End		Double-wound End	
	Top	1.0 inch below top	Top	1.0 inch below top
T_1	1125	1138	1100	1202
T_2	902	915	795	915
T_3	668	670	628	722
T_4	450	450	495	560
T_5	356	351	301	314

thermocouples. The data are compared to similar data obtained using a furnace having a uniform winding extending above the end of the furnace tube. The cementing and insulating of the two furnaces were the same.

The closer winding which is of real value in horizontal furnaces neither avoids the temperature inversion nor provides a uniform temperature zone in the central region. The nearest to uniformity provided by such a winding is in the close-wound region, but that is also a hot zone just below a cold zone; such a zone would be treacherous indeed.

In such furnaces, the top must be heated in some manner. The most convenient way is to extend the winding beyond the closed end of the tube.

4.3. Amplification

The differential signal from any of the less energetic reactions will require amplification for most recorders. To a limited degree, amplification can be obtained in the sample holder itself by use of a thermopile (Fig. IV-5) in which the junctions are alternately in the sample and reference

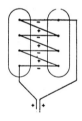

FIG. IV-5. Schematic diagram of a multiple differential thermocouple. From Lodding and Sturm (L12).
The signals are additive so the emf would be four times that of the conventional technique.

specimens; Lodding and Sturm's (L12) arrangement is shown in Fig. IV-6. The sample-holder design must permit locating a number of thermocouple junctions at equivalent positions, in this case the center line of a rectangular parallelopiped.

This technique for amplification has one very distinct advantage—the effects due to size and positioning of thermocouple beads are averaged over the set so that any base line drift *due to these causes* is diminished even while the differential signal is increased. Note, however, that drift due to the differing properties of the specimens is amplified, too. Lodding and Sturm show (Fig. IV-7) thermograms of quartz to illustrate

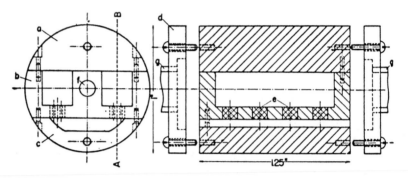

Fɪɢ. IV-6. Specimen holder for a four-unit multiple differential thermocouple. The line A-B refers to the cross section shown on the right. From Lodding and Sturm (L12).

The rectangular cross section permits easiest positioning of thermocouple beads.

the technique. The base line signal is low in magnitude so a peak of fairly low magnitude could be detected.

Another nonelectronic means of amplifying the differential signal can be used easily with optical detectors. The signal is fed into a mirror galvanometer and the movement detected by photocells some distance away. The displacement of the beam is obviously proportional to the distance. The signal may be attenuated by shunting to obtain less sensitive operation. Keith and Tuttle (K14) arranged a split photocell on a recorder pen carriage (Fig. IV-8) so that the photocell and hence the pen followed the beam deflection.

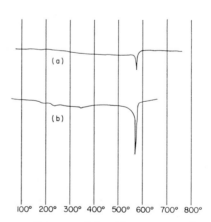

100° 200° 300° 400° 500° 600° 700° 800°

Fɪɢ. IV-7. Thermograms of quartz: (a) with conventional unit, (b) with multiple differential thermocouple. From Lodding and Sturm (L12).

The small inflections ca. 250° and 350°C may be due to impurities.

Generally, electronic amplification will be used. Stabilized electronic amplifiers with high signal-to-noise ratio and low drifts are available. The total amplification of the amplifier-recorder combination should be adjustable, but only in fixed steps. A continuously variable range will almost certainly be less reproducible than a fixed range and has little to offer in compensating advantages while a fixed-step adjustment ought to be accurately reproducible from day to day.

Similarly, a stepwise zero adjustment has a substantial advantage over a continuous adjustment. This zero adjustment ought to be on the slide-wire shunt on the recorder. The reason for having a stepwise adjustment is that the zero can be known at all times, permitting change in amplification with knowledge of the effect. (With continuous adjustments on amplification and zero, by the time the operator has made a couple of changes during a run he has probably lost track of zero and possibly of amplification factor so that he no longer knows the magnitude of his signal.) The reason for putting the zero shift on the shunt is that a compensating signal is avoided. The compensating signal technique introduces more components and more noise. The present author has used both techniques; in the differential thermal analysis apparatus described in Chapter XVII a compensating signal is used because operation in the slidewire circuit is impractical. When the thermogravimetric control and recording apparatus (Chapter XVI) is used—as it is occasionally—for a differential thermal analysis experiment, the author shunts the slidewire to shift the zero.

If an external compensating signal is to be used, a calibrated potentiometer should be used if the zero is to be shifted more than one or two scale ranges away from center. For zero shifts on scale or not far off scale the shifting signal can be applied between amplifier and recorder. At this higher signal level contact noise and such is rarely troublesome. Nearly any amplifier will give a linear output at twice its rated output, particularly under these conditions; the electrical load is, in effect, diminished.

4.4. Placement of Control Thermocouples

In most types of furnaces, any location chosen for a control (programming) thermocouple is a compromise between smoothness of control and precise linearity of temperature rise. For maintaining a steady temperature in the interior of a furnace, assuming no change in demand, keeping the temperature of the heating element nearly constant is quite obviously the best way, for a steady-state heat flow will be established that will be unchanging with time. If the temperature of the furnace winding is controlled, however, the system is insensitive to

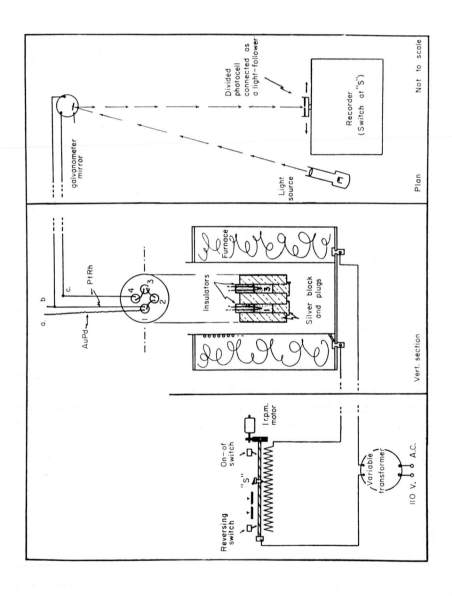

changes in demand; that lack of sensitivity made necessary the earlier assumption (see above) of constant demand. Let us move to the other extreme in control points, i.e., within the material being heated, and consider the behavior of the control system.

If the system happens to be at a steady state and any control functions are in a nonvarying condition, the temperature may possibly remain constant. (Note that in the absence of any proportioning action the steady state is highly improbable.) Any unbalance that does occur is likely to initiate oscillations about the control temperature simply because the heater must gain or lose in temperature to compensate for the unbalance, but this gain or loss is not received immediately at the control point.

> A cooling of the control point, for example, brings about an increase in the heater temperature but all intervening materials must also be heated before the control point is brought back to the set temperature. Since these intervening materials are now warmer than they would be in a steady state the control point is also made warmer than the set temperature so that the heater needs to cool. The intervening materials likewise cool to below their steady-state temperature and the process repeats. The magnitude and frequency of this "hunting" oscillation depends on the nature and quantity of material between the heater and the control point and the type of control system (which determines the relation between any unbalance and the resulting temperature of the windings).

Some types of control systems permit some oscillation as a matter of course; this oscillation would be characteristic of ON-OFF, HIGH-LOW, or adjustable autotransformer control. For many applications it is not troublesome but for accurate smooth control better systems are needed. Even with good control systems the problem of location of the control point is not solved completely. With a control point at the windings the material being heated is at a lower temperature and this lower temperature depends on the demand, i.e., the amount of heat the winding must supply to its surroundings to keep itself (and the control point) at the set temperature. On the other hand, if the control point is in the material being heated a change in temperature will incur exaggerated changes in the temperature of the winding which may induce hunting.

Let us now impose a new condition—a moving set point or temperature. This is the condition of real interest to us, a regular increase or decrease in temperature with time—so we need to consider what point in

Fɪɢ. IV-8. Mirror galvanometer with beam follower. Samples in silver block: (1) unknown quartz; (2) cryolite; (3) reference quartz; (4) K_2SO_4. From Keith and Tuttle (K14).

Up to the limit imposed by mechanical vibration the galvanometer movement can be amplified by further separating the beam follower from the galvanometer.

our system is to rise in temperature at a constant rate. Let us first return the control point to near the furnace winding and note the effect on the region in which a differential thermal analysis specimen might be placed.

As shown above, the interior of the furnace will not be at the control temperature; further, this difference will change with temperature and heating rate. This difference is not generally severe; the initial lag due to low conductivity at room temperature diminishes gradually until a dynamic "steady state" is achieved.

Now put the control thermocouple in the specimen. As heating begins the lag shown in Fig. IV-9 will require the heating winding to supply

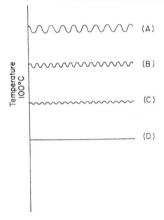

Fig. IV-9. Temperature variation in specimen with control thermocouple located in: (A) isolated cup; (B) metal alloy block; (C) furnace cement ⅛ inch outside of heater winding; and (D) against inside wall of furnace tube.

The control thermocouple should be near the heater for smooth control.

heat rapidly. Since the heater winding is able to heat its environment to some limit far above room temperature, it may warm the furnace tube 100°C or more too high before the control thermocouple is brought to the control point. But now the heater shuts down and the overheated tube keeps up with the moving control point for a while. Since the heater is actually cooling there must soon come a time when the control thermocouple temperature begins to lag behind the control point and a new surge must begin. This effect diminishes at higher temperatures because heat transfer becomes more rapid. The behavior shown in A can be alleviated by proper adjustment of proportional band reset and rate action to approach that shown in D. Note that the controlled temperature is now at the location where the control is wanted; on the other hand, the adjustment of the process control variables, i.e., proportional band, etc., may need to be different for each type of experimental arrangement. This can be a minor nuisance in determining the settings, but once these are found the operator needs only to remember to make the changes when required.

The author's control apparatus was designed to operate from the recorded temperature which means that the control point must be in the sample, the reference, the block, or at some reasonably equivalent point. Generally the block temperature was recorded (and controlled). The later use of more sensitive arrangements required careful readjustment for each system.

4.5. Sample Holders

The use of a sample block is common perhaps to the extent of being prevalent; nevertheless, a considerable number of workers use other types of specimen holders. These may range from a moderate increase in isolation of specimens by inserting a poor conductor between block and specimen to a complete (within the hot zone) isolation of the specimen supports. The present author uses the entire range.

For slight isolation a poorly conducting sleeve may be set in the specimen cavities. Providing the length of the specimen is significantly greater than the diameter this will provide some isolation with the comforting knowledge that the outside of that sleeve is at a uniform temperature.

Somewhat greater isolation is provided by inserting nonmetallic cups into blocks (Fig. IV-10); much greater isolation can be obtained by supporting the specimen only (Fig. IV-11) by the thermocouple wires. The latter degree of isolation is approximated also by support by the thermocouple insulator. Many varying intermediate degrees of isolation have been reported, e.g., Figs. IV-12, IV-13, IV-15, and VI-34.

The effect of the increasing separation is a matter of degree; the approach toward differential calorimetry carries with it the risk of failure to separate—or possibly even to recognize—close-lying thermal effects.

Bohon (B59) enclosed samples of explosives in small cups which were set on the ends of shielded thermocouples. The samples were enclosed by threaded caps either (Fig. IV-12) to seal in the sample and products or to retain the sample but allow interchange of gases between the sample and the furnace atmosphere. (The present author has used similar cups but *sans* cover to allow free access of atmosphere to the sample.)

The apparatus used by Bohon is shown in Fig. IV-21. Note that the Inconel thermocouple sheaths and the baffle plates form a heat conduction path between sample and reference. The interchange of heat is significant (B61) and, in fact, the degree of thermal isolation—and hence sensitivity—can be varied somewhat by adding, subtracting, or re-positioning these baffle plates.

A somewhat unusual sample arrangement has been reported by Saba-tier (S2), by West (W24), and by Rey and Kostomaroff (R18). Three rather isolated cylinders (Fig. IV-13) hold the sample, reference, and a second reference in which to measure the temperature. The temperature reference cylinder may sometimes contain sample rather than an inert material. The fact that there are three sample vessels instead of two

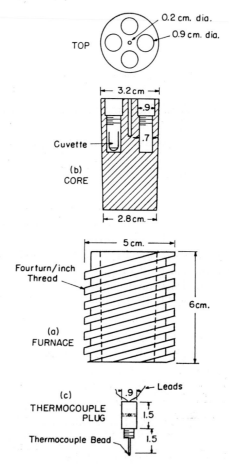

Fig. IV-10. Differential thermal analyses block. (a) Furnace block, Alcoa alumi-num rod stock; (b) cuvette carriage core; (c) thermocouple and mounting. From Barrall and Rogers (B7).

The very coarse winding is of no importance because the block equalizes the temperature. The cuvette provides some thermal isolation of the specimens.

means that they must necessarily be spread out more than two need be and, hence, a portion of each is very near the hot wall. Garn and Flaschen (G12) have pointed out the potential danger of nonuniformity of temperature around the specimen. The wall of the cylinder must be thick enough to transmit heat rapidly, otherwise the reaction front does not move symmetrically from the entire circumference and the peak is spread over a wider range of time and (indicated) temperature. The effect will diminish with increasing temperature.

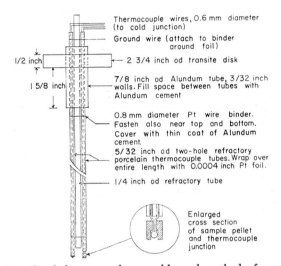

Thermocouple wires, 0.6 mm diameter (to cold junction)

Ground wire (attach to binder around foil)

1/2 inch

2 3/4 inch od transite disk

1 5/8 inch

7/8 inch od Alundum tube, 3/32 inch walls. Fill space between tubes with Alundum cement

0.8 mm diameter Pt wire binder. Fasten also near top and bottom. Cover with thin coat of Alundum cement.

5/32 inch od two-hole refractory porcelain thermocouple tubes. Wrap over entire length with 0.0004 inch Pt foil.

1/4 inch od refractory tube

Enlarged cross section of sample pellet and thermocouple junction

Fig. IV-11. Details of thermocouple assembly and method of supporting sample pellet. From Newkirk (N7).

If the specimen melts the liquid can cling to the thermocouple bead. No thermal contact exists between sample and reference except by radiation (see Chapter VIII.

The nature of the surface of the sample block is as important as the properties of the bulk material. A nickel block may conduct heat more readily within itself than a ceramic block but its emissivity is far lower. This can result in better heat transfer in the ceramic because the temperature drop between wall and block is accentuated. Figure IV-14 is a purely arbitrary representation of this condition. While the metal block has a nearly zero gradient in it, it heats the sample less because it cannot absorb radiation so well as the ceramic.

The isolated sample sleeves in the preceding figure might better be ceramic than platinum.

The author has used a great variety of specimen holders for various studies. The use of a vertical furnace with easily interchanged support pieces makes possible many changes in geometry. Support rods with one, two, four, or even more holes of various sizes enable use of shielded or wire thermocouples in a multitude of arrangements. Two specimen holders in which both sample and reference thermocouples were led through a single ¼ inch ceramic tube (centered in the furnace) are shown in Fig. IV-15. The open-cup holder shown in Fig. IV-15a is used to provide good accessibility of (or to) the furnace atmosphere (see Chapter VII).

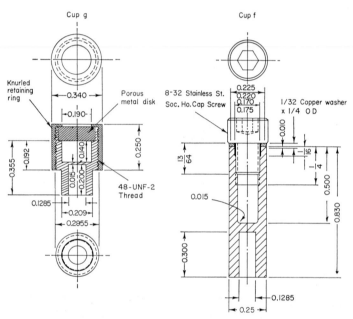

Fig. IV-12. Typical sample cups used by Bohon (B59). *Left:* Isobaric cup g. Porous metal cup permits passage of gases but retains solid sample. *Right:* Isochloric cup f. Dead soft copper gasket provides pressure seal.

The isochloric cup permits pressures of several thousand pounds per square inch.

The reference thermocouple may be placed in a similar cup (and the two symmetrically placed) if the slight base line drift is a problem but for most purposes a thermocouple not quite touching the cup is adequate.

The holder shown in Fig. IV-15b was used with some relatively small samples for which finding reference materials would have been a tedious problem. This resembles a thermal conductivity measurement and the displacement of the base line does indeed depend on the thermal diffusivity but discontinuities are easily detected.

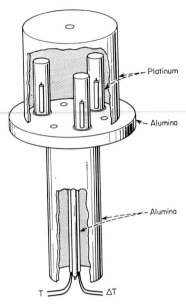

FIG. IV-13. Sample-holder arrangement using a third cavity in which to measure the furnace temperature.

Platinum sleeves are set into the alumina support plate so that the thermocouple bead is centered and along the axis.

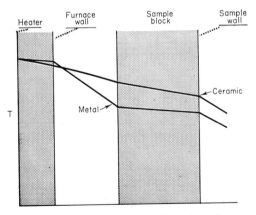

FIG. IV-14. Representation of temperature gradients from heater to sample well.

The temperature drop between furnace wall and sample block is high because of the low emissivity (and absorptivity) of metals.

Figure IV-16 shows a block used for samples which melt and for which a dynamic atmosphere is not needed. The block is set on the support rods used with the standard blocks and the thermocouple led through to re-enter the sample cavity from the top.

4.6. Programming

The general problem and techniques of programming are discussed in Chapter XV. Let us note here the need for programming by observation of the effect of a linearly varying voltage input. See Table IV-2.

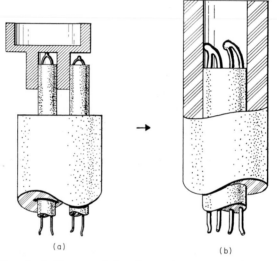

(a)   (b)

Fɪɢ. IV-15. Sample holders used by the author for (a) controlled-atmosphere accessibility and (b) changes in state of certain powdered specimens.

The wall separating the thermocouple and sample in (a) is thin enough to permit sensitive detection of effects. The measurement in (b) is the temperature drop from edge to center. The size of the thermocouple wire is exaggerated.

As part of a study of the kaolinite decomposition in water vapor at various pressures, the present author wished to heat the specimens to ca 700°C and cool without appreciable overshoot in temperature. The only apparatus in the author's custody which would permit controlled heating followed by complete shutdown at a preset temperature was that designed originally for thermogravimetric work. The "control" comprised a motor-driven autotransformer and a limit switch on the recorder. In practice, the voltage input was increased steadily until the thermocouple in the center of the specimen reached 720°C at which time the furnace power was shut off. The heating rate was not constant, but was fairly reproducible (10%) as the decomposition region was approached.

4.7. Recording of Data

The recording of data from a differential thermal analysis requires the simultaneous measurement of the temperature, T, and the temperature difference, ΔT. These may be recorded together or separately in a number of ways. The general problem of recording data is discussed in Chapter XVII; we are concerned here with a comparison of techniques.

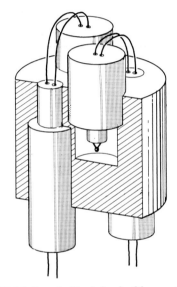

Fɪɢ. IV-16. Sample block for fusible specimens.
The holder was designed in this form to permit easy interchange with the dynamic atmosphere blocks.

The two major recording methods of interest here are (1) T and ΔT vs t, i.e., plotting of both functions on a time-based recorder, and (2) ΔT vs T, i.e., plotting of ΔT on a temperature-based recorder. The accuracy of recording is not the question; with good equipment there would be no difference. The comparison must be on the usefulness of the records. The author is firmly convinced that a time-based—whether or not on the same chart as ΔT—record of temperature is needed, since the operation of control devices cannot be taken on faith. [The need for monitoring is especially great if a range of types of operations is planned, while if the apparatus is to be used, run after run, on a single type of sample (control laboratory type of operation) any failure might possibly be recognized quickly without monitoring.]

The temperature-based record has certain elements of convenience: the records are all the same size and can be stored easily; two or three runs can be recorded side by side for easy comparison; for a fixed range and the proper graph paper, the temperature at any point may be read directly from the chart. The major deficiency is that it does not provide a time-dependent record of events that are themselves time-dependent.

TABLE IV-2

TEMPERATURE OF A KAOLINITE SPECIMEN, CA. 0.20 GM, DURING HEATING WITH LINEARLY INCREASING VOLTAGE SUPPLY TO BASE METAL WOUND FURNACE (FINAL VOLTAGE, 78 VOLTS)

Time (minutes)	Temperature (°C)	Heating rate, average over two intervals of time (°C/minute)
0	20	—
5	22	0.8
10	28	1.6
15	38	2.6
20	54	3.6
25	74	5.0
30	104	7.4
35	148	9.4
40	198	10.2
45	250	11.4
50	312	13.0
55	380	14.2
60	454	15.4
65	534	15.6
70	610[a]	16.0
75	700	—

[a]Reaction temperature range.

The time-based record has somewhat different advantages: the record can be expanded or shortened by changing chart drive speed without effect on the recording ranges; any irregularities in heating or other performance failures can be seen readily; and it provides in interpretable record of events even while the sample temperature is changing very slowly. The major deficiency is that an active experimenter encounters storage problems.

Let us now consider the relative effects of time- and temperature-based recording. First consider a phase transformation as shown in Figs. II-10 and II-11. The peaks of Fig. II-10 are quite sharp, far more so than those of Fig. II-11. The latter figure could be made to approach the former by slowing the chart speed, but that would put a much greater slope on the temperature indication and make more difficult the task of reading the temperature. On the other hand, if a measurement of area were desired, the ΔT vs T would be useless (See Chapter V) since the advance of the chart is not constant.

The major hazard in the use of temperature-based recorders is the possibility of overlooking close-lying effects in phase studies (this might apply to polymer work). Figure IV-17 shows a portion of a cooling cycle of a BaF–LiF mixture in which there are three close-lying thermal effects. The entire range of the peak is only 12°C, so the chart of the

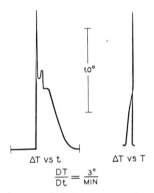

ΔT vs t ΔT vs T

$$\frac{DT}{Dt} = \frac{3°}{MIN}$$

FIG. IV-17. Simultaneously recorded temperature-based and time-based thermograms of a BaF–LiF mixture.

The close-lying effect would not have been detected on a temperature-based recording.

X vs Y recorder (0–1500°C span) moves only slightly—not even the width of the tracing line—between the start of the deflection and the third peak. There is, in fact, a slight elevation in temperature during this period because of supercooling prior to the start of the solidification. Each of the three effects is clearly seen in the time-based plot.

It is true enough that expansion of the T scale to, say, 50°C or less full scale would permit detection of these changes. Use of this scale expansion (with the required zero offset circuitry) would require the willingness to rerun a portion of samples just to examine peaks. Reruns might also be required with time-based recording but the need to make the rerun would be clear. The equivalent of scale expansion is accomplished by the present author by setting limit switches on the temperature pen so that the chart drives only when the temperature is within the selected limits. Only a small amount of chart paper is run off even though the entire run might be quite long in time.

The present author uses both a time- and a temperature-based recorder, often simultaneously (see Chapter XVI). If only one recorder were to be used this author would unhesitatingly choose a time-base, recording T and ΔT on a single chart using a two-pen recorder.

4.8. Multiple Sample Holders

There are advantages in simultaneous differential analysis of a number of samples. It makes possible direct comparison of thermograms of two or more samples, the same sample in a series of dilutions, or comparison specimens for qualitative identification. The major problem of identity of temperature programming from run to run, while still highly desirable, can be avoided for work *specifically limited* to comparisons. In more general work in which the features of each thermogram are expected to have some meaning the usual requirements of nondiscontinuous and reproducible heating rates still apply and the heating rate is preferably linearly programmed.

The question of arrangement of sample cavities in a multiple block is reasonably simple. If the block is fairly conductive one may safely assume that the temperature is the same at the perimeter of each cavity so that, as in Fig. IV-18, the sample and reference may not even need

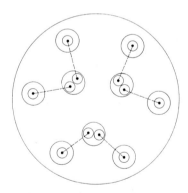

Fɪɢ. IV-18. Multiple differential thermal analysis in a single block (K43). The (numbered) sample holes are symmetrically placed but their accompanying reference functions are unsymmetrically placed in holes not symmetric with the sample holes.

The noncentered reference thermocouples appear to be quite satisfactory. The small base line drift that would probably occur with most samples would be of little consequence in this phase diagram work since it would appear in all thermograms and hence not indicate differences in specimens.

to be symmetrically placed. For many inorganic systems this would be a satisfactory arrangement. Kulp and Kerr (K43) were obtaining phase diagram data. It was convenient to obtain data from a set of six compositions simultaneously. Note that while sample and reference are not symmetrically placed, each sample well is symmetric with the others so even if a radial temperature gradient should exist, the only effect would be a base line displacement of each plot; the samples would still be exposed to the same temperature at their perimeters.

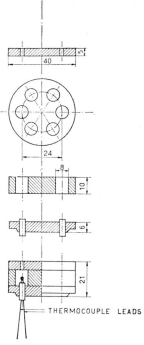

Fig. IV-19. Sample block for multiple DTA; dimensions in millimeters. From de Bruijn and van der Marel (B85).

The three-part block can be cleaned easily.

Another type of multiple differential thermal analysis sample block is that of de Bruijn and van der Marel (B85) shown in Fig. IV-19. This one has radial symmetry and, of course, accommodates three sample-and-reference pairs. It can be disassembled for easy cleaning. One of the interesting features, probably inadvertent, is that with an assembly like this the user could diminish end effects by choosing poorly conducting interfaces and have an uncommonly good approach to symmetric heating.

4.9. Controlled-Atmosphere Furnaces

The physical chemical basis for controlled atmospheres is elucidated in Chapter VII; our purpose here is to show only some of the equipment used. The effect of neutral atmospheres or atmospheres of gases which take part in a reaction is a comparatively recent development; the common practice was, of course, to establish a procedure for running a differential thermal analysis and to relate unknown samples to known specimens. This was reasonably satisfactory for mineralogical use in the days when the technique was used only to establish identity. As equipment was improved the users in all fields attempted to learn more about the reactions themselves.

A natural consequence of this shift in emphasis was a more careful evaluation of sample holders. Disputes such as that centered around the mineral ferrous carbonate, siderite, drew attention to the problem of atmosphere control (see Chapter XIII).

From this increased emphasis on atmosphere effects came the use of controlled-atmosphere furnaces. These evolved quite reasonably; the earliest were simple adaptations of existing apparatus followed by those designed specifically for controlled-atmosphere work. Whitehead and Breger (W30), for example, enclosed a more-or-less standard differential thermal analysis furnace is a vacuum chamber principally to avoid oxidation of organic materials in their samples.

Saunders and Giedroyc (S6) recognized the need for inert (nitrogen) as well as oxidizing (air) atmospheres in differential thermal analysis. They arranged their crucible assembly inside a quartz tube (Fig. IV-20) which they could evacuate and flush several times before adjusting their gas flow through the tube. Their sample cavity was also provided with a cover so that even the controlled atmosphere could be kept free from contact with the sample.

The use of supra-atmospheric pressures is also a consequence of controlled atmospheres; if a furnace must be sealed so that it can be pumped out or so there is no interchange of gas there is nothing to prevent the operator from adding more gas—up to the mechanical limits of the equipment. The general reasons for use of sub- or supra-atmospheric pressures will be discussed in Chapters VI and VII.

A more special use is in the study of explosives; here there is a distinct effect of pressure other than the usual atmosphere effect. The burning, ignition, or detonation behavior of explosives and propellants is dependent frequently on the *total* gas pressure rather than the pressure of some particular gas having some part in the reaction. Bohon (B59) constructed a furnace (Fig. IV-21) having a Monel tube surrounding the specimens and pressure-sealed to the base. Several hundred pounds of pressure can be applied to a sample by pressurizing the entire furnace chamber.

Application of a controlled pressure to a reasonably large chamber gives an approximately constant composition of gas—subject to short-term variations in the vicinity of the sample—and a constant pressure be-

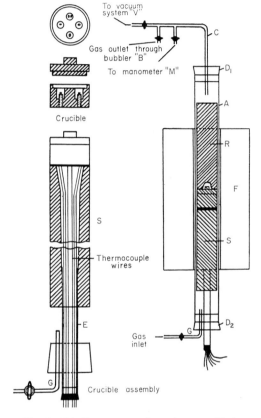

Fig. IV-20. Inert atmosphere furnace (S6).
The atmosphere sweeping up the sides of the tube can remove decomposition products or prevent oxidation.

fore, during, and after the reaction. Another technique found necessary by Bohon was the use of closed containers (Fig. IV-12) which could be pressurized before closing (Fig. IV-22) to provide a quite high initial pressure within only the sample container; the furnace chamber can be operated at atmospheric pressure. This technique permits higher pressures with relatively inexpensive equipment but it requires confinement of product gases with a consequent change in composition *and* increase in pressure as the decomposition reactions proceed.

Whether or not this is a disadvantage depends on the particular experiment; a general answer cannot be given. Berg and Rassonskaya (B40) used supra-atmospheric pressures on more nearly reversible reactions (see Chapter VII, Sec. 7.12).

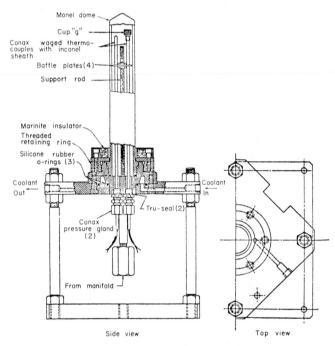

Fɪɢ. IV-21. Pressure furnace for differential thermal analysis. From Bohon (B59).
The lower O-ring seals retain the coolant, the upper seal provides the pressure seal. Baffle plates serve as radiation shields as well as adjustable thermal bridges between sample and reference.

4.10. Subambient Temperatures

The state of a specimen of nonliving material is prescribed by—among other things—the temperature. Each material behaves in a manner dictated by its own characteristics as its heat content is changed. It follows that the common temperatures 273.18°K, 298.18°K, or 373.18°K are of no general importance to such matter. There are thermal events which take place below room temperature quite like those associated with higher temperatures. The only difference in the study of these effects is that we must remove heat from the furnace and sample; this requires

different apparatus from that customarily used. The difference, however, is intrinsically quite small.

Accurate control of temperature by exerting control only on a cooling
process is not common; on the other hand, very extensive experience in
control of heating processes can be drawn upon. The natural result is
that an apparatus designed for subambient temperatures will comprise
an uncontrolled or not closely controlled means of lowering the temperature and a means of controlled electric heating. The controlled heating

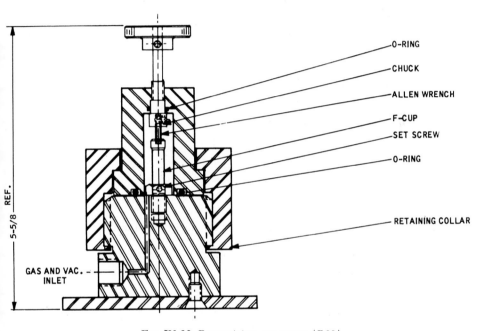

Fig. IV-22. Pressurizing apparatus (B60).
A high pressure of a known gas can be applied to the specimen. The composition
may change drastically in the course of the reaction.

can then supply the compensating energy with quite ordinary equipment.

The actual apparatus design will depend on the nature of the problem. Two examples will be cited—one providing high thermal homogeneity within the system, the other providing a high degree of isolation.

Vassallo and Harden (V3) supplied cooled nitrogen to the outside of
a metal block by use of a helical winding of tubing around the block
(Fig. IV-23). Some cooling control can be obtained by varying the flow
of the nitrogen. The presence of the heater at the center of the block

raises the possibility of a substantial temperature gradient in the block so that noticeable differences in temperature at the inner and the outer edges of the sample might occur; careful programming and control would be needed (see Sec. 4.11).

Reisman (R12) used a Dewar flask which could be filled with liquid nitrogen for cooling (Fig. IV-24). While he uses isolated containers instead of a block, there is no reason why the same general plan could not be used with a block. The existence of a substantial surface area implies that some degree of control of cooling can be applied by varying the pressure over the liquid nitrogen. This control would be difficult to program accurately but the smooth variations would make the heating

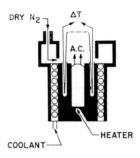

FIG. IV-23. Cross section of heater-cooler differential thermal analysis block. From Vassallo and Harden (V3).

In addition to the cooling gas, dry nitrogen is swept across the top of the block to avoid water condensation or oxidation.

control easy. Note that the heater is between the cooling system and the sample. This arrangement assures that the sample assembly will be affected by a single heat source—or sink; the temperature of this heat source, the wall surface, will presumably be changing smoothly so that no extreme or rapidly changing gradients will occur.

This latter arrangement, with the heat supply interposed between the cooled region and the specimen, is the more common design. In effect, one simply puts a fairly ordinary furnace in a cold environment. The direct contact of heat source and heat sink with the block can be made to work but extra effort is almost certainly required.

4.11. Internally Heated Blocks

Differential thermal analysis blocks are generally heated from external sources for good reason: homogeneity of temperature throughout the block can be approached more closely. Although many designs do not provide real symmetry—for example, a horizontal tube furnace enclosing a cylindrical block whose axis is in a vertical position—they do generally provide a fairly uniform environment. Heat can reach the block from the furnace wall in a pattern which at least approaches symmetry. But symmetry is only a part of the problem. Let us first examine the relative quantities of heat which must be transferred to or from the block and their effects on homogeneity or the temperature changes.

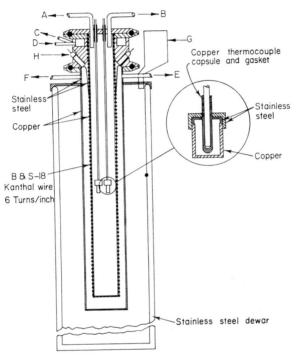

Fig. IV-24. Differential thermal analysis cryostat, 190 to 400°C. A and F, Vacuum valves; B and E, Bleeder valves; C, water inlet; D, water outlet; G, Funnel—liquid N₂ (supply to outer stainless steel Dewar); H, Stupakoff seals (2). From Reisman (R12).

The heater helps provide the precise control of the temperature "seen" by the specimens.

Consider the blocks of Fig. IV-25 in which axially symmetric blocks are heated internally and externally. The externally heated blocks must receive from the furnace wall enough heat to raise the temperature of the block, the sample and reference, and the support and measuring accessories. This implies a furnace wall hotter than the block but only sufficiently hotter to maintain the heat flow. The actual amount of heat transferred will change only slightly over a few hundred degrees and the change will be smooth.

Note that the flow of heat is converging; the relatively large source of heat to the block, i.e., the outer edge, provides heat to an effective cross section which diminishes with distance. This means that even the curvature of the temperature distribution will be less steep in most of the block.

Contrast this with an internally heated block. The small circumference in contact with the heater must convey approximately the same heat to the block assembly as before but through a considerably diminished area. The temperature gradient near the heater is necessarily considerably greater.

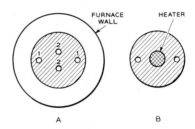

FURNACE WALL   HEATER

A   B

Fɪɢ. IV-25. Representation of blocks heated from A, a furnace wall and B, an interior heater.

Because of the difference in paths, the thermal gradient will be different in the two cases and the outer sample well (1) of block A will see a larger gradient than the inner (2) well.

Let us demonstrate the effect by a simple exercise which is descriptive enough to give some relative numbers but which lacks any vitiating assumptions. That we are dealing with a portion of a long cylinder, i.e., ignoring end effects, is the only controversial assumption. This assumption will change some numbers but will not affect the conclusion.

The equation for steady-state radial flow of heat in a cylinder is

$$q = \frac{2\pi kl(T_2 - T_1)}{\ln(R_1/R_2)}$$

where q is the quantity of heat crossing a radius, k is the thermal conductivity, l is the length, and T_2 and T_1 are the temperatures at radii of R_2 and R_1, respectively. This does not, however, take into account the consumption of heat in simply raising the temperature. Treatments of unsteady-state problems of this nature are—to the best of the author's knowledge—lacking in the literature, so we will use an ingenuous approach which yields answers in the form we are seeking.

Let us put some imaginary boundaries in the blocks of Fig. IV-25. First assume that the internal heater has a radius one-fourth that of the block and that the contact between them is perfect and hence radially symmetric. Now assume a constant heat capacity over a small range of temperature so that we may say that introduction of Q calories per unit time will raise the temperature at the programmed rate and, for the purposes of the immediate discussion, no heat is lost.

For any imaginary radius we can now calculate the area within and without the radius and also the quantity of heat which must cross that boundary. To avoid assigning specific values we will deal in fractions of R, A, and Q. The heat passing a boundary inward is proportional to the area within the boundary and the length of the boundary is proportional to the radius so

$$\frac{Q_{in}}{c} = \frac{Q}{2\pi r} \times \frac{a_{in}}{A}$$

where c is the circumference at r. This yields a measure of the heat flux, the quantity of heat passing unit length of boundary, and hence a measure of the temperature gradient which must exist at that boundary. Since we are dealing with fractional quantities and treating A as unity we can simplify to

$$\frac{Q_{in}}{c} = \frac{Q}{2\pi} \times r.$$

For the internal heating, the quantity of heat passing a boundary is proportional to the area outside the boundary so

$$\frac{Q_{out}}{c} = \frac{Q}{2\pi r} A(1-a_{out}).$$

The values shown in Table I are calculated for several radii from these formulas. The plot in Fig. IV-26 relates the temperature gradients to the radius for the internally and externally heated blocks under the conditions assumed. Only at 0.7R do the gradients compare. The outer pair of specimen walls of block A of Fig. IV-25 would be in regions of temperature gradients approximating those of block B although the variation in gradient from inner to outer edge is considerably less. The inner pair are in regions of temperature gradient much smaller than around the outer holes.

The discussion so far as assumed no heat transfer out of the block. In case A of Fig. IV-25 this is a reasonable approximation, the heating of support structures and thermocouple leads can be neglected. When the block is hotter than its surroundings, it becomes the apparent heat source and flow of heat can no longer be neglected. But note that this heat loss will be affected by the temperature difference between the block and its surroundings (and also by the actual magnitude of the temperature), the geometry, and the atmosphere. Unfortunately, this loss will vary during a run in a manner which will itself differ with, particularly, change of atmosphere. We can, however, note the general effect by plotting some losses in terms of assumed fractions of Q; i.e., the heat crossing a boundary outward must be that previously calculated plus a given quantity so that

$$\frac{Q_{out}}{c} = \frac{QA}{2\pi r}\left(1 - \frac{a}{A}\right) + \frac{Q^*}{2\pi r}.$$

Figure IV-27 shows the effect of heat losses only up to a value equal to the useful heat, Q, although it can easily exceed Q.

The data show that a changing Q^* brings about a change in the thermal environment at the sample well. Since a change in Q^* is inevitable, so is its consequence.

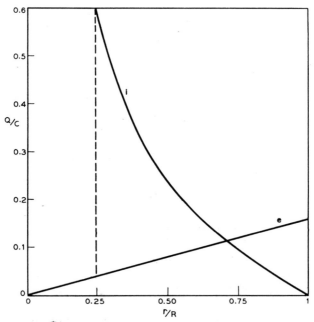

Fig. IV-26. Relative temperature gradients as functions of r/R for internal (i) and external (e) heating. The data of Table IV-3 are plotted using Q_{out}/c at the boundary of the internal heater as the reference value ($= 1.00$).

The temperature difference between inside and outside wall of a sample cavity will be greater for the internally heated block except very near the edge.

4.12. Thermistors as Detecting and Measuring Transducers

The development of differential thermal analysis techniques and apparatus has been an unsteady advance. The entry of a new device or technique may not be generally noted because the reports failed to demonstrate clearly the advantages or new possibilities inherent in the development. For example, controlled atmospheres—even static—have real value, but not until Stone wrote a series of articles demonstrating the use of controlled dynamic atmospheres (see Chapter VII) did many workers do more than speculate about the effect of ambient atmospheres.

TABLE IV-3

EFFECT OF DIRECTION OF HEAT FLOW ON TEMPERATURE
GRADIENT DISTRIBUTION IN CYLINDRICAL BLOCK ASSUMING
NO RADIATION OR CONVECTION LOSSES AND AN INTERNAL
HEATER RADIUS OF $0.250R$

$\dfrac{r}{R}$	$\dfrac{a_{in}}{A}$	$\dfrac{a_{out}}{A}$	$\dfrac{Q_{in}}{c}$	$\dfrac{Q_{out}}{c}$
0.125	0.016	0.984	0.020	—
0.250	0.062	0.938	0.040	0.596
0.375	0.137	0.863	0.060	0.366
0.500	0.250	0.750	0.080	0.239
0.625	0.390	0.610	0.100	0.156
0.750	0.562	0.438	0.119	0.093
0.875	0.765	0.235	0.139	0.043
1.000	1.000	0.0	0.159	0.000

r = radius of boundary under consideration,
R = outside radius,
a_{in} = area inside r,
a_{out} = area outside r,
A = area enclosed by R,
Q_{in} = quantity of heat per unit time moving inward past r,
Q_{out} = quantity of heat per unit time moving outward past r,
c = circumference at r.

The lack of impact is frequently the author's own fault. The introduction of even a minor improvement must be reported with a considered evaluation of its probable use. This ought to take the form of demonstrations of solutions of difficult problems or a clear comparison of techniques.

An example from recent literature of an opportunity lost is the work of Pakulak and Leonard (P4) who reported on the use of thermistors in differential thermal analysis (Fig. IV-28). Obviously thermistors can be used within their temperature limitations and, since they are small and have a low heat capacity but a high temperature coefficient of resistance, a worthwhile extension of technique ought to be obtainable. Very tiny samples in contact with the thermistors ought to yield rather large signals in a properly designed bridge. Further, the low-energy transitions of many organic materials could be detected. Comparison of thermal data with microscopic observation using a hot stage not only could have excited interest but also might have stimulated other workers.

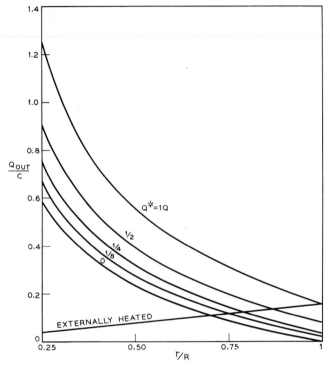

Fig. IV-27. Relative temperature gradients as functions of r/R assuming various relative heat losses, Q^*.

Since Q^* will change with temperature as well as several other parameters the relative environment of a sample cavity in an internally heated block will not remain constant.

In the actual report, Pakulak and Leonard noted that "Because this curve [Fig. IV-29] has a logarithmic nature, using the thermistors directly in a measuring circuit would result in an extremely poor temperature scale. Readings at one end of the scale would show a very small resistance differential for a given temperature differential; those at the opposite end would have very large resistance differentials." So they sacrificed the principal advantage of the thermistor by shunting it by at least an order of magnitude at low temperatures (Fig. IV-30). Having discarded most of the sensitivity and finding there was still more than they could use with ordinary high-heats-of-reaction samples, they diluted the sample twenty to sixty times to obtain readable thermograms (Fig. IV-31) and used a relatively slow (2°C/minute) rate of heating. They even measured the temperature using a thermistor; the temperature lag in their sensing assembly may account for their temperatures of 104, 117,

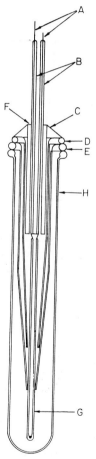

Fig. IV-28. Thermistor sensing element for differential thermal analysis: A, output leads; B, Teflon sleeve; C, electric resistor cement; D, 1 mm centrifuge tube; E, 1.5 mm centrifuge tube; F, two-hole ceramic tube; G, thermistor; H, test tube (P4).

A matched pair of thermistors replaces the differential thermocouple.

and 131°C for the copper sulfate pentahydrate peaks. The first peak is the loss of two waters, the second is the vaporization of these waters.

Rotation of their bridge through 90° would have permitted elimination of the shunts (Fig. IV-32). With thermistors at R_1 and R_2 and ignoring the balancing resistor, R_B, since

$$\frac{\Delta E}{E} = \frac{R_1}{R_2} - \frac{R_3}{R_4} = \frac{R_1}{R_2} - C$$

a fractional change in R_1, e.g., $R_1 + 0.04\ R_1$, will have the same effect at any value of R_1, since R_2 is changing at essentially the same rate. The

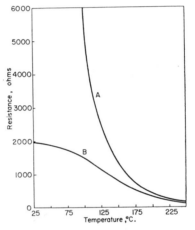

Fig. IV-29. Relationship of resistance of a thermistor and of a thermistor and its shunt to temperature: A, resistance of a thermistor vs temperature; B, combined parallel resistance of a thermistor and its shunt vs temperature (P4).

At the lower temperatures most of the sensitivity of the thermistors is lost by shunting.

zeroing or balancing potentiometer could be put between R_3 and R_4. Some adjustment of resistance might be necessary for impedance matching (see Chapter XV). This matching could be done by using an amplifier or a cathode follower. In spite of the handicap imposed on the system the thermograms obtained by Pakulak and Leonard (Fig. IV-31) show rather good sensitivity.

Some observers might be tempted to use thermistors for all four legs of the bridge, and put, perhaps, an indexing or comparison specimen on one or more of the others or a similar specimen on the opposite leg to double the effect. This may indeed be feasible. Some makers discourage use of thermistors for all four legs of a bridge but the present author has done just that in a chromatograph in which two detectors read into a single recording channel.

The temperature limits are the major problem. The present author has not, to date of writing, found thermistors made for general use above 500°C. Some interesting low-energy transitions occur at lower temperatures so thermistors can have great utility. The best solution to the resistance change problem will no doubt be the use of more than one pair of thermistors. The user might need to have a choice of perhaps five or six sets, each set having a different optimum temperature range.

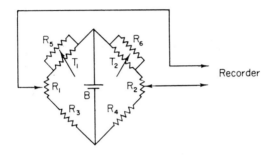

R_1, R_2 = 100 Ω   Potentiometer
R_3, R_4 = 1000 Ω ± 1 %
R_5, R_6 = 2000 Ω ± 1 %
T_1, T_2 = Thermistors – 100,000 Ω at 25 °C
B   = 1 1/2 volt dry cell

Fig. IV-30. Direct current bridge for differential thermal analysis (P4).
The recorder is "looking into" about 1400 ohms near room temperature and only about 100 ohms near 250°C. Maximum sensitivity occurs when the effective resistance of the shunted thermistor is 1000 ohms at around 250°C.

4.13. Insulation

Operation of an uninsulated furnace can be both uneconomical and uncomfortable. Well-insulated furnaces can be maintained above 1000°C with 200–300 watts. We are generally concerned in thermal analysis with heating and cooling so (1) the furnace heater must have sufficient power to raise the temperature at the desired rate and (2) the furnace must lose heat rapidly enough to cool reasonably quickly. These arguments lead generally to low-mass, lightly insulated furnaces or to furnaces with built-in cooling arrangements. The cooling arrangements are generally those used also in subambient temperature work (Sec. 4.10).

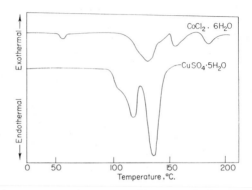

FIG. IV-31. Thermograms of copper sulfate pentahydrate and cobalt chloride hexahydrate (P4).

The thermograms show reasonable sensitivity but slow response; the response behavior is probably due to the isolation of the sensing element.

The present author frequently uses lightly insulated furnaces, confining the heat by the protective cement and outer tube at lower temperatures and by a radiation shield at higher temperatures.

The radiation shield functions by reflection back to the furnace of a substantial portion of the heat radiated. The shield itself, since it can radiate heat outward, does not reach nearly the same temperature as the furnace surface. It functions best in vacuum systems such as that of Martin and Edwards (M15) shown in Fig. IV-33 but it can be used also in air. The slow corrosion of the inside shield in air diminishes the effectiveness after a while but this can be replaced easily.

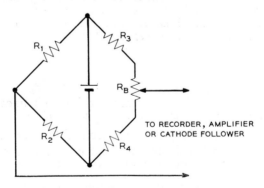

FIG. IV-32. Suggested circuit for thermistor. R_1 and R_2 are matched thermistors; R_3 and R_4 are fixed resistors.

Since a thermistor shows a fractional change in resistance with temperature the sensitivity of this arrangement would change only slowly with temperature.

The radiation shield surrounding a hot furnace in air will be cooled by convection; a very unsteady-state heat-transfer situation arises in which the heat loss can easily vary somewhat from minute to minute. In differential thermal analysis, the heating and cooling of the furnace present a changing demand on the power supply which is far greater than any demand changes from changes in cooling effects. For slowly varying temperature for differential thermal or thermogravimetric analysis the present author cannot recommend the use of radiation shields. A well-insulated furnace will provide greater temperature stability, longer life for the winding, lower power requirement, and a cooler laboratory. If the well-insulated furnace has provision for cooling, the same furnace

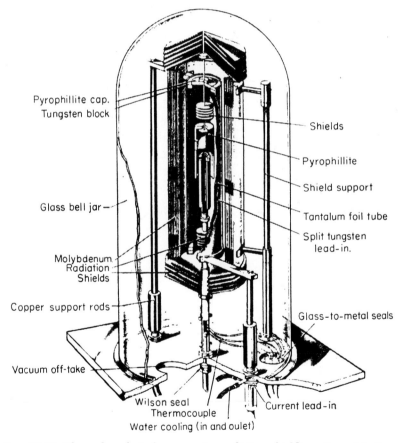

FIG. IV-33. Thermal analysis furnace using radiation shielding. From Martin and Moore (M16).

The shielding restricts heat by reflection and performs effectively as insulation.

could have all the advantages cited at the disadvantages of significantly greater cost and size.

The ordinary commercial insulating materials are well-known: firebrick, magnesium oxide, etc. For not extremely high temperatures, a relatively new material, potassium titanate, can be used. The thermal conductivity is much less than that of magnesium oxide.

4.14. Summary

There is no one superior instrument for differential thermal analysis. The basic apparatus will need to be selected or constructed for the problem on which it will be used.

Horizontal furnaces can be constructed with very low-temperature gradients; vertical furnaces will have noticeable gradients but provide more nearly symmetric heating.

The type of sample holder is chosen principally on the basis of the desired degree of isolation and atmosphere accessibility. Multiple sample holders are useful for comparison runs.

Quantitative measurements other than peak height will ordinarily require a time-based record. An X vs Y recorder plotting ΔT vs T does not show as much; the X vs Y records are more convenient to store.

Controlled-atmosphere furnaces are useful for studying decomposition or oxidation reactions. Pressure effects can also be studied.

CHAPTER V

Evaluation of Differential Thermal Analysis Curves

5.1. Introduction

Before making any detailed study of quantitative measurements or mathematical treatments some concept of the magnitudes involved will be of help. Several clearly different types of reactions could be chosen ranging from decompositions or combustions to crystallographic phase transformations on to second-order transitions. Because of the oft-encountered assumptions of temperature homogeneity and of unchanging or nonaffecting atmosphere the best starting point is a chemical decomposition.

Let us examine the decomposition of calcium carbonate in some detail. We shall mount the specimen in a usual manner—a long cylinder of which we will take a right section. We will consider the outside of the cylinder to be heating at a regular rate. We shall assume, for our immediate purposes, that the decomposition is extremely rapid although this is not essential to the discussion.

As the specimen is heated a temperature gradient is set up from the edge to the center which reaches a nearly steady state. An exactly steady state would require a heat capacity, thermal conductivity, emissivity (if the experiment goes above, say, 400°C), heat-transfer coefficient from container to sample, and heat-transfer coefficient from particle, all constant with temperature, or a fortuitous combination of circumstances. But since we have a quasi-steady state, we can find relations describing the gradient within the specimen merely assuming that certain quantities are constants over any small temperature interval.

Recall the heat flow equation for cylinders. A form of the temperature distribution which satisfies the differential equation is

$$T = \beta \left(t - \frac{R^2 - r^2}{4a} \right)$$

where β is the heating rate, T is the time, R is the outside radius, r is the radius of the point under consideration, and a is the thermal diffusivity.

Now
$$\frac{\partial^2 T}{\partial r^2} + \frac{1}{r}\frac{\partial T}{\partial r} = \text{constant},$$

so substituting our previous expression for T we obtain

$$\frac{\beta^2 T}{2a} + \frac{1}{r} \cdot \frac{\beta r}{2a} = \frac{\beta}{a}$$

obeying the general heat flow equation $\nabla^2 T = \frac{\beta}{a}$.

Using the temperature equation given, we can calculate the temperature difference, $T_w - T_c$, from wall to center during the steady temperature rise:

$$T_w - T_c = \frac{\beta R^2}{4a} = \frac{\beta \rho c R^2}{4k}.$$

We can then insert known or estimated values for the heat capacity, c, the density, ρ, the thermal conductivity, k, and the radius, obtaining a numerical value for this temperature difference. Assume, for the purposes of illustration, the values shown in the accompanying tabulation for the calcium carbonate decomposition.

	CaCO₃	CaO
k	0.0070	0.017 cal/sec cm/deg
c	0.27	0.24 cal/gm/deg
ρ	2.7	1.3 gm/cm³
β	= 6.0°C/min = 0.10°C/sec	
R	= 0.30 cm	

(The density we have taken is for a well-packed specimen, nearly 90% crystal density for calcite, assuming no shrinkage or loss of weight.)

From the preceding equation we can readily calculate the temperature drops from wall to center as 0.20°C and 0.10°C for calcium carbonate and calcium oxide, respectively. (This produces a base line shift of 0.10° or 4 μv using chromel-alumel thermocouples.) Let us next consider the energy involved in the decomposition, i.e., 44 kcal/mole or 440 cal/gm of calcium carbonate.

Imagine first the instantaneous addition of the necessary quantity of heat (for decomposition) simultaneously to our sample and to an extremely stable reference material. The temperature rise of the inert specimen would be ca. 1800°C. Quantities of heat of this magnitude require a tremendous temperature gradient for transport. Since this addition of heat is clearly unrealistic, imagine that we are carrying out a decomposition in our sample holder in such a manner that the last 1% of the sample decomposes in 1 second. We can calculate that 1 cm length of specimen will require 300 calories so we must supply 3 calories to the center. Since we are only concerned with the order of magnitude, we use the steady-state equation

$$\Delta T = \frac{q}{2\,k\pi} \ln \frac{R}{r},$$

the real case being much worse. We are dealing now with a layer of calcium oxide but neglecting the uncertain correction for change in mass,

$$\Delta T = \frac{3.0 \times 2.3}{2 \times 0.017} \approx 64°.$$

This means that to carry out the decomposition so that the last bit occurs at 1% per second we must heat the sample enough to provide at least a temperature drop of 64°C from the wall to the reaction front. The limiting factor in a decomposition of this kind is not the rate of reaction but the supply of heat to the decomposing material. Obviously the heat supply problem is accentuated in thermogravimetry wherein the sample is customarily isolated from the heat source.

Note that each of the quantities involved in the idealized heat transport is changing discontinuously at the time of decomposition and that other quantities are varying continuously with temperature. Deeg (D9) points out that sixteen variables have to be considered even after omitting emissivity; Dilaktorskii and Arkhangel'skaja (D11a) list twenty-five.

The thermal effects during a phase or second-order transition will be less marked but note that the lesser magnitudes call for more careful avoidance of background signal. The residual signal due to actual changes in thermal properties of the sample and reference is relatively large compared to the discontinuous event being studied. The temperature gradients in a polymer undergoing a glass transition, for example, are ordinarily much smaller than in a decomposition but by no means negligible; gradients are—in fact—to be expected because of the low thermal conductivities of such materials.

5.2. General Remarks

There are three important reasons for mathematical treatments of differential thermal analysis curves; of basic interest are the attempts to describe the curves in terms related to the events occurring with the aim —simply—of understanding the process. Another use for measurements is the quantitative determination of materials, or, if the material is known, the determination of energy changes; the third is to estimate the rates of reaction of the material from the slope or from the instantaneous magnitudes of the differential temperature.

So far, the mathematical treatments have been inadequate. Vitiating flaws exist in the treatments offering a precise description. The purely empirical procedure of obtaining a calibration curve is in general use. Nevertheless, the events occurring during a differential thermal analysis are reproducible physical phenomena and are subject to known physical laws and relationships; the problems are that: (1) several processes must be treated simultaneously; (2) the nature of some processes may be changing during the run or vary with the environment; (3) the applicability of a treatment of a particular segment of the process may depend on the history and condition of the specimen; and (4) the several types of reactions render the use of any single description unworkable.

Under (1) we must consider the problems of heat transfer and temperature control and these are already severe (mathematically) in the simple case of a rapid and reversible phase change. If the furnace wall, for example, is programmed to raise in temperature at a constant rate the change in heat-transfer coefficients from wall to block and from block to specimen means that the actual heating rate of the specimen is varying slowly. Programming the rise of the block temperature eliminates only the first but accentuates the problem of control. Within the sample the heat transfer in unreacted and reacted materials will differ and will vary with temperature. During the reaction the temperature distribution within the block will vary because of the change in demand by the sample.

Under (2) we must consider not only the effect of atmosphere and changing atmosphere (Chapter VII) but also the possibility that the over-all reaction being studied is actually a stepwise process whose individual reactions may—and probably do—have heats of reaction and/or of activation which vary greatly and differently with temperature.

Under (3) we must consider effects of particle size and history on heat transfer and surface energy as well as effects of packing on uniformity of heating within the specimen.

Under (4) we must consider the obvious existence of processes that are decidedly rate-controlled, others that are diffusion-controlled, and still others that are instantaneous.

For all these reasons assumptions and approximations are made concerning various parts of the several processes; in many cases the assumptions are clearly not related to the physical event, in others the relation is tenuous at best. The inability to describe the curve satisfactorily leads immediately to inability to integrate mathematically and calculate the amount of material or the heat of reaction from the area and already known parameters such as heat capacity and thence to the need to calibrate the apparatus to determine the effective magnitude of all the parameters under the conditions of the experiment.

This lack—to date—of a really satisfactory treatment should not excuse the active practitioner of thermal analysis from study of the extant treatments. These can still lead to some better understanding of the processes involved and perhaps to some new and superior approach. This chapter necessarily treats both empirical and mathematical approaches to analytical, thermodynamic, and kinetic problems in thermal analysis.

The endothermic peak appearing in differential thermal analysis results from the deviation of the temperature of the material in contact with the thermocouple or other measuring device from the programmed (directly or indirectly) temperature. The cause of the deviation is a change in the thermal characteristics of the sample material. The manner in which the change in properties will affect the heating in the vicinity of the thermocouple depends on the nature and magnitude of the change and, to a limited degree, on some mechanical considerations.

If the change in properties comes as a result of a change in state other than volatilization the change will occur along a moving boundary as described in Chapter II and the movement will be determined by the sharpness of the discontinuity (related to the heat of transition) and the thermal properties of both the high-temperature and the low-temperature forms. The endothermic peak is essentially a record of the movement of this boundary so that it, in turn, reflects the changes in thermal properties. In the case of chemical reaction or decomposition the movement of the boundary can be modified by atmosphere effects, or, in some cases, by a rate-controlling step.

Chemical reactions, including decompositions, will generally be sufficiently rapid that we can assume a clear boundary between unreacted and reacted materials; some, however, are very decidedly rate-controlled* so that each particle reacts or decomposes over a finite time.

*The term *rate-controlled* is used to describe reactions, including decompositions, in which the chemical reaction rate is slow enough so that it determines the over-all rate of reaction. In this sense such reactions may be differentiated from those in which the over-all rate is determined by the supply of heat or by diffusion of gases.

In the latter case the moving boundary would be spread out to a skewed curve. The several effects cited will each affect the magnitude of the differential temperature and, if any quantity is to be calculated from the differential temperature, the several others will need to be considered.

5.3. Peak Shape

The detailed shape of the differential thermal analysis peak has been the subject of considerable empirical treatment as well as some mathematical description. The empirical treatments quite naturally preceded the mathematical as the users of differential thermal analysis sought ways of relating sets of data to each other and to the composition of the materials. The manner of description normally included the magnitude of the peak and some temperature selected to represent the reaction. The mode of selection of the temperature can be surmised: it would be the temperature which remained most nearly constant with changes of quantity of active material, nature of other materials present, heating rate, and any other variables coming to the mind of the experimenter. The fact that the temperatures chosen were frequently heavily dependent on apparatus and procedure was not recognized.

Although the quantitative measure generally chosen was the area of the peak, the difficulty of circumscribing this area properly (Section 5.4) has led to other methods of measurement. Similarly, the shape of the peak has been used to deduce information needed for kinetic studies.

In general, endothermic deflections will look somewhat like one of those in Fig. V-1. A typical phase transformation will comprise (Fig. V-1, A) a continually increasing rise until very near the peak, a slightly rounded peak, and a rapid return to the base line [which may be displaced from the original base line (see Chapter II)]. If the process is seriously rate- or diffusion-controlled the deflection will be relatively broad and the peak (Fig. V-1, C) decidedly rounded. Deflections having some characteristics of each type may occur in lesser degrees of rate or diffusion control or in cases of inadvertent limitation of decomposition products. The oft-mentioned straight-line portion (Fig. V-1, B) may occur in quite large specimens or with a fortuitous combination of thermal properties. There is no reason to expect such a region to be characteristic of all deflections.

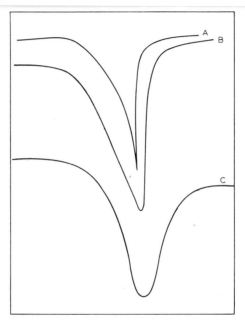

Fig. V-1. Typical thermograms for: A, a rapid phase transition; B, a phase transition deflection with a straight-line section; and C, a rate-controlled reaction.
Simple treatments are impracticable because the shape depends on the nature of the thermal effect.

The shape of the peak is dependent not only on the nature of the material but also on its manner of containment. The presence or absence of a heat sink close to the specimen can and will modify the reaction and hence modify the thermogram. Figure V-2 shows a repetitive thermogram of potassium sulfate; compare this with Fig. II-10. In Fig. V-2, the sample holder was an alumina sleeve which fitted over the supporting tube and extended above it, forming a sample well quite isolated from a similar reference well. Not only is interchange of heat avoided but also each specimen is in contact only with a thin ceramic wall of fairly low heat capacity (not counting the supporting tube). The heat supplied to or taken from the sample must therefore have just come from or be immediately supplied to the furnace wall. (The sample cavity in the block was also ¼ inch nominal ID.) Differences in appearance are quite apparent in both the time-based and the temperature-based (Figs. V-3 and II-11) thermograms. In Fig. II-11 the presence of the heat sink enables a rapid return to the base line on heating through the transformation and a very noticeable shift in the base line. The reverse effect, i.e., a sharp break *away* from the base line, is seen on cooling. The change in thermal properties of the material exercise a de-

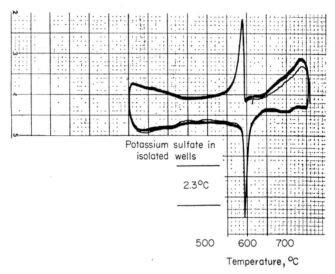

Potassium sulfate in
isolated wells

2.3°C

500   600   700

Temperature, °C

FIG. V-2. Repetitive (seven-cycle) thermogram of potassium sulfate in isolated alumina wells.

Compare with Fig. II-10.

cided effect. In Figs. V-2 and V-3, on the other hand, the sharper deviations from the base line are, in each case, the initial deviations from the base line. The return to the steady state is essentially asymptotic. This is quite reasonable since the isolated specimens comprise, in effect, a differential calorimetry arrangement. The gain in sensitivity, roughly a factor of 2, (note difference in scale) carries the penalty of a lack of sensitivity for close-lying reactions. For seven cycles in Fig. V-2 the peak heights and root mean square deviation were 2.16 ± 0.016 and 1.97 ± 0.01 inches for heating and cooling, respectively. The root mean square deviations are 0.7 and 1.0%, respectively.

The several temperatures that have been used to characterize a deflection include the temperature of onset of transition or decomposition, the intersection of the extensions of the base line and of the "straight-line portion" of the deflection, a similar intersection using an extension of the slope at the inflection point, the temperature at the inflection point, the intersection of extensions of the "straight-line portions" of the rising and falling sides of the deflection, the peak temperature, the temperature of "maximum rate of reaction," and temperature of completion of reaction. These methods are empirical. The peak temperature is the temperature

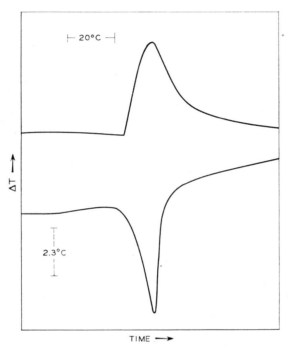

FIG. V-3. Thermogram of potassium sulfate in isolated wells.
The inflection is larger but the return to the base is slower than shown in Fig. II-10.

of interest when the measuring thermocouple is at the center of the specimen. If the measured temperature is that of the edge of the sample, e.g., the block temperature, the temperature of the beginning of the reaction is the important datum. Other points of measurement on or from the peak have no simple significance.

Guiochon (G53) has registered an objection to the use of the term "temperature of onset of decomposition," pointing out that the Arrhenius law, $\kappa = Ae^{-E/RT}$, describing the temperature dependence of reaction rates indicates only that the rate of any reaction will generally decrease along with the temperature. He states further that "there is absolutely no reason why this rate suddenly becomes zero, although it may be that no apparatus can detect it below a certain value of the temperature, characteristic of the apparatus, not of the reaction." This is a quite valid criticism, yet temperatures such as that of "onset of decomposition" are still measured and reported. This is because a more-or-less reproducible temperature is observed under a given set of conditions. The reason must be that the initial (ambient) atmosphere already contains some of the gaseous decomposition product; the presence of a partial pressure of the gas will delay a noticeable decomposition and ultimately permit what appears to be an almost immediate finite rate (see Chapters III and VII).

The temperature at which this finite rate appears will be dependent on the geometry as well as on the heating rate of the sample, but only to a small degree on the rate of flow of a gas over the specimen. (The flow of gas will have a much greater effect after the appearance of the weight change, when the concentration of gas over the sample might limit the diffusion outward.) The vapor remaining within the specimen can affect subsequent decompositions (Fig. III-22).

The general pattern of action in deriving expressions describing the differential thermal analysis peak is to set up a mathematical model, make a number of simplifying assumptions, state the established laws and/or relations for heat conduction or temperature variation, substitute in these laws the quantities applicable to the particular problem, and finally manipulate the expressions until a usable form is obtained. The approach is perfectly straightforward. It is notably unsuccessful because the assumptions necessary to permit convenient mathematical description are not ordinarily physically valid. (This criticism is especially applicable to decomposition reactions, yet these same reactions are cited commonly in evaluating quantitative techniques.)

As Sewell and Honeyborne (S19a) point out, these assumptions are commonly that none of the several quantities needed in the mathematical expressions change during the thermal effect (see Chapter II). These quantities include the thermal conductivity, heat capacity, density and hence the thermal diffusivity, and heat of reaction. (Sewell and Honeyborne carefully restrict their own treatment to reversible phase changes and thermodynamically irreversible decompositions obeying a first-order law with the comment that the type of reactions such as the decomposition of calcite "appears too complex for a general treatment to be useful.")

The quantities assumed as constant all change with temperature but even if we ignore the continuous change of each of these we can scarcely ignore the sudden change in thermal conductivity, for example, when a sample melts. Even crystallographic phase changes differ considerably. The α-β transition in quartz involves two hexagonal structures and a rather small heat of transition. One might expect the listed quantities to be rather similar at temperatures above and below the transition. In contrast, barium titanate undergoes a rhombic-cubic transformation ca. 120°C. This transition also marks the disappearance of ferromagnetic properties (Curie point). To expect the listed quantities to remain nearly the same above and below this transformation would be exceedingly optimistic.

This nonconstancy of important quantities means, essentially, that a simple relation between heat of reaction and temperature difference or peak area does not exist for differential thermal analysis. This does not mean that reasonably accurate quantitative techniques cannot be found. The simplest—and probably the best available—procedure will be the use of differential calorimetry.

Differential calorimetry has its own quota of disadvantages and hence is certainly not a cure-all. If a reaction can be isolated—in point of time— from any other and there is no easy flow of heat between sample and reference a rather good measure of the heat of reaction should be obtainable.

5.4. Precision Analysis

With the increasing use of differential thermal analysis, there is inevitably a compulsion to improve the numerical precision so that accurate heats of transition or decomposition may be obtained or, conversely, by determining the heat effect of the reaction in the sample and in the pure material, an accurate quantitative analysis may be performed.

Various degrees of success have been claimed but success has generally been accompanied by penalties. In several cases, the term "differential thermal analysis" has been used quite loosely; the authors have reported on a technique which can be more reasonably classed as differential calorimetry.

In general, the attempts to describe a differential thermal analysis peak are characterized by unwarranted assumptions based on mathematical convenience; these assumptions were intended to render the differential temperature describable by an expression requiring no great manipulation. These assumptions are recognized as approximations and the final expressions were intended as no more than good representation.

If a certain term, expression, or relation—whether known or unknown

—describes a physical being or process, an approximation must be a simpler term, expression, or relation describing the same phenomenon but not so well as the proper term. Substitution of one process for another is out of bounds. To ignore the physical realities is to vitiate the final result which, one may presume, the author had hoped to use for some real events. In evaluating an expression which purportedly describes a differential thermal analysis curve due to some specific type of thermal effect, one may often save time by examining the assumptions made. If some part of the assumed behavior of the system is unrealistic the final expression may be, in effect, nothing more than an exercise in mathematical manipulation.

Differential thermal analysis was defined previously (Chapter I) as a technique in which heat is allowed to flow from the sample to the reference or vice versa. The function of this heat flow is to permit equalization of the temperature and enable detection of any subsequent reaction. Obviously one may inhibit this heat flow by thermal isolation of the sample, but this tends to cause deflections to persist unduly long times, nullifying the advantages of differential thermal analysis. Admittedly this is a matter of degree; there is no clear separation between differential calorimetry and differential thermal analysis.

The major criterion in the several mathematical representations of the differential thermal analysis curves is whether or not the devisor of the expression was able to ignore the thermal conductivity of the specimen. If this quantity is found to have no effect on the results, the technique used is differential calorimetry and the reader will find that the writer has his sample vessels supported by rods—generally ceramic—or set on a ceramic plate or otherwise isolated from the reference material.

Differential calorimetry is certainly a worthy technique, but the prospective user must be aware of its shortcomings. Differential calorimetry will permit determination of heats of reaction or transition at the cost of loss of ability to measure or perhaps even detect reactions occurring soon after the first. The interval in which interference would occur varies with heating rate and heat of reaction. The calculations are simple and calibration is not even needed in favorable designs. Comparison with a known specimen is sufficient.

Vold (V10) got rather good agreement with literature values for the heats of fusion of stearic and benzoic acids. She recognized that her apparatus was a differential calorimeter and—even more laudably—recognized that confinement of vapors was necessary. On this latter point, she differed from the general run of workers reporting quantitative techniques even though these would consistently use decomposition reactions for calibration.

Quantitative measurements on reversible transformation ought not to be difficult; Grimshaw (G46), for example, found $\beta \rightarrow \alpha$ quartz inversion reproducible to less than 2% diluted in diluted (with alumina) natural specimens. This is quite understandable; the transition temperature is not affected seriously by the rate of heating or cooling and the porosity of the mass is unimportant because no gases have to find their ways in or out. Note, however, that Arens (A12) (see Chapter III) reports that the area of the quartz peak increases with heating rate. The present author believes this to be a heat-transport problem, but in any case the rate of heating should be controlled and reproducible.

Boersma (B58) chooses to go back to differential calorimetry. He points out quite justly several shortcomings of differential thermal analysis and offers a solution. "These shortcomings can be overcome by a new measuring technique (new sample holder) [Fig. V-4] and a new method of diagram interpretation (curve synthesis) [Fig. V-5]."

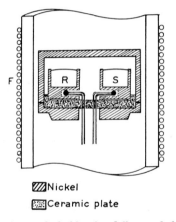

%%%%Nickel
%%%%Ceramic plate

FIG. V-4. Boersma's (B58) sample holder for differential thermal analysis: S, sample; R, reference material; F, furnace.

The isolation of the specimen and reference holders prolong the temperature effects. Better quantitative data may be obtained for completely separable effects but these completely separable effects are less likely to be found.

Boersma's formulas were derived for nickel blocks, in which the thermal conductivity of the block was considered to be so much greater than that of the specimen that its effect could be ignored, and for ceramic blocks, in which the thermal conductivity of the block was taken into account. The equations are given below, together with that for the proposed sample holder.

A. Nickel Blocks
    (1) Cylindrical cavity:

$$\int_{t_1}^{t_2} \theta_0 dt = \text{peak area} = \frac{qa^2}{4\lambda}$$

    where θ_0 = differential temperature,
          q = heat of transformation per unit volume,
          a = radius of cavity, and
          λ = thermal conductivity of sample material.

    (2) Spherical cavity:

$$\int_{t_1}^{t_2} \theta_0 dt = \frac{qa^2}{6\lambda}.$$

    (3) Flat plate:

$$\int_{t_1}^{t_2} \theta_0 dt = \frac{qa^2}{2\lambda}.$$

B. Ceramic Block
    A solution exists only for the spherical case:

$$\text{peak area} = \frac{qa^2}{6} \left(\frac{2}{\lambda_c} + \frac{1}{\lambda} \right)$$

    where λ_c is the thermal conductivity of the ceramic block.

C. Proposed Sample Holder (Differential Calorimeter)

$$\int_{t_1}^{t_2} \theta \, dt = \frac{mq}{G}$$

    where m = mass of sample and G = heat-transfer coefficient between small nickel container and surrounding nickel.

    The sample holder is perfectly suitable for differential calorimetry since, as Boersma points out, the volume or thermal conductivity of the sample does not affect the peak area. They do, however, affect seriously the time interval over which the peak must be observed and therefore can seriously decrease the sensitivity. With samples of any moderate size the peak may easily become so spread out that it overlaps another and Boersma's calculation can be applied to neither. For this eventuality he proposes the use of "curve synthesis."

    Curve synthesis is a technique by which curves for known pure minerals might be added electrically to match the curve obtained from a specimen containing these minerals. Templates are made of curves of the pure minerals and of the specimen. These are examined by a light beam–photocell arrangement and the responses from the several known materials individually attenuated until their sum—as observed on an oscilloscope—reproduces the curve of the unknown. The amount of each material is proportional to the attenuator setting. (The circuit as shown would tend to *average* rather than *sum* the several inputs. In order to add the various input signals should appear across resistors in *series* rather than *parallel.*)

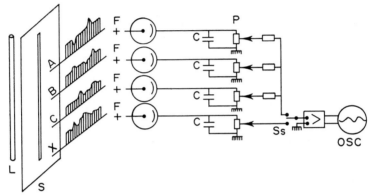

Fig. V-5. Curve synthesis for differential thermal analysis: L, lamp; S, slit; A, B, C, and X, moving templates; F, photocells; C, integrating condensers; P, calibrated potentiometers; Ss, selector switch; and OSC, cathode ray oscillograph. From Boersma (B58).
By optically adding fractions of components Boersma attempted to match the thermogram of the unknown mineral.

The method takes no account of curve shifting by other components (see Chapter VII) and it assumes that the operator is comparing curves of *all* the components; further, comparison of the curves directly will lead the operator to match—or try to match—peak heights rather than areas. The present author does not agree with Boersma's closing statements on the advisability or ease of manipulating an integral curve rather than the raw data. Further, the present author has not heard of any successful use of the curve synthesis procedure. If the data were obtained using a properly chosen dynamic atmosphere, the procedure might well be successful. The present author does not imply that matching peak heights rather than area is an error (see Chapter II). The peak height must be shown to be a linear function of concentration or some empirical correction would need to be applied. This correction might be dependent on the other materials present. A further complication is the quite common shift in peak temperature with concentration as shown in Fig. V-6.

Boersma also formulated the expressions below for the deviation of the peak because of the presence of the thermocouple (Fig. V-7), accounting both for the altered geometry and for heat leakage along the thermocouple wires.

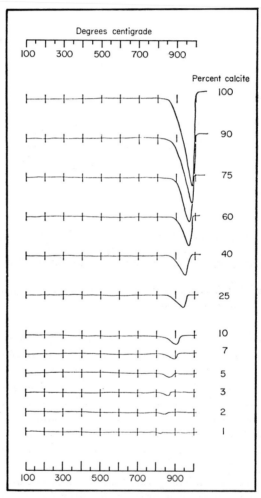

Fig. V-6. DTA curves of calcite-alundum mixtures. The calcite is Iceland spar ground to 120–200 mesh. From Kulp *et al.* (K42).
     Decompositions will customarily show a shift in temperature with dilution.

Correction Added for Thermocouple Interference
(1) Spherical cavity:

$$\int_{t_1}^{t_2} \theta_0 dt = \frac{qa^2}{6\lambda} \cdot \frac{\alpha}{1 + \Lambda/\lambda}$$

where a (correction for altered geometry) equals $1 - r_0^2/a^2 \, [3 - 2r_0/a]$ and Λ (heat leakage correction) equals

$$\lambda_p \frac{r_0}{l} \frac{A}{4\pi r_0^2} \left[1 - \frac{r_0}{a}\right]$$

where r_0 = radius of thermocouple bead,
λ_p = thermal conductivity of thermocouple wire, and
A = cross section of leads.

(2) Cylindrical cavity

$$\int_{t_1}^{t_2} \theta_0 dt = \frac{qa^2}{4\lambda} \frac{1 - \dfrac{r_0^2}{a^2}(1 + 2 \ln a/r_0)}{1 + \dfrac{A}{l} \cdot \dfrac{\lambda_p}{\lambda_s} \cdot \dfrac{\ln a/r_0}{2\pi n}}$$

where l = length of leads.

Two years later, de Josselin de Jong (J9) reported his evaluation of the Boersma (B58) equations. He found, like Speil (S40) but unlike Arens (A12), peak areas essentially independent of heating rate. Several equations for areas or temperature differences predict this independence. The question must necessarily be resolved. If one side or the other has not committed a gross error then the experiments must differ in some important way.

In his determination of the calibration factor for heats of reaction de Jong (J9) finds that a given sample (and thermocouple) height but a varying diameter will yield calibration factors, Ψ, which agree with

$$\Psi = \frac{\text{peak area}}{\omega} = \frac{\rho a^2}{4\lambda} \left\{ \left[1 - \frac{r_0^2}{a^2}\left(1 + \ln \frac{a}{r_0}\right)\right]\left[1 + \frac{\Lambda}{\lambda} \ln \frac{a}{r_0}\right] \right\}$$

values calculated from where ω = quantity of sample, obtained from Boersma (B58). But when the height of the sample is varied, the calibration factor cannot be predicted. Figure III-15 shows that the height of the thermocouple neither maintained (a) a symmetric position in the sample nor (b) a fixed position with respect to either end. His data have undoubtedly met with objections on the first point but his conclusion answers such: "samples 10 and 20 mm high show practically the same area which indicates that it is not the total amount of the reacting material that counts but only the amount present in a disc of unit height." True! so far as it goes, but only because his point of

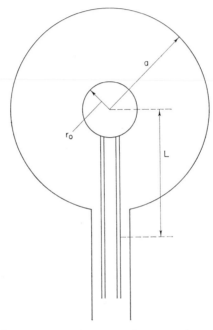

Fig. V-7. Heat leakage through thermocouple wires of lengths *l*. From Boersma (B58).

The presence of sizable metal leads coming from the point of measurement can have a serious effect on sensitivity.

measurement has become deep enough to decrease (almost to vanishing) the effect of exchange with the outside atmosphere. This is strictly analogous to Arens (A12) observation that "deep placement of the differential thermocouple junctions in the samples yield DTA curves with relatively strong endothermic reactions . . . in which the omission of the latter part of the quotation is deliberate (see Chap. III). The peak temperatures should be increasing asymptotically like the area. These temperatures are not shown.

Note: There is a deplorable compulsion to calibrate or evaluate for quantitative work using reactions involving a weight loss; yet only a few authors give *any* sign of recognition that the atmosphere has any importance. The heat of decomposition of copper sulfate pentahydrate is *not* the same when expanding against one atmosphere of water vapor as when expanding against the few millimeters of vapor pressure in the ambient atmosphere. This is because the reactions occur at different temperatures. In the usual sample holder the vapor pressure is at some undeterminate place between those limits. At best, the partial pressure of water approaches one atmosphere during the latter part of the decomposition. The 220 cal per gram determined by de Bruijn and van der Marel (B85) applies to the apparatus and conditions including the relative humidity of the ambient atmosphere. For any other apparatus or conditions the figure is an approximate value. It can be used (with reasonable care) to demonstrate similarity of condition. It may NOT be treated as a fixed, known value. It *must* not be used for calibrating an instrument.

The total heat of the change

$$CuSO_4 \cdot 5H_2O_{(25°C)} \rightarrow CuSO_4 \cdot H_2O_{(200°C)} + 4H_2O_{(0.01\ atm,\ 200°C)}$$

could be determined and would be a fixed quantity by whatever path the change took place. The differential thermal analysis apparatus measures the heat effect only within the sample—more specifically, only in the vicinity of the thermocouple. The heat required to drive off the water will be detected but the temperature dependence of the calibration factor will not.

Boersma's equations, according to de Josselin de Jong, predict (Fig. V-8) that $\Psi/\rho a^2\lambda$ (a function of the heat loss through the thermocouple wires) reaches a maximum for r_0/a of 0.2; i.e., the greatest peak area or

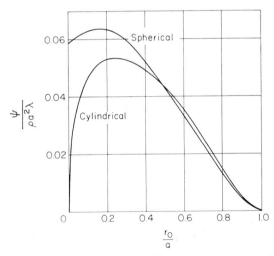

FIG. V-8. Graph of calibration factor ψ according to Boersma's eqs. (4) and (5) for $\Lambda/\lambda = 2$ and for different ratios of thermocouple junction, r_0, vs sample diameter. From de Jong (J9).

The conclusion apparent from the plot would be that one uses different size thermocouple beads for different size sample cavities and that there is a drop in sensitivity with an excessively fine couple (or with a small couple in a large specimen).

the least fractional loss through the thermocouple wires occurs when the thermocouple radius is ca. one-fifth of the sample radius. Further, if one decreases this thermocouple radius toward zero, the function for a spherical sample holder drops off only slightly but for a cylindrical sample holder the value drops rapidly toward zero! One may, then, decrease sensitivity greatly if one uses a small junction in a cylindrical sample but not in a spherical sample—if the relation is valid.

5.5. Area Measurement and the Parameters Influencing It

Examine now the quantity used as a measure of heat of reaction or amount of material, i.e., the peak area. This area is the summation—over the time of the deflection—of the temperature difference,

$$A = \int_{t_1}^{t_2} \Delta T \, dt.$$

The ΔT is the difference in temperature between the sample and reference but the universal assumption in deriving expressions is that the heat of reaction heats or cools the sample and its crucible. A sample block cannot be treated in the same manner because not only will the reaction in the sample heat or cool the block but it will also heat or cool the reference, in either case diminishing the ΔT signal. This effect on the reference is time-dependent and will have a greater effect with the slower heating rates. A high heating rate will carry the reaction to completion before the effect is felt or at least before it reaches the same magnitude. A more rapidly heated specimen may then show a higher apparent heat of reaction than a less rapidly heated specimen. The effect is not seen with isolated cups (differential calorimetry) since there is no rapid transfer of heat from sample to reference.

The discussion above may lead the reader to plan immediately to use the isolated specimen holder so a review of the advantages and disadvantages is in order. The isolated sample and references offer the greater sensitivity to *a* reaction because the heat of reaction needs to affect only the sample and the container; a given quantity of heat can bring about a greater temperature change than if the sample were in a block and, from this, a greater temperature difference than if there is a "low-impedance" path for heat between the sample and the reference. On the other hand, the dissipation of excess heat or recovery of a deficit of heat by an isolated sample is slow for the very same reason. The lack of reasonably free exchange of heat between sample and reference means that thermal effects will be spread over a large temperature range.

The block, with its relatively free exchange of heat, suffers a diminution of peak height and area but permits approach of temperature equilibrium very quickly after completion of one reaction so that a subsequent reaction may be observed as a separate reaction. This is the prime advantage of differential thermal analysis.

The author does not imply that either technique is superior per se to the other. The author uses both and modifications of both. The author does hope to convince the reader that the choice of sample holders must be made on the basis of the problem at hand. Dependence on either one alone prevents thorough exploitation of thermal analysis.

Eriksson (E5) points out that the peak area in differential thermal analysis is always a linear function of the heat of reaction *if* the heat is being produced or consumed at the *same rate at every point in the sample*. For most differential thermal analysis work this is per se a trivial solution since finite times and decidedly finite temperature lags are involved. In conventional apparatus reactions may take 10 or more minutes, the reaction finally ending at a temperature 100°C higher than at its inception. Obviously Eriksson's argument does not apply to such a case, but consider now a small sample one in which essentially every particle is in contact with a common heat sink of low heat capacity. The function of this sink is more to equalize temperature than to supply or remove heat. Under these conditions Eriksson's condition is met or closely approximated and we may conclude that for small specimens not compacted into a sphere or cylinder his relation might hold. The problem of measuring temperature change becomes quite difficult in such an experiment.

Under the conditions generally used in differential thermal analysis the heat of reaction is not being generated or consumed equally in all parts of the sample because thermal gradients do exist. Barshad (B9) showed (Fig. V-9) that the measured heat effect was, in effect, proportional to the amount of heat consumed per unit volume, i.e., the concentration of the active material.

Another source of concern in quantitative differential thermal analysis is the variation of atmosphere which occurs principally in decomposition reactions. It is accompanied, therefore, by peak shifting with changing heating rate. This is reasonable. The peak area is a measure of the heat of reaction, ΔH. The reaction temperature is dependent on the partial pressure of any gaseous product in contact with the specimen, i.e., within the bulk of the specimen. At high heating rates the gas does not diffuse out rapidly enough to maintain any resemblance of equilibrium. The reaction temperature is increased according to the van't Hoff relation, $d(\ln p)/dT = \Delta H/RT^2$, but ΔH is not a constant. Some further effects must be considered.

From Kirchoffs law $(d\Delta H/dT)_p = C_p$; thus

$$\Delta H = \Delta H_0 + \int_0^T \Delta C_p dT \tag{1}$$

and

$$\frac{d \ln K_p}{dT} = \frac{d \ln P}{dT} = \frac{\Delta H_0}{RT^2} + \frac{1}{RT^2} \int_0^T \Delta C_p dT.$$

Ignoring variation with T in ΔC_p,

$$\ln \frac{P_2}{P_1} = -\frac{\Delta H_0}{R}\left(\frac{1}{T_2} - \frac{1}{T_1}\right) + \frac{\Delta C_p}{R} \ln \frac{T_2}{T_1}. \tag{2}$$

This ΔC_p term can, and often will, be greater than the ΔH_0 term so that the observed ΔH increases quite rapidly with increasing partial pressure.

Let us examine the problem graphically (Fig. V-10). At low heating rates the product gas, e.g., water from kaolinite, can diffuse away rapidly enough so that only a small fraction of an atmosphere is present at any time. The material decomposes at T_1 to form dehydrated kaolinite and water absorbing a quantity of heat ΔH_1. These necessarily have some given heat content, H_1, at T_1 and this heat content increases with temperature in a manner dependent on the heat capacities of the prod-

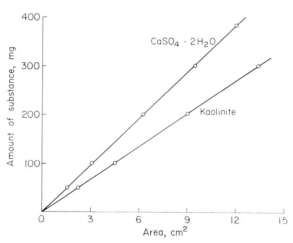

FIG. V-9. Peak areas of the endothermic breaks in DTA curves of various amounts of kaolinite and $CaSO_4 \cdot 2H_2O$. From Barshad (B9).

The materials were dispersed in sufficient quantities of alumina to yield the same volumes.

ucts. At T_2 the heat content is H_2. Now consider a second specimen heated at a higher rate, thereby decomposing at a higher temperature, T_2, because of the increased partial pressure of water vapor, P_2. Since the products must have a heat content of H_2, the heat of reaction at temperature T_2 is ΔH_2 which is obviously greater than ΔH_1.

Now let us insert some values in Eq. (2) and evaluate the significance of the source of error, using the data of Arens (A12) for the specific heats of kaolinite and calcined kaolinite, 0.201 and 0.428 cal/gm/°C, respectively. The molar heat capacities are 51.1 and 75.0 cal/mole/°C, respectively, but we have yet to consider the 2 moles of water. These add another 18.0 cal/mole°C. The change in heat capacity, ΔC_p, is then 62 cal/mole°C. Now, using Arens' peak shift values, i.e., peak temperatures of 545 and 620°C for heating rates of 6 and 10°C/minute, respectively, and using the value of 200 cal/gm as the heat of decomposition, Eq. (2) can be partially evaluated,

$$\log \frac{P_2}{P_1} = -\frac{200 \text{ cal/qm} \times 260 \text{ qm/mole}}{2.3 \times 2.0 \text{ cal/mole deg}} \left(\frac{1}{893°C} - \frac{1}{820°C} \right)$$

$$+ \frac{62 \text{ cal/mole deg}}{2.3 \times 2.0 \text{ cal/mole deg}} \log \frac{893}{820}$$

$$= 1.1 + 0.5 = 1.6$$

and the partial pressure of water vapor within the specimen chamber at the peak temperature is about forty times as high for the rapid

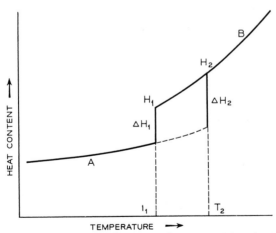

Fig. V-10. Heat content as a function of temperature: A, initial material; B, products.

Since the difference between the total heat contents varies with temperature, so must the heat of reaction or decomposition.

heating rate as for the slow. This value is very likely an exaggeration but there is, nevertheless, a marked effect.

The peak areas can hence be expected to be different at different rates, because at the higher heating rate a higher fraction of the kaolin stays in the unreacted state to any given temperature in the reaction range. This is in addition to the variation in area with equal increments of heat.

That even a given amount of heat does not cause the same magnitude of thermal effect at all temperatures has been shown by Sabatier (S2) and by Foldvari-Vogl and Kliburszky (F12). Sabatier selected materials whose heats of decomposition are well-known from the literature and which decompose at various temperatures, and related the peak area to the heat. His data are shown in Table V-1; they show a progressive

TABLE V-1

Substance	Temperature of dissociation (°C)	Heat of dissociation (Q) (cal/gm)	Area (S) (mv sec/gm)	Q/S
Gypsum	160	153	1720	0.089
$ZnCO_3$	425	114	965	0.118
$MgCO_3$	565	302	2160	0.140
$CaCO_3$	875	404	2120	0.190

diminution in response of the differential signal to a given quantity of heat as the temperature increased.

Even more convincing are the data of Foldvari-Vogl and Kliburszky (F12). They didn't rely on other measurements of heats of decomposition, but measured the effect of known quantities of heat applied electrically. They inserted a resistance heater in the form of a 5.6-ohm spiral filament in one of the sample crucibles and passed a current of 0.68 ampere through it for a period of 3 minutes (1100 cal) each 100°C as the sample was heated to ca. 1000°C. The areas (Fig. V-11) show a progressive decrease with temperature which shows the same general form as reported by Sabatier for actual reactions.

The conclusion to be reached is clearly that one cannot calibrate an apparatus for quantitative measurements at a temperature significantly removed from the temperature at which it will be used. A more positive thought, however, is that one might routinely compare peaks to an electrical standard rather than to the heat from another run; for example, after completion of the heating the furnace could be cooled to the approximate reaction temperature and a quantity of heat approximating the reaction heat added electrically. This would enable convenient comparison with a precisely known amount of heat at essentially the reaction temperature. Exact return to an arbitrarily defined reaction temperature would be pointless; bear in mind that the calibration factor varies by about 10% in an interval of 100°C in Foldvari-Vogl and Kliburszky's apparatus.

This electrical calibration would require a special apparatus. For general or infrequent use calibration with known amounts of known materials would suffice; Ellis and Mortland (E1) suggest those shown in Fig. V-12.

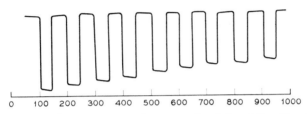

FIG. V-11. Differential temperature and area produced by adding identical quantities of heat at intervals of temperature rise. From Foldvari-Vogl and Kliburszky (F12).

The area per calorie decreases with increasing temperature.

The problem of integrating the area of a differential thermal analysis peak to measure the quantity of heat taken up or evolved has led to a variety of empirical solutions. We are not concerned here with the form of the peak nor with the significance of any part of the deflection; our immediate concern is the evaluation of the integral of $\Delta T\ dt$ from the moment the reaction begins to the moment ΔT returns to the base line. The method of integration can be selected from any of a number of techniques, e.g., measurement by planimeter, square-counting, weighing of the peak area, summation by trapezoidal rule. The major problem is selection of a reference line, that is, the line delineating the boundary at the open end of the recorded peak.

As a general rule materials undergoing reaction or transformation will show a quite marked change in thermal diffusivity and, hence, the steady-state temperature difference, i.e., baseline, will change. This effect may be diminished by dilution or by separation of sample and thermocouple but the peak is also attenuated, although not to the same degree. Further, the question of homogeneity of the dispersed sample will arise. Let us consider, for the time being, only specimens consisting wholly of a sample material whether or not it is already impure.

Figure V-13 shows Berg's (B26) thermogram for potassium nitrate illustrating his techniques for choosing the limits of simple curves. Transitions or reactions in which there is no substantial change in base line
offer no difficulty; the base line is extrapolated from one side to the
other and the area is clearly established. When there is a substantial
change in the base line as the second transition, a slightly more involved
procedure is required. Berg, like Deeg (D9), treated such reactions as
occurring on a front moving inward from the edge of a circle so that, at

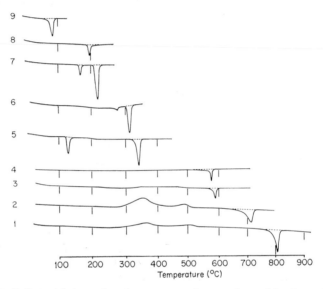

Fig. V-12. Differential thermal analyses curves of materials used for heat of reaction
calibration: (1) NaCl, 8.3%, 0.226 gm; (2) RbCl, 22.7%, 0.232 gm; (3) K_2SO_4, 52.8%,
0.280 gm; (4) quartz, 100%, 0.283 gm; (5) KNO_3, 41.2%, 0.215 gm; (6) $NaNO_3$,
21.7%, 0.230 gm; (7) $AgNO_3$, 53.0%, 0.273 gm; (8) NH_4Cl, 17.2%, 0.208 gm;
(9) *m*-/dinitrobenzene, 32.7%, 0.185 gm. The specimens were diluted with alumina.
From Ellis and Mortland (E1).

*Several calibration materials are needed because of the variation of heat indica-
tion with temperature.*

the time the centrally located thermocouple reached the peak deflection, the transition was complete. The latter part of the curve, then, is
simply a return of the center of the sample to a temperature approximating that of its surroundings. This asymptotic return depends only on
the magnitude of the deflection and on the thermal characteristics of the
specimen and not on the actual heat of reaction generated in or taken
up by the sample material. This does not avoid counting the area but
it does provide a basis for choice of the reference line. On the basis of

the considerations set forth above, in those cases where the thermal characteristics of the sample change enough so that the sample becomes warmer than the reference after the transition, Berg drops a perpendicular from the peak of the deflection to the zero line and joins this intersection to the initial and final portions of the curve. More involved peaks or combinations of peaks require more elaborate treatment as Berg needed to use in his quantitative evaluation of dolomite-bearing minerals. Figure V-14 shows the somewhat overlapping peaks of dolomite mixed

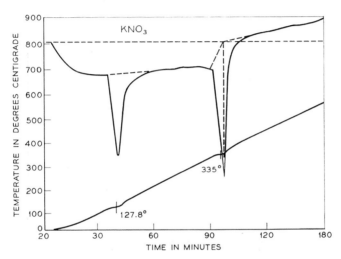

Fig. V-13. Thermogram of potassium nitrate showing ways of selecting the base line. From Berg (326).
The area is selected on the premise that the thermal effect after the peak is due only to a return to the base line.

with calcite and Berg's method of separating the two peaks. The method is intrinsically arbitrary.

Other possible ways of delineating the peak area to be measured include a slanted line joining an empirically selected beginning of the peak to an empirically selected end of the peak, extension of the lower-temperature base line to meet the high-temperature side of the peak, or, if these would not meet, the extension of the higher-temperature base line to meet the initial side of the peak. Both base lines might be extended also to join a perpendicular at the peak temperature. All of these are arbitrary and may be selected on the basis of the shape of the peak; any error will likely be within the experimental error due to other causes so long as peaks of the same shape (preferably of the same type of sample) are being compared.

If the instrument is being calibrated with one material for subsequent use with another, considerable risk of inaccuracy is incurred because the area that may or may not be included in the count can be a significant fraction of the total area. Note that simple experimental error is not involved here; either curve might be reproducible and repeatable. The question is whether to ignore a section—on one or the other of the curves—which could reasonably be included. Unfortunately, the derived expressions offer no help. The before and after base lines are *assumed* to be the same.

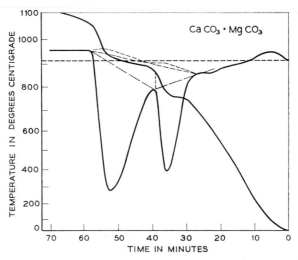

Fɪɢ. V-14. Thermogram of dolomite showing the separation of areas of overlapping curves. From Berg (B26).

    The separation is arbitrary but the error will be a small part of the total area.

An essential feature in measuring the peak area is reproducibility of the total curve. For decompositions the atmosphere effect requires special care by the operator, particularly in packing the sample. A quite sensitive measure of the reproducibility of packing will be the reproducibility of the peak temperature. Despite the considerable body of evidence (i.e., reports) that reproducibility of curves can only be achieved by firm packing of the samples, Kissinger (K29) found that peak temperatures were better reproduced "by loading the sample into the holder, with no packing other than gentle rapping around the outside of the holder. The standard deviation of an individual measurement was found to be 2.6°C, calculated from 25 pairs of duplicate determinations." This attention to reproducibility is convincing.

The reason for this reproducibility lies only partly in the mode of packing; it rests as much or more on the sample geometry. Kissinger used, principally, a tube ⅜ inch by 1¼ inch long. The sensing thermocouple is well-buried. Its atmospheric environment is not pure air certainly, but neither is it pure water vapor. At this distance from the surface, the reaction product (water vapor) cannot escape readily so the partial pressure of water is substantial. With the lesser barrier to diffusion than in a tightly packed sample, this partial pressure will reach some maximum value, probably before the peak temperature, determined principally by this case of diffusion and the heating rate. The observed peak temperature is properly the peak temperature at that particular water vapor pressure. Because of variations in sample holder design, variations in peak temperature will occur and variations in the calculated activation energies must result.

Kissinger's data (Table V-2) shows the peak temperature as a function of heating rate for the ⅜ inch and for some ⅛ inch by ½ inch long sample holders. The differences in peak temperature are in the order of 80°C for the same material, the same heating rate, but a different sample holder.

A further advantage of the thinner samples is the lesser error in establishing transition or "decomposition" temperatures. The huge samples popular in early differential thermal analysis work led to a number

TABLE V-2

DIFFERENTIAL THERMAL ANALYSIS MEASUREMENTS (K 29)

Heating rate[a] (°C/minute)	Peak temperature (°C)				
	A	B	C	H–12	H–13
(a) ⅜ inch holders					
12.5	640	642	635	629	629
10	625	632	615	616	614
6	611	614	611	603	597
4.5	598	599	592	588	583
3	588	584	574	582	568
(b) ⅛ inch holders					
12.5	557	563	544	553	553
10	549	553	530	547	542
6	537	538	520	530	533
4.5	525	528	511	519	517
3	514	523	499	512	508

[a] Heating rates given are nominal values. The actual rates were measured individually for each pattern and varied slightly from pattern to pattern.

of rather arbitrary geometric devices for obtaining a temperature to be designated as the characteristic temperature for that event. When simple phase transformations are spread out graphically over 50°C and dehydrations extend over a spread of more than 100°C, these empirical single temperatures are rather unconvincing.

There is, of course, no question that areas can be measured and, if the analyses are made under properly chosen conditions, related quite well to the quantity of material present. Barshad (B9) showed that the concentration was more closely related to area than total quantity. Some limitations must be observed, but these are generally restricted to decomposition reactions.

Wittels (W35) demonstrated, nevertheless, that a high heating rate (30°/minute) could be used for measurement of high heats of reaction (calcium carbonate, 40 kcal/mole) on small undiluted samples. He reports good linearity of peak area with sample mass from 0.30 to 3.00 mg (Fig. V-15), the smaller quantity giving a heat of reaction of 0.12 cal. In a later work (W36) he shows that the area to mass relation is nonlinear for samples greater than 60 mg in the case of tremolite, a calcium magnesium silicate hydrate.

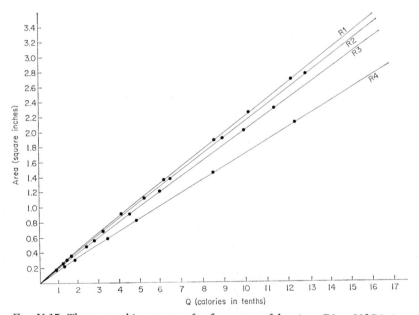

Fɪɢ. V-15. Thermographic response for four rates of heating: R1 = 30°C/minute; R2 = 22.5°C/minute; R3 = 15°C/minute; R4 = 10°C/minute. From Wittels (W35).

The area per calorie varies somewhat with rate of heating but not with the amount of heat.

Wittels pointed out that "samples of large mass are to be avoided when measuring small heat changes by differential thermal analysis" partly on the basis of the data noted above. The present author agrees enthusiastically—especially with the principal clause. The present author does not extend this agreement to the derivation by Wittels of an expression for the heat of reaction. The treatment was empirical; the approach was chosen on the basis of similarity of Wittels' area vs quantity plot to a plot of the function e^x. No theoretical justification is offered.

Wittel's success can be attributed easily to the fact that in this sample size range he finds the area dependence to be linear because he is generating carbon dioxide rapidly enough to form a reproducible atmosphere, i.e., nearly all CO_2. The heat of decomposition will be the same for a range of sample sizes. The higher limit (Fig. V-15) is set by the decreasing response to material at some distance away. Its closeness to the container walls becomes increasingly significant. For smaller samples the limit would be dictated to some degree by a similar reason; i.e., in the same container a relatively greater portion is in good thermal contact with the wall rather than the thermocouple. A very important contribution, however, is the probability that a large and variable fraction of the *ambient* atmosphere permeates the sample. This would be true in the upper part of the specimen and as the sample becomes smaller a centered thermocouple necessarily approaches the top.

In diluted samples some range of near constancy of atmosphere can be obtained with the result that both upper and lower limits could be pushed further. The lower limit would again be the failure to generate an atmosphere at a rate sufficient to keep the heat of reaction nearly constant. The upper limit would be set by the influence of the thermal characteristics of the material on those of the diluted specimen.

With the aid of the data of de Bruijn and van der Marel (B85) we can gain some better picture of the effects. Figure V-16 shows a calibration curve in which the heat in calories is plotted against the area of the peak. The samples were, for convenience, mixed with the required weight of alumina to make up 400 mg; note that we are dealing with *weight per cent* and not concentration. The plot actually has a very straight-line region up to about 20 calories. Near this point corresponding to one-quarter or more of the less-energetic materials a noticeable curvature begins and the data are less well-related from compound to compound. The thermal characteristics of the individual materials will generally begin to exert an influence (on the thermal conductivity for example) on the thermal behavior of the entire specimen. In spite of the curve having been extended unduly far with some of the materials it does show that the heat measured can be related quite well to the amount of material reacting or decomposing. As Barshad (B9) showed (Fig. V-9) the material ought to be dispersed in a constant volume and dispersed to such an extent that the thermal characteristics of the diluent determine those of the whole specimen. In de Bruijn and van der Marel's work the drop in heat effect with large concentration is shown in Fig. V-17. The small deviation by the barium chloride dihydrate is probably due to the lesser volume of a given weight.

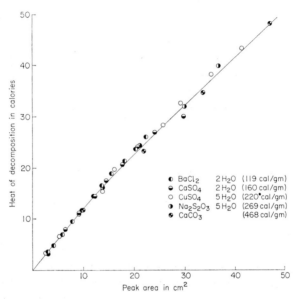

FIG. V-16. Calibration of differential thermal analysis apparatus. Heats of decomposition of some pure substances diluted with intert a-Al₂O₃, the total in the sample holder being 400 mg. *Peak area and heat of decomposition for loss of H₂O from CuSO₄·5H₂O to CuSO₄·H₂O. From de Bruijn and van der Marel (B85).

The well-diluted specimens show a linear relation because the thermal characteristics of the sample material do not contribute greatly to those of the entire specimen.

5.6. Evaluation of Heats of Reaction

The differential thermal analysis technique can be used to determine heats of reaction or of decomposition. Several methods of calculating these quantities have been offered by the difficulties arising from the changing characteristics render these methods inexact. Nevertheless they must be examined and the inaccuracies pointed out so that the pitfalls may be avoided without discarding the entire work.

The question of the exact significance of the differential thermal analysis peak of a decomposition reaction was taken up by Foldvari-Vogl and Kliburszky (F12), who analyzed the steps in the heating and cooling, resolving the heat effects into six quantities. The quantities are given below, with some clarification by the present author.

(1) A quantity of heat, q_1, is needed to heat the specimen from ambient temperature, T_0, to the initial temperature of the thermal effect, T_i, so

$$q_1 = m_1 \int_{T_0}^{T_i} c_1 \, dT + H_1$$

where m is the mass, c is the heat capacity, and H_1 comprises any heat effects at temperatures lower than the reaction under investigation.

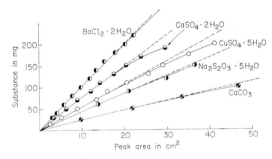

FIG. V-17. Calibration of differential thermal analysis apparatus. Peak areas for endothermal reactions of some substances diluted with inert α–Al_2O_3, the total in the sample holder being 400 mg. From de Bruijn and van der Marel (B85).
The relationship is linear for well-diluted materials.

(2) Some further heat, q_2, is required to change the lattice energy, the decomposition product from the specimen, and, in the case of water, vaporize it, as well as raise the temperature of the residue to the final temperature of the experiment, T_f. (Foldvari-Vogl and Kliburszky used the example of a mineral containing an OH radical so they could later show that for some minerals most of the heat effect detected by differential thermal analysis was heat of vaporization of water rather than the heat required to break chemical bonds.)

If the final temperature coincides with the return to a base line of a differential thermal analysis plot, the area under the curve is a measure of q_2. The changing heat capacity during the course of the reaction ought (except in rate-controlled processes) to be a rather small correction since at their very rapid heating most of the reaction will take place under one atmosphere of water vapor or other product gas and hence over a small temperature range.

Then on cooling:

(3) The decomposition residue is cooled to the ambient temperature, releasing a quantity of heat, q_3, which is not identical with q_1 because both mass and heat capacity are different, so

$$q_3 = m_3 \int_{T_f}^{T_0} c_3 \, dT + H_3$$

where the quantities are defined as previously, except referring now to step (3).

(4) Cooling the product gas (assume it to be water vapor) to 100°C liberates a quantity of heat, q_4.

(5) Condensing the water vapor at 100°C liberates a quantity of heat, q_5.

(6) Cooling the liquid water to ambient temperature liberates a quantity of heat, q_6.

Note that if the product gas were a permanent gas, step (5) would be dropped and steps (4) and (6) would be a single entry.

Now if the decomposition process is carried out in a calorimeter (Foldvari-Vogl and Klibursky's is described in Chapter XII), the quantity of heat supplied, Q, can be measured by the time and magnitude of an electric heating current. The quantity of heat recovered by heating of the calorimeter can be determined from the temperature rise and the total heat capacity. The difference, ΔQ, is an algebraic sum of all six steps, i.e.,

$$\Delta Q = -q_1 - q_2 + q_3 + q_4 + q_5 + q_6.$$

All of these quantities can be determined experimentally except q_2, so that, from known values plus whatever further measurement is needed, q_2 may be calculated.

The value of q_2 determined in this manner is not time-dependent. The change in base line which is common in differential thermal analysis has no bearing, since if the specimen is heated beyond completion of the reaction the difference in heat capacity between unreacted material and residue does not appear in the final determination. The heat required to raise the temperature of the residue appears again as a part of q_3 *so long as no other reaction occurs*.

In essence, Foldvari-Vogl and Kliburszky determine the heat of reaction at room temperature and relate it to differential thermal analysis measuring or calculating the necessary quantities to evaluate the heat of reaction at the temperature of the reaction. The appropriate relationship is

$$\frac{\partial \Delta H}{\partial T} = \Delta C_p$$

so

$$\Delta H_T = \Delta H_{T_d} + \int_{T_0}^{T} \Delta C_p \, dT.$$

The integral on the right comprises the terms described by Foldvari-Vogl and Klibursky as q_1, q_3, q_6.

Their technique ought to be useful not only for evaluation of heats of reaction but even as a quantitative tool. If another reaction occurred prior to the one under investigation, the effect could be calculated if the data are available or the material might be given a preheating to eliminate the interference.

Note that, unlike differential thermal analysis, calorimetric technique does not register heat of vaporization of water as part of the heat of reaction; the heat used in the vaporization is recovered on cooling. This is a major source of error in some dehydrations, those in which the reaction may reasonably be interpreted as $A \cdot xH_2O \rightarrow A + xH_2O(l)$ followed by $xH_2O(l) \rightarrow xH_2O(g)$. Dehydrations or dehydroxylations above the critical temperature of water ($374°C$) would have no vaporization step but the heat of condensation is still recovered.

The figures obtained by Foldvari-Vogl and Kliburszky (F12) will differ from data obtained by differential thermal analysis, as pointed out above, by $\int \Delta C_p \, dt$; in most cases involving hydrates the heat of vaporization will appear as a major portion of this heat, so the values by these authors will be lower than differential thermal analysis (or high-temperature calorimetry) values by this heat of vaporization. In the case of gypsum, they found, by differential thermal analysis, 170 cal/gm and, by their calorimeter, 34 cal/gm. From this latter datum they calculate q_2, the heat of dehydration, as 151 cal/gm.

Sewell and Honeyborne (S19a) treat a differential thermal analysis block and sample arrangement as a multitude of points each obeying a temperature function which is specifically a function of position and time. Each of these points continues its course of temperature rise without regard for the behavior of adjacent particles or points except for certain regions during the temperature interval of the thermal effect. The temperature difference, ΔT, can be treated as the difference between the function $T(P_1,t) - T(P_2,t)$. P_1 is specifically the location of the thermocouple in the sample and P_2 the location of the thermocouple in the reference specimen. The block containing the sample and reference material is assumed to be close to but not touching a furnace wall whose temperature is programmed at a constant rate so that $T = \beta t$. Heat conduction from the furnace wall to the block is assumed to be a function only of the temperature difference between the wall and the surface of the block. All of the quantities with the exception of temperature and time are assumed to be constant before and after the reaction has taken place as well as during the course of the reaction. The treatment is further limited to reversible phase changes and to thermodynamically irreversible decompositions obeying a first-order law.

All points except within the sample and all points in the sample except during the reaction or phase change obey the ordinary heat flow equation $\kappa_i \nabla^2 T = \partial(T)/\partial t$ where the subscript i may refer to any point within the system. During the reaction, the equation for points within the test specimen has an additive term

$$\kappa_s \nabla^2 T = \frac{\partial T}{\partial t} + \frac{L}{C_s}\frac{\partial \alpha}{\partial t}$$

where L is the heat of reaction and α is the fraction of material at P that has reacted at time t. The use of this fraction term demands a continuity of state which is not generally accepted; it implies that in any small region there is a mixture of reacted and unreacted material whose relative amounts are temperature- and time-dependent. The use of the term may be warranted in time-dependent decompositions but probably not in any reversible phase transition.

The customary heat flux continuity equations must also be obeyed; in essence what goes in one side of a boundary must come out the other.

$$\lambda_s(\partial T/\partial n)_s + \lambda_b(\partial T/\partial n)_b = 0$$

and

$$\lambda_r(\partial T/\partial n)_r + \lambda_b(\partial T/\partial n)_b = 0$$

where $\partial T/\partial n$ is the temperature gradient perpendicular to the surface at the point under consideration. On the surface of the block, this continuity equation takes a different form; while the heat transfer into the block is, as above, the thermal conductivity multiplied by the temperature gradient, any heat transfer from the furnace wall to the block depends upon the temperature difference at that point. Assuming the furnace wall at that point to have a temperature equal to βt, the temperature function for the point on the surface of the block is $T(P)$ and the difference between these two terms is multiplied by the heat-transfer coefficient $H(P)$,

$$-\lambda_b(\partial T/\partial n) = H(P)[T(P) - \beta T]$$

where β is the heating rate. Since this H is the sum of two terms, H_R and H_C, heat-transfer coefficients for radiation and for conduction, respectively, and since neither of these is independent of temperature, the assumption that the total heat-transfer coefficient is independent of temperature introduces a serious source of error.

During ordinary operation of the differential thermal analysis run, a steady state will occur or ensue in which the temperature at any point lags behind the programmed wall temperature by some function of its position so that, in general, $T = \beta t - f(P)$, where $f(P)$ depends on the heat-transfer characteristics both of the materials between the point under consideration and the wall and also on the heat-transfer and heat-absorption characteristics of the material further from the wall and to which it must transmit heat. With all the assumptions of temperature independence previously set down the temperature at any point will reach a fixed lag behind the programmed temperature and then heat smoothly at the programmed heating rate of β; hence, the temperature difference between point one and point two, the sample and reference, will reach some magnitude and, until a reaction occurs, have zero slope.

In order to use this $f(P)$ it must be shown that it has the same form as $T(P)$ to the extent of obeying the rules set down so far. Substitution in the general heat-flow equation yields identical results because—on the left hand side—βt is not a function of the coordinate so its derivative with respect to position drops out; $f(P)$ is not a function of time so it drops out, leaving β, which is the heating rate.

In the interface relation, the derivative of βt with respect to position again drops out, leaving the same equation but in f instead of T.

Similarly, on the block surface, the substitution allows the βtr to be subtracted. The same thing happens in the differential temperature at the steady state.

Having established a model for the behavior during the steady temperature rise, Sewell and Honeyborne turn their attention to the events during the phase change. They introduce the peak area function, an integral between two times, one before and one after the reaction, at both of which the temperature differential has returned to a base line which is time- and temperature-independent.

$$W(P) = \int_{t_0}^{t_2} [\beta t - f(P) - T(P,t)]dt$$

where t_2 is a time after completion of the reaction; thus

$$\text{area} = \int_{t_0}^{t_2} [(\Delta T)_0 - (\Delta T)]dt = W(P_1) - W(P_2).$$

In essence, this peak area function is the integral of the difference between the actual temperature and the temperature which is prescribed by the previous considerations. It is, then, the integral of a peak one might observe if the temperature at a point were plotted against the symmetrically located point, the symmetry being with respect to a plane between a sample and the reference specimens. Since this peak area function, $W(P)$, is a function of $T(P)$, we can substitute W into the several equations which T and f must obey and ascertain whether or not the results have any meaning; we shall, in effect, evaluate one side of the equation.

One can easily dispose of the parts that take no direct part—whose roles are as counterpoise, containment, and measuring accessories. This is done by expanding $\kappa\Delta^2 W$ by simply inserting the definition of W on the right-hand side and since $\kappa\Delta^2 f$ is equal to $=\beta$ and $\kappa\Delta^2 T$ equal to $\partial(T)/\partial t$ we get an expression which we recognize as $f(P)$ evaluated between t_0 and t_2, but since $f(P)$ is not a function of time the evaluation is zero.

Similarly, insert W in the equation of continuity at interfaces and expand W by definition, noting that βT is not a function of position, and rearrange terms. Two expressions, one involving F and one involving T, are obtained but each of these expressions goes to 0 at an interface as does, then, the expression involving W. In essence, this establishes that W is continuous across any interface. Again, on the surface of the block, W behaves in the same manner as T or F.

The behavior in the specimen is of greatest importance. Again, expanding W and substituting, the first two terms in the brackets drop out leaving the term involving the several thermal properties times a evaluated between t_0 and t_2. But a goes from 0 before the reaction to 1 after the reaction leaving

$$\nabla^2 W = \frac{-L\rho_s}{\lambda_s}.$$

Thus, from the several results and with the assumptions previously stated, Sewell and Honeyborne conclude that the peak area is proportional to the heat of reaction per unit volume of test sample and is independent of the heating rate so long as it is linear, the rate at which the reaction takes place, or the specific heat of the test sample. It does, however, depend on the conductivities of the several materials of the furnace as well as the heat transfer between the surface of the block and the furnace wall.

Sewell and Honeyborne recognized the several limitations of the treatment just described, but treatments which do take into account, for example, that thermal conductivities, specific heats, diffusivites, and conductances are functions of temperature become at least unwieldy or even intractable.

Complete and exact analysis of the differential thermal analysis peak will require methods of at least this degree of complexity. If we now add in the fact that $f(P)$ is not a function *only* of P but has a temperature dependence it becomes apparent that solution would be impractical. (The temperature dependence of f arises from the variations in heat capacities and thermal conductivities with temperature.) Further, it is apparent that within the sample $f(P)$ [or $f(P, T)$] would have a discontinuity during and because of the thermal event. The discontinuity arises from the change in identity of the material.

The treatment by Deeg (D9), on the other hand, takes into account the changing thermal properties in a nonexplicit manner, but he finds it necessary to point out that, in most cases, it will be impossible to provide a self-contained analytical form of the solution; hence, in the evaluation of basic equations, reliance will have to be placed mainly on numerical and graphical processes.

In addition to Deeg's refusal to make assumptions purely to simplify the mathematics, he treats the reaction temperature range differently. He uses the "advancing reaction front" approach, stating, in effect, that except for a very brief period of time the material at a given point is either in one form or the other—no fractions.

In his treatment, he uses Dirac's δ function (C13)

$$W_B = \lim_{\epsilon \to 0} W \cdot \int_{T_r - \epsilon}^{T_r + \epsilon} \delta(T/T_r)dT$$

which is a step function.

The two approaches to the transition temperature region are compared in Fig. V-18. A segment of time bracketing the transition is taken and the fraction reacting at some given point is plotted. Sewell and Honeyborne's treatment dictates a skewed curve—skewed because of the temperature dependence of the rate of transformation. Deeg's treatment dictates an immediate rise to some high rate followed by a fall to zero when the material at that point has been exhausted. The summations are equally predictable, a nonsymmetric sigmoid curve compared to a rapid rise.

Sewell and Honeyborne's acceptance of coexisting reacted and unreacted material implies a finite and substantial time of reaction of a particle; this implies in turn a rate-determining step. Deeg implies that when the sample reaches a transformation temperature it simply transforms. Deeg's treatment is more descriptive of phase changes but is quite unsuitable for those decompositions which do have a rate-

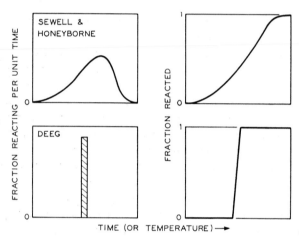

Fɪɢ. V-18. Fraction of any arbitrarily chosen bit of sample reacting or reacted as a function of time (or temperature) as the specimen is heated steadily.

Sewell and Honeyborne's (S19a) treatment assumes coexistence—in a limited region and for a finite time—of reacted and unreacted material; Deeg's (D9) treatment assumes instantaneous or very rapid conversion. For the entire sample, Sewell and Honeyborne's calculations yield a relatively broad peak compared to Deeg's.

determining step. The former treatment shows the effects of studies on clay minerals. Many of their reactions have rate-determining steps and Sewell and Honeyborne's use of the a term takes this into account even though they carefully restrict the applicability of their treatment to reversible phase changes or decompositions obeying a first-order law.

Whether or not a particular thermal effect is rate-controlled can be established fairly easily by two kinds of experiments by changing the heating rate under identical thermodynamic conditions or by changing the size of sample.

The identity of the thermodynamic conditions is crucial; if the reaction is a gas-forming decomposition, the atmosphere surrounding the material should be the pure gaseous product at the same pressure in each experiment or a dynamic atmosphere comprising the product gas. Significant change in temperature of reaction, e.g., peak temperature, with change in heating rate implies a rate-determining step.

Changing the sample diameter, on the other hand, will affect the shape but the peak temperature—measured along the axis of a cylindrical sample—should remain the same if the process is fast i.e., not rate-controlled. The peak will become sharper with the smaller samples. In a rate-controlled process, on the other hand, the shape of the curve ought to remain very nearly the same.

The sharper peaks available with the smaller specimens are not an argument for general use of very small samples. The injudicious use of milligram amounts can lead to sampling errors that often render the data almost meaningless.

Vold (V10) prepared a formula by which heats of reaction could be calculated from differential thermal analysis curves. For a close approach to validity, her final equation must be used with data obtained with a block-type specimen holder, yet she carefully used a pair of

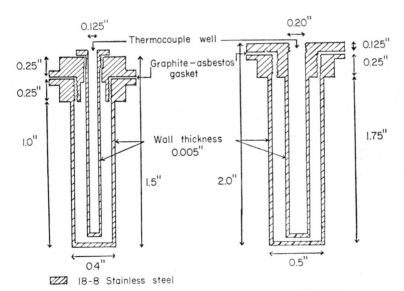

Fig. V-19. Differential calorimeter cells. From Vold (V10).

These cells are suspended in air within a cylindrical furnace. Any vapor was either confined within the cell or allowed to diffuse out through a small orifice.

isolated cells (Fig. V-19). Vold first sets down equations describing the heat flow into the specimen and into the reference:

$$\frac{dq_s}{dt} = K_s(T_w - T_s) + \sigma(T_r - T_s) + \alpha_s(T_0 - T_s) \tag{3A}$$

$$\frac{dq_r}{dt} = K_r(T_w - T_r) + \sigma(T_s - T_r) + \alpha_r(T_0 - T_r). \tag{3B}$$

dq/dt is the rate at which heat is received by the sample or reference, K_s and K_r are the heat-transfer coefficients between the furnace wall and sample or reference, and σ and α are heat-transfer coefficients between the specimens and from specimen to the outside environment at T_0.

The "furnace wall" must necessarily be a surface which presents a uniform appearance to sample and reference specimens *and* from which these specimens may take heat directly; if this is not the case, we must add some more terms. In Vold's apparatus, these would include a term describing the temperature of the outer wall of the cell, a pair of terms describing the transfer of heat to and from the air in the furnace, and, of course, a term describing the transfer of heat through the air. The terms would be nearly identical most of the time so the differences would be small most of the time. Unfortunately, the differences would assume a significant value at a most inopportune time, i.e., during the thermal effect. The heat-transfer coefficients will all be dependent on the nature of the interface between the sample and its container. One can easily deduce what types of specimens will cause severe changes: samples which melt, samples which shrink away from the walls, samples whose decomposition residue has a greatly diminished density, etc. The possibility of significant change would be present quite generally. The isolated sample cell wall will lag in temperature behind the reference cell wall so we have an increased rate of supply of heat to the sample cell, but we have neither a T_w that applies to both cells nor equal rates of heating.

Vold next points out the identity

$$\frac{dq}{dt} = \frac{dH}{dt} = \frac{dH}{dt}\frac{dT}{dt} \tag{4}$$

and segregates the heat content arising from the heat of reaction,

$$\frac{dq_s}{dt} = C_s\frac{dT_s}{dt} + \Delta H \frac{df}{dt} \tag{5}$$

where df/dt is the fractional rate of transformation, and, by substitution, subtraction, and simplification obtains

$$\frac{\Delta H}{C_s}\frac{df}{dt} = \frac{dy}{dt} + A(y - y_s) \tag{6}$$

where $y = \Delta T$, $A = (K_r + a_r + 2\sigma)/C_s$, and

$$y_s = \frac{\left[(C_s - C_r)\dfrac{dT_r}{dt} + \delta K(T_w - T_s) - \delta a(T_s - T_0)\right]}{K_r + \alpha_r + 2},$$

where δK and δa take account of asymmetry in heat transfer. The term y_s is assumed to be a steady-state function of y, essentially a constant for a given experiment or set of conditions. $(C_s - C_r)$, however, is most unlikely to remain constant. In phase transformations, this is often a fair approximation, but in a decomposition such an event would be purely fortuitous; a sizable change in C_s is the rule rather than the exception.

Vold finds the transformation complete when $dy/dt = -A(y - y_s)$, since df/dt is again zero. This point is found by plotting $\log (y - y_s)$ vs t (Fig. V-20); this time of deviation from linearity moving down-

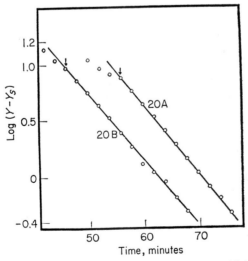

Fig. V-20. Plot for determining constant A. From Vold (V10).

A governs rate at which a thermal steady state is re-established after a transformation occurs. Arrows mark time at which transformation is finished; subsequent points lie on straight lines.

ward in time) marks the time of completion of the reaction. This time corresponds to a point some time after the maximum deflection as in Fig. V-21 (see Section 5.3). Figure V-22 shows the relation between the total and differential heating curves. The reader should keep in mind also that all these "constants" are temperature-dependent.

Note that Vold took no account of the heat transfer within the specimen. There is no objection to this in differential calorimetry, in which entire area is used in computation, but it would be a serious matter in other cases where σ has a significant value. It enters into Vold's work because she was measuring temperatures at the center of specimen and reference and calculating point-by-point values. The rather tardy completion of reaction is probably due to thermal inhomogeneity resulting from loss of heat upward along the sample cells.

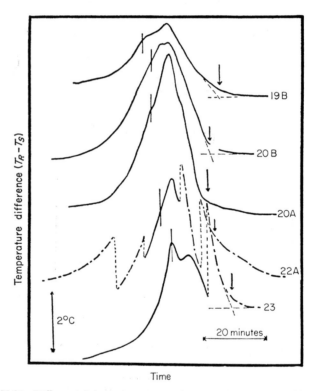

Fig. V-21. Differential heating curves of stearic and benzoic acids. From Vold (V10).

From the points designated by arrows, since reaction is "complete," ΔT returns asymptotically to a new steady-state value.

5.7. Second-Order Transitions

The effect of a discontinuous change of some property on the thermal behavior has been treated by Deeg (D9) with emphasis on its application to differential thermal analysis. The sudden change in a property —whether C_p, ρ, k, or other, will influence the transfer of heat and consequently cause a thermal effect in differential thermal analysis (see Chapter II, Sec. 2.6). The special case of polymers has been examined by Strella (S65).

Strella assumed a cylindrical model in which he lets the surface temperature of the unreacted material hold constant at the glass transition temperature as the interface between the two forms moves in toward the center and, meanwhile, the higher temperature form is treated as a cylinder whose inside diameter is decreasing.

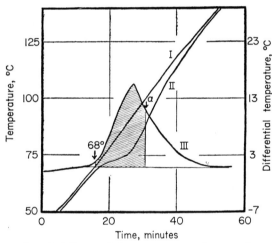

Fig. V-22. Total and differential heating curves for stearic acid and Nujol: I, heating curve for Nujol cell; II, heating curve for stearic acid cell; III, differential heating curve.

At 68°C melting begins. a is time at which calculation shows that melting is completed. Shaded area is that taken into account in calculating ΔH.

From the decay of the temperature distribution in the initial form and the corresponding growth of the resulting form he obtains an expression for the temperature differential between surface and center,

$$\Delta T = \frac{\beta a^2}{4k_2} (1 - e^{-k_2\alpha,t}) + \frac{\beta a^2}{4k_1} e^{-k,\alpha,t}$$

where β is the heating rate, a the radius, k and k_2 the thermal diffusivities, a the first root of the (Bessel) equation $J_0(aa) = 0$, and t the time from the initiation of the transition.

The equation implies a sigmoidal form for ΔT vs T and Strella further deduces that, considering the exponential nature of the equation for ΔT, a plot of log T_{gi} vs heating rate should be linear and extrapolation to zero rate should yield the correct glass transition temperature. Taking the T_{gi} as the inflection points of a number of curves obtained at different heating rates (Fig. V-23) he constructed the plot of Fig. V-24. From Fig. V-24 he obtained a value of 110°C for the correct glass transi-

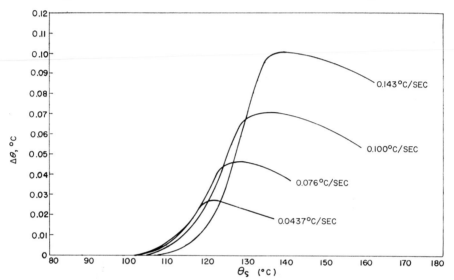

FIG. V-23. Differential temperature vs surface temperature for a polymethylmethacrylate heated at several rates. From Strella (S65).

The change occurs over a substantial time at these not very low heating rates (2.6 to 8.6°C/minute).

tion temperature of polymethylmethacrylate, which "compares quite favorably with Rogers and Mandelkern's value of 105°C (R28). Thus the prediction that the extrapolation of T_{gi} to zero rate would yield the value of the glass transition temperature is considered correct."

As his equation stands, the high-temperature form is not growing at the same rate as that at which the low-temperature form is disappearing; i.e., the decay terms, $e^{-k_n a^2 t}$, should be the same if we are to accept the concept as it stands. The influence of the increased heat capacity may establish the rate at which the interface moves.

The method of extrapolating the data apparently doesn't matter much. The intercept is about the same whether the temperature is in °C as in Fig. V-24 (the mantissa only) or in °K as Strella used for atactic polypropylene. For that matter, a linear plot, i.e., T_{gi} vs heating rate,

of Strella's data yielded 109°C as the "correct glass transition temperature." Further, the initiation of the glass transition should designate the
transition temperature when ΔT is plotted against surface temperature.
From Fig. V-23, this occurs in the 102–106°C range.

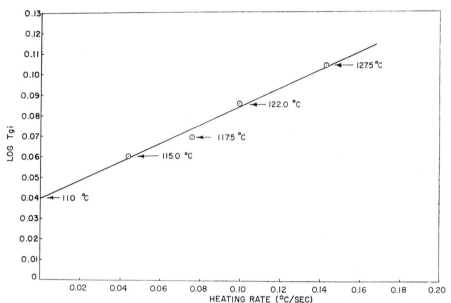

FIG. V-24. Logarithm of the indicated glass transition temperature vs heating
rate for polymethylmethacrylate. From Strella (S65).

*Extrapolation to zero heating rate is used to estimate the correct glass transition
temperature.*

5.8. Summary

Quantitative treatment of differential thermal analysis curves by other
than empirical methods is impractical at present. Detailed calculations
of simultaneous processes would require computers and a set of equations and data not presently available.

The changing of thermal properties as a material is being heated implies that return to the same base line as before the reaction is unlikely.
Empirical methods are used to delineate the peak. So long as there are
no overlapping peaks a high degree of isolation (as in differential calorimetry) favors accurate quantitative determinations.

Approximate mathematical descriptions of differential thermal analysis
curves have been devised, but in order to render the expressions tract-
able assumptions not in agreement with physical reality are needed.
Some inferences may be drawn from the models assumed.

CHAPTER VI

Kinetics

6.1. Introduction

While most crystallographic phase transformations and some decomposition reactions proceed so rapidly that the observed rate of reaction is due to some other limiting feature, some reactions including decompositions proceed at a measurable rate even when atmosphere and temperature conditions are favorable. (Note here that the *observed* rate of change will depend on the *slowest* of the processes involved.) This rate will ordinarily depend on the quantity of unreacted material present and the temperature of the sample. The nature and pressure of the surrounding atmosphere may or may not have a significant effect other than influencing heat transfer. A review of chemical kinetics is outside the scope of this book; any elementary physical chemistry text will provide sufficient background.

One major problem in the study of the kinetics of a reaction by thermoanalytical methods has been the failure to take account of all the factors which might influence the rate. An important question in evaluating kinetic data is whether or not the data are independent of geometry of the specimen. If a reaction can truly be described as first order, then the weight loss should occur in the same manner in a crucible as in a closed chamber or on a flat plate. If, on the other hand, the reaction depends on the nature of the atmosphere surrounding the particles or on the ease of heat transfer—in the case of a changing temperature—the shadow of doubt may reach the proportion of a heavy cloud.

6.2. Homogeneous Reactions

One of the more frequently quoted expressions for rates of reaction is that of Borchardt and Daniels (B67). The expression was derived very specifically for a system in which the (liquid) sample and reference are stirred (Fig. VI-1) so that the temperature of the sample or reference may reasonably be considered to be uniform. Intrepid followers have applied the expression to solid-state reactions without satisfying this homogeneity condition. There are twelve assumptions involved in Bor-

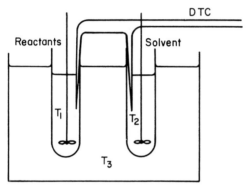

Fig. VI-1. Differential thermal analysis apparatus of Borchardt and Daniels (B67) for obtaining kinetic data for reaction occurring in solution.
The stirring assures temperature homogeneity.

chardt and Daniels' derivation. We will consider only six of them, including (1) the uniform temperature condition above.

We have already (Chapter II) seen how a reaction front proceeds from the wall of the sample holder inward in solids so the extension of the expression to solids is automatically void because the uniform temperature assumption is out of the question. Three of the assumptions are —at best—approximations; these are (2) the heat-transfer coefficients of reactants and products are equal, (3) the heat capacities of reactants and products are equal, and (4) these quantities, plus the heat of reaction, do not change over the temperature range of reaction. Note that these three (see below) are the only ones which would require the temperature difference to return to zero after the reaction and, further, Borchardt and Daniels' plot (Fig. VI-2) does *not* show a return to zero even with stirred liquid specimens.

Assumption (2) will depend greatly on the nature of the materials and the container surface. Just as heat transfer in solids is governed greatly by the nature of interfaces, so can we hypothesize that adsorption of solute on the container surface will influence the heat-transfer coefficient. The relative polar characteristics of solute (both unreacted and reacted) and solvent must be considered.

Assumption (3) will probably be reasonable in dilute solutions of such a nature that the heat of solvation is low. A substantial fraction of the heat-capacity difference could be due to desolvation. Dilution of the specimen will diminish the signal so a compromise must be made. Bor-

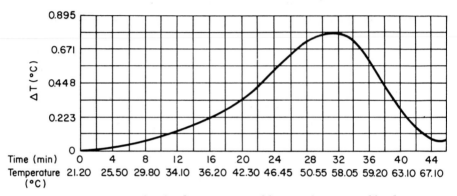

Fɪɢ. VI-2. DTA curve for the decomposition of benzenediazonium chloride. Temperature difference between the reactant solution and inert liquid is plotted as a function of temperature and time. From Borchardt and Daniels (B67).

Even under especially good experimental conditions the differential signal cannot be expected always to return to zero.

chardt and Daniels used a 0.4 M solution, which is not very dilute; a heat-capacity difference can reasonably be expected. At this level of concentration, the change in heat capacity before and after the reaction can well be significant.

Note, too, that formation of a second phase would affect the heat capacity of the solution. If a reaction product were an immiscible fluid or insoluble the likelihood of unchanging thermal characteristics would indeed be remote.

Assumption (4) is related to this last effect since $d\Delta H/dT = \Delta C_p$ and, of course, desolvation and desorption from the surface would both be temperature-sensitive.

These three assumptions, then, are only approximations when applied to stirred liquid samples; applied to powdered solid specimens they are untenable.

The assumption (5) that the heat effect—as measured by the differential temperature—is proportional to the number of molecules reacting in unit time can be applied only to thermally homogeneous systems. It is satisfactory for the stirred samples but not for solids. That the heat effect detected by a thermocouple is influenced by the distance of the reacting materials from the thermocouple has already been shown (Chapter II). The reaction of a given quantity of sample at the edge of the specimen will not produce the same effect as reaction of the same quantity adjacent to a centrally located thermocouple. The reaction of a cylindrical sample is not proceeding most rapidly at the peak of the differential temperature; in many cases it is complete.

The assumption (6) that the kinetics of a reaction can be described by a single rate constant is acceptable for systems that might be studied by Borchardt and Daniels' method but its applicability to solid reactants must be approached with caution and vertified for the system under investigation.

6.3. Heterogeneous Decompositions

A considerable weakness of such extensions—or original derivations, for that matter—is that in the systems of most interest, i.e., decompositions, these various "constants" undergo rather drastic change. Decompositions such as that of kaolin cannot be expected, in the usual nondynamic atmosphere experiment, to follow a single rate expression; nor can decompositions be expected to follow a single rate expression if the concentration of reaction products is allowed to vary.

Freeman and Carroll (E14) by appropriate differentiation, integration, and division, proceed from $k = Z \exp - (E^*/RT)$ where k is the specific rate constant, Z is the frequency factor, E^* is the activation energy, and R is the gas constant, and

$$- \frac{dX}{dt} = kX^x$$

where X is the concentration, mole fraction, or amount of reactant and x is the order of reaction, to find

$$\frac{- (E^*/R) \Delta (1/T)}{\Delta \ln X} = \frac{\Delta \ln(- dX/dt)}{\Delta \ln X} - x.$$

That conclude, of course, that a plot of

$$\frac{\Delta \left(\frac{1}{T}\right)}{\Delta \log X} \quad \text{vs} \quad \frac{\Delta \log(- dX/dt)}{\Delta \log X}$$

should result in a straight line with a slope of $\pm E^*/2.3R$ and an intercept of $-X$. Freeman and Carroll proposed to take the necessary data from a single thermogravimetric experiment in which several tenths of a gram of sample were heated at a rate of 10°C/minute.

Implicit in their derivation were the assumptions that (1) the order of reaction is the same throughout the reaction, (2) the atmosphere had no effect, and (3) the temperature was the same throughout the specimen. The first of these assumptions is not necessarily correct; the other two are clearly untenable (see Chapter II). In their experiment using calcium oxalate monohydrate, not only will the presence of air, rather than water vapor, permit variations in the vapor pressure of water within and about the sample and hence affect the rate of dehydration, but also the air affects the nature of the second reaction. In air, the carbon monoxide moiety of the oxalate ion oxidizes readily to carbon dioxide. The reaction is rapid and sharply exothermic. In Freeman and Carroll's experiment, this reaction took five minutes as compared to the few seconds it would take in a smaller sample. The reason for this is discussed in greater detail elsewhere (Chapter VII), but in essence the rate is dependent on the entry of oxygen; however, diffusion of the oxygen inward is inhibited by the nitrogen which diffuses in too but is not consumed and by the carbon dioxide which is being evolved. The third reaction, decomposition of calcium carbonate, is a rapid and reversible reaction. It will proceed at a rate far more dependent on the diffusion outward of the carbon dioxide than on a reaction rate constant. Furthermore, the size of specimen used by Freeman and Carroll is in the range frequently used in older differential thermal analysis apparatuses; at 10°C/minute, temperature differences of 20°C or more are easily obtained.

On the other hand, Murray and White (M45) measured the rate of weight loss of kaolin under constant (furnace) temperature and concluded that the dehydroxylation in the 500–600°C range is a first-order reaction. They eliminated the extracrystalline water by heating to constant weight at 430°C; they then raised the furnace temperature rapidly to the desired temperature and observed the weight loss as a function of time. They plotted their data with the appropriate coordinates and concluded that over the bulk of the decomposition range the decomposition followed a first-order law.

Murray and White wrote the first-order law in the form

$$\frac{dl}{dt} = k(l_\infty - l)$$

where l_∞ is the total (see below) loss of combined moisture and l is the actual loss at time t. This yields the integrated form

$$\log \left(\frac{l_\infty - l}{l_\infty} \right) = -kt.$$

This equation has the interesting property that "l_∞ cannot be assumed as known but is got by plotting the logarithm of the amount decomposed in a constant time interval Δt against t, the time at the beginning of the interval"; in other words, l_∞ is *not* the amount of water which is lost all together but is simply an integration constant. If this expression is to have any physical significance the magnitude of l_∞ must be quite close to the actual total weight loss; otherwise we must look for another effect. Actually, the magnitude of l_∞ is sufficiently different to cast some doubt.

One other effect is the rate at which the material reaches the decomposition temperature. Obviously, if a sample held in, say, a crucible is exposed to a hot surface the temperature will not rise instanteously to the new temperature; heat must be transmitted from the surface to all parts of the interior. Since heat will flow only from a warmer to a cooler body a temperature gradient must necessarily exist. (Any treatment demanding an assumption of equal temperatures throughout a specimen during heating is automatically suspect.) Let us examine the possible effect of geometry by use of some simplifying heat-transfer assumptions that have at least some resemblance to physical reality. In addition, let us assume that under the extant conditions of water vapor pressure, particle size, and previous history there is some one temperature at which each particle will decompose.

> The assumption of a reaction temperature is used here only as a tool to show some relative effects. There is no reason to doubt that the dehydroxylation of kaolin and similar decompositions of a number of other minerals are rate-controlled. For our purposes, however, we can raise the temperature high enough to cause a conveniently high rate of reaction. The real fact of the rate control will only bring about a diffuseness of boundaries between reacted and unreacted material.

Now recall the conditions of the Murray and White experiments, i.e., the rapid heating of a furnace to a temperature above the decomposition temperature and measurement of weight loss vs time of a crucible suspended therein. Let us consider a full crucible with length $>>$ diameter. Concede that the crucible wall will reach the decomposition temperature instantaneously and the material in contact with the wall will decompose. The wall continues heating to the furnace temperature and transmits heat to the specimen. The outer material of the specimen receives heat from the direction of the wall, warms up to the decomposition temperature, decomposes, and subsequently passes heat onward to the material farther in—which performs in the same manner. Consequently, there is a decomposition temperature front advancing toward the center uniformly from the vertical wall (neglecting small effects at the bottom) ahead of which front is unreacted material and behind which is reacted material. As this front advances its diameter and hence its area decrease. If we assume that this front advances at a uniform rate,[*] $dr/dt = $ constant, where r is the radius of the front, and the area must be proportional to r. This implies that the quantity reacting is proportional to r.

The volume of the unreacted material is proportional to r^2, i.e.,

$$V = \pi r^2 h$$

so that

$$\frac{dV}{dr} = 2\pi h \cdot r$$

but $dr/dt = $ constant, hence

$$\frac{dV}{dr} \cdot \frac{dr}{dt} = \frac{dV}{dt} = 2\pi h \cdot r\kappa \text{ constant} = \kappa r = \frac{\kappa (V)^{1/2}}{\pi h}.$$

The cylindrical crucible may be simple to treat since if the length is sufficiently greater thas the diameter the effects of atmosphere will disappear; this ease of mathematical treatment does not bring about any closer resemblance to physical reality. Let us now consider the common practice; this practice would lead to use of an ordinary crucible, length 1.3–2 times the diameter, partly filled with the specimen. This approximates the condition discussed in Chapter VII. But the events described therein lead to the establishment of a reaction front which as a simplification could be treated as spherical.

Let us make the same assumption of constant advance (dr/dt is constant) but now the volume must be expressed differently, i.e.,

$$V = \frac{4}{3}\pi r^3$$

or

$$\frac{dV}{dr} = 4\pi r^2$$

so

$$\frac{dV}{dr} \cdot \frac{dr}{dt} = \frac{dV}{dt} = 4\pi \kappa r^2 = V^{2/3}.$$

Under these conditions the disappearance of unreacted material will follow a one-half order rate law in a cylinder and a two-thirds order law in a sphere.

[*]This is no more real than Murray and White's assumption of uniform temperature. The intent here is to show the probable effect of geometry on the rate of reaction.

With different assumed geometries, then, different conclusions may be reached with these—and presumably with any—assumptions. (Note that if the material were laid on a flat surface and this surface were kept at a steady, uniform temperature the reaction would appear to be zero order.) The conditions stated above do not coincide with physical reality. There are complicating effects—principally thermal diffusivity change and heat of reaction—which would affect the advance of the reaction front. Nevertheless, the appearance of a first-order decomposition can be approximated by nonfirst-order reactions for reasons of geometry and atmosphere. In the poorly defined geometry represented by a partly full crucible in an uncontrolled atmosphere an extensive treatment would be a waste of time.

This discussion obviously does not establish the actual order of the kaolin decomposition. It is intended only to show that there is considerable reason to question the conclusion of Murray and White. A first-order reaction would depend only on the quantity of unreacted material and the temperature; yet Stone (S60) and the present author have shown an atmosphere dependence and Murray and White "have had certain indications that sample size, type of container, and other environmental factors may have an appreciable effect on the rate of decomposition observed."

Murray and White (M46) extended their consideration of the kinetics of kaolin decomposition to calculate the shape of differential thermal analysis curves. In particular, they calculate a peak temperature which they also describe as the temperature at which the reaction is proceeding most rapidly. This is consistent with their assumption of temperature homogeneity but not with physical reality. The effect might be achieved, however, by thoughtful or fortuitous placement of thermocouples. Note from Fig. VII-9 that under the heating conditions specified the last portion of material to decompose is not at the center, but below the center. A thermocouple at the center of the specimen would show probably a maximum or possibly a sharp change in slope as the reaction front passed it. (The nature of the change would depend on the relative thermal diffusivities before and after the reaction as well as on the heat of decomposition. The situation is probably not analogous to Smyth's (S36) exercise showing the effect of noncentered placement of thermocouples.) Regardless of the shape of the curve one may safely say that the reaction is not yet complete at the time or temperature of the differential thermal analysis peak in a process whose rate is determined (limited) by chemical kinetics.

We can eliminate the heating from the bottom by the simple expedient of specifying a depth much greater than the diameter. We have not eliminated the top; i.e., diffusion of gases will still occur, although the effect will be attenuated in the lower regions. This means that the reaction front will advance only slightly inward before the atmosphere enrichment will require the major movement of the front to be from the top down. A thermocouple at the center (with half the specimen beneath it) will now show a maximum while a very substantial portion of the specimen has not yet reacted. Note that if the thermocouple is sufficiently deep in the sample hole the effects of the ambient atmosphere can perhaps be neglected for most work: the partial pressure of the product gas will be high enough by the time the reaction front reaches the thermocouple location that small deviations may be unnoticeable. The thermocouple would have to be placed deep enough so that no dilution effect could be seen.

Murray and White's decomposition curves calculated from the rate constants obtained from the thermogravimetry data are shown in Fig. VI-3. They bear a rather good resemblance to differential thermal

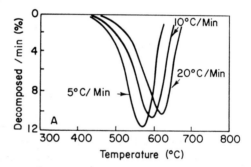

Fig. VI-3. Percentage decomposition per minute against temperature during heating of Supreme kaolin at constant heating rates of 5, 10, and 20°C/minute. From Murray and White (M46).

Calculated decomposition curves assuming first-order reaction kinetics with rate constants determined by static methods. At low heating rates the decomposition proceeds more rapidly than at higher rates!

analysis curves until the effect of heating rate is studied with a little care. These curves show the effect of heating rate on peak temperature in the proper direction, but the relative magnitudes of the peaks are decidedly not in agreement with experiment. The specimen heated at 5°C/minute reaches a greater rate of decomposition than that heated at 20°C/minute! Yet, the former spends about 20 minutes at rates greater than 4%/minute while the latter spends only about 5 minutes at such rates. According to Murray and White's calculations, the depletion of unreacted material becomes the major effect when the decomposition is about 70% complete causing the dehydroxylation to slow down; this figure corresponds to the peak temperature or "turning point"; it is also a figure accepted both frequently and uncritically as the degree of reaction to be expected at the peak temperature—for any reaction. Note that Murray and White cited evidence found and advanced a hypothesis. They recognized the probability of effects of water vapor, for example, and they were aware of the lowering of "dehydration temperatures" at subatmospheric pressures. These latter points would naturally not be known by later workers whose only contact with Murray and White's work is through reading of abstracts.

Sewell (S19) extended Murray and White's work to take account of thermal gradients in the specimen. *With the assumption that Murray and White were correct in their basic conclusion* Sewell pointed out that the turning point, i.e., the temperature at which the reaction proceeds most rapidly, could be expressed by

$$\exp (E/RT_M) = ART_M^2/\beta E$$

where T_M is the turning point temperature, β is the heating rate, E is the activation energy, and A is a constant (from the Arrhenius rate equation). Sewell derived relationships between T_M and the peak actually observed in differential thermal analysis. Unfortunately, the expression for the temperature of the center of the specimen predicts that the peak temperature for dilute samples should be higher than for undiluted samples. This is obviously not in accord with physical evidence (see Chapter III, so Sewell concludes that the equation describing a first-order reaction "cannot be regarded as more than a first approximation to the laws describing the dehydration of kaolinite" and suggests the possibility of an atmosphere effect.

> Let us remember now that a first-order reaction is one in which the reaction proceeds (at a given temperature) solely as a function of the quantity of the— or one of the—reactants. For the kaolinite dehydroxylation this would obviously be the unreacted material. The intervention of any physical condition or property other than quantity and temperature requires some other classification.

Brindley and Nakahira (B79) have concluded that if the effect of water vapor can be eliminated the dehydroxylation is indeed first order. They measured the rates of decomposition of a number of discs of kaolinite of various thicknesses, plotted log w/w_0 vs t (Fig. VI-4), extrapolated the values for various thicknesses to zero thickness (infinitely thin disc), and found a straight-line relationship which corresponds, of course, to a first-order reaction. (The w/w_0 is the fraction of total weight loss.) The times taken to reach a given fractional weight loss, w/w_0, vary in quite good agreement with a linear relationship $tw/w_0 = c + kh$, where h is the thickness and hence c is the time at zero thickness; the agreement appears to be good not only in the initial (straight-line) portion but also in the curved part of the plot.

Brindley and Nakahira use the rate constants determined from the initial portions of the curve to establish the inherent behavior of kaolinite; they were able to show (Fig. VI-5) that the rate constant at each of several temperatures varied linearly with thickness. They established further that an Arrhenius plot is linear *only* for infinitely thin discs (Fig. VI-6). The same general behavior was demonstrated by halloysite, another kandite.

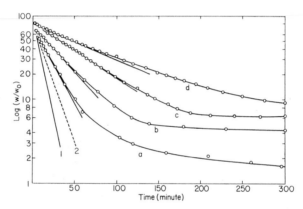

Fig. VI-4. Variation of log (w/w_0) with time for kaolinite disks heated at 497°C; (w/w_0) is expressed as a percentage of the total weight loss by dehydroxylation. Curves a, b, c, and d correspond to disks of thickness 0.38, 0.83, 1.55, and 2.68 mm, respectively. Curve 1 is the extrapolated curve for an infinitely thin disk and curve 2 corresponds to a very thin layer of uncompacted powder. From Brindley and Nakahira (B79).

The weight loss is decidedly dependent on the geometry of the specimen.

These experiments do indeed indicate that the kaolin dehydroxylation is kinetically a first-order reaction, but the reader must bear in mind that these experiments are quite different from those of Murray and White. The stated warning by Brindley and Nakahira, also implicit in the curvature of the weight loss data of Fig. VI-4, that at temperatures in the 450–520°C range kaolinite tends to react only to some given degree, must be also remembered. Murray and White had also noted that there was no clear line of demarcation between the loosely held water and water of constitution.

Neither of these pairs of authors has really eliminated the effect of water vapor. The concentration of water in ambient air is far from negli-

gible, yet the variation might be small enough to escape notice. According to handbook (L1a) values, at 25°C a' change from 84% to 42%
relative humidity means a drop in absolute humidity from 20 to 10 mm
of mercury. As a sample is heated, the water diffuses out of the particles
of the specimen as long as the temperature is high enough to vaporize
said water in the face of this extant partial pressure. Even assuming
that the water vapor can escape from the furnace into the surrounding

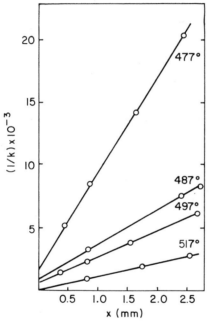

Fɪɢ. VI-5. Variation of reciprocal rate constant, $1/k$, vs disk thickness for kaolinite
disks at various temperatures. From Brindley and Nakahira (B79).
The distance through which vapor must diffuse has a very clear effect on the rate.

atmosphere, the partial pressure in the furnace can only drop toward
that of its surroundings; it cannot drop below. This would explain the
tendency toward incomplete dehydroxylation in Brindley and Nakahira's
work if a real equilibrium vapor pressure exists.

In recent work, Holt, Cutler, and Wadsworth (H22) have studied
kaolinite under rather different conditions. They, too, point out the need
for experimentation which avoids the effect of water vapor and proceed
to heat their specimens in vacuum. The specimen was applied to a platinum screen as a paste or slurry, then dried at 130°C in preparation for
the dehydroxylation.

The data, obtained by heating at pressures less than 1 μ of Hg, indicate that the rate of dehydroxylation is inversely proportional to the thickness of the dehydrated layer, i.e.,

$$\frac{dx}{dt} = \frac{k}{x}$$

where x is the thickness of the dehydrated (or dehydroxylated) layer. This means, of course, that

$$x^2 = 2kt$$

or, since the fraction reacted, R, is proportional to x for this constant-area arrangement, $R^2 = 2kt$

This is the parabolic rate expression and indicates that the decompo-

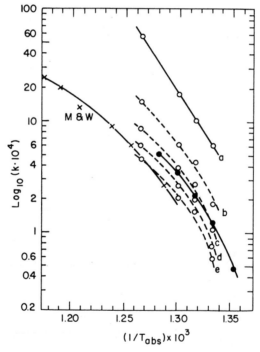

Fig. VI-6. Arrhenius plots for log k vs $1/T$ (absolute for kaolinite). Curves a, through e correspond to disks of thickness 0, 0.5, 1.0, 1.5, and 2.0 mm, respectively. Curve (M&W) shows data by Murray and White. Solid circles show experimental data for sample held in a small platinum crucible. The Arrhenius plot is linear only for curve a corresponding to the infinitely thin disk. From Brindley and Nakahira (B79).

In an infinitely thin specimen the decomposition should follow a first-order law.

sition process is diffusion-controlled, slowing down not from scarcity of
material but from the increasing difficulty of eliminating products. Holt
et al. report that the linear relationships (Fig. VI-7) between R^2 and
t hold to 50% decomposition "after which it starts to change" in a direction not specified. They attribute the nonlinearity to a "decrease in surface area brought about by the fact that the smaller particles are
completely dehydrated before the large particles." In essence, this means
that the rate of reaction is governed by diffusion within the individual
particle rather than through the pores in the bulk of the specimen.

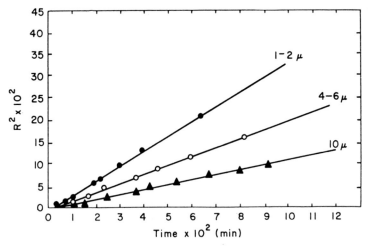

Fig. VI-7. Parabolic plots for three size fractions of kaolinite at 400°C. From
Holt *et al.* (H22).
Up to 50% decomposition the rate is inversely proportional to the amount reacted.

The intrinsic similarity of decompositions of the various particle sizes
of Fig. VI-7 is demonstrated in Fig. VI-8, in which Holt, Cutler, and
Wadsworth arbitrarily selected fractional decomposition, $R = 0.30$, and
obtained an expression for $2k$ and substituted so that

$$R^2 = R_{0.30}^2 \, \tau/\tau_{0.30}$$
$$= 0.090 \, \tau/\tau_{0.30}$$

where $\tau_{0.30}$ is the time during any run at which $R = 0.30$. Now the data
from the three particle size fractions can be plotted together as in Fig.
VI-8. The behavior of each of the three fractions is quite similar to that
of the others.

Holt *et al.* also showed at low pressures of water vapor the parabolic
relationship held; increasing water vapor decreased the rate (Fig. VI-9)

of decomposition in a linear manner at these lower pressures. They report that at moderate pressures, e.g., 4.5 mm of Hg at 420°C, the process
undergoes some change that renders the kinetics of the decomposition
first order, in agreement with the several studies in air. The major conclusion which one might reach is that, while knowledge of the kinetics
of dehydroxylation of kaolin under a number of sets of experimental
conditions has been obtained, the intrinsic behavior may not yet be
known. The pressed discs of Brindly and Nakahira (B79) are quite different from the dried slurry of Holt, Cutler, and Wadsworth as were the

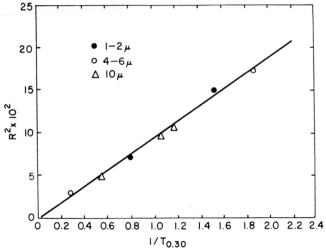

Fig. VI-8. Plot of R^2 vs $1/\tau_{0.30}$ at 400°C using three size fractions. From Holt
et al. (H22).
  *The agreement indicates that the actual differences in rates are due only to dif-
ferences in area.*

environments used. Neither set of authors could measure initial behavior
satisfactorily because (even disregarding the fact that the control temperature is not reached quickly by the sample) the basic measurement
constitutes a small change in a large quantity. This is a procedural
error common to nearly all these experiments. While the present author
has no desire to minimize the utility of thermoanalytical techniques in
general, he also advocates selection of the best tool for the job at hand.
The proper measurement—certainly for the initial behavior and probably
for the whole experiment—is the rate at which water is released. Weight
loss is only an indirect measure of it.
    The fact that a thermocouple junction measures the temperature of
its immediate surroundings cannot be used to infer that more distant

materials do not affect the temperature at all. The magnitude of any effect will depend on the geometric relation; material between the specimen and the heat source, for example, must inevitably influence the heating of the specimen. This effect was neglected by Kissinger (K30) in his evaluation of shapes of peaks and the relation of these shapes to

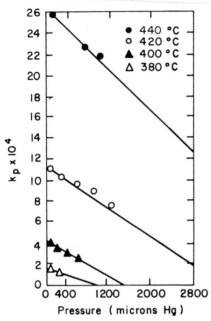

Fig. VI-9. Parabolic rate constant vs water vapor pressure at four temperatures. From Holt *et al.* (H22).

At low pressures the rate constant varies inversely with the pressure of water vapor.

the order of the decomposition kinetics. He set up expressions for the quasi-steady-state heating: at the center of the reference,

$$T_r = T_0 + \phi t - \frac{\phi \rho c a^2}{4k}$$

and at the center of the sample

$$T_s = T_0 + \phi t - f\left(\frac{dq}{dt}\right)$$

where ϕ is the heating rate, a is the radius of the cylindrical specimens, $f(dq/dt)$ is a function of the reaction rate, dq/dt being the rate of heat absorption per unit volume, and the other terms have their usual significance.

The differential temperature,

$$\theta = T_s - T_r = f\left(\frac{dq}{dt}\right) - \theta\,\frac{\rho c u^2}{4k}$$

and

$$\frac{d\theta}{dt} = f'\left(\frac{dq}{dt}\right)\frac{d^2q}{dt^2}.$$

From this last equation he concluded that when d^2q/dt^2 was zero $d\theta/dt$ must necessarily be zero. Since $d^2q/dt^2 = 0$ implied maximum rate of reaction and $d\theta/dt = 0$ a maximum temperature difference, the peak in the differential thermal analysis deflection must occur at the moment of the maximum rate of reaction. In the utopian case, i.e., reaction occurring equally in all parts of the specimen and unchanging thermal characteristics, this would be a reasonable conclusion.

The conclusion still represents—approximately—the behavior of the material in the immediate vicinity of the thermocouple, but only so far as the small region can be considered to react homogeneously. The temperature of this region has already, during the quasi-steady-state heating, lagged behind the outside of the specimen by several degrees. The material at the edges will continually be at a higher temperature than that at the point of measurement and the progress of the reaction takes up heat that would otherwise serve to warm the central region, accentuating the difference in rate. The material at the periphery will be significantly further reacted than that at the center at any time after the reaction starts until that at the edge is approaching complete reaction. As the reaction at the edge subsides it can pass on in greater amounts the energy necessary to carry out the reaction in the central regions. Note that a cylinder with some arbitrary thin wall, say 1/1000 inch, occupies a much greater volume of space with the same radius as the sample holder (i.e., at the edge of the sample) than with a radius of, say 10/1000 inch, enough to surround the thermocouple. Much more of the sample is at the higher temperature. We can easily infer that the maximum rate of reaction occurs well onto the low-temperature side of the peak; when the center of the sample reaches the maximum temperature lag in most cases the reaction is nearly complete.

(All this takes no account of the atmosphere effect which will cause a reaction rate variation from top to bottom of the specimen holder. All the materials cited by Kissinger show such effects.)

We have seen that Kissinger's method is an approximation because the basic assumption is invalid. Since no rigorous treatment exists approximation must be used; it is advisable, hence, to examine the closeness of the approximation to physical reality. Kissinger ascertains an expression for the temperature of maximum rate of reaction in terms of the order and extent of reaction by differentiating the rate expression

$$\frac{dx}{dt} = A(1-x)^n e - (E/RT)$$

with respect to t and setting the expression equal to zero, obtaining

$$\frac{E\phi_2}{RT_m} = An(1-x)_m^{n-1} e - (E/RT_m)$$

where the subscript m refers to conditions at the peak temperature. [Compare with Sewell's (S19) equation assuming first-order kinetics.]

By integrations and substitutions Kissinger arrives at $n(1-x)^{n-1}_m = 1 + (n-1)\ (ZRT_m/E)$ which says that as n becomes smaller so also does the quantity of material not yet decomposed at T_m. This agrees in principle with the implied observation that in a reversible phase transformation (zero order) the reaction is complete when the peak temperature is reached. From the variation in the quantity decomposed at T_m with order of reaction Kissinger proposed the use of a "shape index" to estimate the order of reaction. Figure VI-10 shows his calculated plots for several orders of reaction.

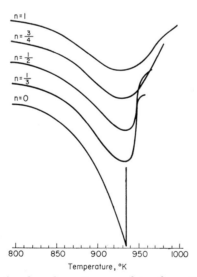

FIG. VI-10. Effect of order of reaction on plots of reaction rate vs temperature for constant heating rate, frequency factor, and activation energy. $E/R = 20,000$; $\ln A = 16.00$. From Kissinger (K30).

The activation energy and frequency factors are arbitrarily selected but their influence on the relative shapes is small.

From these curves, or from curves in general, the slopes at the inflection points are taken (Fig. VI-11) and the ratio of these slopes is used as
a measure of the assymmetry of the peak. At these inflection points
d^3x/dt^3, the rate of change of reaction rate, i.e., $d^2/dt^2 (dx/dt)$, is zero,
so Kissinger does the differentiations and with some substitutions is
able to calculate the relation between shape index and order of reaction
as shown in Fig. VI-12.

The straight line of the lower plot is described by

$$n = 1.26S^{1/2}.$$

Some curves showing the experimentally determined S and n are shown
in Fig. VI-13.

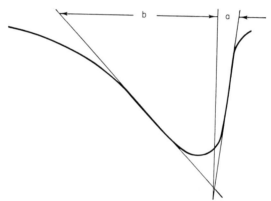

Fig. VI-11. Method for measuring amount of asymmetry in an endothermic differential thermal analysis peak. Shape index = S = a/b. From Kissinger (K30).
*Actual determination of an inflection temperature is not required. The probable
error in determining the slope is less when the inflection point is difficult to establish.*

These apparent orders of reaction are obviously influenced by experimental conditions since agreement among authors is not very good.
Particle size and geometry of the specimen will have a considerable
influence, especially since the atmosphere is not that of the gas being
evolved.

With the understanding that some invalid assumptions have been
made and approximations are introduced, Kissinger's method can be
used as a rough guide to the apparent order of the rate law followed by
various decompositions *under the experimental conditions used;* the
shapes of the curves vary in the proper manner.

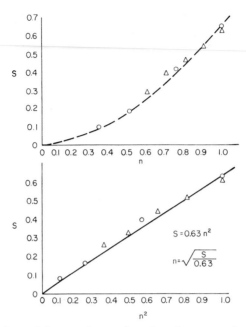

Fig. VI-12. Values of shape index S plotted as functions of n and n^2. Key: $\triangle$, calculated; $\bigcirc$, measured on curves of Fig. VI-10.

The relatively good agreement between calculated and measured slope ratios shows only the consistency of the mathematics.

6.4. Reversible Decompositions

Calcium carbonate is frequently cited as an example of a reversibly decomposing salt. The temperature at which it begins to decompose is determined by the pressure of carbon dioxide in contact with the surface of the particle. Janz and Lorenz (J4) have reported that when the prescribed temperature is passed, either heating or cooling, the material begins to decompose or recompose very quickly; this says nothing about the rate but shows that even the occurrence or nonoccurrence is dependent on the carbon dioxide pressure. Cremer and Nitsch (C26) studied the decomposition by volumetric measurements (avoiding the very marked heat-transfer problem found in thermogravimetry) at various pressures (Fig. VI-14) of carbon dioxide. They deduced that overlapping processes of nucleation and crystal growth would explain the data and, further, that at a given pressure the reaction is of the two-thirds order. This is in agreement with crystal growth dependence.

The many treatments of reaction rates by thermal analysis appear to

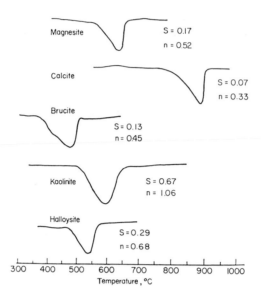

FIG. VI-13. Typical differential thermal analysis peaks for materials used in present study. From Kissinger (K30).

The calcite decomposition—which is probably not rate-controlled—approaches $n = 0$.

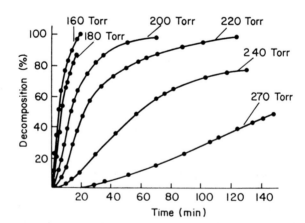

FIG. VI-14. Decomposition of calcium carbonate at 850°C. From Cremer and Nitsch (C26).

The rate of decomposition varies greatly with the pressure of carbon dioxide.

show a common disbelief in equilibrium or reversible processes. The idea of a simple reversible dehydration or similar process obeying a first-order rate law is patent nonsense; the probability of its following first-order kinetics is vanishingly small. Chapter VII treats the atmosphere effect in detail; we shall see herein sufficient evidence to impress on the reader the need to study Chapter VII.

Berlin and Robinson (B48) used thermogravimetry in their study of reaction rates. They had derived a relation for the reciprocal of the absolute temperature,

$$\frac{1}{T} = -\frac{R}{E_2}\Big[\ln\Big(\frac{d\alpha}{dT}\Big) - \ln(1-\alpha)^Z - \ln A_0\Big(\frac{\Gamma M}{W_0 N} S_2 \nu \bar{N}\Big)\Big]$$
$$+ \frac{R}{E_2}\ln\Big(\frac{dt}{dT}\Big)_c$$

wherein a is the fraction decomposed, Z is the exponent describing the change in area, A, at the interface between reacted and unreacted species such that $A = A_0(1-a)^Z$, and

$$\Gamma = \Big(1 - \frac{\nu_B M_B}{\nu_A M_A}\Big)^{-1}.$$

They suggest the use of a T_2, the temperature at which the reaction is virtually complete, as a means of relating data obtained by different authors in different laboratories on different types of equipment. (Their T_2 is found by estimating from the plot or data the temperature of the last detectable change in weight.) By measuring T_2 at several heating rates and plotting $1/T_2$ vs $\ln(dt/dT)_c$, they anticipated a straight line with a slope R/E_2 and an intercept of

$$\frac{R}{E_2}\ln A_0\Big(\frac{\Gamma M}{W_0 N} S_2 WN\Big).$$

Now let us examine the assumptions. There is, of course, the implied assumption of temperature homogeneity but in addition they recognize that da/dT and $(1-a)^Z$ are dependent on the thermobalance, assuming, however, that they remain constant for a given balance. Since the exponent Z is, in essence, the order of the reaction kinetics followed, said order varies from thermobalance to thermobalance.

The plot yields an activation energy from the slope and it is with this that we are concerned. Using the data of Richer and Vallet (R19), they obtain plots A and B of Fig. VI-15. The plots yield activation energy values of 44 kcal per mole for the decomposition of calcium carbonate in nitrogen and 210 kcal per mole in carbon dioxide. Since the determination of activation energies is a popular pastime, let us examine now their physical significance.

The activation energy is a quantity which takes into account the fact that thermodynamically favorable reactions do not proceed spontaneously and speedily. It may be pictured as an energy barrier separating the stable species such that a quantity of energy must be added to either species to produce an activated species which may or may not become the other species as it gives up its energy. In a reversible reaction a sufficient number of particles are being supplied with this activation energy so that there is a recognizable tendency for interchange and consequently equilibrium. Equilibrium implies that in a given time the

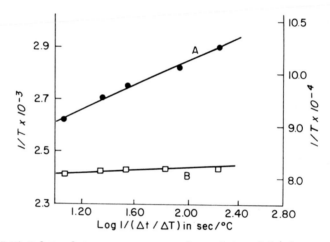

Fig. VI-15. Relation between temperature of completion of the decomposition and the heating rate. $1/T \times 10^{-4}$ scale: (A) $CaCO_3$ powder in dry N_2; (B) $CaCO_3$ powder in CO_2. From Berlin and Robinson (B48).

The slope is R/E_2 where E_2 is the activation energy. For calcium carbonate the value varies greatly with composition of the atmosphere.

number of particles leaving any state is equal to that entering the state; i.e., for a single one-step reaction the forward and reverse rates are equal. In the case under consideration, the nature of the activated species can be deduced easily; it must be an energized calcium carbonate,

$$CaCO_3 \rightleftharpoons CaCO_3^* \rightleftharpoons CaO + CO_2.$$

Figure VI-16 shows a two-dimensional representation of a one-step process such as we are considering. A particle ($CaCO_3^*$) that can pass over the barrier can fall into either stable phase A ($CaCO_3$) or B + C ($CaO + CO_2$) without regard for the state from which it came; thus the rate equation in either direction must include a term expressing the probability that the particle will pass over the barrier rather than dropping back.

The forward reaction rate constant, using rather simplified kinetics, may be expressed by

$$k_f = A_f \theta_f(P) \exp - (E_f/RT).$$

where A_f is a constant lumping together all the terms we do not presently wish to compare and $\phi_f(P)$ is some function of the pressure of carbon dioxide.

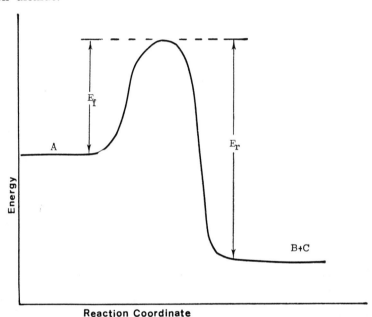

Reaction Coordinate

Fig. VI-16. Two dimensional representation of energy relation of reaction $A \rightarrow B + C(g)$.

The activated state formed by adding energy E_f to E_a can go to either stable state. The activated state for the reverse reaction requires not only energy Er but joining of B and C. It, too, can fall to either stable state.

This atmosphere dependence of the forward reaction ought to be a very secondary effect, probably related to diffusion of gas out of a particle. This much is in qualitative agreement with the data of Cremer and Nitsch (C26). However, the direct effect of this limiting step may be to permit a transitory equilibrium pressure of carbon dioxide within the particle. In this (quite probable) case, the true rate of reaction is likely zero order, but appearing to decrease with decreasing concentration of unreacted because of the increasing diffusion path as the surface and subsurface layers react. This diffusion step would vary with total pressure as well as with carbon dioxide pressure because the outward migration of carbon dioxide would be repressed somewhat by a high concentration of gases (i.e., a shorter mean free path). Even should the measured forward rate have an apparent dependence on the pressure of carbon dioxide this may well be due to other causes than to $\phi_f(P)$ in the rate expression having real significance. Measurements of the rate of decomposition as a function of particle size and total pressure as well as carbon dioxide pressure would be needed to resolve the question. Cremer and Nitsch (C26), working with pure carbon dioxide atmospheres and a single type of calcite, deduced that the rate of decomposition is determined by a nucleation velocity and the growth rate of the CaO crystallites—and that these two processes are dependent on the pressure of carbon dioxide.

Returning to the question of the activation energy, this quantity is evaluated by calculating the rate of the reaction at each of several temperatures and plotting an appropriate function of temperature (e.g., log k vs $1/T$ for first-order reactions). The activation energy is calculated from the slope of the plot. The calculation assumes that the chemical reaction is the rate-controlling step in the process and that the observed rate of reaction is a true description; i.e., the entire specimen is undergoing reaction at that rate at the moment under consideration. If this is not the case, some qualifications must be made.

> Wendlandt (W18), for example, calculated the activation energy for the dehydration of calcium oxalate monohydrate (Fig. VI-17) as 27 kcal/mole, using the method of Borchardt (B66). Comparing this value to Freeman and Carroll's (F14) 22 kcal/mole, Wendlandt points out "the slight difference between results may be attributed to the effect of particle size, heating rate, furnace atmosphere conditions, and so on." Which curve of Fig. VI-17 he used was not specified.

This activation energy is a physical quantity whose value should not vary significantly with experimental conditions. If there is a severe variation the experimental procedure is at fault. The technique for reconciliation of thermogravimetric data from one apparatus to another takes no account of atmosphere effects and neglects entirely the fact that the rate of recombination of carbon dioxide and calcium oxide is increasing with the pressure of carbon dioxide (in the immediate vicinity of the particles) as well as with temperature.

6.5. Critique

Attempts to apply methods using a progressively changing temperature to determine a highly temperature-dependent quantity (the rate of reaction) have generally lost touch with the straightforward approach of making the easiest measurement. In the case of kaolinite, for example, the measurements of the rate of reaction involved problems in heat transport, in temperature homogeneity, and in atmosphere effects. These arose from the thermal isolation and the shape and method of support of the sample. Further, the initial stages of the decomposition are of special interest, but at that stage thermogravimetric methods have their smallest validity. (The entire sample and support are being weighed to establish—by difference—the loss of a very small part of the entire weight.)

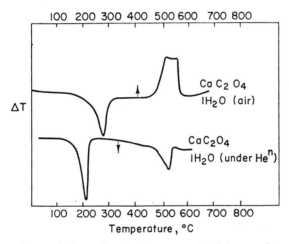

Fig. VI-17. Differential thermal analysis curves of calcium oxalate monohydrate. From Wendlandt (W18).
The peak (200–300°C) for the dehydration was used to calculate the activation energy by the method of Borchardt (B66).

Let us instead support this sample on a thermostatted heat sink in such a manner that it can take up heat rapidly from the sink and let the sample be in a thin layer so that the temperature gradient is indeed negligible. Now let us pass across the sample a stream of gas so that the gaseous decomposition products are carried from the sample into a detector such as is used in gas chromatography.

Since these detectors can measure in the microgram range the measurement of the initial decomposition can be performed with more sensitivity than with a thermobalance and yet the sensitivity can be adjusted easily to measure higher concentrations with the same relative accuracy. Under these conditions the sample temperature is known and is known to be very close to uniform. The only problem remaining is that of the changing atmosphere.

The effect of the changing atmosphere can at least be diminished considerably by good contact between gas and sample. If the incoming gas stream contains none of the product gas, the partial pressure will not be known but will be small. A better arrangement would be to supply a gas stream having a known concentration of the product gas (water in the case of kaolinite). With such a stream the concentration of water vapor is at least some minimum value; whether or not it rises substantially will depend on design and flow. A differential detector can still measure the small increase due to decomposition.

From this point on, the design of the system will be determined by the nature of the information sought. A partial pressure carbon dioxide can be supplied for carbonate decompositions or even a mixture including both carbon dioxide and water vapor if both may be given off. For irreversible reactions any ordinary carrier gas could be used. If analysis of products is required, repetitive gas chromatography would be useful (see Chapter XIV).

6.6. Summary

Like quantitative descriptions of differential thermal analysis curves, attempts to establish the kinetics of a reaction from thermogravimetric or differential thermal analysis data require untenable assumptions. The mathematics required for a rigorous treatment does not lend itself to a practicable solution. Several additional data, e.g., changes in heat capacity and thermal conductivity, would be needed.

The atmosphere effect must be taken into account. Reversible decompositions will be affected by accumulation of products. Irreversible reactions may be affected by accessibility of reactant.

Use of other experimental techniques is indicated.

CHAPTER VII

Atmosphere Control

7.1. Introduction

Many of the reactions studied by differential thermal analysis involve weight loss and this weight loss is often the result of a more-or-less reversible decomposition. The effect of the surrounding atmosphere is therefore of extreme interest. It is the author's experience that a simple description of the effect of atmosphere is not convincing; examples of misleading data are necessary. This chapter will contain a more extensive review than was considered appropriate for other topics.

Let us note first a range of effects on a single material, ammonium perchlorate, without an attempt to reach any conclusion except that the conditions of the experiment have a decided effect and hence the experimental conditions must be controlled—or at least known. Figure VII-1 shows Stone's (S58) data using dynamic atmospheres. The reaction in the 400°C region is a decomposition whose products vary from author to author.

The influence of the atmosphere on the behavior of the specimen can be varied by design. To some degree it will depend, in nondynamic systems, on the sample geometry. For a given sample geometry the effect will depend on whether the atmosphere is static, flowing, or dynamic. For our purposes a flowing atmosphere is defined as one in which the gas is passed through the furnace and around or over the sample holder and a dynamic atmosphere is one in which the gas passes through the sample cavity or chamber. A static atmosphere is one in which there is no forced flow of gas. The most important influence is, of course, the nature of the gas in relation to the reaction under investigation.

Bohon's (B59) curves on the decomposition of ammonium perchlorate

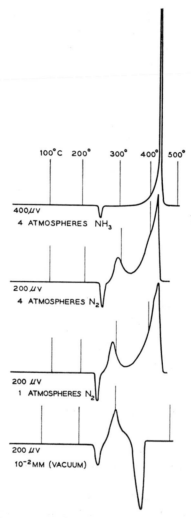

Fig. VII-1. Effect of pressure and gas composition on decomposition of NH_4ClO_4 diluted 1:1 with alumina. From Stone (S58).

The purely exothermal reaction in ammonia changes with atmosphere composition and pressure to an endothermal reaction under vacuum. In the absence of ammonia a lower-temperature exothermal reaction appears.

(Fig. VII-2) under some rather special conditions appear prima facie to disagree with Stone's (Fig. VII-1) data; qualitatively they can be related. The curves are shown here for easy comparison; the explanation is postponed to Section 7 of this chapter.

7.2. History and Critique

Rowland and Lewis (R34) were among the early users of controlled, static atmospheres. While a part of their work was concerned with use of a neutral atmosphere to avoid combustion or other oxidation, the more interesting curves are those obtained using carbon dioxide (Fig. VII-3).

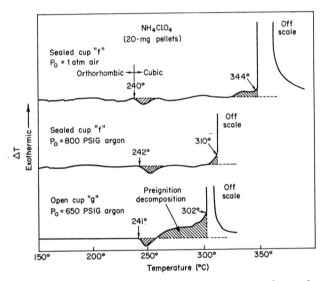

FIG. VII-2. Effect of pressure and product escape on pyrolysis of ammonium perchlorate (20 mg pellets). From Bohon (B59).
The mass action law requires that the presence of a product gas should inhibit a decomposition.

Siderite is cited elsewhere (Chapter II) in pointing out the evils of orthodox sample holders. In oxygen the lesser heat effect of the carbonate decomposition is completely hidden. Rowland and Lewis state: "between 450°C and 530°C the endothermic effect of the dissociation of CO_2 is accompanied by oxidation of FeO, so that the first part of the curve is a compromise. When a temperature of 530°C is attained, sufficient CO_2 is liberated to prevent the oxidation of the FeO, and a modified endothermic loop is registered. At about 570°C the evolution of CO_2 decreases enough so that the FeO can oxidize, and an exothermic loop is recorded. The small exothermic mound between 750°C and 850°C is registered when the iron oxide becomes hematite. In a CO_2 atmosphere the iron is not oxidized and a larger, uninterrupted endothermic loop is obtained."

The magnesite and calcite curves show clearly the effect of an atmosphere of the product gas. The deflections break away from the base

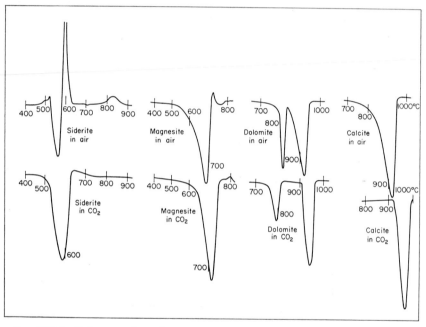

Fig. VII-3. Carbonates heated in air and in carbon dioxide. From Rowland and Lewis (R34).

Temperatures of reactions vary and in some cases the nature of the reaction is different.

line more sharply and at higher temperatures than in air. This behavior is to be expected since the temperature must become high enough to cause an equilibrium vapor pressure of one atmosphere instead of the 2×10^{-4} atmospheres common in ambient air.

The effect of pressure change in controlled atmospheres is rather strikingly demonstrated by Stone's (S54) data shown in Fig. VII-4. The peak for magnesite is shifted only slightly while that for a calcite impurity is shifted by ca. 200°C. This might lead one to conclude from the van't Hoff relation that the heat of decomposition of magnesite is much greater than that of calcite. While this is apparently true, reaching such a conclusion from only the evidence here would be reasoning in circles since heats of decomposition are often determined from just this sort of shift of decomposition temperature. A very necessary step is to establish the reversibility of the decomposition.

An interesting approach to the question of atmosphere was taken by Hill and Murphy (H13). They heated a sample block from below with a heat lamp. This block was encased in three pieces of firebrick. The top piece had a piece of aluminum foil in the hollowed cover section. They report that the second peak in Fig. VII-5, "although much lower than the reported boiling point of 220.3°C, corresponds to the volati-

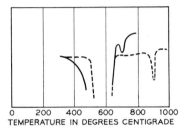

0   200   400   600   800   1000
TEMPERATURE IN DEGREES CENTIGRADE

FIG. VII-4. Differential thermal analysis of magnesite in carbon dioxide: _____ 16.5 mm of Hg; - - - - - - - 750 mm of Hg. From Stone (S54).
The calcite peak is shifted much more than the magnesite.

lization of 1,4-dibromobenzene from the sample holder. The position of the lamp ensures the existence of a thermal gradient in the system, which provides a driving force for the sublimation [*sic*] of 1,4-dibromo-benzene. . . . Thus, nonequilibrium conditions exist providing for continuous removal of the gaseous phase and replenishment from the liquid. Because of this, liquid-gas transitions would be expected to give broader peaks, at temperatures below recorded boiling points." The authors report this as a perfectly reasonable phenomenon to be accepted and endured! They fail to point out what possible use one might have for volatilization temperatures under uncertain conditions. The arrangement would have no use whatsoever for mixtures since the composition would be continuously changing in the volatilization temperature range; yet as a separation technique it must obviously rank as somewhat less than trivial.

The solution is confinement of the vapor so that it must reach a vapor pressure essentially equal to the ambient pressure before it could escape from the immediate vicinity of the sample. The answer was available in the literature. Vold (V10) had reported 10 years earlier—an experiment in which water vapor was made to escape through a hole drilled in the side of the sample cell. This confinement made certain that the water vaporized under a partial pressure essentially equal to the ambient pressure.

Kissinger *et al.* (K31) had a much better knowledge or understanding of the atmosphere effect. They believed "the decomposition of the

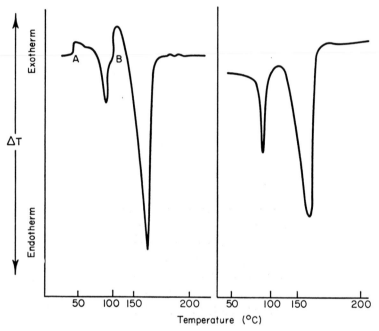

Fɪɢ. VII-5. Differential thermal analysis of 1,4-dibromobenzene. *Left:* 50% in Al₂O₃; manual control. *Right:* 20% in Al₂O₃; programmed voltage. From Hill and Murphy (H13).

When no design precautions are taken a process involving vaporization will yield good results only by chance.

type solid → solid plus gas takes place essentially at a pressure of one atmosphere of the gas evolved when studied by the DTA-TGA under conditions . . . described." They did overestimate the difficulty of diffusion of gas into the sample from the ambient atmosphere. The ⅜-inch opening at the top of the sample holder presents a tremendous area for exchange of gas with the atmosphere above; further, the ⅜-inch total cross section of the sample also permits diffusion from the surface down into the bulk of the sample. At temperatures in the region of 400°C carbon dioxide and oxygen molecules are traveling at a velocity of 20,000 sample holder lengths per second; even considering the tremendous number of collisions, the rate of diffusion within the sample will be high. The only reasonable barrier to interchange of gases is a long narrow path.

7.3. Effect of Interchange of Gases

Consider Fig. VII-6, in which a vessel containing a sample is decomposing reversibly, giving off vapor X into an atmosphere of N. The sur-

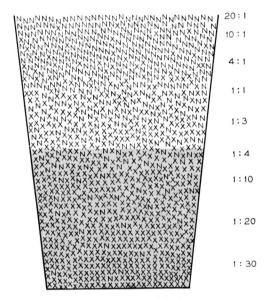

Fig. VII-6. Crucible containing reversibly decomposing specimen.
As decomposition product X is formed it tends to diffuse out into the ambient atmosphere. Since the diffusion is slow amongst the particles of sample the relative amounts of the neutral atmosphere, N, and X will vary with depth in the container. The N : X ratios shown were selected arbitrarily.

rounding gas being initially pure N the concentration of N will vary at some given instant with depth in the vessel, both above and within the specimen. The diminution in N with depth is obviously the result of the evolution of X, but even while this gas is being evolved some N will remain in—or reach—all parts of the vessel simply because gases diffuse rapidly. Of greater importance, the proportion of N and X is not the same in various parts of the vessel. Let us consider the consequence of this rather obvious fact.

As the vessel is heated the walls will reach a "decomposition temperature" first and the reaction will begin. Product X will displace some N initiating a concentration gradient essentially perpendicular to the walls. The center is not yet hot enough to decompose and the concentration of X is a further bar to decomposition so the material toward the center is unaffected as yet.

While the concentration of X is increasing in the bulk another effect—the interchange with the ambient atmosphere—begins to exert an influence. The material near the top of the sample has a lesser concentration of X because of diffusion interchange with N from the environment, i.e., the X diffuses out and N diffuses in. Therefore, this material will react fairly soon after that which is in contact with the wall even though material nearer the wall but deep within the specimen is at a higher temperature. This latter material must reach a still higher temperature because of the concentration of X amongst the particles.

The concentration gradient of X (Fig. VII-7 and VII-9) at the sides is steep in the immediate vicinity of the reaction surface because this is the source of product X, but a more-or-less steady change should go on toward the center with a nearly steady-state vertical gradient set up when diffusion and decomposition are balanced.

The temperature, on the other hand, advances steadily from the sides.

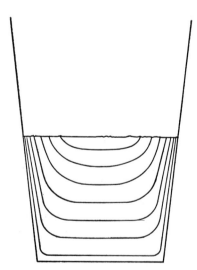

Fɪɢ. VII-7. An arbitrary representation of the concentration gradient of product gas during the early stages of a decomposition.

The concentration is initially high along the sides because that is where the reaction is preferentially occurring and diffusion is slow.

If the temperature lag due to absorption of the heat of reaction is neglected, the temperature distribution in a large thin-walled vessel can be described by Fig. VII-8.

The atmosphere in the immediate vicinity of a given small particle dictates the temperature at which that particle will decompose. Each of the product gas isobars establishes an area which must reach a unique temperature. These isobars are in continual motion; obviously the product X concentration around any particle will tend to diminish after that particle has decomposed.

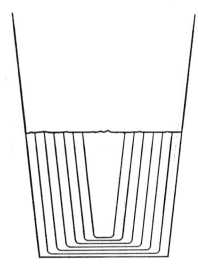

Fig. VII-8. An arbitrary representation of the temperature gradient during a decomposition.
The heat is supplied mostly through the sides of the vessel.

All of this means that a large and bulky sample decomposing in contact with an atmosphere other than the product gas is constrained by known physical laws to have a sizable temperature range of decomposition. It further means that the actual conditions under which various parts of the sample decompose are thermodynamically different (Fig. VII-9), and in at least a few cases the observer risks the occurrence of different reactions in different parts of the vessel. This effect accounts in turn for the nonstoichiometric weight losses obtained more than occasionally.

The deplorable consequences described above may be avoided, even with large samples. Obviously if a single product gas is involved decomposition in an atmosphere of that gas will avoid different reactions regardless of sample geometry. If another atmosphere is used it may be kept in dynamic contact with the sample in the manner of Stone (S50) or Lodding and Hammell (L11), or if it is administered as a static or quasi-dynamic atmosphere in the manner of Rowland and Lewis (R34) or Saunders and Giedroyc (S6), respectively, the sample must be in a thin layer in the manner devised by the present author (G17) or Paulik, Paulik, and Erdey (P11) to permit rapid interchange with whatever atmosphere is supplied and hence to maintain an atmosphere within the sample approximately like that above. A third solution is to avoid diffusion from the atmosphere into the sample (G16). Let us examine, with the aid of thermodynamics, the origin of the troubles and the reasons why the solutions are available.

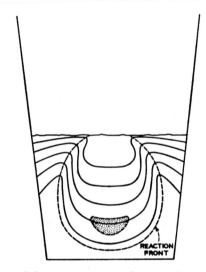

Fig. VII-9. The effect of the temperature gradient on the concentration gradient. *The reaction temperature is prescribed by the concentration so that the reaction front moves in more rapidly at the top. The front moves downward rather fast, too, so that the last material to react is usually a pellet close to, but not at, the bottom.*

7.4. Reversible Decompositions

Take the case of a reversible decomposition of a carbonate,

$$MCO_3 \rightleftharpoons MO + CO_2.$$

This reaction is governed by both rate and equilibrium constants but let us assume that at the temperatures of interest both the decomposition and recomposition proceed very rapidly; we can then ignore rate constants and concern ourselves with the more important problem of equilibrium.

The equilibrium constant for such a reaction is expressed as

$$K = \frac{[MO] \, [CO_2]}{[MCO_3]},$$

but since the oxide and carbonate are both solids their activities (or concentrations) are generally taken arbitrarily as unity so that

$$K = [CO_2]$$

or

$$K = P_{CO_2};$$

that is, the possibility that the oxide and carbonate will coexist at some given temperature depends only on the pressure of carbon dioxide over the system. If the pressure actually existing is not the equilibrium pressure the reaction will proceed in the direction which will tend to bring about this condition.

From this we can see that at some reasonably high temperature if a carbonate is put under a vacuum it will decompose completely, while if an atmosphere of carbon dioxide were supplied to it it would stay as the carbonate. The only condition permitting coexistence of both solid species is maintenance of the equilibrium pressure, but this is a difficult condition to impose on a system by external control. Deviation in either direction will permit disappearance of one species or the other.

Let us examine the actual physical occurrences in a system comprising a specimen of our metal carbonate, MCO_3 and, over it, an infinite volume at a fixed total pressure of carbon dioxide. Since one of the initial conditions is existence of the carbonate, the temperature of the system is below that for which the fixed pressure is the equilibrium pressure, so let us heat the specimen. When the carbonate reaches and exceeds the appropriate temperature, it will begin to decompose and will continue to do so until it is gone. Now let the specimen cool. When the temperature drops below the equilibrium temperature for this fixed pressure of carbon dioxide the oxide will begin to take up carbon dioxide and convert back to the carbonate. Again the process will go to completion without much regard for the amount of temperature drop. Let us contrast these occurrences with those in a slightly different system.

Consider the same system, a quantity of metal carbonate in an infinite volume with the same pressure of carbon dioxide, but now this carbon dioxide pressure is not the total pressure. Let us add some other gas so that this carbon dioxide pressure is only a few per cent of the total pressure. Again let us heat the specimen. Again the specimen will reach and exceed the same equilibrium temperature but now the evolution of carbon dioxide from the carbonate causes an enrichment of the gas in the immediate vicinity of the specimen so that the decomposition will be retarded. Given sufficient time, however, the carbon dioxide can diffuse away into the infinite volume bringing the partial pressure in the immediate vicinity back toward the initial partial pressure remitting additional carbonate decomposition. Note that the end result is the same: the carbonate will decompose completely. Now let this specimen cool. When the temperature drops below the equilibrium temperature the specimen begins to convert back to the carbonate, depleting the carbon dioxide supply in the immediate vicinity. Since an infinite volume is available, more carbon dioxide diffuses in, allowing further reconstitution of the carbonate. Again the end result is the same; there is, however, a quite different speed of reaction because of the effect of diffusion.

7.5. Pressure-Temperature Relation

We have seen from the above discussion that at a given pressure of carbon dioxide there is some definite temperature at which the metal carbonate will decompose. We can infer that there is a definite relationship governing the equilibrium pressure at various temperatures. The relationship may be found with the aid of a few statements from rather elementary thermodynamics. Remember that for such reactions

$$K = P_{CO_2}$$

but

$$\Delta F = RT \ln K, \qquad \text{so } \Delta F = RT \ln P_{CO_2}$$

or

$$\frac{\Delta F}{T} = R \ln P.$$

The variation of the change of free energy with temperature is given by

$$\frac{d(\Delta F/T)}{dT} = \frac{-\Delta H}{T^2}$$

so

$$\frac{d(R \ln P)}{dT} = \frac{-\Delta H}{T^2} \text{ or } \frac{d \ln P}{dT} = \frac{-\Delta H}{RT^2}.$$

This is the familiar van't Hoff expression. Several important considerations may be deduced easily from examination of a typical plot of this expression, as in Fig. VII-10.

Consider again the vessel shown in Figs. VII-6 to VII-9 and assume that the material in it has an equilibrium pressure of P_a at ambient temperature T_A, but that the ambient partial pressure of carbon dioxide is P'_A. The material is obviously stable. Let us heat the specimen. Upon reaching T'_A the material may start to decompose but any decomposition raises the partial pressure of carbon dioxide in the immediate vicinity in turn slowing the decomposition. The carbon dioxide, however, can and will diffuse away so if heating was stopped just above T'_A the material would decompose as rapidly as the product gas could diffuse away. We are concerned, generally, with dynamic systems so let us

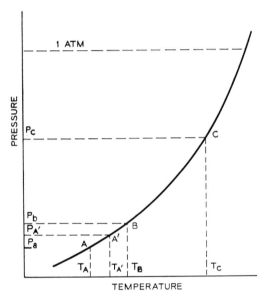

Fɪɢ. VII-10. Van't Hoff plot for a reversible decomposition.

At any temperature to the right of that corresponding to the actual local partial pressure the material will tend to decompose, to the left, recompose.

continue the heating. The decomposition of the carbonate will enrich the gas in the immediate vicinity so that as a material reacts the material near it sees a change in environment; as the partial pressure is increased to P_b the material in that environment cannot decompose until T_B is reached. If diffusion is slow because of geometry and sample size the partial pressure of carbon dioxide may reach P_c so that the decomposition is not completed until T_C is reached. This reaction which will occur at any static temperature above T'_A is now, because of somewhat inhibited diffusion, spread out over the temperature range from T'_A to T_C.

Let us consider some effects of various sample and atmosphere arrangements to avoid this spread-out temperature range problem. Conside first the behavior we might expect in a dynamic atmosphere with a partial or total pressure equal to P_b. A dynamic atmosphere is specifically a stream of gas passing through the sample; each particle may be assumed to be surrounded by an atmosphere identical with that entering the sample vessel.

As soon as the temperature exceeds T_B the sample will begin to decompose. This condition is essentially the same as a sample decomposing in an infinite volume of carbon dioxide at a total pressure of P_b so the sample will decompose completely at any temperature above T_B. Note that diffusion is unimportant because an atmosphere with a carbon dioxide pressure of P_b is continually supplied to each particle. The time required for the reaction will be generally dependent on the rate at which heat can be supplied to the specimen.

Reactions taking place in a dynamic atmosphere of the gas produced during the reaction will, in general, take place in a very narrow temperature range. The start of the reaction should be clearly manifest.

Take now a quite open sample vessel and put in it a thin layer of the specimen. Expose this now to a *static* atmosphere with a *partial* pressure of carbon dioxide of P_b. (In an atmosphere comprising only carbon dioxide this reaction would occur quickly as described earlier but it is important to consider a more general case.) When the temperature T_B is reached and exceeded the decomposition begins, as usual, but with the thin, spread-out sample diffusion of carbon dioxide out of the sample is rapid and the sample decomposes rapidly over a short temperature range. Under the same heating conditions the decomposition in this mixed atmosphere will occur over a somewhat longer temperature range than would the decomposition in pure gas (because of the need for diffusion), but this range will be considerably smaller than for the same reaction at the same heating rate in a crucible or block because the diffusion is so much more rapid.

7.6. Inhibited Diffusion

Let us now consider the opposite extreme in atmosphere accessibility. This time we will put the sample in a cavity opening to the atmosphere only through a long narrow tube (Fig. VII-11). The cavity is packed with the powdered sample so that the only air remaining in it is the small amount between particles. From Fig. VII-12 we can deduce the behavior of the specimen. Assuming for this case that the ambient partial pressure does not exceed P_A, as the temperature exceeds T_A, the equilibrium vapor pressure exceeds P_A and decomposition begins. The first hint of decomposition brings about a substantial increase in the amount of gas present so that an equal volume of gas must be forced out of the cavity. The gas forced out will be mostly air, so that the partial pressure of the product gas is increased from P_A to P_1. Considering that the volume expansion from the solid to the gas is likely to be on the order of 1000 and that the open space among the particles is likely to be only a few per cent, one may conclude that the amount of material which needs to be decomposed to increase the partial pressure significantly is quite small. This increase, however, is but the first of a series of infinitesimal steps. When the temperature exceeds T_1 a further quantity must be decomposed raising the partial pressure to P_2 raising the decomposition temperature to T_2 raising the pressure to P_3 raising the decomposition temperature to T_3, etc.

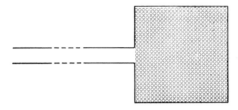

Fig. VII-11. Closed or inhibited diffusion vessel.
Gas can escape easily under a pressure gradient but exchange of gases is slow in the absence of a pressure differential.

This series of infinitesimal steps will continue until P_i is equal to P_{atm}, still with the decomposition of only a small part of the sample. The atmospheric pressure is of course the limit since a diffusion path does exist through the long narrow tube. Since this diffusion path does exist the sample can decompose rapidly and over a small temperature range. Thus, by preliminary decomposition of a very small portion of the sample material, the bulk of it is decomposed, at one atmosphere pressure, over a small temperature range.

The general effect is a narrowing of the reaction temperature range, consequently permitting better discrimination for close-following reactions and probably a more reproducible peak area. (This latter should follow because the effect of packing on diffusion into and out of the sample will disappear.) In practice the long diffusion path need not be tubular. The author uses cylinder-and-piston sample holders for thermogravimetry (Fig. VII-13) and for differential thermal analysis (Fig. III-23). The clearance is about 0.05 mm in either device.

Note that the decomposition occurs at the ambient total pressure rather than at specifically one atmosphere. Hence one may bring about the decomposition of a material at any experimentally convenient pressure. The gas surrounding the vessel need not bear any resemblance to the product gas yet because the movement of gas occurs in just one direction; the decomposition will take place under the applied pressure of the product gas. This consideration is of some importance in studying samples whose products might be difficult to handle in a pure state or in substantial amounts.

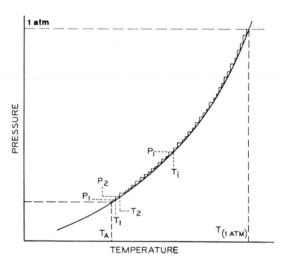

Fig. VII-12. Van't Hoff plot for a reversible decomposition with inhibited diffusion.

As the material decomposes the newly formed gas displaces the ambient air in a series of infinitesimal steps, each in turn raising the temperature required for continued decomposition. Most of the material decomposes only when the ambient temperature is reached.

7.7. Some Results

Essentially concurrent with the author's work (G16, G17) on sample holders for thermogravimetry, Paulik and co-workers (P11) were discovering the merits of a shallow sample holder. Since their concern was, in part, for more effective use of their particular apparatus (P10), they attached a thermocouple to the underside of their platinum pan (Fig. VII-14) and rested the pan on three points on the support tube. Their comparison of curves used different materials from the present authors— but the results are in agreement in principle. Figure VII-15 shows their results for calcium oxalate dihydrate, one of a number of excellent test specimens. The center group of curves is the sort of data Paulik *et al.*

obtain directly by derivative thermogravimetric analysis (see Chapter X). The thin layer of specimen does not permit build-up of water vapor, so the dehydration occurs more readily. The oxalate decomposition is exothermic in air

$$CaC_2O_4 + \tfrac{1}{2}O_2 \rightarrow CaCO_3 + CO_2$$

but endothermic in carbon dioxide (curves 3)

$$CaC_2O_4 \rightarrow CaCO_3 + CO.$$

Note that the differential thermal analysis in the crucible (curve 2) shows what might be interpreted as a pair of exotherms. This sort of

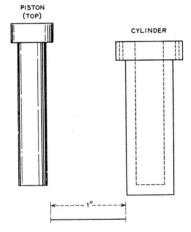

Fig. VII-13. Sample holder for thermogravimetry in self-generated atmospheres. From Garn and Kessler (G16).

Closed-chamber specimen holder. The piston provides a greatly restricted opening and hence highly inhibited diffusion of gases (see also Fig. III-23).

trouble often occurs with crucibles or other massive samples. It becomes clear on careful deliberation that the air within the sample and that diffusing in could oxidize the first carbon monoxide formed, but the carbon monoxide and dioxide tended to keep oxygen out of the crucible so the decomposition required heat until it slowed down enough so that oxygen could diffuse in again to react with the remaining carbon monoxide. The total decomposition reaction, then, comprises a single exothermic and a single endothermic reaction. The exothermic reaction involves a greater quantity of heat (compare curves 1 and 3), and under reasonably well-defined thermodynamic conditions one or the other reaction will be seen while under the unsteady, uncertain, and uncontrollable conditions in a crucible both reactions may or may not be observed. The exact nature of the curve will depend both on the geometry and the heating rate. Note too that the carbonate decomposition in the crucible begins at a temperature, ca. 630°C, at which the shallow pan-in-air decomposition is proceeding rapidly but the reaction is not complete until about the same temperature (>900°C) as in the carbon dioxide atmosphere. See also Figure VI-17.

Calcium oxalate monohydrate does not always show an exotherm when heated in air. Freeman and Edelman, in their examination of electrical derivative techniques (F15), obtained a thermogram (Fig. VII-16) much like the one Paulik *et al.* obtained in carbon dioxide (up

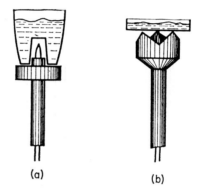

(a)   (b)

FIG. VII-14. The sample holders of Paulik *et al.* (P11).
The thin layer of specimen in (b) *does not permit a high concentration of product gas to accumulate.*

to about 700°C), but this was because the initial dehydration of the quite large and deep sample drove the air out. Loss of carbon monoxide presumably occurred in an atmosphere initially of water vapor. It is quite apparent that air did not diffuse to the region of the thermocouple until the decomposition was complete.

Pyrite (Fig. VII-17) is much less simple. In the shallow pan in air two oxidations can occur but one (iron) effects a weight gain while decomposition of the disulfide—to what appears to be an oxysulfide and sulfur (which oxidizes)—effects a weight loss. The differential thermogravimetric (DTG) analysis plot looks rather like the differential thermal analysis of calcium oxalate hydrate in a crucible in air (Fig. VII-15). Here, though, it appears to be a question of initiation temperatures and rates. Oxidation of ferrous iron obviously begins before decomposition of the disulfide. Just as obviously the disulfide decomposition is more rapid than the iron oxidation, since the thermogravimetric as well as the "DTG" curve shows a continuation of iron oxidation at the end of the first reaction. The final weight loss—to the oxide—is apparently endothermic.

Curves obtained in the crucible in air are uninterpretable except for gross features. The iron oxidation begins followed quickly by a general but erratic disulfide decomposition. One might guess that the ingress of oxygen from the air is not a uniform process—that there is reasonable

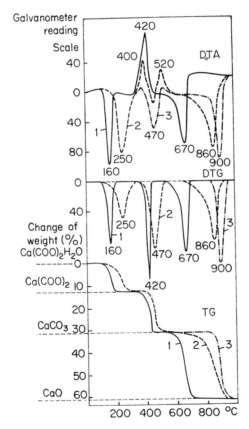

FIG. VII-15. The decomposition of calcium oxalate hydrate: Curves 1 in air in the free-diffusion sample holder of Fig. VII-14b; curves 2 in air in the crucible of Fig. VII-14a; and curves 3 in carbon dioxide in the crucible. From Paulik *et al.* (P11).

Note that curves 2 and 3 coincide in the first step in each case because the carbon dioxide is not evolved. The nature of the atmosphere is immaterial except to the extent that water vapor may be present.

evidence that surges occur. Accounting for each of the peaks in the "DTG" curve would require, first of all, a vivid imagination. This paragraph is, admittedly, opinion; one might make a case for some intermediate sulfides, citing the curves obtained in nitrogen. From there it is a simple step to postulate, in turn, corresponding oxysulfides.

Figures VII-1 and VII-2 or ammonium perchlorate may now be related and the apparent inconsistencies elucidated. Note that the specimen

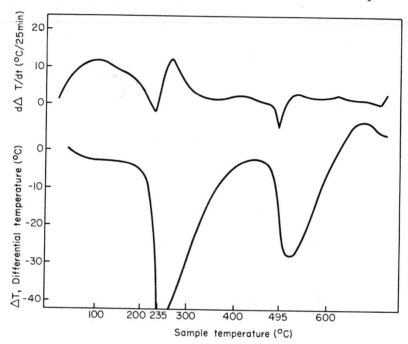

Fig. VII-16. DDTA (derivative differential thermal analysis) and DTA curves of calcium oxalate monohydrate. From Freeman and Edelman (F15).

Ten-gram samples in glass test tubes were used so the calcium carbonate decomposition was not reached.

sealed in air not only must retain its decomposition products in the immediate vicinity but must decompose in the presence of a very substantial pressure of one of them (oxygen). The total pressure is not of great interest; the partial pressure of any product gas is. Compare first with Stone's curve in ammonia; in each case the supression is considerable. Now compare the first curve of Fig. VII-2 with the second; no product gas is initially present so the decomposition occurs at a lower temperature. Since the gases are restricted, the temperature of the rapid decomposition is still set back more than in the third case.

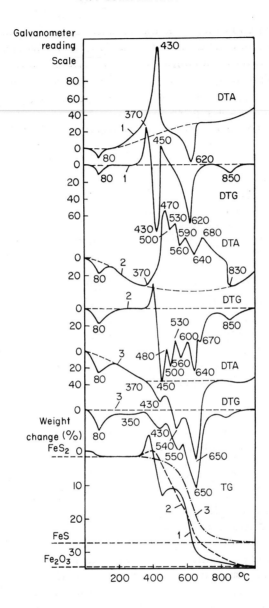

Fɪɢ. VII-17. Thermal analysis of pyrite. Curves 1 in air in the shallow sample holder; curves 2 in air in the crucible; and curves 3 in nitrogen in the crucible. From Paulik *et al.* (P11).

The rapid surges in curves 2 might be the result of several quite similar steps; the oxidation of some of the sulfur not only depletes the atmosphere but also fills the crucible with a heavy gas which slows down the entrance of oxygen for a time.

In the open cup experiment the initially formed products can diffuse away readily and their effect is only slightly felt. This would correspond to the dynamic nitrogen atmospheres used by Stone but modified by the slowness of diffusion.

The reader may question the applicability of the mass action law to an exothermic reaction. The discussion in Chapter II pointed out only that crystallographic phase changes were unquestionably irreversible if exothermic. While we may conclude prima facie that the decomposition of a perchlorate is irreversible and that equilibrium states are hence nonexistent, we might admit that a particular reaction is possibly reversible but that the thermodynamic equilibrium highly favors the decomposition. But this concession may not be required here since we can suggest an alternative. From Stone's curve obtained in vacuum, we might very easily postulate an endothermic (and probably reversible) step preceding—and prerequisite to—the exothermic decomposition such that the exothermic decomposition does not occur until a sufficient concentration of products (probably within the particles) has been built up.

7.8. Effect of Presence of Gas Other than Product or Reactant

Before introducing the concept of dynamic atmosphere it is appropriate that we make an overwhelming case against improper control of atmosphere. We will examine a few experiments in which the present author has concluded that interpretation or technique was faulty because of atmosphere effects. These are selected only as examples; there are many, many thermograms, including some of the present author's, that could be more informative if redone with proper atmosphere control.

The work by Crandall and West (C25) on oxidation of cobalt-alumina mixtures shows the problems encountered when the experiment is not planned specifically to obtain the information needed. Their use of the standard differential thermal analysis technique (G41) led to some rather doubtful conclusions (Fig. VII-18). Crandall and West apparently took the thermocouple temperature as the temperature of the entire specimen. The present author's interpretation of their differential thermal analysis data—assuming that the thermocouple bead is at or very near the center of the specimen—is that the indicated peak temperature occurs in the higher temperature runs at the time the reaction front reaches the bead. The present author also takes issue with their conclusions on rate-controlling factors. At the lower temperatures, oxygen reaches all particles very soon and the oxidation proceeds inward at each particle. The rate-controlling factor cannot be the diffusion of oxygen but has to be the oxidation rate of the cobalt. At higher temperatures, e.g., 700°C, the oxidation is so rapid that it depletes the oxygen. As oxygen diffuses into the nitrogen atmosphere in the sample vessel, it is taken avidly by the first unoxidized cobalt it encounters; at this temperature, then, the rate-controlling factor must necessarily be the diffusion of oxygen. The reaction front moves into the sample vessel at a progressively slower rate because of the progressively longer diffusion path, accounting for the tailing-off after the maximum.

The studies could have been more lucid had oxygen been used in place of air. The depletion of the oxygen at the reaction front draws in—purely as a volume change effect—only about an 18% replacement.

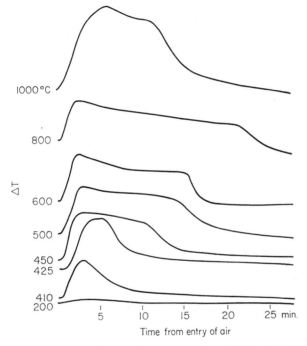

FIG. VII-18. Differential thermal oxidation curves for 50% Co—50% Al₂O₃ mixtures at high temperatures. From Crandall and West (C25).

The present author suggests that the rate-determining step at the higher temperatures is the diffusion of oxygen into the sample cavity.

In effect, oxygen is diffusing from an 18% level at the top of the sample vessel to the reaction front at a 0% level. Suppose, though, that oxygen had been used. The oxygen would sweep in as a replacement for that used up. While the reaction would be very rapid at the higher temperatures, the rate-controlling step ought to be the oxidation of the metal. A dynamic atmosphere like that suggested by Stone (S58) would be most helpful in this study. A stream carrying definite partial pressures of oxygen at a high flow rate would give a nearly uniform environment to the entire sample.

Kissinger and co-workers (K31) made an attempt to interpret the decompositions of manganous and ferrous carbonates by simultaneous differential thermal analysis and thermogravimetric analysis and by X-ray and electron diffraction. The X-ray and electron diffraction techniques are, of course, static-heating experiments but conclusions may still be drawn with caution. The differential thermal and thermogravimetric analysis experiments provide good correlation of data between the two techniques since the data were obtained simultaneously with essentially identical specimen holders. Identical specimen holders provide for similar inhibitions of diffusion of product or reactive gases. Such determinations provide relatable information which does not necessarily have any thermodynamic significance. Their data on all carbonates are subject to reinterpretation.

A cylindrical sample holder $\frac{3}{8}$ inch in diameter and $1\frac{1}{4}$ inch in depth can provide a rather extensive range of environments during a decomposition. Their assumption that ferrous carbonate necessarily decomposes first to ferrous oxide and carbon dioxide, the ferrous oxide then oxidizing to ferric oxide, is not well-supported by the data which they show. The more probable interpretation, under equilibrium conditions at least, is that the first reaction to occur is the oxidation of a part of the ferrous iron to the ferric iron on and near the surface. This gives rise to the slight exothermic effect shown in their 3°C per minute heating rate (Fig. III-3). This oxidation cannot take place in the mass of the specimen because of the ensuing decomposition with evolution of carbon dioxide. The oxidation does continue wherever oxygen can get into the sample from the surface. The process of oxidation and the process of decomposition are quite separate phenomena except when evolution of carbon dioxide prevents the oxidation of ferrous to ferric iron.

Borchardt (B65), in his apparatus for instructional purposes, used a block with holes 2 inches deep, thereby achieving, inadvertently, atmosphere confinement to a greater degree than is customary. Since his thermocouple junction was only slightly raised from the bottom the conditions set forth for a closed-chamber sample holder were approached. for this reason he was able to show the two-step dehydration of $BaCl_2 \cdot 2H_2O$. His text and thermogram also suggest that part of the time the first decomposition of $CuSO_4 \cdot 5H_2O$ and the vaporization of the resulting liquid water could be detected as separate steps. A high degree of reproducibility and ease of interpretation could be gained by adding sample to a depth of about $\frac{1}{4}$ inch, then inserting a close-fitting rod to create a long narrow diffusion path.

The attempt by Walton (W3) to achieve greater sensitivity by forming the sample into a pellet has been mentioned previously (Chapter VI). Examine the 600°C dehydroxylation shown in Fig. VIII-12. The deflection starts at a significantly lower temperature in the isolated sample and continues to essentially the same temperature as in the block. The attentive reader will conclude that the reaction begins at a low temperature because of the exposure to the atmosphere. To this extent it resembles the free-diffusion sample holders. This is simple enough. Let us next consider the sample block and the sample dimensions. Within the $\frac{3}{8}$-inch-diameter sample cavity there is no less than $\frac{1}{2}$ inch of greatly compacted sample between the thermocouple and the atmosphere. This is enough distance to prevent rapid diffusion and the last parts of the sample decompose, in effect, under nearly one atmosphere of water vapor.

Actually with such a heavily compacted body the $\frac{1}{2}$-inch separation between thermocouple and atmosphere is more than enough. The $\frac{3}{16}$-inch lateral separation appears to be enough. In other words, the latter part of Walton's isolated-sample dehydration curve shows that the center of the specimen is decomposing under ca. one atmosphere of water vapor.

The resemblance of the exposed pellet curves to a melange of "free-diffusion" and "closed-chamber" effects is due to the sample size, yet this problem can only be vitiated—not eliminated—by decreasing the size, so long as the pellet technique is used at all. Brindley and Nakahira (B80) reported that even with thin and loosely compacted samples the isothermal dehydroxylation of kaolin proceeded as a first-order reaction ($-dx/dt = kx$, where x is the quantity of unreacted material) at first, then slowed down. With pressed-disc samples, the reaction was slowest both initially and finally for the thickest samples. Relating this information back to the case of the pellets, the material on the surface is not influenced by the amount of material beneath it. The dehydroxylation will begin at a low temperature. The water vapor that forms inside cannot diffuse out readily and hence inhibits the decomposition until either the water vapor diffuses out or the temperature is raised, permitting a higher vapor pressure of water. The question of the order of reaction is discussed in Chapter VI.

Even the choice of "inert" atmospheres can affect the behavior of the sample and hence the appearance of the thermogram. The use of helium, for example, will cause severe deviations because of its special properties of very high diffusivity and thermal conductivity. As a dynamic gas it will provide another—and important—means of heat transfer, tending to diminish differential signals by serving as an infinitely large heat sink. This behavior contributed to the diminished signal found by the present author (Chapter XIV) in one of his early experiments in effluent gas analysis.

Wendlandt's (W18) curves for calcium oxalate monohydrate in air and in helium provide a striking example. The endothermic peaks in the 200–300°C range are the same process in each case, the dehydration of the monohydrate, yet if these peaks were separately presented, even an experienced observer might well fail to recognize them as the same process occurring in the same material. The reasons for the difference in the peaks are the two cited properties of helium. See Figure VI-17.

The major effect is the rapidity with which helium interchanges with other gases. The entry of helium in among the particles lowers the partial pressure of water vapor, enabling decomposition at a lower temperature. A secondary effect is the improved transfer of heat by this interparticulate helium. The more uniform temperature within the sample permits decomposition over a narrower range of temperatures.

The conclusion to be reached is necessarily that decompositions require precise control of the atmosphere. The mere supply of a particular gas over the sample holder is not enough; indeed, from Section 7.6 control of the gas *over* the sample holder may not be necessary.

7.9. Dynamic Atmosphere Differential Thermal Analysis

One of the most significant steps in thermal analysis since the introduction of the differential thermocouple was the development of apparatus permitting the passage through the sample of selected and controlled dynamic atmospheres. This was mainly the work of Stone (S50–S55, S58, S60), with an improved (in some ways) approach later by Lodding and Hammell (L10, L11). Some work had been reported (R34, S6) in which the sample—enclosed in a cavity or cup—was heated in an atmosphere of a selected neutral, reducing, oxidizing, or product gas. Product gas is used here and elsewhere in this book to mean a gas resulting from a decomposition.) Even with the usual rather massive samples, static atmosphere heating is a perfectly sound technique so long as the object is to avoid a decomposition, for example, the use of nitrogen or argon to avoid an oxidation, or if a single decomposition occurs and the atmosphere is the product gas.

Consider first a case in which a hydrated carbonate is heated in a static atmosphere of carbon dioxide and let us arbitrarily select this hydrated carbonate such that the water and carbon dioxide are given off at widely separated temperatures. (This latter condition is only a convenience). As the sample is heated to the decomposition range of the hydrate the dehydration will begin and will proceed at a rate tending to set up an equilibrium pressure of water vapor. Since the original atmosphere was not water vapor its real identity is almost immaterial. (Diffusion rates of water vapor in various gases will have a small effect.) The hydrate will tend to decompose over a wide range of temperatures just as though the atmosphere had been air.

The dehydration completed, the sample approaches in temperature the decomposition range of the carbonate. Since a large temperature interval was specified most of the water vapor will have diffused out of the sample holder. The decomposition begins, then, in an atmosphere of carbon dioxide with a small amount of water vapor. The onset of decomposition, at a temperature determined by the relative amounts of water and carbon dioxide deep in the sample holder, expels the water vapor as the decomposition proceeds. Most of the decomposition occurs in the atmosphere of the product gas and hence over a small temperature range.

Now let these same reactions occur with a lesser temperature interval between the decompositions. The hydrate decomposition will tend to remain the same but the onset of the carbonate decomposition will occur at a lower temperature because the water vapor has not had time to diffuse out. Still the effect may not be great since a small amount of carbon dioxide will expel the water vapor; but consider the logical extension, i.e., the case in which the equilibrium vapor pressure of carbon dioxide over the carbonate has a measurable value within the decomposition range of the hydrate. Now as the hydrate decomposes, and the water vapor partial pressure increases, the partial pressure of carbon dioxide necessarily decreases. At some temperature the hydrate decomposition is occurring rapidly enough to diminish the partial pressure of carbon dioxide below the equilibrium vapor pressure of carbon dioxide and the carbonate will begin to decompose. A mixture of water vapor and carbon dioxide will be given off from the sample because the presence of either of the gases will diminish the partial pressure of the other and accelerate the reaction producing that other. Eventually, the lower-temperature hydrate decomposition will run its course, the temperature difference signal will approach—but not reach—the base line, and the remainder of the carbonate will decompose. Note that even the dehydration will be complete at a lower temperature than if the carbonate decomposition did not occur so soon. [This is the lowering of the decomposition temperatures of mixtures noted by Arens (A12) and by Webb and Heystek (W11).]

Now examine the effect of a dynamic atmosphere of carbon dioxide on the same systems. The effect is quite straightforward. The water vapor is swept out rapidly and never achieves any substantial partial pressure. The dehydration occurs at a significantly lower temperature and has no effect on the carbonate decomposition. The dehydration peak is not particularly well-defined. The carbonate decomposition takes place sharply over a small temperature range determined by the actual pressure of the carbon dioxide. To complete the picture, however, we must consider a static atmosphere of water vapor and dynamic atmospheres of water vapor and of a mixture of water vapor and carbon dioxide.

In static water vapor the hydrate will remain unchanged until the equilibrium vapor pressure reaches the furnace pressure. If the hydrated carbonate has no appreciable equilibrium pressure of carbon dioxide we have no serious complications; at the appropriate temperature the hydrate will begin to decompose. Since the hydrated specimen is at a higher temperature than it could reach in the carbon dioxide atmosphere, let us assume that at this temperature we have a few millimeters vapor pressure of carbon dioxide from the carbonate. The dehydrated carbonate will tend to decompose to maintain the pressure but the dilution in the water vapor keeps the pressure low—and not only due to diffusion. The movement of the freshly released water vapor from the bulk of the sample into the surrounding atmosphere sweeps the particles with a pro tempore dynamic atmosphere of water vapor. Initially, then, the carbonate decomposes rapidly—as long as the dehydration continues. When there is no hydrate to decompose the carbonate decomposition will slow to a rate only sufficient to keep each particle surrounded by the equilibrium vapor pressure of carbon dioxide as long as possible. The reaction will proceed as described in Section 3 of this chapter.

In a dynamic atmosphere of water vapor (pure or diluted) the hydrated carbonate will again be stable until the equilibrium vapor pressure reaches the pressure (or partial pressure) of water vapor in the steam. At this point it will start to decompose and if the carbonate has an appreciable vapor pressure (as we postulated before) it will also begin to decompose. In this case, however, the dilution of the carbon dioxide continues so that the carbonate decomposition peak follows close behind the dehydration peak and is not well-separated from it.

Lastly, consider a dynamic atmosphere of a mixture of carbon dioxide and water vapor. The proportions are not very important as long as there is a substantial fraction of each; let us arbitrarily use, for example, carbon dioxide saturated with water vapor at 25°C before it enters the furnace. The hydrate will begin to decompose when the equilibrium vapor pressure exceeds the partial pressure of water in the gas stream. Assuming a flow rate sufficient that the carbon dioxide partial pressure is not changed substantially, the hydrate will decompose completely—over a short temperature interval—without effect on the carbonate. At the appropriate temperature the carbonate will in turn decompose, also over a short temperature interval. The two reactions are now, however, clearly separated in temperature and in time. The degree of separation in temperature would depend, for a given material, on the actual partial pressures of the two gases. The separation can hence be varied by changing said pressures.

Note that the arguments above can describe, just as well, a mixture of a carbonate and a hydrate. The only difference would be that the equilibrium vapor pressures would now be independent of each other; i.e., the discontinuity of carbon dioxide pressure as the hydrate decomposed would not occur. Similarly, the arguments are by no means limited to carbon dioxide and water. Figure VII-1 shows the effect of ammonia in repressing a reaction in which one of the product gases is ammonia.

7.10. Apparatus for Dynamic Atmosphere Differential Thermal Analysis

Two varieties of dynamic atmosphere differential thermal analysis furnaces are in common use, that (Fig. VII-19) described by Stone (S58) and that (Fig. VII-20) described by Lodding and Hammell (L10); they differ basically in the direction of flow of the gas. Stone introduces the gas into a manifold below the furnace chamber from whence it is admitted to the sample and the reference through a pair of capillaries. After passing upward through the specimens it mixes with the chamber gas which may or may not be the same gas.

> The present author very strongly suggests the use of the same gas unless there is good reason to use another. Back-diffusion of the chamber gas can occur even at moderately high rates of flow of gas.

In the Lodding–Hammell apparatus the dynamic gas is sent first into the furnace chamber from which it flows downward through the sample and reference and out through the tubes which also support the block and lead the thermocouple wires.

Each technique basically has its own advantages which render it better —for some purposes—than the other. Each can be modified, however, to obtain some of the attributes of the other; there is, for example, no chemical reason why the operation of either cannot be inverted to resemble the other. The barriers are physical and mechanical.

With the understanding that modifications are possible in either case we will consider and compare the basic design of each.

The Stone apparatus uses a sample block heated by a furnace element quite separate from the gas enclosure. The block is secured to the gas-flow tubes. Since the furnace element is positioned on the base by water and electrical connections and the block is also carefully positioned, the heater and the block are positioned quite reproducibly with respect to

one another. The Lodding–Hammell apparatus uses ceramic cups
(which are, in essence, sleeves set part way over the support rods)
heated by a furnace winding applied over the furnace chamber tube.
Since the support rods and the furnace chamber tube are secured at
some distance from the hot zone, the cups and the furnace are less

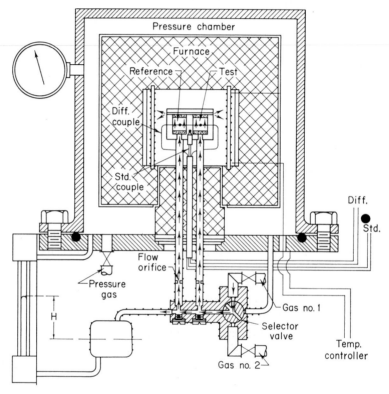

Fig. VII-19. Dynamic atmosphere differential thermal analysis furnace. (Courtesy
of Robert L. Stone Co.)
The dynamic gas flows upward from manifold through orifices and specimens and
escapes into the pressure chamber.

likely (in the absence of special techniques) to be reproducibly and
symmetrically positioned. If a block is substituted for the cups, a substantial misalignment may permit the block to touch the furnace wall
and be heated very unsymmetrically. The use of varying pressure on the
O-ring seal to position the furnace with respect to the specimen is of
little use because it would need to be done not only at each run but even
during each run, using the differential signal as a guide. This might

compensate for gross differences in the thermal properties of sample and reference materials when this sort of compensation is not particularly desirable. Further, balancing the heating in this manner is a unidirectional adjustment. The information gained is only that sample and reference specimens are symmetric with respect to a plane perpendicular to and at the midpoint of a line joining the sample and reference thermocouple junctions. The specimens may still be much closer to the furnace

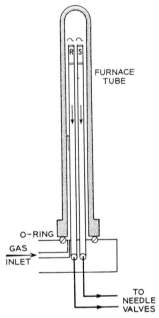

FIG. VII-20. Dynamic atmosphere furnace of Lodding and Hammell (L10).
The dynamic gas passes from the furnace chamber through the specimens out of the furnace and thence through flow measuring and control equipment.

wall on one side than the other; such positioning will tend to smear out the thermal effect. This type of positioning error would be quite irreproducible.

The present author uses a modification of the Lodding–Hammell furnace because of its other advantages but eliminates the positioning error. The furnace flange (Fig. VII-21) determines the positioning of the furnace chamber accurately; the O-ring is used properly only as a sealant. The support rods are positioned so that the top ends of the rods are directly above the support tube positioning holes in the base. When assembled, then, the sample and reference, whether in block or cup, are symmetrically positioned with respect to the furnace.

Letting the gas flow downward through the specimens then out of the furnace permits (*a*) collection of product gases for continual repetitive or subsequent analysis (see Chapter XIV) with minimum dilution and (*b*) separate and nearly independent control of flow through the two specimens. The flow of gas can be monitored to assure not only actual rate but also volume. Variations due to differing impedance to flow or to possible clogging can not only be detected but also corrected.

Water vapor cannot be used as a dynamic gas in the Lodding–Hammel method except at pressures or partial pressures less than the ambient temperature vapor pressure, at least with practices current at the time of writing. The Stone method permits the preheating and superheating

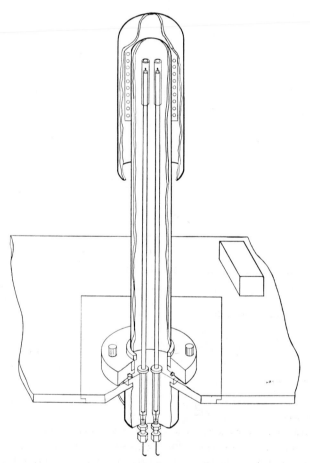

Fig. VII-21. Dynamic atmosphere differential thermal analysis furnace. (Courtesy of Apparatus Manufacturers, Inc.)

The author's design provides for reproducible positioning as well as for microsamples and the several types of atmosphere control.

of the water vapor so that dry steam can be introduced to the sample cavity.

Preheating of gases is not only possible but also necessary with the Stone method. The entry of gas at ambient temperature into a sample at—say—400°C could bring about a rather severe temperature gradient at a right angle to the ordinary gradient. The Lodding–Hammell method uses gas from the furnace chamber which can be assumed—in the absence of a nearby cold surface (see Chapter III)—to be very near block or cup temperature at any heating rate. Preheating without a separate controller would produce an effect which varied with heating rate and possibly with temperature.

A properly constructed furnace of the Lodding–Hammell type can be used easily with isolated samples because the temperature gradients in the hot zone are low. This likewise permits a flexibility of sample support —for example, microsamples as described in Chapter VIII, Sec. 8.2—which is impracticable in a zone heated only from the sides and with a very sizable cool surface above it.

Techniques requiring a change of dynamic gases are generally easier with the Stone technique. The hold-up volume of the manifold is low and the transition from the initial to near the final composition is swift (Fig. VII-2). In the Lodding–Hammell arrangement the furnace chamber must also be cleansed of the initial gas so that the complete change might well take several minutes.

Handling of fusible samples is similar in the two methods. The sample may be mixed with enough diluent to hold it when molten or small cups may be put in the sample chamber. The latter is easier with the Lodding– Hammell arrangement because the cup can rest against the thermocouple bead.

7.11. Experimental Results

The utility of controlled and/or dynamic atmospheres is seldom exploited to near its capabilities. Indiscriminate use will lead to a lack of appreciation of the merits of control. Comparisons of the effects of dynamic gases that have no significantly different action on the specimen (e.g., nitrogen and helium or, usually, oxygen and air) are uninformative and hence useless.

In planning an experiment the degree of confinement and the nature of the possible reactions must be considered. The use of a controlled atmosphere—except to prevent a reaction such as oxidation or if the atmosphere is a product of the reaction being studied—when the specimen is not in good contact with the atmosphere is quite without merit. Likewise, if the nature of the reaction is known and a single gas is involved a dynamic flow is not ordinarily beneficial. Since the temperature or even the nature of the reactions can vary with atmosphere, definitely known conditions must be used; the use of these definitely known conditions is rewarded by more informative thermograms.

Fig. VII-23 shows thermograms obtained from a coprecipitated magnesium manganese iron oxalate hydrate. (The desired heating product is magnesium manganese ferrite.) Each curve is different from the others not from lack of control of heating conditions but because the environ

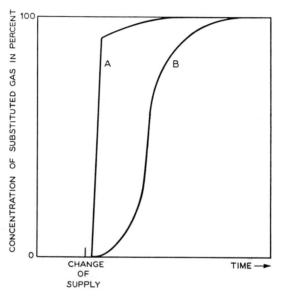

Fɪɢ. VII-22. Representation of the time dependence of gas proportions during change of gases in the (A) Stone and (B) Lodding–Hammell furnaces.

The change will not be completely sharp in the Stone furnace because the gas in the differential manometer will exchange very slowly. The entire furnace chamber volume of the Lodding–Hammell furnace damps the change. The change should be effectively complete in the latter in a small number of minutes.

ment of the specimen was established for each thermogram. The curve obtained in the closed chamber shows a quite sharp dehydration ca. 200°C and a less well-defined oxalate breakdown peaking ca. 460°C. This latter is—for most oxalates when heated separately—an evolution of carbon monoxide to form the appropriate metal carbonate; some, however, lose carbon dioxide to yield the metal unless oxygen is available (see Figs. VIII-6 and XI-15). In either case this a highly irreversible decomposition so a carbon dioxide atmosphere could not be expected to have a substantial effect. In dynamic carbon dioxide, therefore, this peak is rather similar to that obtained in the closed chamber. The slight downward shifting suggests that the temperatures ought to be sensitive to carbon *monoxide* pressure since the major effect here is dilution of the carbon monoxide.

The dehydration peak is shifted to ca. 170°C in dynamic carbon dioxide because the water vapor is swept out rapidly and can achieve only a low vapor pressure. Roughly the same effect is observed in dy-

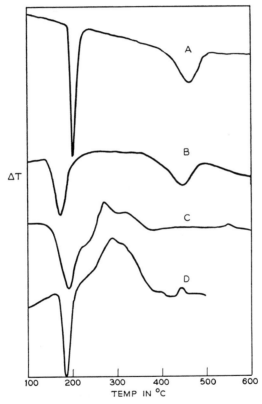

Fig. VII-23. Thermograms of coprecipitated magnesium manganese iron oxalite hydrate in A, closed-chamber sample holder; B, dynamic CO₂; C, dynamic O₂; and D, shallow pan sample holder in air. No attempt was made to obtain equal peak heights in the various runs. Thermogram D was terminated at 500°C because the sample holder was aluminum.

Since materials may show greatly different thermograms under different atmosphere conditions, well-selected atmosphere conditions can be used to derive information about a sample.

namic oxygen but the shift is not so great because the bottled oxygen has a higher water content than the "bone dry" carbon dioxide.

The exothermic peaks (250–350°C) in the dynamic oxygen are–as one might expect–due to the oxidation of the various oxalate species (see Fig. VIII-3).

The presence of oxygen permits oxidation of the carbon monoxide moiety of each species more or less separately. While it is reasonable to assume that a mechanical mixture of the oxalates would show a greater definition of oxidation peaks, the coprecipitated material will have intermediate energy states at boundaries of crystallites or at metal ion substitutions. The later oxidation ca. 550°C is probably manganese going to the +3 state.

In static air the behavior of the material is much as in dynamic oxygen except for the oxidation ca. 450°C. Note that the principal oxidation peaks are not quite the same shape as in dynamic oxygen. This is understandable; in dynamic oxygen the partial pressure of other gases cannot become very high and each particle is surrounded by a continually refreshed atmosphere of oxygen while in static air the oxygen in the vicinity of the specimen becomes depleted not only because of use but because of the formation of the carbon dioxide. Four volumes of carbon dioxide are formed for each volume of oxygen reacting and, since a volume of oxygen diffusing in from an air atmosphere also brings along more than four volumes of nitrogen, it is clearly possible to blanket the specimen and prevent–briefly–an oxidation that would otherwise have occurred during the general oxidation.

We can see from this last curve the possible hazard of a static atmosphere. Such anomalies will be particularly apparent when the specimen reacts with the–or part of the–atmosphere to form another gas. If the product were a solid (oxide, for example) the only effect of reaction with a part of the atmosphere would be dilution as in the case of Crandall and West (C25) (see Fig. VII-18).

The important feature in dynamic atmosphere work is that reactions may be selectively affected. The sweeping through of carbon dioxide during a dehydration has the same effect as nitrogen, argon, or cyclobutane; i.e., the concentration of water vapor is kept extremely low and the dehydration takes place at a lower temperature than in even a static atmosphere. If a subsequent (reversible) decomposition of the sample produces carbon dioxide the peak will be very clearly defined compared to the corresponding peak in other gases. Even for rather similar reactions separations of peaks can be accomplished. The van't Hoff relation describes the manner of change independently for each reaction. If a pair of dehydrations are describable by the two curves of Fig. VII-24 and the intersection occurs very near the ambient partial pressure of water the peaks will not be separable by ordinary techniques but can be by proper atmosphere control.

Consider the case of gypsum, calcium sulfate dihydrate. Fig. VII-25 shows thermograms of the dihydrate and the two hemihydrates. Note that the hemihydrates are already beginning to decompose before the dihydrate is completely gone. This would quite obviously present diffi-culties if one were to attempt to detect or measure a small quantity of

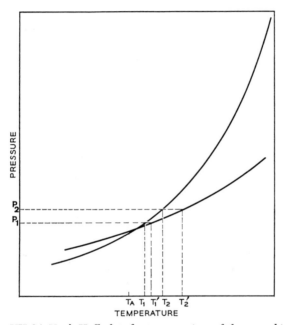

FIG. VII-24. Van't Hoff plots for two reactions of the same kind.

Even though the two reactions may occur together at some particular pressure a change in pressure will separate them on the temperature scale. The separation, $T_i'-T_i$, will vary regularly with pressure.

dihydrate in either hemihydrate unless, of course, one controls the atmosphere properly. Kuntze (K48) showed (Fig. VII-26) that such control was easily achieved for this particular case.

In Fig. VII-26a, even 1% of the dihydrate is barely discernable in a dry atmosphere; this would be true at the slower heating rate, too. The reason is that at the low water vapor pressure the hemihydrate begins to decompose at about the same temperature as the dihydrate in water vapor, however, the hemihydrate decomposition is set back enough (Fig. VII-26b) so that $\frac{1}{10}\%$ dihydrate is readily detected and measured.

7.12. Pressure Effects

The variation of the temperature or even nature of thermal effects with atmosphere has now been demonstrated, along with the concept of variations with pressure (Fig. VII-1, VII-2, and VII-4; see also Fig. V-29). Not only can the use of pressure changes be informative in studying an already known effect but also the use of pressure effects can lead to discovery of, for example, new states of matter (G8).

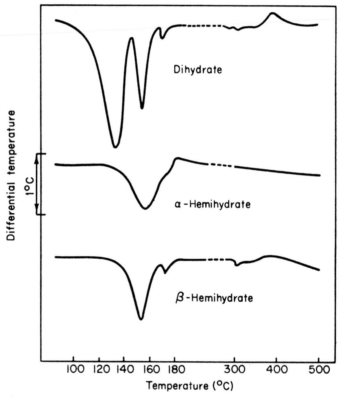

Fig. VII-25. Differential thermograms of synthetic hydrates of calcium sulfate. From Kuntze (K48).

The dihydrate goes to the β-hemihydrate at atmospheric pressure.

The apparently simple dehydration of barium chloride dihydrate becomes rather complex at pressures above atmospheric. At one atmosphere the weight loss occurs in two steps, the first near 100°C so that the water can vaporize immediately and the second well above the boiling point. If we increase the pressure on the system we change the boiling point of water in a well-documented manner (L1a); further, we change the temperatures of the weight losses in a manner depending on the heat of dehydration so we can calculate this quantity if we wish. But of even more interest, we may reach a pressure at which some new crystal structure or composition is stable.

Figure VII-27 shows this author's data at several pressures. The data were obtained using the closed-chamber sample holder of Fig. III-14 in a furnace like that of Fig. VII-21. Supra-atmospheric pressures were

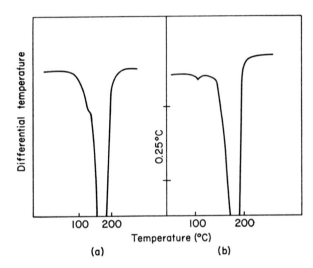

Fig. VII-26. Differential thermograms of hemihydrates containing small amounts of dihydrate. (a) Dry atmosphere, 1% dihydrate, rate of heating 10 cal per min. (b) Atmosphere saturated with water vapor, 0.1% dihydrate rate of heating 6 cal per min. From Kuntze (K48).

The differing heats of dissociation of the hydrates permit separation of peaks by changing the pressure.

obtained by applying a gas pressure to the furnace chamber from a cylinder. The identity of the pressurizing gas is essentially immaterial; whatever is used, the decomposing hydrate must supply an equal pressure before the decomposition can become rapid.

At pressures above one atmosphere the initial loss of water simply leaves a wet sample; the water does not vaporize until a higher temperature, the second peak, is reached. In addition, another thermal effect is indicated by the small peak separating from the second dehydration. At four atmospheres this new effect is well-separated, but at eight atmospheres still another effect appears. Whether or not these two additional effects are both weight losses is not clear at the time of writing. It is probable that many hydrates have several forms with lesser hydration at elevated pressures. Modification of furnace design to permit higher pressures will allow greater latitude in studying these.

Other possible and inadvertent effects of use of pressure must be recognized. Consider a particle of a clay at a temperature in the dehydroxylation range. The water must diffuse out of the particle as part of the total process. If the atmosphere is something other than water, diffusion outward is more rapid if the pressure is low than if it is high since there are less of the other molecules bouncing about at the low pressure.

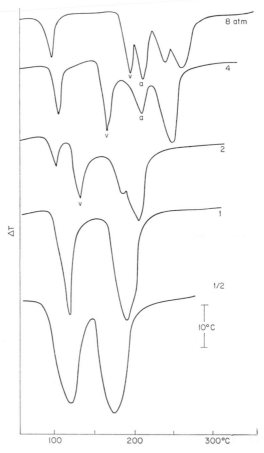

Fig. VII-27. Thermograms of barium chloride dihydrate in self-generated atmospheres at various pressures. From Garn (G8a).

At the higher pressures new phases appear.

Stone's (S58) data on Ca-montmorillonite (Fig. VII-28) show the effect. Even a dynamic atmosphere, keeping the water vapor at the surface near zero, causes a considerable shift of dehydration or dehydroxylation temperatures.

Note that this shift will be seriously time-dependent because the nitrogen and water are continually interchanging. The appearance of the thermogram would be significantly dependent on heating rate. In a water

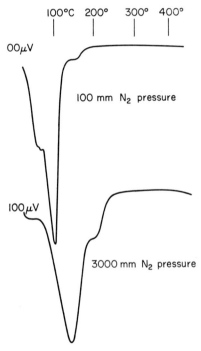

Fig. VII-28. Removal of low-temperature water of a Ca-montmorillonite. From Stone (S58).

At the higher pressure the diffusion outward is repressed so the thermal effects occur at higher temperatures.

atmosphere, whether dynamic or self-generated, the diffusion takes place by reason of a pressure differential created by the decomposition. Any change in appearance of the thermogram would be solely due to the rate of dehydroxylation, not diffusion.

Berg and Rassonskaya (B40) observed pressure effects with the assembly shown in Fig. VII-29. They set a crucible containing the sample into the pressure chamber and also had no provisions for highly inhibited interchange with the pressurizing gas; consequently their data were not so well-defined as can be obtained by the present author's technique.

7.13. Summary

Most of the reported examples of use of dynamic atmospheres are designed to extract specific information rather than to show the benefits thereof. For the present purpose, the offering of an extensive series of comparisons would become tedious. The purpose of this chapter was to

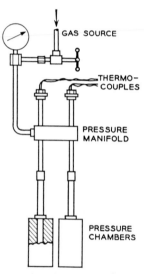

Fig. VII-29. Pressure system for thermal analysis at elevated pressures. From Berg and Rassonskaya (B40).

No matter what the pressurizing gas—unless it reacts with the sample—the atmosphere during a decomposition becomes principally the product gas at the applied pressure.

demonstrate the need for atmosphere control of some sort so that the experimenter could choose the optimum conditions for the particular experiment. Some general examples of applications are given in Chapter XIII.

In brief, the static controlled atmosphere combined with easy interchange of gases provides a control over reversible (and some irreversible) reactions in which the atmosphere is a reactant or product, without effect on other reactions. If another reaction should evolve another gas, there is obfuscation to some degree reaching as a limit the equivalent of no atmosphere control. It is best used for study of specific reactions and by using the gas undiluted.

A dynamic atmosphere provides a control over reactions in which the dynamic gas is a reactant or product similar to the static atmosphere but with a different influence on reactions yielding other gases as products; i.e., these other gases are kept at very low levels of concentration so that the decompositions occur at lower temperatures while those involving the dynamic gas as a product occur at higher temperatures. The technique has the advantages that the type of reaction may be easily identified by changing the identity or pressure of the dynamic gas and that gaseous decomposition products may be easily swept out for identification or determination (see Chapter XIV).

The self-generated atmosphere provides better-defined peaks for decompositions without the need for specific control of atmosphere. It is used as the principal exploratory technique and on those occasions when supplying an atmosphere of the decomposition product gas is impracticable.

CHAPTER VIII

Special Techniques

8.1. Introduction

Differential thermal analysis is by no means a perfected art. The apparatus commonly used in differential thermal analysis has evolved by reason of its applicability to a reasonably wide range of problems. The great utility of the technique, however, leads to its use in cases wherein the usual methods are of marginal or submarginal value. The enterprising observer will thereupon devise a modification more suited to his needs.

The user of differential thermal analysis as a research tool must be willing to evaluate his own particular needs and change his approach accordingly. This will be more successful than just dropping a sample into whatever apparatus is around and hoping the curve will be helpful.

8.2. Small Samples

Over the period of development of differential thermal analysis, the size or weight of sample generally used has naturally decreased. The use of 10 gm or so of sample brings about uncertainty because at moderate heating rates the temperature drop from edge to center will be a score or more degrees. This raises the possiblity of a second reaction already beginning at the edge influencing the flow of heat inward and hence affecting the shape of the observed peak.

There are very understandable investigations of smaller samples. The present author, when there is reason, uses samples down to the tenths of a milligram range instead of the 20–200 mg which generally yield more reliable data. These small samples must be used with caution lest they become an experiment in instrumentation rather than a source of information about the sample.

Thermal analysis of extremely small (1 mg) samples imposes special problems because of the need for concurrent temperature homogeneity between sample and reference and low heat capacity and conductivity of the sample holder. The thermal isolation of the sample is necessary to provide a reasonable lag or lead in temperature to permit detection of the thermal event; this isolation causes unusual difficulties in providing a reference thermocouple at an almost exactly equivalent point. The almost exactly equivalent point is a point which undergoes temperature changes very similar to the sample point under all ordinary heating and cooling cycles. Such a point is required because of the ultimate need or desire for higher amplifications. Presently available techniques and commonly available detecting and recording apparatus are quite easily able to detect the low energies of decompositions or even phase transformations in samples no larger than a few micrograms. The real gains in sensitivity must come from design of the sample environment. Generally, microsamples will be examined by differential calorimetry, i.e., comparatively isolated sample holders, because of the greater sensitivity. This isolation should be modified only so much as may be necessary to (1) reduce drift to reasonable limits and (2) permit separation of close-lying reactions (see Chapter III).

Rogers (R26) uses micro differential thermal analysis for a quite understandable reason. His samples are principally explosives. Since the decomposition is exothermic and atmosphere-independent, the atmosphere accessibility is of no importance. The principal function of his sample holder (Fig. VIII-1) is to provide a compact sample in good thermal contact with the reference material. The reference material

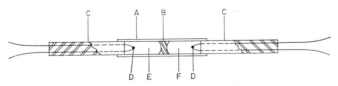

Fig. VIII-1. Differential thermal analysis cell: A, cell body; B, plug; C, thermocouple insulation; D, thermocouples; E, sample compartment; and, F, reference compartment. From Rogers (R26).

Sample and reference are in good thermal contact, leading to low drift.

could probably have been omitted and the thermocouple pushed against
the barrier. Any small base line drift would be trivial compared to the
effects in which he was interested.

The present author's work with small samples (G5) was done with full
cognizance of the importance of atmosphere accessibility and hence took
a route somewhat different from those of other workers. Attempts to provide good temperature agreement while retaining some thermodynamic significance led to development of sample holders which comprise
a means of measuring the temperature of a thin layer of material. There
is obviously no merit in having an extensive area covered by this sample; hence the small area and the thin layer result in a small sample,
0.1 to 2 mg. This free-diffusion technique then becomes necessarily a
microtechnique. The advantages of essentially reproducible and nearly
constant atmosphere conditions are obtained only with rather small
samples in any reasonable size furnace. The advantages of the other extreme in atmosphere accessibility, i.e., the inhibited-diffusion sample
holder, are described in Chapter VII. Design to accommodate smaller
samples was simple.

The free-diffusion sample holders comprise, in general, a thin sheet of
metal to which one or more fine dissimilar wires has been welded.
One form comprises a heavy wire (0.020 inch) platinum vs platinum–
10% rhodium thermocouple to which a 0.005-inch sheet of gold is
welded (Fig. VIII-2). A 0.005-inch platinum–10% rhodium wire is
welded to the bottom of a slight depression in the sheet. The fine wire
must be of the same composition as one of the thermocouple wires so
that the gold may function as the joining member of a differential
thermocouple.

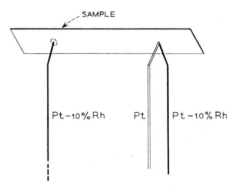

FIG. VIII-2. Micro free-diffusion sample holder. From Garn (G5).
The gold sheet acts as the joining wire of the differential thermocouple. The sam-
ple is placed directly over the junction with the fine wire.

The relatively heavy wire of the thermocouple provides at least a small heat sink so that thermal effects in the sample are not transmitted along the foil sufficiently to affect the temperature signal. The fine wire and thin foil are used to afford as high a degree of thermal isolation as practicable. The need for a thin layer of specimen with a reasonably homogeneous temperature not only permits the use of small samples but also implies that a reference material—to give more or less compensating temperature effects—is not needed.

The sample holder (Fig. VIII-2) is supported on a ceramic tube inside a vertical furnace. The leads are connected to an amplifier and an x-y recorder such that the temperature is measured across the thermocouple leads directly while the potential difference between the two platinum– 10% rhodium wires (ΔT) is amplified before being fed into the recorder.

The thermogram of cobalt oxalate hydrate (Fig. VIII-3) shows good

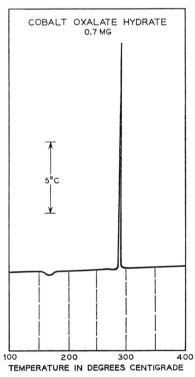

FIG. VIII-3. Thermogram of 0.7 mg cobalt oxalate hydrate. From Garn (G5). *The ease of entry of oxygen permits rapid enough oxidation to cause a 15°C exothermic deflection.*

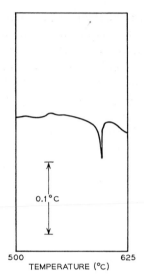

FIG. VIII-4. Thermogram of potassium sulfate (0.1 mg). From Garn (G5).
The local cooling permits ready detection of phase transformations.

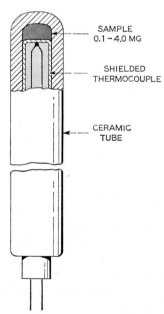

FIG. VIII-5. Inhibited-diffusion sample holder for small samples. From Garn
(G5).

Even with shielded thermocouples very small effects can be detected.

agreement with the weight loss ·curve of Chapter XI. Any remaining error is most likely in the temperature measurement in thermogrametry. Thermograms of phase transitions are not affected by the nature of the sample container. Figure VIII-4 shows the *α-β* transition in a 0.1-mg sample of potassium sulfate.

The inhibited-diffusion sample holder (Fig. VIII-5) comprises, in its simplest form, a glass or ceramic sleeve fitting snugly over a commercial shielded thermocouple, $\frac{1}{16}$ OD. Reaction products which escape freely

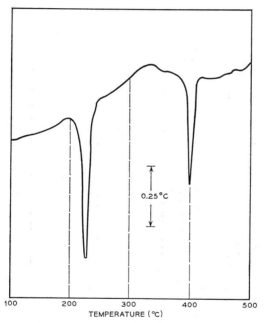

0.25°C

TEMPERATURE (°C)

Fɪɢ. VII-6. Thermogram of 0.3 mg cobalt oxalate hydrate. From Garn (G5).
The inhibited diffusion eliminates exterior atmosphere effect for small samples as well as large. Compare with Figs. VIII-3 and XI-15.

from the free-diffusion sample holder are retained because of the long, narrow escape path. The major portion of the decomposition takes place in one atmosphere of the product gas, and consequently the reactions occur at some higher but more reproducible temperature than with other sample arrangements. Reactions with atmosphere oxygen do not take place.

Figure VIII-6 shows a thermogram of cobalt oxalate hydrate and Fig. VIII-7 shows one of copper sulfate pentahydrate. Even with the small 0.3- and 2.0-mg samples the deflections are well-defined. The base line drifts significantly because of the difficulty of matching but the drift is not enough to inhibit measurement.

The work of Mazières (M21) with specimens in the tens of micrograms range shows both a particular use and a limitation of small samples. The use is in the study of effects of lattice strain or imperfection, in this case induced by irradiation; the limitation is the possibility that a particular sample of the material under investigation might show deviations in behavior of no interest in the particular study. The furnace is shown in Fig. VIII-8.

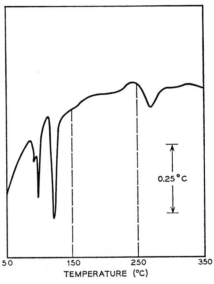

Fig. VIII-7. Thermogram of copper sulfate pentahydrate. From Garn (G5).
The effect of the first dehydration and subsequent vaporization of water ca 100°C can be seen clearly.

The three microsample holders are used in the manner described in Chapter IV, Sec. 4.5. There is, of course, no sample block of the usual type. The heat effect need only be large enough to affect the temperature of the very small cup. This is surrounded by a chamber which is—hopefully—very symmetrically heated. The great sensitivity is shown in Fig. VIII-9, where the droplet of mercury has enough heat of fusion $(2.8 \times 10^{-5}$ cal) to produce a melting endotherm of more than half a degree. (A furnace designed to permit subzero operation was used.)

The study of effects of radiation, strain, etc., might very advantageously be carried out by microtechniques. Figure VIII-10 shows data on irradiated lithium fluoride. Note the variation in curves a, e, f, and g;

the conclusion is clearly that the history of the particle has a very important effect on the thermogram.

A more general conclusion is that, if one obtains thermograms of single particles or small assemblages of particles, the thermal and physical history of the individual particles will show effects superimposed on the thermal effects characteristic of the material. In larger quantities the variations among the individual particles would be diluted and only the characteristics common to all would persist. It follows that if one plans to study the intrinsic properties of a material one must use a specimen in which nonintrinsic properties can be destroyed or at least diluted. The thought of running enough differential thermal analyses for a statistical treatment is appalling.

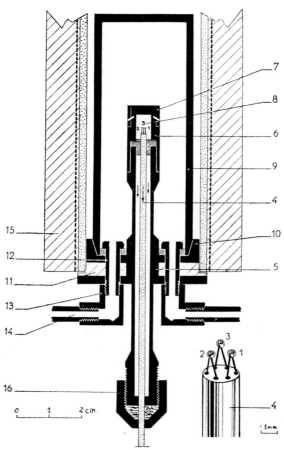

Fig. VIII-8. Furnace and sample holder for differential thermal analysis of very small samples. From Mazières (M21).

Samples down to a few micrograms can show very easily detectable thermal effects.

In summary, very small samples can be used effectively if used intelligently. Atmosphere control is just as important as with larger samples and must be used with more care. The characteristics peculiar to a given particle may have sufficient effect on the thermogram to lead the user to ascribe these characteristics to the whole sample (see also Chapter XI, Sec. 11.1).

8.3. Pelleted Samples

Walton (W3) attempted to obtain better sensitivity (Fig. VIII-11) by pressing the specimens into pellets and supporting these pellets on the

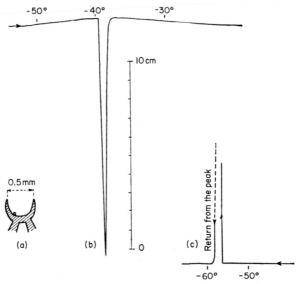

Fɪɢ. VIII-9. Thermogram of a droplet of mercury, showing heating and cooling peaks. From Mazières (M21).

The melting of 10 μg Hg gives a signal of ca. 0.8°C.

thermocouple insulators but otherwise isolated from the furnace wall. He compared these pellets with similar ones heated in a block and reported "a much greater sensitivity . . . in the low-temperature range than with . . . the Inconel block." This means that in the dehydration of kaolin a greater pen deflection was obtained with the isolated sample than with an identical pellet in the block. This is no guarantee that the curve is more useful.

The inflection (curve C, Fig. VIII-12) for the isolated sample is about 20% greater in peak height than for the pellet in the block (curve B); unfortunately, it is also about 60% broader. This means that any other reaction overlapping this nearly 200°C interval will interfere and be interfered with. Sensitivity, however, must be judged on the ability of the technique under examination to detect a material in small quantities, to detect it as a separate entity in a mixture, or to separate reactions within a single material. Obtaining a greater deflection is not in itself a suitable goal. The curves offered by Walton would lead the present author to choose the block technique. The reasons for the appearance

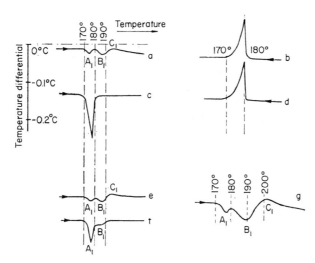

Fɪɢ. VIII-10. Thermograms of irradiated fragments of lithium fluoride: a, first heating, b, first cooling, c, second heating, and d, second cooling of a single fragment; e, part of another fragment; f, the other part of this fragment after preheating at < 160°C; and g, rapid (30°C/minute) heating of another fragment of the same crystal. From Mazières M21).

On very small samples, localized effects can appear to have significant influence in the characteristics of the material.

of the thermograms of the isolated samples are discussed in Chapter VII. The broad low-temperature deflection in curve C is probably due to differences in heat transfer. The emissivity of the calcined reference can be expected to be higher than that of the sample (see Chapter III).

Pellet techniques can be useful, however; they, like other techniques, must be used with discretion—selecting the best method to obtain the most instructive data. Newkirk (N7), for example, uses a pellet technique for phase equilibria studies. Since no decompositions are involved, the exposed surface is not in itself advantageous; the advantage lies in the elimination of any sample holder at all. The work reported is in the 1300–1500°C range so heat transfer occurs principally by radiation. A sample holder serves no function except—when necessary—to hold the sample.

Newkirk presses his samples in a mold and sinters them at a temperature ca. 50°C below the first liquidus formation. A hole is drilled in the specimen, it is slid over the thermocouple wires, and the thermocouple

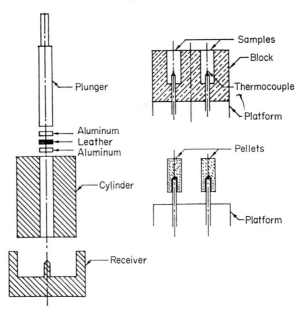

Fig. VIII-11. Cross sectional diagram of equipment for pressing and mounting pellets. From Walton (W3).

The pellets are supported by the thermocouples and are exposed directly to the wall of the furnace.

wires are joined in a rather large bead (0.025-inch wire, 0.070-inch bead). The bead then supports the sample (Fig. IV-11). Another simplification is possible here, the elimination of a reference body. To the thermocouple, the sample appears at a shield, shading it in part from direct radiation from the furnace wall, i.e., intercepting much of the radiation and reradiating at a lower temperature. This condition can be easily simulated by drawing the reference couple up so that it is partially recessed in the protection tube. Quite satisfactory curves (Fig. VIII-13) were obtained.

8.4. Fluidized-Bed Differential Thermal Analysis

A case in which improper use of a new approach vitiated the results was the fluidized-bed differential thermal analysis reported by Basden (B14, B15). His arrangement, shown in Fig. VIII-14, provides for fluidizing both the external heat-transfer medium and the pair of specimens.

A fluidized bed is an arrangement in which a bed of particles levitate by reason of an upward gas stream through the bed. Figure VIII-15 shows the nature of the velocity-of-flow effect of the gas stream. At low flows, the gas must penetrate the bed by diffusing through the tedious paths between the particles; as the flow is increased, the pressure drop across the bed increases. At some point dependent on the nature (particle size, density, etc.) of the bed the upward push exceeds the downward pull of gravity and the particles will be lifted. Lifting of the

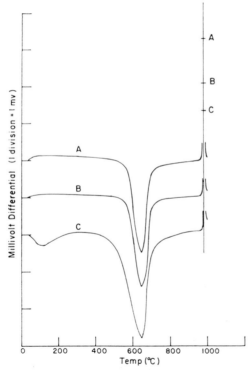

Fig. VIII-12. Differential thermal analyses of kaolin: A, Hand-packed specimen heated in Inconel block; B, pressed, dried sample heated in Inconel block; and C, pressed, dried sample heated in air. From Walton (W3).

The exposed pellet technique shows a greater deflection (C) but its broadness shows an even greater increase; this leads to a greater possibility of overlapping reactions.

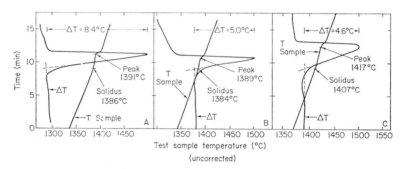

FIG. VIII-13. Typical differential thermal analysis curves obtained by pellet method for some compositions in the system CaO–2CaO•Fe$_2$O$_3$–12CaO•7Al$_2$O$_3$. From Newkirk (N7).

The absence of any sort of heat sink permits a quite large ΔT signal.

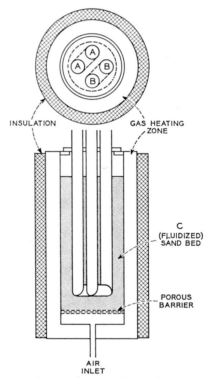

FIG. VIII-14. Fluidized-bed differential thermal analysis apparatus. From Basden (B14).

Fluidized-bed heat transfer is used not only for the gross heating of sample and reference but also to achieve thermal homogeneity within each of the two specimens.

particles expands the openings so the pressure gradient across the bed drops rather sharply. This would tend to permit the particles to drop back into a bed except that the consequent formation of narrow paths would increase the (local) upward force and the particles would again levitate. The result is a rapid, more-or-less turbulent movement of the particles both vertically and laterally. This rapid movement and the consequent frequent collisions provide rapid transfer of heat and hence very good temperature homogeneity within the bed.

If Basden had fluidized either the heat-transfer bed or the pair of specimens, some advantage should accrue for reasons explained below; fluidizing both gave the plots shown in Fig. VIII-16 and in which the

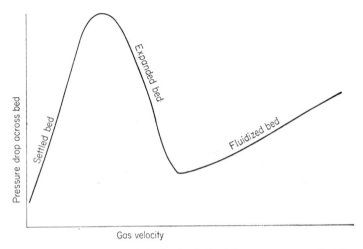

Fig. VIII-15. Fluidization of finely-divided solids. From Zenz and Othmer (Z1).
When the gas velocity becomes high enough, the particles lift with little motion, allowing a decrease in the pressure drop. Continued increase in gas velocity lifts the particles so that they are individually supported and free to move.

principal distinguishing features are (besides the peaks due to introduction of steam) the sudden shifts (ca. 40°C) due to agglomeration of the Liddell and Greta specimens. The general trend of oxidation shown in the bottom set of curves illustrates the over-all problem.

The benefits of fluidized-bed systems are derived from the rapid motion, but this rapid motion brings about the loss of identity of any single particle and hence the inability to measure the properties (especially the temperature) of any except the whole group. Consider a relatively cool fluidized bed in contact with a suddenly heated wall. While the mass of the bed is still cool, the particles impinging on the wall are heated to a temperature far greater than their counterparts away from the wall. The hot particles circulate into the cooler regions, losing heat to the cooler particles they encounter but leaving many particles pro tempore untouched and still cool. The apparent temperature of the bed rises nonetheless because any measuring device we would care to use treats the particles on a statistical basis. We have, then, in such a system a distribution of particle temperatures over a range from the initial

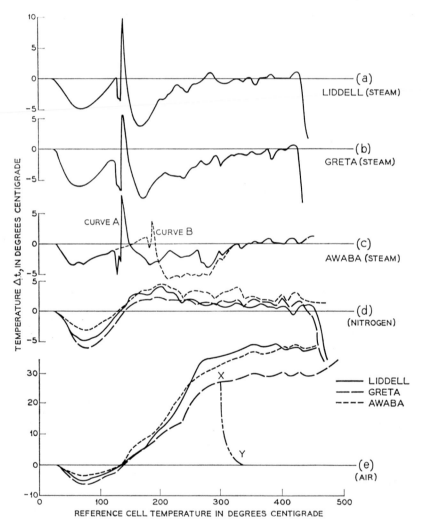

Fig. VIII-16. Differential thermal analysis of coals by the fluidized-bed technique. From Basden (B15).

Other than the effect of steam injection the only sharply defined feature is the agglomeration of two of the coals.

(for a short time) temperature to something approaching the wall temperature.

Now examine the technique used by Basden. The sample and reference cells are set into a hot fluidized bed thus reproducing the conditions just described. Some of the coal particles are heated substantially above the measured temperature; others are not. When—in the presence of oxygen—the particle can oxidize, it will oxidize, contributing to an exothermal indication at a relatively low temperature. The general exothermic trend in Fig. VIII-16 is due, then, to a steady increase in the rate at which the particles reach the reaction temperature. A number of reasons can be advanced for the leveling off. One of these is the combination of the decrease in unreacted particles and the increase in ease of reaction. (Since the particle is already approaching temperature, the likelihood of a collision raising it to the reaction temperature is increasing.) Another condition contributing to the trend is the probability of successive reactions. In fluidized-bed specimens, these will necessarily be smeared together for the reasons given above. Still another factor contributing to the poor resolution in Basden's studies is the probable interruption of exothermic reactions by cooling. Recall that in a non-fluidized bed of particles heated from a wall a temperature gradient from the wall inward (Chapter II) will be set up. For endothermic changes, a reaction front moves from the wall inward as the temperature of reaction is reached and passed. An exothermic reaction, on the other hand, can supply not only heat to continue its own temperature rise but also heat to warm the neighboring—inward—particles so that they, too, reach the reaction temperature. The process (unless a second phase such as oxygen is needed but is in short supply) is self-sustaining and is consequently rapid. Now contrast this to Basden's fluidized-bed thermal analysis.

Assume only that each particle will react chemically with oxygen (other than by ordinary combustion) as long as the particle is at or exceeds some temperature T_r and as long as the particle is not completely reacted. Let a fluidized bed of these particles be exposed to a suddenly heated ($<T_r$) wall. The first multitudes of collisions will probably not raise a significant portion of the entire specimen to T_r but eventually this must happen. As previously described, the hot particle—in the normal course of circulation—will collide with many cooler particles and give up heat to them, warming them—but to temperatures less than T_r. The net effect is a partially reacted particle and a number of particles warmer than they would have been in the ordinary course of heating; the over-all effect is an exothermal trend. As the general temperature level is raised, the partial oxidations will occur more and more fre-

quently, and the general effect shown to the observer—by the recording equipment—will be an increasing exothermic effect while the measured temperature is still below T_r. The increase must stop eventually because of the formation of completely reacted particles, but since these are ready for further oxidation in this stepwise process the shape of the curve would be difficult to predict. The curves given by Basden are, at least, not in contradiction to this discussion.

The fluidized-bed technique for maintaining a nearly uniform temperature in the specimen, we may conclude, will lead to uninterpretable results if a wide range of particle temperatures is permitted. It would be necessary to control the rate of rise of the wall temperature. The use of fluidized beds for both specimens and heat transfer in differential thermal analysis is subject to uncertainty because the huge (apparent) thermal conductivities leave little to measure. Use of a fluidized bed for heat transfer to an orthodox specimen could be quite useful because of the temperature homogeneity.

Fluidized-bed specimens may lead to some interesting results. Eriksson (E5), for example, showed that the peak area was proportional to the heats of reaction if the reaction were occurring at the same rate throughout the specimen. Borchardt and Daniels (B67) derived expressions for determining the kinetics of reactions assuming temperature homogeneity; they necessarily confined their use to stirred liquids. Fluidized beds may permit better use of Eriksson's work and a *valid* extension of Borchardt and Daniels' work to reactions of solids. The experiment would best be done in rather isolated specimen holders.

8.5. Furnaces Providing Visual Observation of Specimens

There is occasionally a need—and frequently a desire—to keep the specimen under visual observation during the heating cycle. There is no question that the observation may be useful. Hogan and Gordon (H20) attacked the problem by heating their test tube specimen holders from below with a laboratory electric "burner" (Fig. VIII-17). They pointed out that thermomicroscopy was not well-adapted for measuring thermal effects because of the space needed for the sample and measuring elements. Programming and recording were both inhibited greatly by heat-transfer problems after the appearance of a liquid phase (Fig. VIII-18); part of their difficulty in programming was due to the relatively small heat reservoir and part to the location of the control point for their controller. A control point should not be located at any point where it might be affected by short-term variations in the specimen, i.e., heat effect, unless one is deliberately permitting the disturbance (see Chapter IV). A better approach ought to be the use of an ordinary quartz tube furnace with some apertures in the winding to permit the visual observation.

The most important consideration is the avoidance of any direct path for loss of heat, i.e., there must be a heated surface or a space containing heated gas between the specimen and the observer. This is because the observer does not see the part of the specimen the thermocouple "sees"

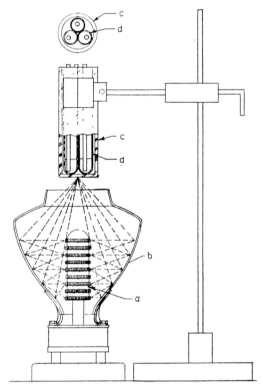

Fig. VIII-17. Schematic diagram of electric Bunsen burner and sample tubes: a, Heating element; b, aluminum reflector; c, quartz tube; d, borosilicate glass sample tubes. From Hogan and Gordon (H20).
The sample can be observed from the side as well as the top.

and hence is looking at a part of the specimen which is almost certainly at a measurably different—and likely at a severely different—temperature from that indicated by the recording system. In Hogan and Gordon's apparatus the temperature of the observed material is no doubt hotter than that near the thermocouple; on the other hand, if a sample block is heated directly and one attempts to look at the surface of a specimen, the observed point is no doubt cooler than the indicated temperature. A transparent dome above a directly heated block will require deep immersion of the specimen so that observation would be impractical. The high convection currents would cause the outer portion of the block to lag too greatly behind the inner regions. A filled sample cavity would experience a considerable gradient at elevated temperatures.

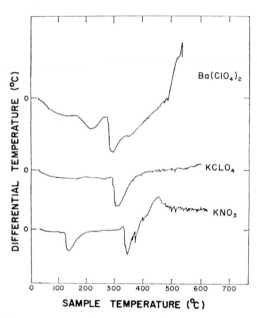

Fig. VIII-18. Representative DTA curves obtained by using electric Bunsen burner. From Hogan and Gordon (H20).

The exothermic displacement of the signal after appearance of the liquid phase is due to the greater transparency of the liquid to the radiated heat. The "noise" may be due to sample movement resulting from bubbling.

The disparity in the case of the block will increase with temperature for the quite obvious reason that loss or gain of heat by radiation becomes more important. If the block is heated from an exterior wall by radiation and/or convection, the problem will be serious only if a large portion of the exposed spherical angle projects toward cool surfaces.

8.6. Change of Atmosphere

Differential thermal analysis need not be done only by changing the temperature regularly. Thermal effects are in some cases detectable upon changing the total pressure or the partial pressure of a gas. Stone (S58, S59) uses both techniques. In studying catalysts he raises the temperature in an inert atmosphere then injects the desired atmosphere and observes the transient change in temperature resulting from the absorption or, more particularly, the chemisorption of this gas on the active catalyst. The heat generated is taken as a measure of catalytic activity.

Crandall and West (C25) used a rather similar technique in studying the oxidation of cobalt. The sample was brought to the selected temperature in flowing nitrogen and a flow of air substituted for the nitrogen. Oxidation of the cobalt is observed as an exothermic reaction. The reaction was not instantaneous; measurements continued for ca. 30 minutes. The reasons for the slowness of reaction are discussed in Chapter VIII.

Stone (S58) also diminished the pressure as a function of time to determine the moisture content of samples. Within a porous somewhat moist specimen an equilibrium will be set up between the moisture on the particles and in the air in the interstices. This condition can persist because the exchange of air between the sample and its surroundings is slow. Now let us decrease the pressure at a steady rate. The adsorbed water will tend to evaporate to maintain the partial pressure corresponding to the vapor pressure at the room temperature, but eventually the total pressure will be diminished below the vapor pressure (see Chapter VII) and evaporation will be accelerated, giving a measurable thermal effect. Stone provides the example shown in Fig. VIII-19. The evaporation will cool the sample, tending toward a steady state in which the new temperature will correspond to a water vapor pressure equal to the instantaneous total pressure. Since the total pressure is decreasing constantly, the evaporation cannot cool the sample to a steady state, but the over-all effect of the accelerated evaporation is a rather sharp thermal effect which can be related to the total moisture.

Stone uses the peak height as a measure of the moisture content. Essentially the peak height—rather than the area—would be a measure of the mass of water available for evaporation at the time the vapor is suddenly pulled away. At room temperature heat transfer will not be very rapid so that the peak height should depend directly on the amount of water (hence indirectly on the total amount of water) and inversely on the heat capacity, with only one condition: the evaporation must be rapid; the entire peak should be obtained in a few seconds. If, because of surface conditions, the evaporation becomes slow, some more elaborate calibrations may be needed.

8.7. Pyrosynthesis

Dunne and Kerr (D17) measured thermal effects during pyrosynthesis by differential thermal analysis while investigating a series of solid solutions of lead sulfide (galena) and lead selenide (clausthalite) using the technique previously reported by Bollin *et al.* (B62). They sealed the weighed constituents into a Pyrex tube having a thermocouple recess (Fig. VIII-20). A similar tube was used as reference. The reaction temperature increased as the sulfur was increased (Fig. VIII-21 and VIII-22). Differential thermal analysis curves (in air) of the synthesized materials are interpreted by the authors as evidence for a con-

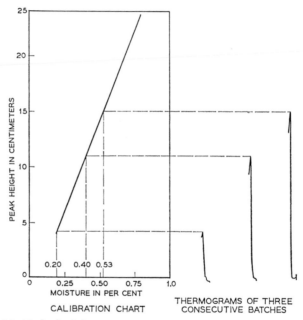

Fig. VIII-19. Method of determining moisture content of dry powders by evacuation. Sample, undiluted; thermogram, room temperature; instrument range, 20 μv. From Stone (S58).

The sudden vaporization as the furnace pressure is brought below the vapor pressure of water provides a measure of the amount of water.

tinuous series of solid solutions, even though some of these curves show two distinct oxidation peaks (D17). These two minerals have nearly the same lattice parameters so one might readily suspect a complete series of solid solutions. The present author is not ready to dispute the conclusion but he is ready to point out that the thermal data offered are not adequate proof. An alternative interpretation of Figs. VIII-21 and VIII-22 can be supplied.

Consider the curves shown in Fig. VIII-21. They are characterized by a huge exothermic peak due to reaction of lead with sulfur, selenium, or both. Selenium reacts ca. 160°C and sulfur ca. 210°C, 50°C difference. The exotherms go off scale in each case indicating—from examination of the description of Bollin *et al.* (B62)—a temperature difference substantially greater than 12°C. This large difference is indicated on a thermocouple separated from the reacting specimen by a layer of Pyrex so it is easily conceivable that the temperature within the sample reached 210°C and initiated the lead-sulfur reaction. Since this is exo-

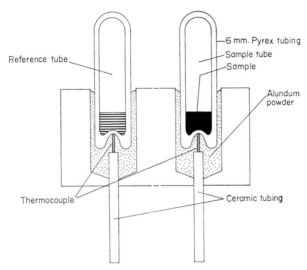

Fig. VIII-20. Sealed-tube specimen holders for relatively low-temperature thermal analysis. From Bollin *et al.* (B62).
The recess in the tube ensures that a large spherical angle around the thermocouple is directed toward the sample.

thermic there would be no recognizable indication with the experimental method used. (The present author has found sudden temperature increases of more than 100°C in some reactions.) The variation of initiation temperature with quantity of the lower temperature–reacting species is almost certainly no more than a concentration effect. The sharp increase of initiation temperature at the high-sulfur end is a consequence of the lack of enough selenium to raise the temperature locally to the lead-sulfur reaction temperature.

In this sort of experiment it is essential that the *sample* temperature be recorded rather than the furnace or reference temperature (see Chapter IV).

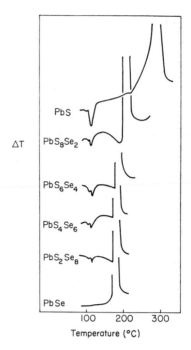

ΔT

100   200   300

Temperature (°C)

Fɪɢ. VIII-21. Differential thermal pyrosynthesis (DTP) curves. The samples comprise a 20 mole % synthetic PbS-PbSe series. From Dunne and Kerr (D17). *Endothermic deflections are to the right.*

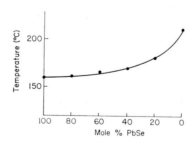

Fɪɢ. VIII-22. Pyrosynthesis reaction (formation) temperature vs molar composition. The samples listed are those whose DTP curves are given in Fig. VIII-21. From Dunne and Kerr (D17).

The reaction temperature is increased only slightly until the sulfur content is very high.

8.8. Differential Calorimetry

In Chapter I differential calorimetry and differential thermal analysis were compared on the basis of sensitivity and the reasons and precautions set forth. We are now in a position to examine a particular type of differential calorimetry, i.e., that in which the temperatures of the sample and reference containers provide the differential signal.

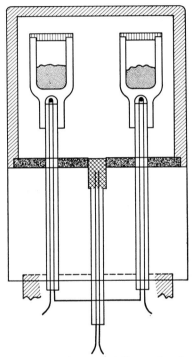

Fɪɢ. VIII-23. Sample holder for dynamic differential calorimetry. From Schweite and Ziegler (S15).
For isolated reactions, heat changes can be measured with good precision.

Schweite and Ziegler (S15) used sample holders of the type shown in Fig. VIII-23 to obtain quantitative data on some decompositions. Note that these differ from Boersma (B58) sample holders in that Boersma measured the temperature in the major heat-transfer path while Schweite and Ziegler provided no special heat path but simply compared the temperatures of the bottom portions of the holders. The temperature distribution within the specimen is of no concern since the measurement is made over the entire thermal effect. Reproducible data on isolated heat effects can be and have been obtained in this manner.

The measurement of temperature of the sample holder yields a thermo-gram with a smoothed-over indication of the thermal event, the actual heat absorption or evolution having to cause a change in temperature of the sample holder as well as that of the sample itself. Further, the tem-perature of the sample itself is not known particularly well, the possible error being very greatly dependent on the sample holder size and de-sign.

Note that a relatively large specimen will have a major influence on the measured temperature with a reasonably thin sample container but the temperature gradients within the sample are also large and the cen-ter of the sample may be at a temperature quite different from that measured. Similarly, if the sample is small in relation to the holder the temperature effect becomes dependent on possible variations in heat transfer to the specimens; even though these variations are relatively

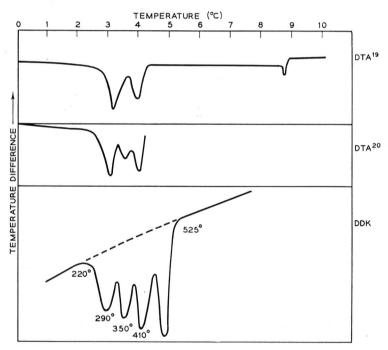

Fig. VIII-24. Dynamic differential calorimetry and differential thermal analysis of lead carbonate. From Schweite and Ziegler (S15).

The temperature gradient in the sample and the lack of heat transfer between sample and reference inhibit approach of the signal to any base line between peaks because (1) both reactions are occurring at the same time in different parts of sample and (2) the "decay" time of the temperature difference is too great.

minor in a large sample because of averaging, a change in the heat transfer for any reason would cause a more serious change in temperature lag than in a large sample. Figure VIII-24 shows Schwiete and Ziegler's thermogram of lead carbonate. The additional peak is not explained.

The present author uses specimen holders rather similar to those of Schwiete and Ziegler (Fig. IV-15), but only when the information sought calls for that particular technique.

8.9. Heats of Explosion

The violently exothermic reaction of an explosion provides an essentially instantaneous quantity of heat which—even with special apparatus —would be impracticable to measure continuously. The customary method of determining heats of explosion is by calorimetry, but since this normally requires a substantial sample there is a need for a method better adaptable to small samples. Bohon (B60) used a form of differential calorimetry, the apparatus for which is described in Chapter IV. In essence, Bohon measures the decay curve as the sample cell returns to the furnace temperature to calibrate the apparatus. The heat generated during the explosion is then calculated from the area under the peak in the conventional manner (see also Vold V10).

Providing that the heat is generated over a brief interval of time as in Fig. VIII-25 and assuming near constancy of heat capacity, emissivity,

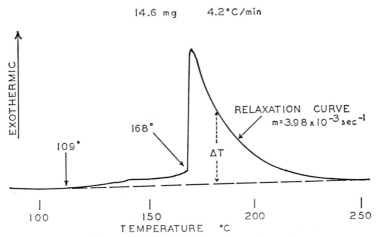

Fig. VIII-25. Thermogram of JPN propellant. From Bohon (B60).

The change in temperature with time after the explosion is used to measure the heat of explosion. JPN is a homogeneous solid propellant comprising principally nitroglycerin and nitrocellulose.

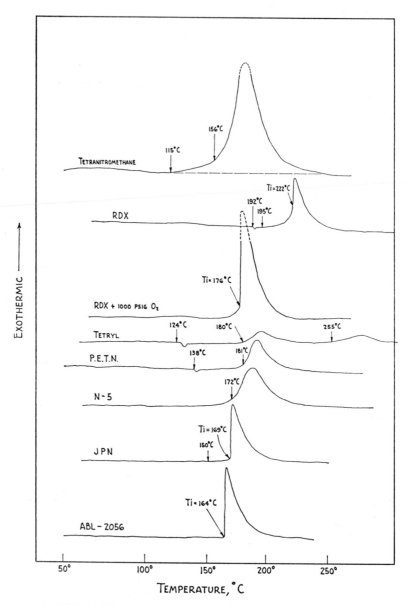

Fɪɢ. VIII-26. Thermograms of some explosives. From Bohon (B60).
The reaction in some cases is very rapid, indicated by a steep rise from the base line.

and such, the return follows the decay law,

$$\frac{d\Delta T}{dt} = -m\Delta T.$$

Experimentally the return to the base line follows the decay law only approximately so actual measurement of the area under curve is more suitable. The area measurement would have to be used in those cases (Fig. VIII-26) where the reaction was slower.

8.10. Freezing Range Measurements in Clays

The melting point of a pure bulk material can be reasonably expected to be reproducible; when the material is deformed its melting behavior may change very appreciably. From a thermodynamic point of view a layer of water absorbed on a clay is deformed relative to bulk water. It follows that determination of the temperature range through which the water on a wet clay melts might be related to the amount of water actually absorbed. Rosenthal (R31) used the arrangement shown in Fig. VIII-27 to measure "freezing ranges" of clay-water mixtures, relating data such as those of Fig. VIII-28 to the plasticity of the clay, a high

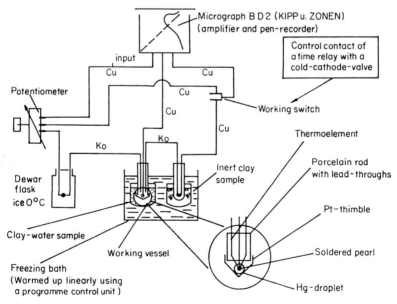

Fɪɢ. VIII-27. An apparatus for the freezing analysis of clay-water systems. From Rosenthal (R31).

Any supercooling effects are eliminated by cooling at least to −55°C.

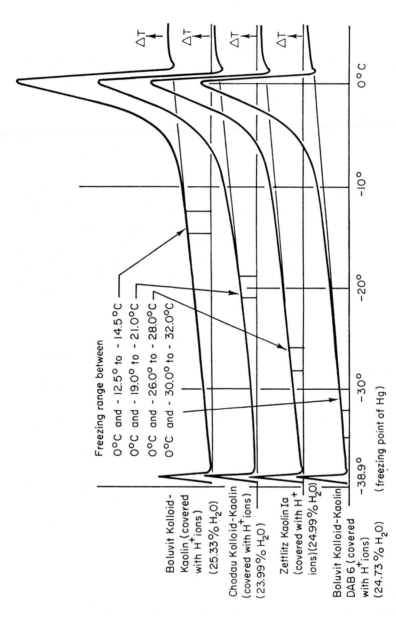

Fig. VIII-28. Freezing curves of kaolin. From Rosenthal (R31).
The lower the temperature of the "freezing range" the greater the plasticity.

degree of water adsorption—indicated by a wide freezing range—corresponding to a high plasticity.

8.11. Derivative and Differential Techniques

In differential thermal analysis we have already departed from use of the primary signal, i.e., the temperature of the sample. We have done so in order to gain sensitivity in detecting changes. An important question is whether or not there is any advantage in continuing further. The procedures can (prima facie) be very simple and for crystallographic phase changes the interpretation should in fact be simple. Let us first consider the differential techniques and subsequently the derivative.

Double differential thermal analysis is a technique in which a reactive specimen is compared with a reactive reference. The present author has attempted—on a few occasions—to detect shifts in reaction temperature of superficially identical specimens by treating one as sample and the other as reference. This is done in the hope that equal reactions at identical temperatures will cancel each other's thermoelectric effect and supply a straight-line plot. Another method of use is to attempt to subtract the thermal effect of one (or more) materials so as to permit better observation and measurement of the thermal effect of another component. One example of the author's use of this technique was an attempt to measure the Curie point shift in isotopes of nickel (S9). Samples of Ni^{60} and Ni^{62} were compared with Ni^{58}. Readable variations were obtained although no conclusion could be reached because impurities, especially copper, could have affected the Curie point to a greater degree than the additional mass.

A prospective user of the method must necessarily demonstrate that his sample containers are heated very uniformly. If either leads the other in temperature, its contents will begin to react first and show a portion of the thermal effect. This will soon be cancelled or diminished by the thermal effect in the other container. Since the reaction in the first container is concluded while reactive material is still present in the other, the total thermal effect will finish with a more or less symmetric (to the first) deflection.

The major proponent of the technique is McLaughlin (M29). His optimism is not entirely justified but with proper care the technique should be of use in special problems. McLaughlin's illite: kaolinite mixtures are, in general, attempts to observe and measure illite in the presence of kaolinite. He concedes that "the quantitative analysis of kaolinite and illite mixtures are . . . fraught with difficulties. . . ." One of these difficulties was his inability to subtract out the kaolinite reactions by placing an equal amount (diluted with alumina) in the "reference" cavity. One source must—in this case—be unsymmetric heating.

McLaughlin also points out the effect of wet and dry mixing on the high-temperature reactions: ". . . in wet mixes the exothermic peak (ca. 950°C) due to kaolinite is considerably lower in temperature . . ." and "a tendency also for the 850°C endothermic reactions due to illite to sharpen. . . ." Although McLaughlin specifies only "mechanical mixing" a reasonable assumption is that a ball mill was used. Ball milling for extended periods has been shown to be deleterious to differential thermal analysis peaks (M28). Shaking in water may in time cause as many fractures of crystals but water is immediately available for adsorption on any active regions as well as to prevent local heating.

Let us now compare the effects of the grinding with the wet mixing. The additional surface energy gained during the dry grinding lowers and broadens the differential thermal analysis endotherm because it produces surface regions with a wide range of energies. The first reactions must consequently be rather diffuse in the dry mix compared to a thoroughly hydrated wet mix. But this only applies to the first reaction in which a recrystallization takes place. From this point on the reactivity will depend on the other attributes of the mixing methods, i.e., differences in particle size, crystallinity, and intimacy of mixing. The "sharpening" of the 850°C illite endotherm is probably the result of comparing a fully hydrated with an incompletely hydrated system. The lowering of the kaolinite exotherm is attributed by McLaughlin to catalysis by the breakdown products of the illite, but Stone and Rowland (S60) and the present author (G9) have found that decomposition of kaolinite in water vapor tends to lower the temperature of and broaden the exotherm (Fig. VIII-29).

In the use of this technique, the experimenter must satisfy himself that symmetry of heating exists. A reasonable test is the use of identical specimens in each cup in a separate run. These specimens must have (in ordinary differential thermal analysis) an endotherm or exotherm with at least as great a slope and maximum deflection as the specimens under investigation. A double differential thermal analysis of these specimens will establish limits of significance for the sample of interest; that is, a deflection must be greater than the maximum deflection in the test run before any confidence may be placed in its reality. The same criterion must be established for the subtraction of thermal effects.

Almost inevitably, any worker determined to perform double differential thermal analysis must sacrifice uniformity of heating of the individual specimens, i.e., cylindrical chambers, in favor of symmetric heating of the two specimens. For this purpose, some type of gradient heating arrangement may be best. An example, conceived but not tested by the author, would comprise a three-leaved bar with cubic sample cavities cut into the center leaf. The loaded sample holder would be inserted partly into a vertical furnace and allowed to heat from the top down. The atmosphere effect would be essentially that of a closed chamber.

A technique using two identical samples but having asymmetry of heating *and* of thermocouples was proposed by Freeman and Edelman (F15). Two 18-mm-diameter test tubes were set in an eccentrically located Nichrome block; the test tube nearer to the wall had a thermocouple junction 5 mm from the bottom of the tube while the junction in

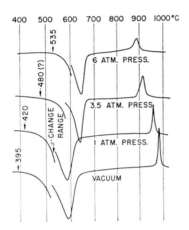

Fig. VIII-29. Thermograms of kaolinite under different pressures. From Stone and Rowland (S60).

The fact that the water vapor pressure must reach different levels in the several runs leads to a change in environment during dehydroxylation sufficient to affect the exothermic reaction substantially.

the other tube was 8 mm from the bottom. The sample nearer the furnace is somewhat warmer as the furnace heats up and consequently reaches the temperature of any thermal event more quickly. In the case of a phase transition, such as in Fig. VIII-30, the temperature differential drops toward zero as the transition front moves inward. (Note that this is an experimental ΔT rather than $d\Delta T/dt$; the scale shown by Freeman and Edelman is calculated.) It drops very near to zero because the ordinary heating of the "reference" brings its temperature at the thermocouple close to the transition temperature as the material near the "sample" thermocouple undergoes transition. The assymmetry of the latter portion of the upper plot is due to the geometric asymmetry. Both samples are returning toward steady-state heating but are not at identical points (in time) of the return nor is the temperature differential taken between corresponding points.

The appearance of such a plot will be sensitive to spacing and to heating rate. This could be alleviated somewhat by putting the differential thermocouple in a single sample (see Fig. IV-15b).

The general purpose derivative techniques suggested by Campbell *et al.* (C4) use electromechanical amplification to obtain a signal large enough to differentiate and record without further electronic amplification. The slidewire shaft of the recorder measuring the primary function

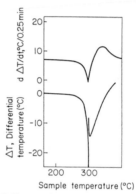

Fig. VIII-30. Derivative differential (upper) and differential (lower) thermal analyses of potassium perchlorate. From Freeman and Edelman (F15).

The upper curve measures the differential temperature between eccentrically located samples. Symmetry cannot be expected.

(Δt, Δw, etc.) is fitted with a "retransmitting" slidewire. Movement of this slidewire as the recorder pen moves changes the voltage (Fig. VIII-31) read off the slidewire at the contact. This voltage is supplied to a differentiating capacitor; since direct current cannot flow through a capacitor the charge on the capacitor will follow the position of the slidewire. If this charge should change due to movement of the slidewire, a current must flow through the resistor on the right-hand side to charge—or discharge—the differentiating capacitor to the new level. This flow of current creates a potential drop which can be measured by the second recorder (see Chapter XV).

Generally, in constructing such a circuit one would choose capacitors and resistors so that the time constant, RC, was less than the pen speed (time required for full-scale travel) of the recorder and the resistance was not greater than the input impedance of the recorder. Too large a time constant will mean that the recorder can follow a charging current and produce a record showing a false rounding or slow approach to a steady value, much like an overdamped balance or galvanometer. Too large a resistance will result in loss of sensitivity. Campbell *et al.* were faced with an additional problem, a "noisy" recorder. Their solution was a smoothing capacitor across the recorder input. Since this capacitor has to be charged and discharged, it becomes the major contributor to the time constants of 4 seconds for the upper and 40 seconds for the lower circuit. They offer the curves shown in Fig. VIII-32.

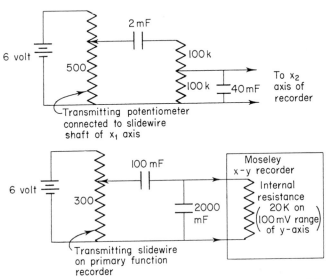

Fig. VIII-31. Circuit diagram for R-C differentiation. Top: R-C differentiating circuit for use with potentiometric recorders. Bottom: R-C differentiating circuit for use with Moseley x-y recorder. From Campbell (C4).

The movement of the recorder pen shaft changes the voltage on the differentiating capacitor causing a current to flow during and shortly after the movement. The heavy filtering by the 40- and 2000-mfd capacitors is required to avoid signals due to the "jitter" of the recorder shaft on which the transmitting slidewire is mounted.

Their major error was in their choice of the signal to differentiate. The jitter that is common on a number of kinds of recorders does not—or should not—affect the input signal appreciably. This input signal can be differentiated by a similar circuit (Fig. XVI-9) and amplified electronically if necessary to produce a rapidly responding system. The same type of circuit may be inserted between amplifier and recorder. The present author has done this merely as an exercise and obtained good, readable curves (Fig. VIII-33). Since the present author has not yet seen any real gain in the use of a derivative signal in differential thermal analysis, the resistor and capacitor were soon put back in the electrical-parts drawer. (Thermogravimetry is quite another question; see Chapter X.)

8.12. Sealed Tube Sample Holders

A frequently occurring problem involves samples which decompose before melting or at least before the thermal effect of interest. If the product gas is easily handled and if the equilibrium pressure is not very high, ordinary controlled atmosphere techniques may be used. If, however, the pressure is unduly high or if the gas is not easily handled, sealed sample holder techniques may be needed (see also Sections 8.7 and 8.9).

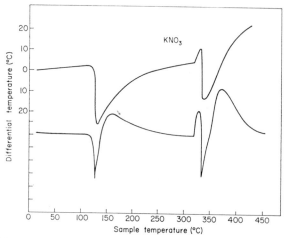

Fig. VIII-32. DDTA and DTA curves of potassium nitrate. From Campbell *et al.* (C4).

The asymmetry in the lower plot is attributable not only to the sample but also to mechanical and electrical characteristics.

Many fluorides, for example, have quite substantial fluorine vapor pressures below their melting points. The pressure at the melting point of the salt may be several atmospheres. Fluorine is, of course, quite difficult to handle at these pressures and temperatures near 1000°C. In the author's laboratory the customary solution is the use of sealed tubes (see Fig. VIII-34). These sealed-tube sample holders are constructed from 20 mil platinum–20% rhodium commercially available tubes. The tubes are ¼ inch in diameter. In use, a 1- to 2-inch section of tubing is cut off with an ordinary tubing cutter, and one end is crimped with a cable cutter fitted with rounded jaws to permit crimping without breaking the metal. The crimped end is then welded securely using a carbon arc.

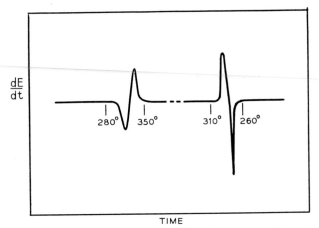

FIG. VIII-33. Derivative differential thermal analysis curves for potassium perchlorate using the differentiating circuit of Fig. XVI-9 at the output of the amplifier. *The asymmetry is almost entirely attributable to the sample (see Fig. II-11).*

The sample is now loaded into the open end to the extent of one-eighth to one-third the total depth of the tube, and the open end is crimped and welded in the same manner as the other end. The welding takes only a few seconds and the tube is held in a vise which serves as a heat sink. No evidence of decomposition of sample was encountered. At this point, or, if the operator is confident, after the thermocouple wires are attached, the tube is safety-tested. This is customarily done

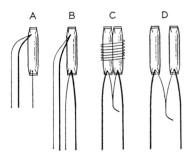

FIG. VIII-34. Ways of connecting sealed-tube sample holders: A, Single thermocouple and single wire; the thermocouple may be at top or bottom. B, Two thermocouples; fairly smooth furnace control is possible using the upper thermocouple while the sample temperature is read from the lower. C, Sample and reference tubes, joined; the tubes are held together by a wrapping of wire. D, Sample and reference tubes, separated.

The separated tubes offer best ultimate sensitivity while the joined tubes offer superior resolution of close-lying effects. The ΔT signal was taken from the platinum wires in each case.

by placing the tube in a muffle at a temperature at least approximating the maximum temperature to be reached during the thermal analysis. In the absence of any audible or visual evidence of failure, the sample tube may be used. The thermocouple system may comprise a platinum vs platinum 10% rhodium thermocouple and a platinum wire. The platinum–platinum rhodium is spot-welded to the tube near one end and the platinum wire is spot-welded to the tube near the other.

Now with the tube properly supported in the furnace the thermocouple wires may be connected to the recorder treating the two platinum wires as the outside legs of a differential thermocouple, the platinum-rhodium tube being the joining member. If the temperature measured is that of the top of the tube, the temperature difference between the top and the bottom is measured by the differential thermocouple; thus any inflections detected can be associated quite accurately with the temperature of the sample itself. Thermal effects can reach the thermocouple at the top, resulting in a less neat thermogram without in any way affecting the validity of the data. This arrangement was used during a portion of the work because the measuring thermocouple was part of the control system. A temperature gradient is built up along the tube with the type of furnace the author was using at that time but the thermal effects (Fig. VIII-35) are still clearly defined. The gradient quite naturally in-

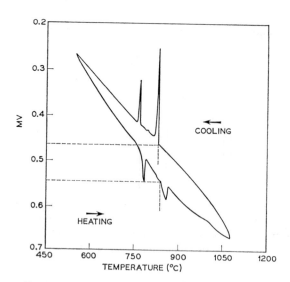

Fig. VIII-35. Thermogram of a BaF₂–LiF mixture.

The phase changes are sharply defined and reproducible even though a substantial temperature difference is set up.

creases with temperature and is somewhat different on the cooling from on the heating cycle.

Somewhat more elaborate systems were also used with a reference sealed tube. These were connected as shown in Fig. VIII-34 for various needs, i.e., varying degrees of isolation and, hence, sensitivity (see Fig. VIII-36).

Sealed tubes are not necessarily a good general technique. In phase diagram work, for example, there is the everpresent possibility of segregation and *de facto* variation in composition. Repetitive heating could lead to very well-defined segregation which might remain relatively

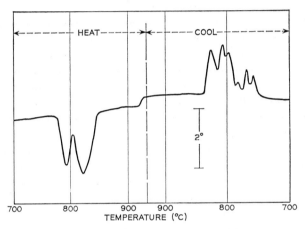

Fig. VIII-36. Thermograms of a chromyl fluoride–potassium fluoride mixture using the twin-tube arrangement of Fig. VIII-34c.

The ease of heat transfer approaches that of a block so that good separation of effects is possible.

steady from cycle to cycle. The small holders will not prevent segregation but the high sensitivity will make detection easier. The symptom is a changing temperature of one or more thermal effects from cycle to cycle. Segregation is inevitable in phase diagram work. The freezing-out of one phase separates it from the melt so that the two phases cannot generally reunite at any significant rate on heating. For this reason the heating cycle of a specimen undergoing a number of changes is likely to show a very few effects while the cooling cycle shows, as in Fig. VIII-36, each effect. The segregation becomes serious only if it persists while the sample is supposed to be molten.

An additional possibility which might vitiate the results is decomposition of the specimen. In small sealed tubes any reversible decomposition will not go far unless the vapor pressure at the melting point is very high. Whether or not an irreversible decomposition has occurred must be determined by examination of the specimen after the thermal study is complete.

8.13. Summary

There are many variations on the general method of differential thermal analysis, each having some advantages. The user of the technique is well-advised to prepare to take advantage of more than one approach.

Very small samples can be used quite easily, even with control of atmosphere effects. The lower size limit will be set by the applicability of the data to the whole specimen.

Pelleted samples present a large surface for interchange of gases with the atmosphere. If this is taken into account, the technique is useful. It presents the ultimate in practicable sample isolation.

Fluidized-bed heating may be usable for heat transfer to samples or within the sample itself but not both. If the use within the sample is successful, some valid kinetic data may be obtainable.

Visual observation of specimens during heating will require special design to avoid strong convection currents.

Changing of atmosphere or pressure can yield useful information. The furnace should permit dynamic-atmosphere or free-diffusion operation.

Several types of reactions may be studied. If the atmosphere needs to be excluded or the products contained, sealed sample holders of various types may be used.

Derivative or differential techniques could be usable if careful preparation were made.

CHAPTER IX

Thermogravimetric Analysis

9.1. Introduction

For the purpose of this discussion, consider thermogravimetry to comprise continuous or frequently repeated measurement of the weight or change in weight of a specimen as it is subjected to a temperature program. Generally, it will include automatic and continuous recording of weight or change of weight as the sample is heated. The temperature programming and/or control is usually of the same general nature as for differential thermal analysis and is described in another chapter. The concern here is over the means of weighing, the conditions affecting the specimen, and the significance of results.

The measurement of weight and temperature as the specimen is being heated is not simple. Before considering the mechanical and electrical systems needed let us first consider some of the special problems. These problems comprise principally heat transfer and the consequent temperature lag, changes in buoyancy, and movement of gases by convection or by design.

9.2. Heat-Transfer Effects

The fact that the specimen is being weighed requires that mechanical contact with the specimen be extremely slight; otherwise the sensitivity and possibly the accuracy of the measurement will be impaired. This condition then requires that heat be transferred from, generally, a nearby hot wall to the specimen holder. In turn, a temperature difference between wall and specimen is implied, and we can deduce easily that a temperature measurement anywhere but in the specimen will be in error. This error must be evaluated to determine whether or not trying to place the thermocouple in the specimen is worthwhile. If a satisfactory measurement can be made from a thermocouple supported very near the specimen, the additional mechanical linkage involved in leading thermocouple wires to the specimen is another and unnecessary source of error.

Newkirk (N5) made a quite thorough study of sources of error in Chevenard thermobalance; from the present author's experience the data cited herein are applicable to thermobalances generally. (A Chevenard thermobalance comprises a torsion balance, a counterweighted assembly to support the specimen above the level of the beam, and a furnace surrounding the specimen holder.) Newkirk programmed the temperature rise of his furnace and measured at several temperatures the difference in temperature between his control thermocouple in the furnace and another thermocouple in the crucible. The results in Fig. IX-1 show the extent of the lag. His data agree qualitatively with those the present author obtained with a bottom-loaded balance (Chapter XVII).

The error could be expected to be small at lower heating rates; fortunately these are the heating rates more commonly used in thermogravimetry. But now consider the effect of the specimen. In the Chevenard balance, like many others, a very light specimen holder

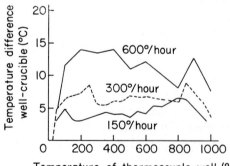

Fig. IX-1. Effect of heating rate on temperature lag of the specimen holder. From Newkirk (N5).

The difference does not continue to increase with temperature because heat-transfer processes become more effective at higher temperatures.

is used and consequently the specimen contributes much or most of the heat capacity. It is not surprising, then, that the presence of a specimen alters the temperature lag noticeably. Newkirk made a set of measurements corresponding to those shown in Fig. IX-1, but with quantities of calcium oxalate hydrate in the crucible. The data in Fig. IX-2 show the increased lag for the dehydration ($CaC_2O_4 \cdot H_2O$ $\rightarrow CaC_2O_4 + H_2O$) and for the subsequent decomposition of calcium

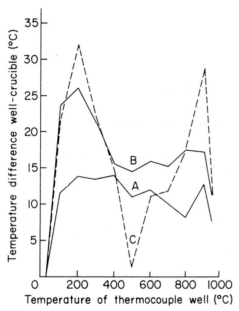

Fig. IX-2. Temperature lag due to sample. Decomposition of $CaC_2O_4 \cdot H_2O$. Heating rate 600°C/hour: A, crucible only; B, crucible + 0.2 gm $CaC_2O_4 \cdot H_2O$; C, crucible + 0.6 gm $CaC_2O_4 \cdot H_2O$. From Newkirk (N5).

The temperature lag varies the most at the temperatures of greatest interest.

carbonate ($CaCO_3 \rightarrow CaO + CO_2$); in between, however, the larger specimen gives off enough heat during the oxalate decomposition ($CaC_2O_4 + \frac{1}{2}O_2 \rightarrow CaCO_3 + CO_2$) to bring the crucible very near the furnace temperature. The important feature is that the reaction changes the temperature lag in the reaction region, so special effort or precautions would be necessary to get reliable temperatures of reaction from thermogravimetry.

It must be recognized that thermogravimetry will only rarely approach equilibrium. The transfer of sufficient heat to warm the sample may take place quite readily but decomposition of a few hundred milligrams of sample will require such a quantity of heat that the temperature will lag severely (see Chapter V, Sec. 5.1). Figure IX-3 shows the curves of Belcher *et al.* (B23a) on potassium acid phthalate in which a heating rate as low as 0.5°C/minute gives an effect much closer to a heating rate ten times as fast than to a zero heating rate. The results obtained by thermogravimetry may well appear to be significant because repeatable numbers can be stated. Nevertheless, the data must be interpreted with some understanding of the physical or chemical processes.

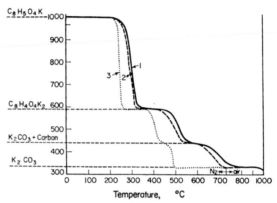

Fig. IX-3. Weight loss curves for potassium acid phthalate at (1) 5°C/minute, (2) 0.5°C/minute, and (3) isothermal heating at successively higher temperatures. From Belcher *et al.* (B23a).

Isothermal heating will bring about reaction at far lower temperatures than is customary in thermogravimetry. Thermogravimetric data must be used with great caution in estimating thermal stabilities.

9.3. Buoyancy and Gas Flow

When a specimen is heated in ambient air or any gas of comparable density, the apparent weight changes with temperature due to the change in weight of the displaced gas; the specimen appears to gain weight as it is heated. Simons, Newkirk, and Aliferis (S26) have examined the effect; their curve is shown in Fig. IX-4. The weight change is more rapid at lower temperatures. The simple solution is to decrease the volume of the sample holder but there are advantages to larger sample vessels. The effect must be recognized; from there on a choice of procedures is available. The principal choices are (1) calibration and correction and (2) use of twin furnaces. The former procedure is easier; the latter is generally better.

An apparent buoyancy effect can result from application of power to the heater windings as a step function. The sudden application of a

higher voltage heats the furnace wall quickly but because—at low temperatures—heat is transferred to the sample holder mainly by convection,
the flow velocity increases markedly. The rapid rising of gas along
the wall displaces the cooler gas down the center so that it impinges on
the sample holder, creating thereby an apparent weight gain. Lukaszewski (L17) has given (Fig. IX-5) rather dramatic evidence of the effect.
The effect is transitory because it depends for its existence on a rather
drastic temperature difference between wall and specimen holder. It
will be aggravated by a cold top (see Chapter IV); even though

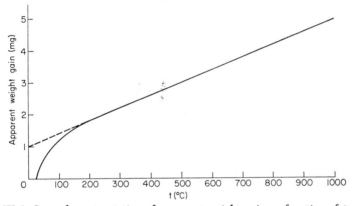

Fig. IX-4. General representation of apparent weight gain as function of temperature. From Simons *et al.* (S26).
*The gain in weight is the diminution of weight of the gas displaced by the
specimen holder plus the specimen.*

Lukaszewski had inserted a plug well into the heated zone (Fig. IX-6)
the plug surface is slow to heat because of the poor thermal contact and
will remain relatively cool because it can conduct heat to the top of the
furnace. Alumina is not a very good thermal insulator; magnesia would
have been better.

Controlled atmospheres are used in thermogravimetry for various purposes (see Chapter VII). One important use is the shifting of decomposition temperatures as illustrated in Fig. IX-7. The separation of reactions should be observable and controllable in thermogravimetry just as
in differential thermal analysis.

As thermogravimetry is usually practiced, very often the choice is simply between an oxidizing and a nonoxidizing atmosphere. In the latter
case, there is reason to have a flowing rather than a static atmosphere.
A flowing atmosphere is, by definition, an atmosphere which moves past,
around, and/or over a specimen but not through it. The fact that there

is a flow in the vicinity of a specimen being weighed creates some rather severe problems. A general movement of gas past a body exerts a force on it. Movement of gas may arise inadvertently, for example by convection, as well as by intention. Newkirk (N5) has made some useful measurements on the Chevenard balance. The present author believes them to be generally applicable.

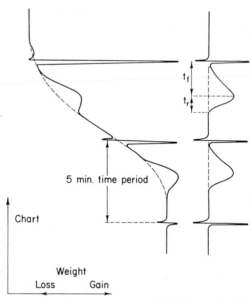

FIG. IX-5. A thermogravimetric record (diagrammatic), showing the effect of thermal pulsing in the furnace: t_r, rise time; t_f, fall time. From Lukaszewski (L17). *The sharp pulses are time marks.*

The usual technique for atmosphere control with Chevenard balances is to bring the gas in at the top of the furnace tube and let it escape through the opening at the bottom through which the sample support rod passes. The downward movement of the gas pushes down slightly on the sample holder, as shown in Fig. IX-8; this effect varies, naturally, with rate of flow of gas.

Duval (D18a) has suggested that proper venting of the furnace at the top could permit flow of air from bottom to top (convection) so as to avoid the apparent weight gain. Newkirk examined the effect of venting (Fig. IX-9) and found rather wide variations. The top opening of 0 mm has already been discussed. The buoyancy effect, however, is mitigated by an upward sweep of air if a small opening is provided. If the top is completely open, the sweep of air becomes a rush, and the

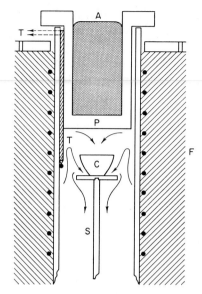

FIG. IX-6. The hot zone of a standard thermobalance furnace: A, alumina powder; P, refractory ceramic plug; T, thermocouple; F, furnace wall; C, crucible; S, support assembly. From Lukaszewski (L17).

A cool surface above a heated zone will accentuate convection.

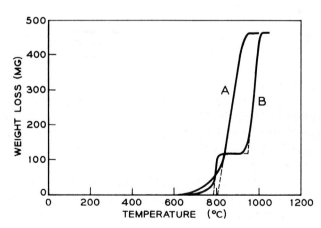

FIG. IX-7. Decomposition of a mixture of calcite and dolomite in streams of (A) air and (B) carbon dioxide. From Gibaud and Gelosa (G24).

The decomposition temperature of calcite is heavily dependent on the pressure of carbon dioxide.

sample appears to lose weight rapidly. An 8-mm opening yields a quite small effect but Newkirk points out that this is dependent to some degree on heating rate.

For the type of work Duval does—i.e., examination of analytical precipitates to determine whether or not they are suitable for a rapid thermogravimetric analysis—the solution is easily deduced: establish, by trial and error, the conditions which will yield an apparent weight gain of near zero for a crucible of given mass and geometry and a precipitate

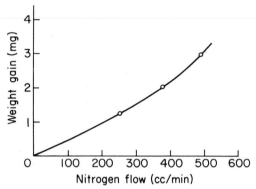

Fig. IX-8. Effect of gas velocity on apparent weight gain of one porcelain crucible at room temperature. From Newkirk (N5).

This error should increase somewhat with temperature because both volume and velocity of the gas will increase.

of a given volume. This sort of answer is hardly suitable for general purpose thermogravimetry, so under ordinary conditions users of thermobalances will need to evaluate the flowing atmosphere and buoyancy effects for each type of specimen holder and sample volume.

One technique for avoiding convection streaming when a flowing gas is used by heating the gas and passing it from top to bottom of the furnace in the manner of Vassallo (V3). He filled the upper portion of his furnace tube with glass wool (Fig. IX-10) and because the glass wool was partly in the heated zone the incoming nitrogen had plenty of warm surface to encounter before it entered the open part of the chamber. Not only is the gas hot but it would tend to emerge from the glass wool at a fairly uniform rate; this uniformity of flow should also lead to more uniform temperature distribution.

9.4. Twin-Furnace Operation

The soundest way to avoid errors from gas flow and convection is by balancing the effects both figuratively and literally. If one suspends or supports a holder with an appropriate amount of nondecomposing material in an identical furnace and any gas and voltage supplies are fed equally to each, all the physical effects on the sample should be felt equally by this reference; no movement or force should register except change in weight by the sample. Note that both hot-zone volumes and cold-zone volumes should be balanced.

Obviously, this type of operation calls rather specifically for an equal-arm beam balance, but there are a number of reasons for using such a

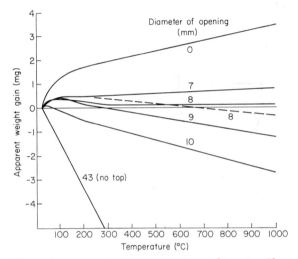

Fig. IX-9. Effect of top opening on apparent weight gain. Chevenard thermo-balance, heating rate 300°C/hour: —, one porcelain crucible, Coors 230-000 (about 4 gm); - - -, two crucibles. From Newkirk (N5).

The apparent weight loss with two crucibles is probably because the moving stream of air has an additional edge to push on.

balance anyway (see Chapter X). The advantages to be gained are several: the calibrations and corrections are avoided; one may use specimen holders of considerable variety; one may use the differential technique of deKeyser (K22).

The present author uses twin-furnace operation. The Ainsworth thermobalance (G13) (Chapter XVII) had been equipped with two furnaces from the beginning; conversion to top-loading simply meant that shorter, lighter furnaces were mounted above instead of below the beam. No new problems were encountered and some were avoided (see Chapter IV).

A major—but often unrecognized—problem in systems using a gas flow is the possibility of contamination due to the upstream diffusion of oxygen, for example. Consider a Chevenard balance operated in a reasonably customary manner with a gas—perhaps nitrogen—entering at the top and exiting through the support-rod hole. There is, true enough, an outward flow that will tend to decrease the entry of oxygen but note that an operator will use as small a flow as he deems safe to avoid disturbing the measuring process. Even at room temperature oxygen is bouncing around at about ½ km per second so the idea of a noticeable percentage being able to ricochet against the general flow presents no strain on one's credulity.

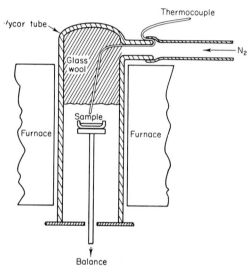

Fig. IX-10. Modifications of Stanton thermobalance. From Vassallo and Harden (V3).

A more nearly uniform temperature is achieved and mechanical disturbance avoided by bringing preheated gas in at the top.

The present author has encountered the problem a few times—enough to make him wary. In general, whenever a system is designed so that two nonidentical gases meet and mixing ahead of the designed meeting point is undesirable special care in design or use will be required. Early models of a commercial gas-density detector permitted diffusion from the sample stream back to the detectors; gases evolved by samples in the Lodding–Hammill type of furnace will diffuse upstream to the furnace chamber unless a small orifice or a high-velocity flow is provided; the Stone type of furnace can permit chamber gas to diffuse back to the sample, so the operator is well-advised to use the same chamber gas as dynamic gas unless there is good reason not to.

This diffusion upstream can be avoided by causing at some point a very high velocity flow or by introduction of a long, narrow flow path. In many applications the high velocity would be undesirable so the long path must be used.

Soulen and Mockrin (S39b) put a long exit path for the flowing gas in their Chevenard balance (Fig. IX-11) but for a different reason. They wished to prevent condensation of decomposition products on the cold support rod. The present author suggests that a major part of the improvement was due to the more effective inhibition of oxidation.

9.5. Top-Loading vs Bottom-Loading

The analytical balance is designed so that the material being weighted-is suspended from the beam. If one plans to make a series of weight

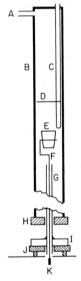

Fig. IX-11. Section through nickel muffle with nickel sleeve in place around crucible support: A, gas entry tube, ¼-in. nickel tube, to Teflon coupling and inlet hose; B, nickel muffle, 1⅝ in o.d. × ⅛ in. wall, 16⅛ in. long; C, nickel thermowell, ¼ in. o.d. × ¹⁄₃₂ in. wall, bottom 9¾ in. from bottom of muffle; D, baffle welded to thermowell to divert incoming gas stream, 11¹⁄₁₆ in. from bottom of muffle; E, crucible; F, crucible support; G, nickel sleeve, ¼ in. o.d. × ¹⁄₃₂-in. wall, 8¹⁵⁄₁₆ in. over-all length, passes through and is silver-soldered to its base, I; H, threaded cap for muffle; I, nickel base soldered to sleeve G, 2 inches diameter × ⅜ in. thick, bottom ⁷⁄₁₆ in. from bottom of sleeve; J, ceramic platform; K, bottom of crucible support. From Soulen and Mockrin (S38b).

The downward flow of nitrogen through the tube enclosing the crucible support effectually prevents upward diffusion of oxygen.

measurements on a hot sample, one puts a balance above a furnace and inserts some heat shields. It is natural that many thermobalances have been designed from that point of view. The present author has constructed three of that type. For most purposes their operation is satisfactory. In controlled atmosphere work (in closed systems) there are some disadvantages.

Consider a balance with one or two furnaces beneath it and equipped with some shields through which the support wire passed. [The non-controlled atmosphere thermobalances (G3) constructed by the present author had three significant barriers to the passage of hot air from furnace to balance: a split disc directly on top of the furnace tube; the metal table on which the balance sat; and the metal base which supported the balancing mechanism. Each of these, and the bottom of the balance case, had a ¼-inch hole for passage of the support wire. Rising heat was spread quite effectively.] So long as hot gases are kept out of, and from the bottom of, the balance case, no trouble from heat should occur. In an open system, the heat can be led away easily. Now let us attach the furnace to the balance by some air-tight contrivance so that we may use a vacuum or pressure and so that we may use a controlled static atmosphere. This mechanical connection greatly diminishes our ability to spread or otherwise dispose of heat. Let us consider the consequences.

Heat is transferred to the balance by conduction and convection. Conduction along the walls of the furnace tube ought to be a fairly trivial problem; in a moderately long tube there is plenty of opportunity to lose heat to the surroundings. One might even encourage this with a fan or cooling coil. The problem inside is not so simple. Convection implies the presence of a gas so let us note first that, if the thermobalance is being operated in a vacuum, there should be no trouble; the amount of heat that can be transported up a support wire can be neglected easily.

When a substantial amount of gas is present, the possibility of conveying heat to the balance chamber increases enormously and provisions must be made to avoid this transfer. We face, however, the condition of having a cold zone above a hot zone. The measures taken to avoid transfer of heat may induce erratic behavior; see Chapter IV on the effect of a temperature inversion in differential thermal analysis. We cannot, for example, interpose a cold surface with no other precautions; this would set up a rather forceful stream of gas and induce a temperature-dependent error. The present author used a series of discs, each with a hole in the center but otherwise nearly filling the tube, to stop radiation and convection. This was partly successful; the balance could be used quite satisfactorily under diminished pressures but much less well at atmospheric. More precisely, at atmospheric pressure it did not operate satisfactorily at high temperatures. Some combination of interposing a barrier and cooling should work satisfactorily, but the mechanical problems led the present author to look with favor on top-loading.

Top-loading results in an array of hot and cold zones in their proper order; this immediately eliminates convection and diminishes conduction. The problems that arise are mechanical; they require some special effort but nothing very difficult. One mechanical problem is that of furnace handling. Bringing a tube furnace upward to enclose a sample holder is not difficult even by hand, i.e., without mechanical guides. It is less easy to bring a furnace down to enclose a sample holder without touching it so a mechanical contrivance will be helpful to lower and lift the furnace or furnaces.

The ordinary beam balance supports the load from hooks which are in turn supported by knife edges. This flexible suspension requires that the center of mass of the load on each end of the beam be below the hook so a top-loading sample holder must be counterweighted, as in Fig. IX-12, for the sample assembly to keep it in a reproducible position in the furnace. (Since the weight of the assembly is—in effect—at the knife edge, any tilt may permit unequal heating, but the measurement of the weight will not be affected.) The weight of the counterbalance and sample holder assembly should not exceed the rated maximum loading for the balance; the change in sensitivity of the balance should then be of no concern. Most important, the counterbalance should be designed so that it is not the weight-limiting feature. The counterweight should be short and have a substantial cross section; if a significant part of the mass is near the fulcrum it is of little use. The material near the fulcrum should be only of sufficient mass to provide rigidity.

The lever arm relation is a summation, i.e., for the top portion

$$W_T D_T = \sum_{d=0}^{d=l} w_n d_n$$

where w and d refer to weight and distance from the fulcrum and l is the total length; a similar summation of the top portion holds for the bottom. But to keep the sample support in a vertical position

$$W_B D_B > W_T D_T$$

in any position of the support arm. Since the total weight is limited, the length may need to be extended. An arrangement using relatively little weight to good advantage, then, would comprise an appropriate mass at the end of a rod or tube. In the present author's design the sample-supporting tube is 12 inches, but the counterweight rod is 20 inches long. The counterweight need not be equal in weight to the sample and sample holder, but was made sufficiently heavy to keep the support tube vertical. The actual length of the counterweight tube will generally be limited by the space available.

9.6. Connections to Balance Beam

Mechanical connection to the beam or suspension system of balances is to be avoided wherever practicable; even thermocouple leads must be tolerated only as a necessary evil. If the measurement system requires connection between the moving and stationary parts there are ways of making any damping, drag, or tension effects rather small. The manner of attaching electrical connections depends on their use. Thermocouple connections may be made through fine copper or thermocouple wires (see Chapter XVI). For displacement-measuring systems a connection

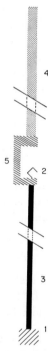

FIG. IX-12. Counterweight for top-loaded beam balance.
The counterweight (1) should be as far from the fulcrum (suspension hook) (2) as is experimentally convenient. The counterweight support (3) should be a thin-walled plugged tube. This and the upper tube (4) are cemented into the bracket (5). The sample holder is set on top of the rod. Thermocouple wires may be led through the rod.

permitting limited movement with as little drag or tension as possible is required; Reisman (R12) and the present author use single large loops of fine wire. For null balance the present author prefers a helix which can be easily bent or stretched so that at null the wire has no influence on the beam position (Fig. IX-13).

For current-carrying wires the connection should be made where the inevitable drag or tension will have the least effect, i.e., near the center knife edge on a beam suspension balance; Waters (W8), for example, passes the coulometer current through a helix attached to the beam near the central support.

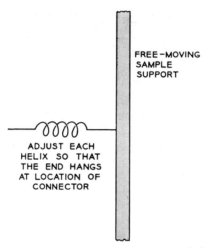

FREE—MOVING
SAMPLE
SUPPORT

ADJUST EACH
HELIX SO THAT
THE END HANGS
AT LOCATION OF
CONNECTOR

Fig. IX-13. Thermocouple connection to balance.
The helix can be bent until the end rests without force on its stationary terminal. When secured, there will be no appreciable effect on the balance.

In general, the deleterious effects of mechanical connections may be diminished most in a null or force-restored null balance because the same force—if at all measurable—is operative at all times since the beam remains in the same position. [Papailhau (P5a)—see Chapter X—even connects gas-carrying tubes to his sample support.] Any significant force will manifest itself only by an increase in the unbalance required to initiate restoring action. Whether or not the effect will be significant in a pseudo-null balance will depend on the magnitude of the force.

The arguments advanced above are not limited to beam balances. They apply to as well to spring, torsion element, or any other support system. The essential distinctions here are only between the devices that do or do not operate at or near a null position.

An exception might be granted in a case in which the mechanical connection is made through a sensing element; for example, Bartlett and Williams (B12) used a strain gage on the beam end opposite the sample suspension. The vertical strain from balance table to beam was measured to follow the weight change.

Intermittent mechanical contact between a moving and a stationary support system is not necessarily deleterious; as long as the beam or other moving part can move to its proper position after each disturbance the balance operation need not be impaired. Note that the intermittent rebalancing action used by Ewald (E8) should not have any effect on a beam already at null because the position-indicating arm is first locked in position by a movement parallel to the knife edge, the rebalancing movement—if any—takes place, and the indicating arm is finally released. No torque is exerted about the knife edge except by the specimen or the chain.

Now consider the position-sensing device (Fig. IX-14) used by Simons *et al.* (S26) with a Chevenard balance. The contact plate is driven downward by the recording mechanism until contact is made whereupon the recorder mechanism reverses the drive, withdrawing the contact plate until the connection is broken; the contact plate and hence the recorder sense the extent position of the beam, but in so doing a small force is exerted briefly.

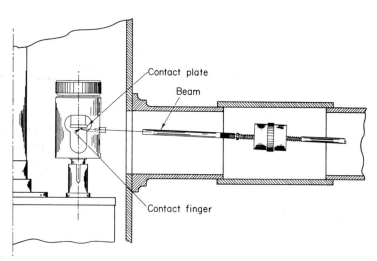

Fɪɢ. IX-14. Position-sensing mechanism for pen-recording Chevenard thermobalance. From Simons *et al.* (S26).

The slight intermittent force from the contact plate will tend to keep the beam free-moving.

This small force, even though it is present about half the time, may actually improve the sensitivity by providing an additional cyclic movement which will particularly aid in eliminating surface tension effects in oil dampers, etc. In heavier systems such as one may use on an equal-arm beam balance the cyclic movement will help to overcome inertia. The very noticeable solenoid action of linear variable differential transformers may perform a quite similar function.

Whether or not this movement is a real help will depend very heavily on the particular design. The important conclusion from this discussion is that it is not per se an adverse condition.

9.7. Precautions

Balance mechanisms, whether beam, spring, or other, are generally designed for sensitivity rather than sturdiness and general invulnerability.

Vibration is a common and well-known hazard so that it need not be discussed in great detail, with one exception. There is a moderately widespread belief that analytical-type balances are unsuitable for long-term operation as thermobalances because of wear of the knife edges. Modern laboratory buildings will not often be subject to enough vibration to cause any short-term error at analytical accuracy. (If the vibration is sufficient, other balances will need vibration-free mounts.) The author's three thermobalances showed no signs of deterioration in sensitivity during his use of them even though some runs lasted for over 2 days.

Whether or not such wear does occur, the best policy is to choose the instrument that will perform best in the intended use. If the choice, on this criterion, is an analytical balance type of thermobalance, the sensitivity can be checked every few months for signs of loss of sensitivity from wear. A good test for many systems is observation of the electrical displacement or restoring signal on a galvanometer to see whether or not the signal changes smoothly as the weight changes. Evaporation of a drop of isopropanol should be sufficient. The signal should be taken as near as possible (electrically) to the transducer.

Vacuum balances will, of course, degas as the system is pumped down. As little paraphernalia as possible should be within the evacuated volume. Metal, glass, and many other smooth surfaces well-exposed present no great problems. Confined spaces will slow the pump-down (as well as changes of atmospheres).

In addition, for high-vacuum operation, the out-gassing of components must be taken into account, along with possible changes in frictional coefficients of moving components.

Corrosive gases must be kept out of the balance mechanism region. (The term "corrosive gas" may require different definitions for different apparatus.) If a corrosive gas is being used or formed some counterflow of a "safe" gas can be used to keep the corrosive gas away from the balance mechanism. The opening connecting the balance chamber to the weighing chamber must be a reasonably long and narrow path to avoid back-diffusion (see Chapter VII).

Some materials will creep badly; for example, oxides that form glasses readily may creep over the wall of a crucible and up or down the support. If there is a large temperature gradient, part of the sample may be very significantly hotter or colder than the remainder.

Magnetic effects must be carefully avoided. The first thermobalance constructed by the author (G3) was put to use by another group in a study of polymer additives. The balance oscillated through nearly its full 100 mg range. The low-temperature furnace used in place of the platinum wound furnace had many turns and their stainless steel sample holder responded nicely to a magnet. The holder had been pulled against the side of the tube and the friction caused a dead zone of ca. 80 mg.

9.8. Summary

The need to isolate the sample mechanically from its immediate surroundings accentuates the heat-transfer effects seen in differential thermal analysis. Further, the new problem of mechanical forces arising from buoyancy and intended or unintended gas flow must be taken into account.

The generally poor heat transfer leads to low heating rates.

Buoyancy can be corrected for by calibration or automatically compensated by twin-furnace operation.

Convection is avoided by proper furnace design, most easily by use of top-loaded balances.

Connections to the sample support must afford extremely small torques or, in the case of null balance instruments, small or very highly reproducible torque.

CHAPTER X

Thermogravimetric Apparatus

10.1. Introduction

The devices used to perform continuous weighings while heating a sample have been quite varied. A remarkable degree of ingenuity has been thrown into the outwardly simple problem of providing a minute-by-minute record of the weight of a sample as it rests in a furnace. The devices must be classed first in the two broad categories, beam-balances and other weighing devices.

The beam balance is to the weighing device much as differential thermal analysis is to calorimetry; that is, by hanging an essentially equal weight on the other end of the beam small changes in weight may be detected. Both high accuracy and high sensitivity are possible. Weighing devices in general provide a measure of the total weight. The taring or reference point is commonly electrical and is essentially independent of the actual weighing mechanism. Because of this arrangement the weighing device must attempt to detect small differences in a large quantity and relate these differences to a reference whose constancy depends in large part on the stability of the electrical and electronic systems. The user of any such weighing machine is constrained to use as light a sample support as possible so that the sample is a substantial fraction of the total weight. He must then sacrifice the advantages of massive or closed-chamber sample holders. The user of a balance of ordinary analytical characteristics, on the other hand, can load a 120-gm sample holder with 80 gm of his specimen and measure a 90-mg loss with an accuracy approaching that of an analytical balance or certainly to ca. 0.2 mg—a change of 1 in 4×10^5 in sample weight. The present author has a strong bias in favor of equal-arm-beam null balances; in some special cases it may well be expedient to use some other weighing device but this author knows of no case in which such devices are demonstrably superior under comparable conditions.

10.2. Beam Balances

The analytical balance is frequently used in construction of automatic recording balances. It is designed to operate at null; i.e., the weight suspended from one end of the beam is counterbalanced by adjusting the *weight* suspended from the other end of the beam so that the beam, when free to move, will remain in a horizontal position and the pointer is at the center of the scale. The definition of null balance is necessary because it has been misused. The analytical balance may be put to use as an automatic recording balance in four ways: null balance, force-restored null balance, pseudo-null balance, and displacement measurement (Fig. X-1).

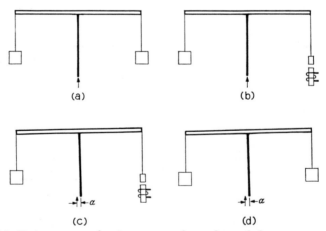

Fig. X-1. Various ways of using an equal-arm beam balance as an automatic and/or recording balance. (a) Null balance; the weight is adjusted to keep the beam balanced. (b) Force-restored null balance; a force, e.g., magnetic, is applied to compensate for changes in weight. (c) Pseudo-null balance; a force which varies with displacement keeps the balance near null. (d) Displacement measurement; for small angles the displacement is very nearly proportional to the weight change.

10.3. Null Balance

The null balance system is not only esthetically pleasing, especially to the physical or analytical chemist, but also inherently more stable. Basically, the balance does not require frequent calibration or checking. The only question that should arise is: "Does the balancing system function?" The question of linear response does not appear. The primary need is a system for adding or removing weight in response to an unbalance signal such that the unbalance signal is caused to disappear when the weight is rebalanced.

The present author has built two null balance instruments (G3) (Fig. X-2). In each case, a linear variable differential transformer was used as an unbalance detector. The unbalance signal supplied a servoamplifier-motor arrangement with directional as well as go-no-go information. The motor moved the balancing chain to restore balance. These were true null balance instruments since the differential transformer and core were adjusted so that at balance there was no force exerted on the balance beam and the motor was not driving. The beam was first balanced with all power off and the chain position noted. With the power on but

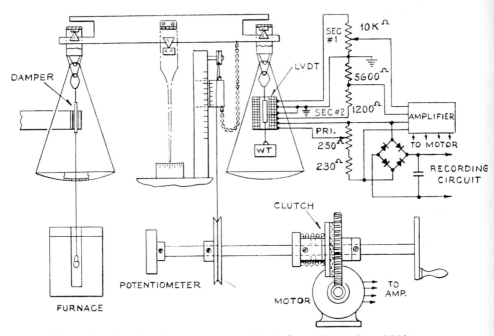

Fig. X-2. Outline drawing of automatic recording balance. From Garn (G3).
The magnetic and electrical nulls are adjusted to coincide with the mechanical null. The balance is always at null except during a weight change.

the motor disconnected from the chain, the transformer core was adjusted along the threaded support rod until the balance stayed at null. [This step is necessary because of the solenoid action of the transformer on the core except when the core is centered (see Chapter XVI).] With the balance now truly at null, the electrical system was adjusted so that the motor did not drive. With the gear train reconnected, the sensitivity was adjusted to a minimum "dead zone" and stable nonhunting operation. That the balance was operating at null could be checked at any time by shutting off the electrical power. In the absence of maladjustment the beam remained stationary.

In the first of these two thermobalances (this instrument is presently in use by another group at Bell Laboratories), a commercial servo-amplifier of the type often used in strip chart recorders was used. There is obviously no need to convert the transformer output to direct current when it must be converted back within the amplifier. A better solution is to bypass the chopper and feed the signal directly to the first amplifier stage. To avoid misconnection resulting in phase reversal, the transformer was supplied directly from the amplifier. Both of these worthy purposes could be accomplished easily by removing the converter (chopper) from its socket and substituting a plug wired to the transformer input and output circuits. The second thermobalance, still in use by the author at the time of writing, makes use of a commercial transformer-amplifier-motor combination.

A rather similar apparatus was constructed by Hyatt *et al.* (H30) using a dual photocell detector to operate the chain-drive motor. The operation of this sort of balance with any reasonable drive speeds brings about a situation in which unbalance produces a constant restoring velocity for all except very small displacements. For these small displacements the restoring velocity is proportional to displacement. The chain motion continues until balance is reached, but the beam moves beyond null because of its momentum, and the chain must move again to correct this false unbalance. For these small displacements the chain velocity decays exponentially as the beam swings toward null; that is, since

$$\frac{dv}{dt} = -kx,$$

$$v = e^{-kt},$$

but the chain has already been driven past the proper balance position and hunting normally ensues.

Three corrective measures are available. One is to slow the movement of the chain so that the beam and load can follow closely enough to enter the detector dead zone before the chain has moved enough to move the rest point beyond the dead zone. This is the solution adopted by Hyatt *et al.* who drive the chain at 0.1 mg/second over a 100-mg range. [The present author (G3) uses a drive speed of about 0.5 mg/second over a 100-mg range. This faster range is suitable for nearly all samples. A few exothermic decompositions cannot be followed accurately.] The second solution is velocity damping using the magnetic damping apparatus normally supplied with analytical balances and perhaps augmented with fluid or additional magnetic damping. The third is the addition of electronically controlled magnetic damping.

An ingenious combination recording and balancing system was devised by Ewald (E8). He supplied the unbalance signal from photoelectric cells to an electromechanical strip chart recorder (Fig. X-3). The pen shaft of this recorder also raised—or lowered—a balancing chain so that a direct record of the amount of chain was obtained.

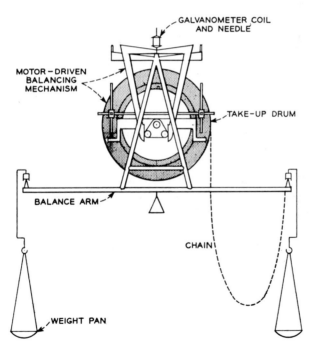

Fig. X-3. Null-type recording balance constructed from mechanical galvanometric recording potentiometer. From Ewald (E8).

At a moderate sacrifice of sensitivity the recording system becomes the balancing system as well. The period and/or damping of the balance must be adjusted so that the balance is not on a back swing at the time of the next balancing action.

In general, null balance instruments suffer from a limited range. The chain-adjusting types described above are limited to the range prescribed by the chain. This limitation is not severe because (1) sample size can usually be adjusted, (2) chains of different weights can be used, (3) more than one point of suspension on the beam can be provided, or (4) weights may be added or subtracted automatically when the chain reaches the limit of travel. The major barrier to substantial downward change of range by either (2) or (3) above is the inherent sensitivity of the balance. The author, once having a prescribed sample size and a need—or at least desire—for greater sensitivity, soldered a pointed wire on the opposite (center) end of the adjusting screw supporting the chain. With the chain end supported at this new point, a range of ca. 29 mg, instead of the usual 100 mg, was obtained. The weight-loss record was quite satisfactory.

10.4. Force-Restored Null Balance

The force-restored null balance instrument differs from the true null balance instrument only in the method by which the balance is maintained at the null position. This is generally, of course, by the action of a solenoid pushing—or pulling—on a core suspended from one end of a beam. In an automatic balance (not a thermobalance) the author helped design, a differential transformer-amplifier-motor combination like that described in the previous section was geared to a helical potentiometer which supplied the solenoid. The voltage across a precision resistor was read. The voltage across the helical potentiometer could be changed to obtain different sensitivities, e.g., ranges of a few milligrams up to several grams.

Among the force-restored null balance apparatuses is the automatic recording vacuum microbalance of Cochran (C17), who used a servo-system to adjust the current through a solenoid to bring the beam back to its original position much as described above. The detector (Fig. X-4) is a variable permeance inductor. The two portions of the winding of the inductor form two legs of an alternating current bridge so that a change in the relative inductive reactances introduces an unbalance. The unbalance supplies a potential to a servoamplifier which moves a balancing potentiometer, steadily changing the restoring force until the unbalance signal disappears.

The balancing circuit is customarily adjusted so that the electrical null coincides with the mechanical null which implies that at balance the transducer should have no effect on the balance system, although Cochran says "the transducer exerts forces of several hundred to zero micrograms on the probe, depending on position, frequency and voltage." Ob-

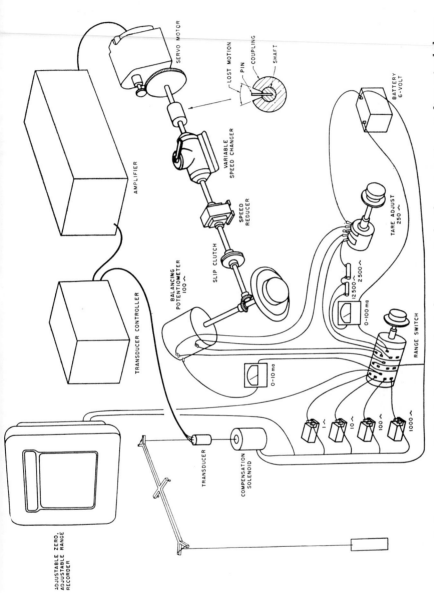

Fig. X-4. Arrangement of electrical and mechanical components for the automatic recording microbalance. From Cochran (C17). *The built-in "lost motion" permits recording of slowly varying weight changes without providing damping.*

viously, when an unbalance occurs, the change in inductive reactance must appear as a magnetic pull, but this should disappear when balance is restored.

No electrical or mechanical damping was used by Cochran. He avoided the problem neatly by building in a "dead time" as opposed to a "dead zone." His mechanical coupling deliberately employs a "lost motion" angle so that a reversal of signal must exist for some time before it results in a change of restoring force. Under these conditions, as the balance is driven back to—and beyond (see below)—null position the resulting reversal of signal would tend to cause oscillation, but even though the beam may move beyond null for a few seconds the lost motion is not used up before the beam has swung back to null and on to the side of the original displacement. The driving motor then starts back in the first direction without ever having transmitted any movement to the balancing potentiometer. The oscillation will die out mechanically without any effect if the balance is at null. Note, however, that there is no real loss of sensitivity because if the balance is not at null the oscillations will not be centered about null and eventually the greater portion of time spent on one side of null will cause the motor to nudge the potentiometer one to several times until the oscillation is centered. This "lost motion" type of operation requires that the dead time be not less than one-half the period of the balance. There is consequently a sacrifice of response speed.

The need for this dead time substitute for damping is partly the result of design. It appears to the present author that the servoamplifier is almost constantly overloaded with signal. Cochran reports that "the servomotor runs at nearly constant speed." One must infer from this that any appreciable displacement will bring forth a full-speed approach from the balancing system. Since the signal cannot reverse until the null point is passed, the beam position will change at an essentially constant rate toward null. Because of inertia, it must necessarily lag somewhat so that, by the time the beam position is at null, the restoring force is already too great—or too little—to maintain the null, so from this and from its momentum the beam will overshoot. In the ordinary course of events position-correcting action will not begin until about one and one-half periods have elapsed. The correction ought to be completed in a few periods.

The behavior just described should have no important effect on the type of study Cochran reports (oxidation of aluminum). A continually changing weight will give a record appearing to waver back and forth about a line which should be a satisfactory index. For systems in which discrete weight losses or gains are to be measured the arrangement is probably unsatisfactory, but then one hardly ever tries to study these systems on microbalances because the question whether or not the small sample was representative would arise.

10.5. Pseudo-Null Balance

The pseudo-null balance instrument uses, in general, a restoring force to keep the balance beam near null, but the magnitude of this restoring force is governed by an unbalance signal. Since a displacement signal is required to maintain the restoring force, that force cannot act to return the balance to null without destroying the displacement signal that must exist to initiate the restoring force, etc.

Consider a general case in which a displacement signal controls the current through a solenoid. The measured quantity is the voltage drop across a resistor in the solenoid circuit and, hence, the current through the solenoid. The one controlling requirement is that throughout the range of the balance

$$i = k\Delta w$$

where i is the current through the solenoid, Δw is the change in weight, and k is a proportionality constant.

In order to generate this current, a displacement from null, x, must exist. Without specifying the nature of the detector, let us assume that the current generated is directly proportional to the displacement, i.e.,

$$x = k'i.$$

Now let there be a change in weight, Δw_1, and let a steady state ensue, so that

$$i_1 = k\Delta w_1$$

and

$$x_1 = k'i_1 = k'k\Delta w_1$$

except that a portion of the weight is represented by the displacement, x_1. This is not an obvious problem since if the change in weight is doubled, i.e., $\Delta w_2 = 2\Delta w_1$,

$$x_2 = 2k'k\Delta w_1,$$

twice as much weight is represented by the displacement itself. In the absence of any change except in weight, the system is capable of supplying a proper measure of a change in weight, as long as the balance beam is held close to the null position, that is, in the limited region where displacement may be considered proportional to changes in weight.

In most pseudo-null balances the displacement is kept small; hence, nonlinearity of the current-displacement relation is not a significant problem because the measured quantity is the restoring force and the error will be the additional (or lesser) voltage required to bring the beam from the proper (linear) control point to the actual control point. (For the purpose of this limited discussion the control point is the position of rest at which the displacement signal generates restoring force necessary to maintain the displacement.) The pseudo-null instrument generally has a high signal/displacement relation so that the displacement error is small. This high response to position change brings about two requirements: dynamic damping and good voltage stabilization.

Consider a beam at balance with a zero restoring force and let a change in weight occur. The beam tends to move to the position which provides the appropriate restoring force. The momentum of the beam and load carries the beam beyond the "control point" as defined above whereupon a strong restoring force stops and reverses the motion and carries the beam beyond the control point in the other direction, etc. Since the restoring force is proportional to the displacement, i.e.,

$$\frac{d^2x}{dt^2} = -kx,$$

we have a classical harmonic oscillator. This oscillator will tend to hunt unless damped. This damping will generally need to be acceleration damping as practiced by Brown *et al.* (B83) or Mauer (M20) rather than the velocity damping provided by the usual magnetic dampers.

The high signal/displacement relation alone is enough to require good voltage stabilization. Consider a system at rest at some reasonable displacement and vary the power supply voltage. Since the detecting system is off null, it will immediately see a change in signal strength almost irrespective of the nature of the detector. This will require a change in position of the beam to restore (nearly) the original restoring force. A recurring variation in the supply voltage will cause recurring momentary deviations with small persistent deviations. This is in an ideal system in which the same supply variation did not affect the damping circuitry. In a nonideal (real) system, the damping circuit will sense the variation in supply voltage as a change in displacement signal and supply an opposing force where none is needed. This causes a real displacement, and the balance oscillates, at least briefly. For the reasons given, a pseudo-null balance instrument must be provided with a good voltage-stabilized power supply.

The linearly increasing displacement signal is simply the easiest to use for illustration; it is common with electrical displacement detection systems but not with optical systems; long-term stability is essential. A circular spot of light activating one of two photocells would be reasonably typical. Brown *et al.* (B83) used such a spot arranged so that there was a small dead zone between the two photocells. (This dead zone does not seem to serve any useful purpose since a displacement is required to do any measuring.) When the spot falls on a photo-cell the area increases rapidly and nonlinearly as the spot moves onto the photocell. They very naturally fitted this detector with a highly effective damping system. Without it a small overshoot due to mechanical momentum could supply a restoring force large enough to start the balance back toward null and possibly into the dead zone. If the momentum carries the beam beyond null and the light spot encounters the other photocell, a sharp surge of current in the solenoid would arrest the beam and start it back in the original direction where it would again encounter a surge, leading to anharmonic oscillation. Their damping system provided a current opposing any change so that the beam would move at a low velocity as long as the restoring force was not equal to the gravitational force at that displacement. The damping current kept the movement slow enough so that the signal could die out and the beam could stop without overshoot.

10.6. Displacement Measurement

The displacement-measuring instrument depends on the nearly linear variation of displacement angle with change in weight. The assumption of linearity is satisfactory for small angles since $\sin a \approx a$. Only the ordinary magnetic damping is required, but because a signal proportional to displacement must be generated this system, too, must have a voltage-stabilized power supply. In this case, the voltage stabilization need be only as good as the accuracy required, since no parts will tend to initiate hunting.

Figure X-5 shows a simple displacement-measuring system. The

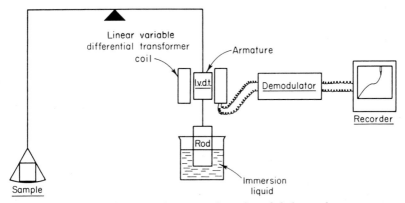

Fig. X-5. Schematic diagram of converted analytical balance for automatic recording. From Gordon and Campbell (G35).

For small angular displacements the signal is proportional to the weight change.

linear variable differential transformer (Chapter XVI) gives an output quite reproducibly dependent on position. The limit of use will be dictated by the balance at both extremes. The sensitivity will depend on the minimum weight difference needed to cause the balance to move and the usable range will be limited by the curvature of E vs w plot. Calibration will be required.

10.7. Miscellaneous Beam Balance Systems

Several variations in detecting or balancing systems have been tried. Whether or not a particular system becomes popular is not solely dependent on its capabilities; there are important human factors in play, too. The unique feature of the system may be beyond a potential buyer's or builder's experience; for example, not many—in the author's opinion —would venture to build a sensitive weight-measuring system using strain gages as sensing elements, yet they have been used. Very few of those who might need recording balances are familiar with strain gages. Similarly, the unique feature of the measuring system might be relatively inconvenient to use and would be rejected summarily on this account. This is not an entirely unreasonable attitude; in many cases, the user will be interested only in the data—not in the means of obtaining them. A third human factor is predilection or prepossession. The present author, for example, is quite unlikely to consider use of a spring for a weighing device under ordinary conditions of experimentation; on the other hand, some workers look with dismay at the use of knife edges for the protracted periods common in thermogravimetry.

Some variations used in connection with beam balances are reviewed below with comments where appropriate. The reader may pick and choose if he plans to build or be better prepared if he plans to buy.

Capacitance null indication was used by Crandall and West (C25) in their thermobalance (Fig. X-6). The detector itself is not at a null condition, but the oscillator circuit may be tuned so that the balancing motor reverses at the mechanical null. The actual detecting elements in a system of this kind would be a pair of plates—one stationary, one attached to the beam—forming a capacitance in the grid circuit of the oscillator. This circuit is then tuned so that an output-stage relay will operate or fall back when the balance is at null. A motor connected to the relay then drives the chain in the appropriate direction.

The fact that the chain is always moving is only a minor disadvantage. The moving parts will wear out faster, but since the balance is always swinging the sensitivity is somewhat better than in the case where a deflection of some minimum value is needed to operate the balancing mechanism. The mechanical backlash—even if very small—can avoid the appearance of a wavy record. This mechanical backlash ought to be the limiting feature on the sensitivity of recording. The amplitude of this backlash will depend on the speed of the motor and the period of the balance. The actual period of oscillation will not be that of the free-swinging balance; the balance will perform as a driven oscillator, but the frequency of this driven oscillator will depend on the variables cited above. If the motor drive is slow, the period of the driven oscillation

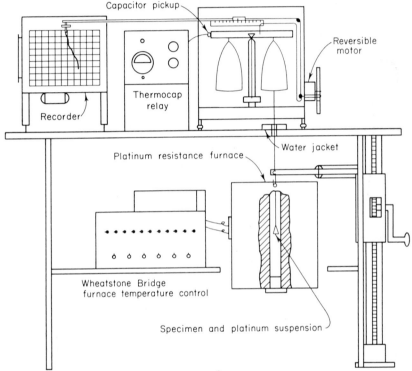

FIG. X-6. Automatic recording balance with furnace. From Crandall and West C25).

The recording pen is coupled mechanically to the chain-drive mechanism.

will approach that of the balance and the amplitude will be low. Let the speed be increased and the amplitude, too, will increase; from the time of the swing of the balance past null to the time of its passing in the other direction the motor will be driving at full speed in a single direction. The actual speed must be a compromise between that needed to follow a weight change properly and that which gives a decently small wiggle.

The long-term (few-hour) drift of the oscillator would probably not be serious. The null detector can be reset very conveniently at the start of a run, but, on the other hand, this resetting is almost certainly necessary.

A magnetic repulsion system has been used to maintain a balance beam at an apparent null (Fig. X-7). The detecting beam oscillates with small amplitude about a null position. When the balance beam tends to move because of a change of weight the increased or decreased repulsion makes the upper beam tend to follow. The upper beam is returned to null

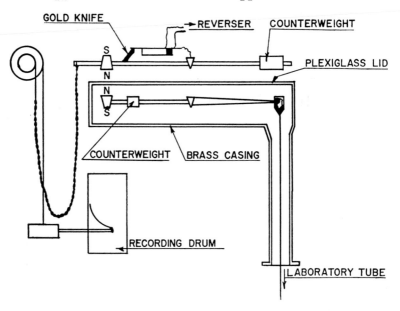

Fig. X-7. Testut null-type vacuum thermobalance with servo-operated chain for restoring force and electromechanical null detector. From Gordon and Campbell (G35).

Essentially all control and measuring equipment is outside the chamber.

so that the lower beam is constrained to return to nearly null. The nearness of approach to null will depend on the strength of the magnetic field. In general, the behavior is similar to the pseudo-null balances described earlier.

Another technique for adding or subtracting weight is by electroplating a metal onto or stripping it from an electrode hanging from the beam. Waters (W8) used a photoelectric detector to drive an amplifier which pushed an electric current through an electrolytic cell in the proper direction so that the weight of the hanging electrode assembly equalled that of the sample assembly (Fig. X-8). This is intrinsically a null system—as long as a displacement exists a restoring action continues. The measured quantity is the current flowing through the cell so the primary record is essentially a derivative, the rate of change of weight with time. Integration of the current presents the user with the total weight change as a function of time. The balancing and recording systems should be very dependable; if this arrangement were to be used in a controlled atmosphere or vacuum system the electrode support ought to pass through a small orifice and the electrolyte covered with a layer of vacuum pump oil.

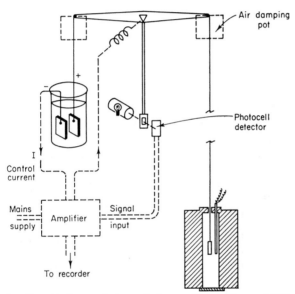

Fig. X-8. Differential thermobalance. From Waters (W8).
The beam is kept at null by electrochemical addition or subtraction of weight. The current required to maintain balance is recorded; this current is initiated and controlled by means of the photocell detector.

10.8. Nonbeam Systems

Some thermobalances use direct suspension of the sample. Magnetic suspensions have been used in other applications (B19) and a thermobalance using a magnetic suspension is reportedly being prepared for commerical sale.

Spring suspensions are often used. Some springs, including quartz-fiber springs, have been used for sensitive measurements of weight (or apparent weight) in closed systems many times. Hooley (H23) used

such a spring in a thermobalance (Fig. X-9), measuring the displacement with a linear variable differential transformer whose core was
part of the suspension system and whose coils were outside the enclosure.
The sample then hangs down into a furnace chamber. The entire volume
may be evacuated or a gas may be made to flow through the chamber to
supply a constantly replenished known atmosphere.

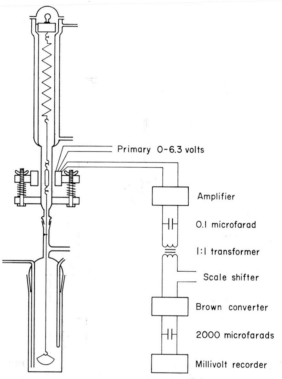

Primary 0-6.3 volts

Amplifier

0.1 microfarad

1:1 transformer

Scale shifter

Brown converter

2000 microfarads

Millivolt recorder

Fɪɢ. X-9. Balance and the recording circuit. From Hooley (H23).
The spring enclosure is water-cooled to provide uniform response along the spring.

Hooley showed (Fig. X-10) that there is a linear region for the spring
he used. Within this region the output of the differential transformer is a
reasonably accurate measure of the weight. The total load for linear
response is about 0.7 gm for the spring he used. The situation of a cold
zone above a hot zone (see Chapter IX) is unavoidable with this type
of suspension.

Wendlandt (W19) devised a strain gage support from which he sus-
᎐ᑦ his specimens (Fig. X-11). The system should be relatively
ᑦle; Wendlandt cites a tolerance of a 1-lb overload without

damage for ±0.15-ounce gage, a fiftyfold overload. On the other hand the capacity is low and very frequent calibration is likely to be needed.

Other systems may permit top-loading. The cantilever support used by Kertzmann (K18) shown in Fig. X-12 allows quite rigidly prescribed positioning of the specimen but at the sacrifice of considerable sensitivity since the support arms must resist torque in any direction but the vertical.

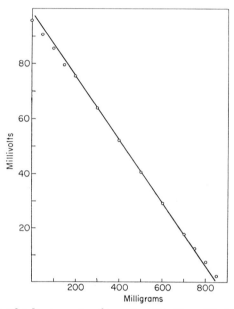

FIG. X-10. The linear region for spring D^1. From Hooley (H23).
This particular spring can be used from about 250 to 700 mg with a two-point calibration.

10.9. Pressure Thermobalances

Rabatin and Card (R1) constructed a high-pressure (600 psi) thermo-balance (Fig. X-13) using a torsion balance and an optical displacement-measuring system. The furnace is mounted above the balance to avoid convection heating of the balance itself. The top contains not only the furnace but also (Fig. X-14) a thermocouple placed so that it is within the sample crucible when the top is let down into place. At 7°C/minute they obtained the curves shown in Fig. X-15. At high pressures the reactions are not necessarily the same as at ambient pressure. Operation at a series of pressures may supply useful thermodynamic data.

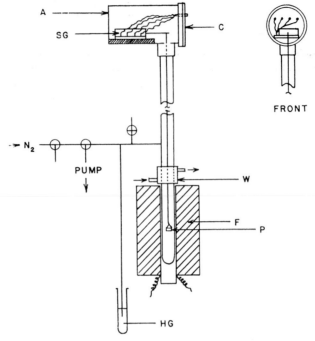

FIG. X-11. Schematic drawing of strain gage thermobalance. From Wendlandt (W19). A, aluminum cylinder housing; SG, strain gage transducer; C, plastic disc; W, water-cooled standard taper joint; F, furnace; and P, sample pan.

The position of the sample supporting arm is sensed by the relative changes in resistance of the gage arms.

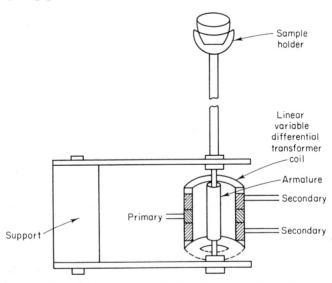

FIG. X-12. Cantilever deflection-type load cell with differential transformer as transducer for measuring. From Kertzmann (K18), as given by Gordon and Campbell (G35).

A somewhat different approach to high pressures was taken by Biermann and Heinrichs (B50a). They enclosed a horizontally positioned spring in a side arm on their chamber and supported their specimen and holder in the furnace above (Fig. X-16). The detecting and damping system provided the counterweight. Since their displacement-measur-

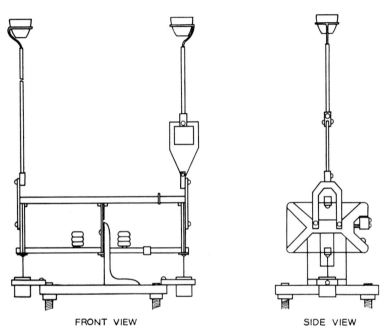

FRONT VIEW   SIDE VIEW

Fɪɢ. X-13. Torsion thermobalance assembly for pressure operation. From Rabatin and Card (R1).

The right-hand arm was used for counterweighting and supporting the displacement-indicating flag. This single-furnace thermobalance compensates for buoyancy changes due to pressure but not for temperature.

ing transducer, a single-ended linear variable differential transformer (see Chapter XVI), was inside they needed to provide adjusting devices to "zero" the support mechanically. This is no great problem; a number of sealing devices which allow movement of shafts are commerically available.

The single-ended transformer (see Chapter XVI) permits simpler circuitry than would a null type; the phase angle is always the same so directional discrimination is not needed. The useful sensitivity will depend on the reproducibility of the bending of the torsion arm. Their curve for Mohr's salt (ferrous ammonium sulfate hexahydrate) is given in Fig. X-17.

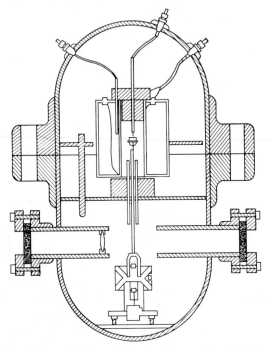

Fig. X-14. Cross section of thermobalance pressure chamber. From Rabatin and Card (R1).

A thermocouple is positioned so that when the top is put in place the junction is within the sample crucible. The rounding of the right-angle corners in the pressure vessel contributes greatly to safety by diminishing stress fatigue.

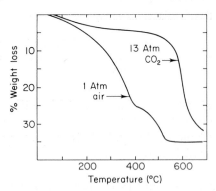

Fig. X-15. Thermograms for decomposition of manganous carbonate in air and in 13 atm carbon dioxide. From Rabatin and Card (R1).

The presence of carbon dioxide represses the decomposition of the carbonate and the absence of oxygen prevents oxidation of MnO to Mn_2O_3 until rather high temperatures are reached.

Note that both of these high-pressure thermobalances have the furnace *above* the weighing mechanism. The present author has found top-loading to be better (in closed systems) even at somewhat subatmospheric pressures. At elevated pressures the gas would inevitably heat the balance chamber in a suspended-sample arrangement. Interposition of a cooling barrier would set up severe currents at only a few hundred degrees.

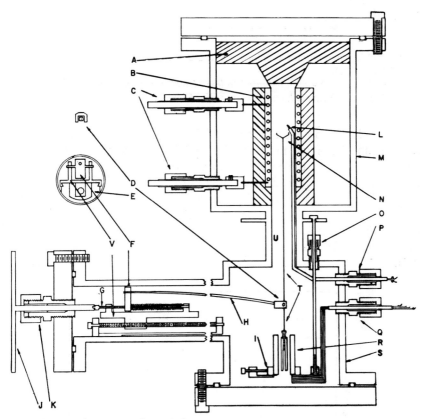

FIG. X-16. High-pressure thermobalance. From Biermann and Heinrichs (B50a). *The position-sensing transducer is also the counterbalance.*

10.10. Differential Thermogravimetry

Just as differential thermal analysis makes use of transient differences in temperature as a means of detection—and sometimes of measurement —of a reaction, so one may also use transient differences in weight. Consider the reasonably typical weight-loss curve in Fig. X-18, curve A.

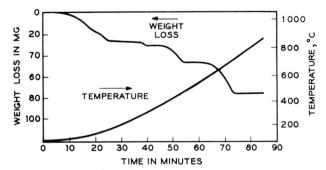

Fig. X-17. Thermogram obtained on heating Mohr's salt. From Biermann and Heinrichs (B50a).

The weight changes are attributed to loss of water, water, ammonia plus hydrogen, ammonia plus sulfuric acid, and, finally, sulfur trioxide.

Since we have no generally successful way to permit mass to enter or leave a specimen we must regain equilibrium by allowing our reference to change in the same manner. Figure X-18, B, shows a pair of curves slightly displaced in temperature and the difference between them. This difference is approximately the derivative of the original curve and such a signal may be obtained by plotting the derivative curve. That technique is discussed elsewhere (Chapter VIII); we are here concerned with the differential curve; how to get it and how useful it is.

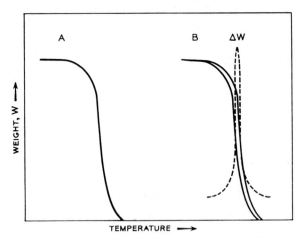

Fig. X-18. Differential thermogravimetry by the twin-furnace technique.

If two weight losses as in curve A occur closely spaced in time so that they over-lap as in B, a difference signal ΔW gives an indication of the rate of weight loss.

The technique of de Keyser (K22) is perfectly straightforward. He heats two identical samples in a twin-furnace balance as shown in Fig. X-19. One of the furnaces being slightly hotter than the other, de Keyser obtains the difference between the two separate plots as illustrated in Fig. X-18, B. His comparison of differential thermal and differential thermogravimetric analyses of magnesium carbonate (apparently a basic magnesium carbonate) is shown in Fig. X-20.

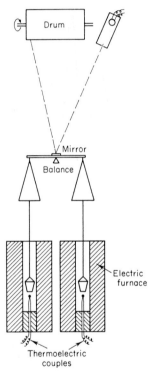

Fɪɢ. X-19. Twin-furnace differential thermogravimetry apparatus. From de Keyser (K22).
Identical samples in two furnaces—one lagging slightly in temperature—give transient indication of weight changes.

The general similarity of the curves in Fig. X-20 could be predicted; differential thermogravimetry has the same general advantages over thermogravimetry that differential thermal analysis has over calorimetry (Chapter II). It has a distinct advantage over differential thermal analysis in that the base line must necessarily return to zero in the absence of a reaction. Obviously it use is limited to study of those reactions involving a reasonably rapid weight change. Kaolin, for example, will show the drying and dehydration but not the exothermic reaction ca. 1000°C (see Chapter VIII). This is not necessarily a disadvantage.

The present author has strong doubts that satisfactory quantitative data may be derived from the technique even though de Keyser suggests that if one determines the total weight loss the weight loss of any

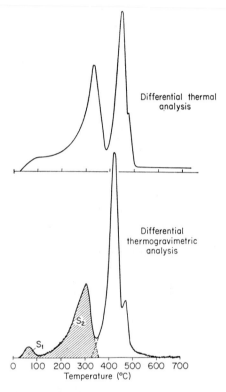

Fig. X-20. Differential thermogravimetric and thermal analyses of "magnesium carbonate." From de Keyser (K22).

one reaction may be calculated from its relative area. The major problem is the nonconstancy of the $\Delta W/\Delta T$ that one is trying to measure; a second is the nonequal rates of reaction and nonequal temperature dependence of rates of reaction when two or more weight losses are involved.

The nonconstancy of ΔT is an apparatus problem and is not easily solved; de Keyser used a resistor in series with one of the furnace windings and apparently fed both from the same power supply. This in effect means that a set and almost constant fraction of the total voltage is dissipated in the resistor and furnace no. 2 of Fig. X-19 will have a voltage input of, say, 95% that of furnace no. 1. At higher and higher temperatures and hence voltage input the relative power total dissipation, $P = E^2/R$, remains the same but in the lagging furnace circuit we encounter a greater and greater lag because not all of the lesser power in the furnace no. 2 circuit is dissipated in the furnace. If, for example, the furnaces have 10 ohms resistance and the lagging resistor is ½ ohm, the actual relative power dissipation in the lagging furnace is 0.91. This naturally brings about a greater and greater temperature difference between the furnaces and hence between the specimens. Under the best conditions otherwise equivalent reactions would give quite different areas. All this does not gainsay the utility of the technique for detecting and studying reactions.

Before considering ways of obtaining a more nearly constant ΔT for the differential let us examine more carefully the nature of the measurement, i.e., the quantity we are attempting to measure, and evaluate the utility of the data. We are bringing about two separate reactions which proceed independently and we are measuring as a function of *time* the difference in completeness of the two reactions. (Whether we plot this difference against time or temperature has not the slightest effect on the reaction.) The rate of reaction is a function of both temperature and time so that the actual measurement is

$$\int_0^t \int_{T_r}^{T + \Delta T} f(T,t)\, dt\, dT - \int_0^t \int_{T_r}^{T} f(T,t)\, dt\, dT.$$

The fact that the rate of reaction changes with temperature means an unsymmetric peak must be expected because a unit of area does not have the same quantitative significance at various times during the course of the reaction. If a unit of area cannot be expected to maintain the same value (in milligrams per second) during one reaction, one cannot hope that a unit of area during some later reaction would have meaning even close to that in the previous reaction. Even assuming a constant ΔT, not only would the second peak be asymmetric within itself but the different rate constant and activation energy will cause a different response.

It can be argued justly that asymmetry in a reaction peak does not affect its utility for quantitative measurements. The objection is raised only for those cases in which (1) area is assigned a definite value and summation of the area under a deflection is considered to be evidence that some precisely stated quantity of material reacted or (2) two or more reactions occur and, from knowledge of the total weight loss, changes in weight are attributed to the various reactions in proportion to the areas of their peaks, i.e.,

$$\frac{\Delta W_1}{A_1} = \frac{\Delta W_2}{A_2} = \frac{\sum_i \Delta W_i}{\sum_i A_i}.$$

Quantitative measurements will require calibration using known quantities of the reacting species under well-controlled conditions.

Since the technique ought to be useful in qualitative work, it is worth while to consider possible improvements. The use of a resistor for lagging one furnace has already been shown to have serious disadvantages, yet the entire value of the system is concerned with this temperature difference. The use of two separate control systems is likely to permit fairly wide and rapid variations in a small ΔT; this would probably have no advantage. One furnace must be programmed and the other made to follow at some definite separation.

Since the system is now being considered principally for qualitative studies, we are not concerned with a very precise interval of temperature. It is enough that one can maintain an approximate ΔT and that this ΔT does not change rapidly or discontinuously. The appropriate control technique is to maintain a constant potential difference between thermocouples in the two furnaces (Fig. X-21). The variation with temperature of thermocouple response should be of no significance here.

Note also that this technique provides a convenient means of controlling sensitivity of selectivity of a process. By adding a way to vary the voltage added across the resistor (Fig. 21b) one may order a small ΔT for high selectivity or a large ΔT to avoid overlooking slow reactions. Too large a ΔT may permit reactions to go to completion in one furnace at a time. This is potentially a limit to the sensitivity.

The related technique of derivative thermogravimetry as described by Paulik *et al.* (P10) (see Chapter XI) depends on the rate of mechanical movement of the sample and support. Since it is not an absolute measurement, it would tend to be insensitive at low rates of weight loss. The derivative technique of Waters (W8) would be usable since it is a null balance technique.

The reader must bear in mind, while evaluating the technique, that it is—or should be—capable of detecting loss of a milligram or so in a 100-gm sample without interferring with detection of another reaction. Similarly, loss of even a number of grams will not interfere with the subsequent detection of milligram quantities.

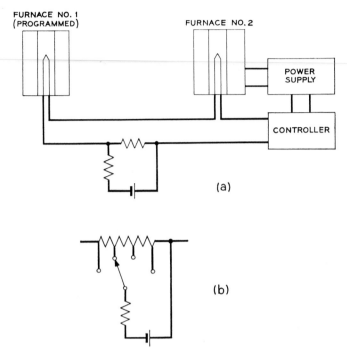

Fɪɢ. X-21. Suggested control system for differential thermogravimetry.

With the left-hand furnace controlled by the programming equipment the right-hand furnace can be made to lag or lead by a (a) fixed or (b) an adjustable amount. An added signal of zero in (b) would permit simple twin-furnace operation.

10.11. Summary

Beam balances may be operated at null by true mechanical balance or by use of a restoring force. They may be held near null by application of a restoring force or the displacement of the beam can be measured.

Nonbeam balances usually comprise some spring device. The displacement is usually measured but null operation is practicable.

While nonbeam balances can be made very sensitive to absolute weight change, the beam balances can measure (with good accuracy) a much smaller percentage weight change.

Differential and derivative thermogravimetry are often useful or convenient. Differential thermogravimetry has better potentialities but its use requires considerable care.

CHAPTER XI

Simultaneous Measurements

11.1. Introduction

In the separate practice of the arts of differential thermal and thermogravimetric analysis it will occur to many workers that, since both techniques involve observation of a sample during heating, the two measurements could be done simultaneously and poor correlation of data eliminated *ipso facto*. The advantages accruing from getting more than one set of data from the same sample at the same time are reasonably clear. A comparison of the two sets may be made with assurance that a reaction or other phenomenon apparent from one set of data can be related to an event apparent from the other set at the same temperature (or time); further, there is a *prima facie* saving on equipment and time. The first argument as it stands is true enough, but serious question of the need or advisability of correlating data in this way can be raised; the second is potentially a snare and a delusion.

The present author has from time to time concluded that two or more techniques could be used simultaneously and proceeded to carry out the experiments. While these experiments have been reasonably successful (e.g., G18 and G7), the general utility of the combination may not be worth the expenditure of time, equipment, and energy. In the second paper cited (G7) the benefits to be derived from a frequent qualitative analysis of the gaseous decomposition products of a thermal analysis were obvious. The nature of the reaction could be determined rather easily and the products of successive reactions could be separately identified. Mixtures of two gases could be separated into their components. An apparatus was assembled which could perform a differential thermal analysis and a continuous thermal conductivity measurement on the effluence, and, more important, at fixed intervals of time the effluence was sampled by a gas chromatograph (see Chapter XIV).

The concept was quite satisfactory; each analysis could be carried out; the method was discontinued anyway. The occurrence of trouble in one of the techniques was frequent enough to discourage use of the combination. In more recent experiments a sample is heated and the gases repetitively sampled for gas chromatography but, aside from measuring the temperature, nothing else is attempted. A separate sample is taken for differential thermal analysis. Since equipment is available a continuous gas analysis can be run as a possible aid in correlating data, but this is an added benefit only occasionally used. The important set of information is generally the differential thermal analysis.

In advocating simultaneous differential thermal analysis and thermogravimetric analysis or any such combination, the argument may have sometimes been raised that, unless the measurements are made simultaneously, they have no significance; they were not made on the same few hundred granules and another portion might behave quite differently. We may presume that a chemist with analytical training would not advance such a claim, for an important part of such training is in intelligent sampling.

If the sample is not representative of the whole, conclusions based on the behavior of the sample may not be extended to the whole. If the sample is properly taken to be representative of the whole, another portion properly taken should also be representative of the whole, and the behavior of one portion can be related to the behavior of the other, and the properties determined on these portions can be attributed to the whole.

The present author has encountered several types of opportunities for improper sampling. A common case is that in which a reaction—usually thermal—has not proceeded in the same manner or to the same degree in one part of the vessel as in another (see Chapter V). Another case is that in which a surface exposed to the air oxidizes or takes up water to a different degree than the interior. A third case is that in which each particle has characteristics somewhat different from others. An example of this third case is a polymer the present author studied rather briefly. The material was in coarse granules, so a few—or even one—could be used as a specimen. The results were highly irreproducible because the polymer had been strained deliberately and each granule could be expected to differ from any other. The selection of two pieces having essentially identical thermal properties would have been fortuitous. In each of these cases there are real differences, and the operator must either sample properly or refrain from making sweeping conclusions from a little bit of dust.

The possibility of irreproducible sampling is also the most probable lower limit to the size of a differential thermal analysis specimen (see Chapter VIII). The smallest practicable specimen, in the opinion of the author, will be that below which any quantity fails to show the thermal effects observable in a larger quantity. Extremely small specimens, such as those used by Mazieres (M21), will presumably be used only for studies of reversible phenomena or with the understanding that the properties of the specimen are not necessarily representative of any larger quantity.

Let us return now to the first reason for simultaneous determinations. The importance of designing an experiment to obtain unambiguously the information needed cannot be overemphasized. It is not enough to point with pride at some curves and relate a bump on one to a cant on another in serene confidence that the same event caused both. This is hardly thermal analysis. Ideal conditions for each of the techniques discussed in this monograph differ and, indeed, they differ even within a single general technique such as differential thermal analysis. The apparatuses for simultaneous determinations are perforce restrictive; the need to make one measurement must necessarily influence or limit the manner in which the second measurement must—or may—be made. If a compromise is made which sacrifices any advantage of either technique, the gain is probably not worthwhile; there is—in fact—a real possibility that the data are entirely meaningless.

The author does not by any means imply that simultaneous measurements should not be made—only that they must be made properly. Several of the techniques mentioned in Chapters I or XII could be done in combinations without detriment to any.

11.2. Differential Thermal plus Thermogravimetric Analysis

A case in which data may be vitiated with particular ease is that of simultaneous thermogravimetric and differential thermal analysis. Generally one may obtain data having relatability by simultaneous use of well-known techniques (Fig. XI-1). In the former case, orthodox techniques call for a moderately large sample and slow heating rates but in the latter case smaller samples and faster rates are the rule. The use of thermogravimetry implies a weight change and probably more than one.

If a leg of a differential thermocouple is stuck into the relatively large thermogravimetry sample and a slow heating rate is used the thermal effects—being time-dependent—will be small in magnitude and quite spread-out (in time). Recording ΔW or ΔT vs T (X-Y recorder) will eliminate time effects but see Chapter IV. If the heating rate is increased substantially, the weight loss reaction may be finished at the edges before the effect is even noticeable at the center. This temperature difference might be enough that a subsequent reaction would begin before the material at the center had undergone its first reaction.

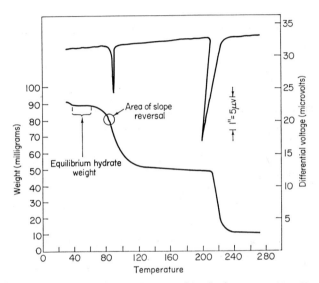

FIG. XI-1. Simultaneous differential thermal and thermogravimetric analysis of cesium carbonate hydrate at an average heating rate of 0.33°C/minute. From Reisman (R12).

A high-sensitivity amplifier and ΔT vs T recording shows temperature effects clearly but note that the lower-temperature thermal effect appears to occur over only part of the weight change.

In differential thermal analysis, one deliberately and with aforethought induces a temperature difference at the moment of reaction in apparatus designed to enhance this temperature difference as much as possible without preventing detection of subsequent reactions. In thermogravimetric analysis, one would like the specimen to lose instantaneously whatever weight it ought to lose under the experimental conditions. In the former technique, a temperature gradient within the sample is necessary and desirable; in the latter, a gradient must be avoided as far as possible and a minimum endured only reluctantly. In the former, dependence of magnitude of signal is naturally a function of heating rate; in the latter, any shift in reaction temperature with heating rate is to be deplored. The two techniques are not compatible. A combination must inevitably compromise the utility or sensitivity of one or the other technique, at least with the techniques common at the time of writing.

If one chooses to employ a high rate of heating, and thus get sensitive differential thermal analysis, temperature gradients within the sample will consequently spread out the weight loss. This will be the extent of the impairment if one is using an atmosphere of the product gas or a closed chamber (Chapter VII); in other cases atmosphere effects will displace the reaction temperature. If, on the other hand, one heats the material slowly, one loses a considerable part of the sensitivity of the differential thermal technique.

Agreement of thermogravimetric and differential thermal analysis data may be obtained in a number of ways. The author has a strong bias in favor of sets of data each obtained under the same known and reproducible thermodynamic conditions whether or not the data were obtained on the same sample at the same time; other attempts to obtain agreement are possibly meaningless. It is quite true that decomposition curves may be obtained which show thermal effects and weight changes in the same temperature ranges. Three popular ways are by simultaneous measurements of weight and temperature on the same specimen, simultaneous measurements on separate but contiguous specimens, and measurements of the two effects in separate experiments but in the same (type of) sample holder.

The good agreement in temperature of the thermal and the mass effects can lead to—or be used to support—some quite unwarranted interpretations or oversimplifications. An example of the latter is Borchardt's measurement of initial reaction rates from differential thermal analysis data (B66). Borchardt derives an equation for the rate of reaction, i.e., the fraction converted per unit time:

$$\frac{-dn/n_0}{dt} = \frac{2\Delta T}{\tau \Delta T_{max}}$$

where he assumed (*a*) that the differential thermal analysis peak can be approximated by a triangle of base τ and height ΔT_{max} and (*b*) that the rate of reaction so calculated applies to the temperature at which the height of the peak is ΔT. By using only low values of $\Delta T/\Delta T_{max}$ he found "initial reaction rates" for magnesium, carbonate, calcium carbonate, and kaolinite. For verification he obtained thermogravimetric curves using a sample holder of the same internal geometry. These sample holders were cavities—open at the top—¼ inch in diameter and ⅜ inch deep. The furnace atmosphere was static air and the heating rate 12°C/minute.

Borchardt selected a $\Delta T/T_{max}$ value of ⅒, determined the corresponding temperatures from the differential thermal analysis plots (Fig. XI-2), and calculated the reaction rates shown in Table XI-1. From the thermogravimetric data, he measured the rate of weight loss ("observed

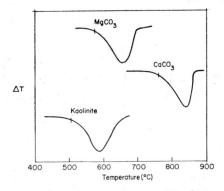

Fig. XI-2. DTA patterns of magnesite, calcite, and kaolinite. The marker on the curve indicates the point where $\Delta T = 0.1\ \Delta T_{max}$. From Borchardt (B66).

The weight loss ratios at the 0.1 ΔT_{max} were calculated from the first-order reaction law and compared with the experimental values.

rate" of Table XI-1) at nearly the same temperatures and found reasonable agreement. The agreement is reasonable but the assumption that these numbers then describe the rates of reaction for these materials at the given temperatures is not. Each number applies only to the *particular* sample geometry with the *particular* packing at the *particular* heating rate because the decomposition is not occurring at the same rate in all parts of the vessel.

TABLE XI-1

"Initial Reaction Rates" Determined by Borchardt (B66)

Material	DTA temperature (°C)	Calculated rate (%/minute)	Observed rate (%/minute)
MgCO₃	579	1.67	1.90 at 580°C
CaCO₃	762	2.11	2.78 at 759°C
Kaolinite	506	1.29	1.28 at 506°C

The very earliest decomposition takes place, of course, in air, but there is a fairly rapid increase in carbon dioxide (or water) concentration. Even with the loose packing of the calcium carbonate, 8.27% of theoretical density, particle size, 6.3 μ, by the time 1% of the material had reacted enough carbon dioxide had been liberated to fill the intergranular voids a couple of times. Nevertheless, these voids are not filled with product gas because of interchange with the ambient atmosphere. The rapidity of interchange will depend not only on the geometry of the sample holder but also on the ease of diffusion within the voids. With this loose packing the interchange could indeed be rapid. Because of this loss of carbon dioxide to the ambient atmosphere, most of the reaction is occurring either near the surface where the carbon dioxide concentration has been attenuated by diffusion or at the wall where the material is hotter than in the interior of the specimen holder (see Chapter VII). The reaction rate is consequently an average rate applicable only to the conditions of that particular experiment. The data would be essentially reproducible and would have significance if they were obtained in an atmosphere of the product gas. Note, however, that two of these materials used as examples are quite different in nature, the simple decomposition of a carbonate as compared to dehydroxylation of a layered mineral (see Chapter VI). A quite different heating rate dependence can be expected.

By a variation on standard techniques, a reasonable approximation to simultaneous differential thermal and thermogravimetric analysis might be performed without serious impairment of either technique. Consider again the requirements: (1) the decomposition or other reaction must cause a measurable deviation from steady-state heating; (2) the temperature must be virtually the same throughout the sample.

The latter requirement is met easily by the thin-layer technique previously discussed, except that the sample holder is no longer massive. Since we can measure the temperature of the sample we no longer need to assure ourselves that the sample temperature is increasing steadily. We may, then, use a low–heat capacity but high–thermal conductivity component in contact with the sample and follow its temperature. This arrangement might take the form of a thin metallic disc—isolated thermally from the furnace walls—on which the sample rests. Its temperature could be compared with that of a point near—but not in contact with—it. This device could be readily adapted to either the free-diffusion or the closed-chamber sample holder (Fig. XI-3 and XI-4) (see Chapter VII). The signal from a measuring thermocouple in contact with the metal disc is compared with the signal from a thermocouple slightly below it.

The result is not strictly differential thermal analysis but the same sort of data can be obtained: a small signal with some drift and the thermal effects imposed on it. The usual amplification and recording apparatus would be needed. (The author is merely suggesting, not advocating.)

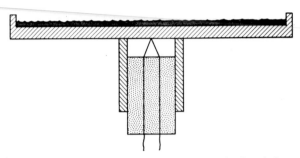

FIG. XI-3. Free-diffusion sample holder for top-loading balance.
The holder is set down on the support rod which also carries the thermocouple.

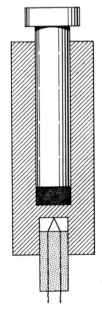

FIG. XI-4. Closed-chamber sample holder for top-loading balance.
The thickness of the barrier between the sample and thermocouple should be inversely dependent on the skill of the fabricator. The mass of the holder may prevent its use on any but beam balances.

11.3. Apparatus for Simultaneous Differential Thermal and Thermogravimetric Analysis

One important attempt at simultaneous differential thermal and thermogravimetric analysis was that of Papailhau (P5a), who constructed a weighing apparatus (in which he could do differential thermal analysis at the same time and on the same sample) which remained at a stationary balance point by reason of a variable fluid displacement action on a cylinder fastened to the sample support (Fig. XI-5). A weight loss causes the breaking of an electrical circuit. The breaking of the circuit causes a motor to lift a second cylinder from the fluid to decrease the displacement by the first by changing the level of the fluid. An index coupled with the motor movement follows the position of the control

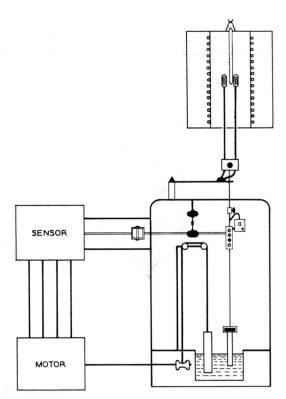

Fig. XI-5. Apparatus for simultaneous differential thermal and thermogravimetric analysis. From Papailhau (P5a).

The temperature effects and weight loss of a single specimen are measured. The fluid level is changed to maintain null.

cylinder, either recording its position on a strip of paper or registering it on a millivoltmeter.

Papailhau (Fig. XI-6) adds another feature—a dynamic atmosphere. A dynamic atmosphere (see Chapter VII) is potentially extremely useful because it permits determinations by both techniques under thermodynamically known and reproducible conditions, so some of the objections to simultaneous determinations are not applicable (Fig. XI-7). The major problems are mechanical. Note (Fig. XI-6) that Papailhau uses a straight length of tubing. Any significant curvature would bring about a noticeable change in torque with any change in gas flow because an increase in flow—and hence in pressure—would tend to

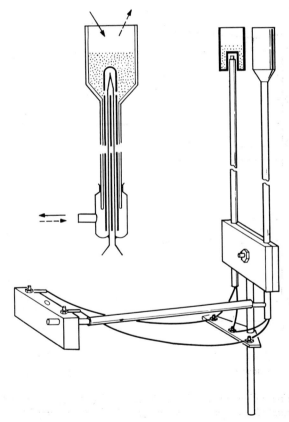

Fɪɢ. XI-6. Arrangement for passing a controlled atmosphere through a sample and measuring both temperature and weight changes. From Papailhau (P5a).

The mechanical connections have relatively little effect since the balance operates at null.

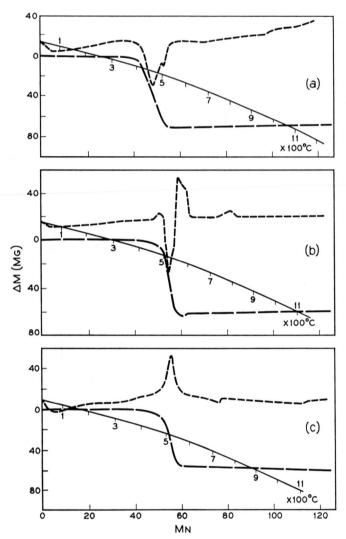

FIG. XI-7. Simultaneous thermogravimetric and differential thermal analysis of siderite in dynamic flow of (a) nitrogen, (b) air, and (c) oxygen. From Papailhau (P5a).

The known thermodynamic conditions in (a) *and* (c) *permit accurate interpretation. The attenuated oxygen supply in* (b) *leads to incomplete reaction (see Chapter VII).*

straighten the tube. If Papailhau were measuring displacement instead of maintaining a null position his calibration curve would be just that —a curve.

The matter of inserting a thermocouple into the sample has been faced—and solved—a number of times. The present author uses a helix of fine wire bent so that the stationary end hangs naturally to the point at which it is fastened (see Chapter IX). Papailhau uses a direct lead with only a slight loop. This is effective in his apparatus because it is a null instrument. Since there is no appreciable change in position any force which might be exerted between the fixed and movable parts will at least be constant.

The same constant-force argument can be applied to the tubing joining the fixed and movable parts. While the coupling might have some effect on the sensitivity, no other error is involved as long as the flow of gas is constant.

Papailhau used samples ranging from 165 to 300 mg in a geometry approximating a crucible. The thermal effects agree, of course, with the weight changes but these weight changes are quite drawn-out affairs. Any sizable reaction extends over at least 100°C. Part of the reason for the wide temperature range is the heating rate, part is the size of the sample. Papailhau heated his samples at the common differential thermal analysis rate of 10°C/minute. This is far too fast to obtain reasonable transfer of heat to a sample (see Chapter III), and especially is it difficult to heat a mass of 0.3 gm at such a rate and expect to have anything approaching uniformity. Even the dynamic atmosphere does not help for, like Stone (S50), he brings the gas to and through the sample and into the furnace chamber but, unlike Stone, he does not preheat the gas.

Paulik and co-workers (P10) used a sort of mechanical derivative with electrical pickup to do simultaneous differential thermogravimetry and, on the same specimen, thermogravimetry and differential thermal analysis. The sample and a reference material are heated in the same furnace (Fig. XI-8) and ΔT, ΔW, and dw/dt are all plotted as functions of time. The dw/dt signal arises from movement of a coil within a permanent magnet; this response should be accurately linear as long as the beam is very nearly at null and the magnet and coil are so designed that electrical response is linear with movement.

The useful weight loss range of a balance of this type is dictated by (1) the mechanical range of linear electrical response and (2) the mechanical range of constant displacement response $d\theta/dw$. Another limit is imposed on the differential thermal analysis. Movement of the sample with relation to the reference should tend to displace the base line because of the temperature gradient within the furnace.

Weltner (W13) reports curves as shown in Fig. XI-9 using the apparatus of Paulik *et al.* (P10), where the thermogravimetric curve is also shown to demonstrate how much more informative is derivative thermogravimetric analysis as compared to simple thermogravimetric analysis. The present author believes that the thermogravimetric curve could be made decidedly more informative by proper attention to sample holders (see Chapter VII). Paulik *et al.* (P11) later improved the sample holder (Fig. VII-14).

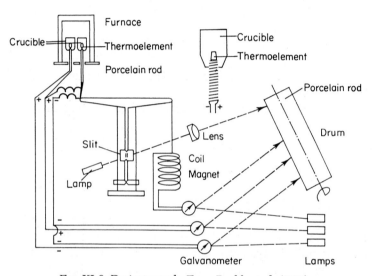

FIG. XI-8. Derivatograph. From Paulik *et al.* (P10).
The balance position is recorded directly by use of a slit on the point arm and T, ΔT, and dw/dt by use of appropriately connected galvanometers.

The technique is obviously usable to detect reactions and has the advantage over the deKeyser (K22) technique in that the area of a deflection is relatable directly to the loss in weight—as long as the limitations given above are heeded.

The technique should not be extended to very low-mass weighing devices because of the possibility of regenerative feedback between galvanometer and detecting coil. A very light balance could possibly have an oscillation period somewhere nearly equal to the period of the galvanometer. Displacement of the galvanometer during the change of position of the magnet induces an opposing voltage during the deflection —i.e., work is done on the galvanometer—but, as the movement drops to zero and reverses, the return of the galvanometer to its rest or zero position induces a voltage opposing the drop-off of detecting coil voltage and hence aiding the movement of the magnet—i.e., work is done by the galvanometer. This work would tend to carry the magnet beyond its new rest point so that it would need to return, thereby starting a galvanometer motion in the other direction, etc. Fortunately, the amount of work that could be done by the galvanometer would not be sufficient to sustain oscillation. The extra deflection would be a nuisance and could at times hinder interpretation of the curve.

This oscillation has an analog occasionally encountered by the unwary. If one attempts to supply a potential to a fairly high-speed, low-range, recording potentiometer from a potentiometer having a short period galvanometer as a null indicator, oscillation may occur if the galvanometer is neither locked nor shorted. Unless

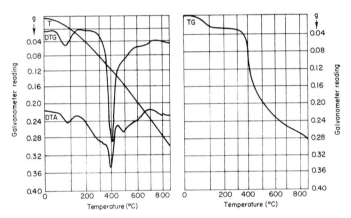

FIG. XI-9. Simultaneous thermogravimetric and differential thermal analysis of coal. From Weltner (W13).
The DTG and DTA curves show good agreement; the TG plot shows little detail.

the recording potentiometer slide-wire contact is already at the proper potential the unbalance will cause motion of both the meter movement and the recorder slide-wire. The slide-wire movement will tend to stop at the set potential but the meter is probably deflected full scale. Its movement back to null induces a voltage which sends the recorder slide-wire further in the direction of initial movement, causing the meter to deflect the other way, causing the recorder to overshoot again. The major difference between this case and the galvanometer-magnet coil case is that this former is a driven oscillator. The work supplied to the slide-wire permits continuous oscillation.

An example of the problems encountered in simultaneous determinations is offered by Kissinger *et al.* (K31) in their studies on manganese(II) carbonate (Fig. XI-10). The differential thermal analyses in the 400–600°C region show striking effects at the highest heating rate compared to the lower heating rates—yet at this highest heating rate, the detail of the weight loss curve is lost, leaving very little to which to relate these effects. The weight loss curve at 10°C/minute, for example, loses the shoulder ca 450°C seen at the lower heating rates but shows no new detail which might be related to the very sizable thermal effects. These authors were careful to use the same geometry for both speci-

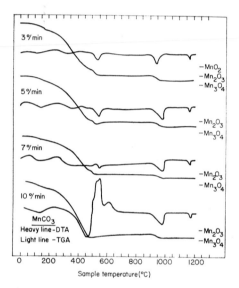

Fig. XI-10. Differential thermal analysis and thermogravimetric analysis patterns of reagent-grade manganese carbonate, MnCO₃, at various heating rates. From Kissinger *et al.* (K31).

The differential thermal analysis shows the most detail at heating rates at which thermogravimetric analysis shows the least.

men holders; the loss of detail is due to incompleteness of one reaction before the start of the next, partly because of the high heating rate and partly because of the atmosphere effect (see Chapter VII).

The atmosphere can be taken into account rather easily. The thin-layer technique—affording free interchange of gas between sample and atmosphere—has been used by McAdie (M24) for simultaneous differential thermal and thermogravimetric analysis. He uses two pans suspended on the same rod (Fig. XI-11) and measures the temperature of each by use of a thermocouple pressed into a hole in the disc. By control

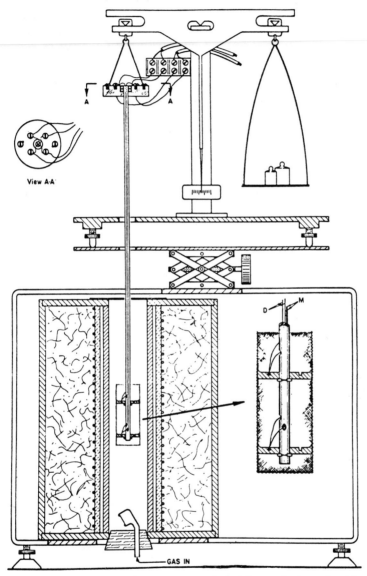

View A-A

GAS IN

FIG. XI-11. Simultaneous thermogravimetric and differential thermal analysis apparatus using free-diffusion sample holders. From McAdie (M24).
Since known thermodynamic conditions can be obtained, the data are meaningful.

of the flowing atmosphere, decomposition steps can be separated as shown in Fig. XI-2 and XI-3.

The simultaneous determinations by Reisman (R12) were done under a considerable range of heating rates with the intention of keeping the specimen near equilibrium at all times. His specimens were contained in

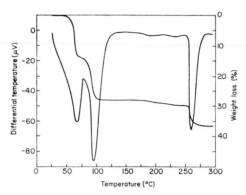

Fɪɢ. XI-12. Simultaneous thermogravimetric and differential thermal analysis of copper sulfate pentahydrate in air. From McAdie (M24).

The constant partial pressure of water vapor permits clear separation of the first two steps of the dehydration. Compare with Fig. XI-14.

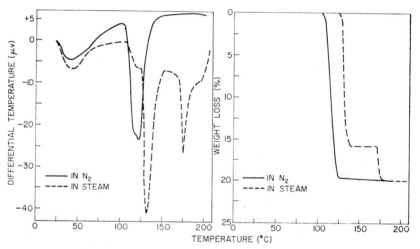

Fɪɢ. XI-13. Simultaneous thermogravimetric and differential thermal analysis of calcium sulfate dihydrate in nitrogen and in steam. From McAdie (M24).

The clear separation of the first reaction permits a better quantitative measurement of the dihydrate than by differential thermal analysis.

split crucibles mounted at the end of a counterpoised rod, both thermal effects and weight change being measured on the same sample. The work is in large part vitiated, unfortunately, by his choice of sample holders. His inability to obtain more than a minor slope anomaly for $CuSO_4 \cdot 3H_2O$ (Fig. XI-14) at a heating rate of 0.56°C/minute must be compared to McAdie's well-developed plateau (Fig. XI-12) at about twice the heating rate or to the present author's very clear break (G4) at 2°C/minute. The partial pressure of water vapor is by no

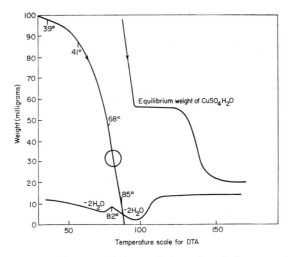

Fig. XI-14. Partial simultaneous differential thermal and thermogravimetric analysis of copper sulfate pentahydrate at ca. 0.56°C/minute. From Reisman (R12).
The lack of a clear inflection is due to nonhomogeneity of the sample during the dehydration. Some material has gone to the monohydrate before all the pentahydrate has gone to the trihydrate.

means equal throughout the crucible, and consequently the material is not all in the same state nor is the relative composition constant from top to bottom.

Similarly, the thermal and mass effects in rubidium carbonate hydrate are very probably well-described by his heating of a sample in an oil bath except that the solid crust is almost certainly the anhydrous carbonate. The crust forms quickly over the melt, showing further loss until the water vapor pressure can break through—rather than diffuse through —when the temperature is raised sufficiently.

An interesting method of detection of changes of state makes use of the adsorption of diffusing gas at interfaces between crystalline regions.

Bussiere *et al.* (B91) devised a simultaneous differential thermal analysis, thermogravimetric analysis and effluence detection using this principle. The applicability of the method would be rather uncommon but this does not imply that it may not be of great value in some particular case.

Thorium, on radioactive decay, gives off the short-lived rare gas, thoron. The gas diffuses out of the crystal of a thorium salt in the normal course of events, some escaping before further decay, but some part of the gas will tend to remain in interstices, along grain boundaries, and at other high-energy sites. During reactions or simple phase transformations, the grain boundaries are disturbed and the gas can escape more easily. If a stream of gas is passed over—or preferably through—the specimen and it is monitored by a radiation detector somewhere downstream, the additional radioactivity during a disruption can be detected. A simultaneous recording of thermal effects, change of weight, and radioactivity is shown in Fig. XIV-17.

Note that the second weight loss, the conversion of the dihydrate to the monohydrate, is reflected only by a gradual increase in radioactivity of the gas stream. This is because even a reversible event would show a time-dependent response to the "emanation analysis"; the gas must have an opportunity to return to a stable level. If the heating were stopped at 100°C and at a later time the sample were rerun, it is possible that the dehydration in the 150–200°C range would also be shown by increased "emanation." In this case, however, another behavior might be encountered. The first dehydration has very probably already caused a change in crystal structure; this one need not. Water might well be driven off without severe disturbance of the lattice and without this disturbance no disruption of grain boundaries is likely to occur. The decrease in emanation ca 300°C is very probably a dilution effect during the decomposition of the oxalate ion.

In any case in which simultaneous determinations are contemplated, the experimenter must consider whether any of the measured phenomena are time-dependent or history-dependent. If any are, special care in planning the experiment is required. Note that even in the common practice of simultaneous differential thermal and thermogravimetric analysis the differential signal is time-dependent while the weight of the specimen may be time-dependent, but for a reversible decomposition in a controlled atmosphere it is much more temperature-dependent.

In most cases the advantage lies with execution of separate experiments, each planned to extract information in the best possible manner. The present author does thermogravimetric and differential thermal analysis on separate apparatuses and at different times (Chapter XVII) yet has no trouble obtaining relatable data. The important consideration is the agreement of thermodynamic conditions, in particular the atmosphere and its degree of confinement (see Chapter VII). Figures XI-15 and XI-16 show thermogravimetric and differential thermal analysis data for cobalt oxalate hydrate and lead carbonate in which there is no difficulty relating the effects.

Nearly the ultimate in simultaneous operations was attempted by Blazek (B55) who constructed a thermobalance with provision for recording a differential thermal analysis and a gaseous decomposition

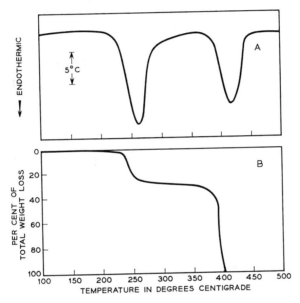

FIG. XI-15. Thermal (a) and mass (b) effects in the thermal decomposition of cobalt oxalate dihydrate in a closed-chamber sample holder (Figs. III-23 and VII-13). From Garn (G4).

The dehydration and the loss of carbon dioxide show clear agreement. The cobalt oxalate is degraded to the metal.

product analysis simultaneously with the thermogravimetric analysis. Like Kissinger *et al.* (K31) or McAdie (M24) he used separate specimens but unlike these other authors he did not use the same geometry. The furnace (Fig. XI-17) had two chambers, one for the thermogravimetric analysis and the other for the gas and differential thermal analysis. The latter chamber (Fig. XI-18) has separate holders for the differential thermal analysis and for the gas analysis samples. Fortunately Blazek used only inert gases passing through the furnaces so that, while each specimen might react somewhat differently as a function of time, the disagreement would be relatively small. The need to place three different sample holders so that each is heated equally is already rather difficult when they are the same shape; vertical furnaces can be expected to have temperature gradients. When at least one of the samples (differential thermal analysis) is necessarily going to be heated unsymmetrically because of its shape, really good agreement is out of the question. The one simultaneous differential thermal and thermogravimetric analysis reported (Fig. XI-19) shows poor agreement. While the differ-

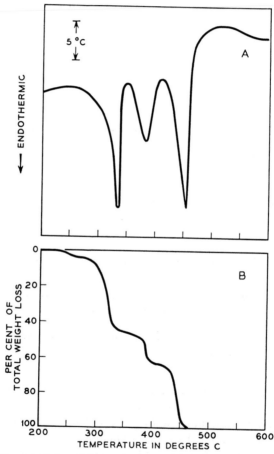

Fig. XI-16. Thermal (a) and mass (b) effects in the thermal decomposition of lead carbonate in a closed-chamber sample holder. From Garn (G4).

Each loss of carbon dioxide is clearly separated because the decomposition— in each experiment—occurs in an atmosphere of carbon dioxide.

ential thermal analysis peak coincides with the completion of the weight loss at the lower-temperature weight loss ca. 300°C, it occurs ca. 100°C after the weight loss at the higher-temperature decomposition.

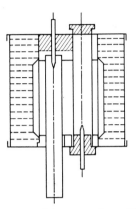

FIG. XI-17. Section of furnace. From Blazek (B55).
The thermogravimetric sample is in a crucible—supported from the balance be-neath—in the left-hand chamber.

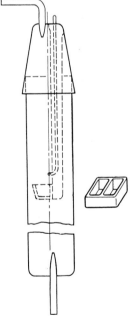

FIG. XI-18. Quartz casing for gas analysis and DTA. From Blazek (B55).
The several containers are not all positioned for equal heating.

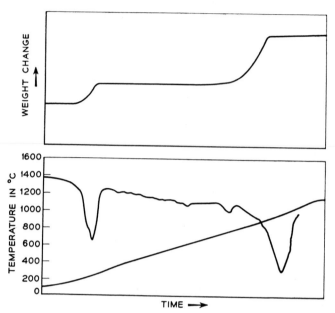

Fɪɢ. XI-19. Decomposition curve of manganous sulfate. From Blazek (B55).
The thermogravimetric sample is probably located higher in its chamber than is the differential thermal analysis sample in its chamber. Not only is the temperature higher but also the heat transfer would be better.

11.4. Summary

The conditions of sample size, geometry, heating rate, etc., which are best for one type of measurement may be quite incompatible with the conditions best for another. Properly chosen experiments can yield better data by separate experiments. Differential thermal analysis combined with thermogravimetry will often lead to poor results.

Nevertheless, if compatible techniques (see also Chapter XII) are chosen and experimental conditions set up so that any needs incident to the taking of one masurement have no influence on any other, a number of parameters can be measured simultaneously and the data will have meaning.

Other
Techniques

12.1. Introduction

From time to time problems appear in which differential thermal or thermogravimetric analysis is unsuccessful. Assuming that a thermal technique for dynamic analysis is needed, one of several special techniques may be appropriate. The techniques discussed in this chapter are generally less useful than differential thermal or thermogravimetric analysis and for this reason are unlikely to be widely used; nevertheless any of them might be useful in some specific case. The techniques may be used as detection methods or, in some cases, as primary measurements providing specifically the desired information.

No exhaustive examination of the literature in these fields has been undertaken; rather specific examples have been selected. This chapter is intended in large part to acquaint the experimenter with these other modes of attack on a problem. A secondary purpose is to offer sufficient instruction to enable the experimenter to avoid some of the possible troubles.

12.2. Dilatometry

The measurement of dimensions or volume as the material is heated or cooled is principally useful when these specific data comprise the information sought. As a means of detecting changes in state it is advantageous in only a few cases. Nevertheless it can be used and the reader should have some acquaintance with the techniques and limitations. Note that the relative nonutility for *detecting* changes does not imply nonutility for *studying* the changes.

Several techniques for measuring linear expansion are useful. Dial gages, micrometers, telescopes, linear variable differential transformers, interferometers, and X-ray diffraction patterns have all been reported.

All of these except the last measure the linear expansion of the specimen as it is set in the apparatus. For nonisotropic materials the expansion will presumably differ and additional experiments with differently oriented samples may be needed. X-ray diffraction measurements yield expansion data for all directions if the lines have been properly catalogued.

During the preparation of this monograph an experimental dilatometer for both sub- and supra-ambient temperatures was constructed at Bell Telephone Laboratories by H. A. Sauer (S7). The measuring and programming systems were the same for both ranges but since the heat conducting and insulating problems are different in the two ranges different test chambers were used. In either case the test chamber (Fig. XII-1) is heated or cooled by a circulating gas whose temperature is controlled by the programmer. Measurements may be recorded, then,

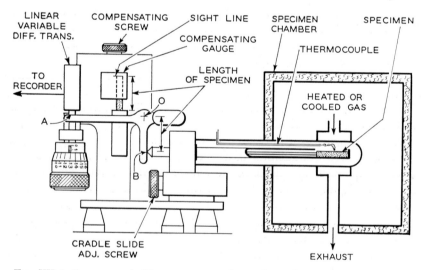

Fig. XII-1. Programmed dilatometer providing sub- and supra-ambient temperatures. From Sauer (S7).

Linear expansion of a rod is recorded directly as a fractional change.

as the specimen is heated, as it is cooled, or at constant temperature.

The sensing element is a linear variable differential transformer whose rectified output is recorded directly. The mechanical linkage to the transformer is through an adjustable mechanical amplifier (the pivot arm). Adjustment of the compensating screw of Fig. XII-1 to bring the top of the specimen to the sight line moves the pivot arm so that the contact point from the bearing rod is precisely one sample length from the fulcrum. In effect, the linear variable differential transformer sees a fixed length of specimen, in this case 100 mm long, and the change recorded is the change in 100 mm of specimen. The transformer may be moved by the micrometer screw for calibration and for zeroing.

Volume expansion is of special value for organic materials and particularly those which are not highly oriented. (Mechanical measurements of linear expansion generally require some firm mechanical contact which could cause deformation of soft specimens.) Fluid displacement is, of course, the simplest method of observing volume changes.

The usefulness of the technique for organic materials is a consequence of the low thermal conductivity of these materials and the occurrence of glass transitions in polymeric materials. The low heating rates ordinarily needed to obtain a reasonably small temperature gradient render the base line discontinuity difficult to detect. Higher rates of heating that cause a significant time lag between the initiation of the change at the edge and completion at the center quite naturally cause a rounding of the discontinuity. While these transitions can usually be detected by differential thermal analysis, static methods such as dilatometry are at least not out of place and are sometimes necessary.

The system of Loasby (L9) illustrates the use of volume expansion. The changing displacement of the sample in Fig. XII-2 is converted to linear motion by the bellows. The large sample and relatively small volume of oil permits rather good sensitivity. The maximum sensitivity is obtained by (1) designing the sample so that it just barely fails to touch the sides at maximum temperature and (2) adding just enough oil to the bellows to bring it out of contact with the sample. Some mechanical amplification can easily be obtained by enclosing the specimen in a rigid container attached to a narrower bellows or, of course, by measuring the volume expanding into a narrow tube. The former would usually be unnecessary because adequately sensitive measurements for most purposes can be made without the mechanical amplification. The second would simply require a different method of measurement. The volume expansion dilatometer can be constructed over a considerable range of sensitivities depending on the particular needs of the user. For temperatures more than just slightly different from ambient the sample chamber of Fig. XII-2 would be enclosed in a thermostatted bath. Note that the specimen need not be a single massive piece. While this massive specimen would provide better sensitivity, small chunks of material can be used. These latter could be expected to reach thermal equilibrium more quickly.

The dilatometers using position-sensing transducers to obtain an electrical signal to record will generally need to be calibrated. The calibration may, in fact, be required before and/or after each run; the linear

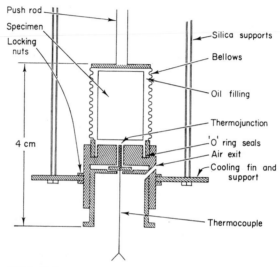

FIG. XII-2. Volume expansion dilatometer. From Loasby (L9).
Expansion or contraction in all directions is converted to unidirectional movement.

variable transformer often used gives a good, sensitive measure of changes of position but an essential part of the experiment will be the simulation of the run by an accurately known change. Lieberman and Crandall (L7) devised a self-calibrating dilatometer (Fig. XII-3) which recorded change in fractions of a fixed unit. They attached an optical grating to the end of their support rod so that it moved as the specimen expanded or contracted and passed a light beam through this and another grating. The measured intensity of the light falling on a photocell is recorded but only an uncalibrated measurement is needed. If the output is simply adjusted so that the recorded maximum and minimum intensities do not go off scale, a plot such as that in Fig. XII-4 will be obtained as the sample expands or contracts. For a 500 lines per inch grating, a full deflection is obtained then for each 0.00100 inch of movement and the sensitivity will likely be limited by the perfection of the grating, i.e., the accuracy of reading of the maxima and minima. The accuracy will only be compromised in that particular cycle; the integral traverses of grating lines will be unaffected. An absolute accuracy of, say, ½% of scale, rather than a relative accuracy, is obtained.

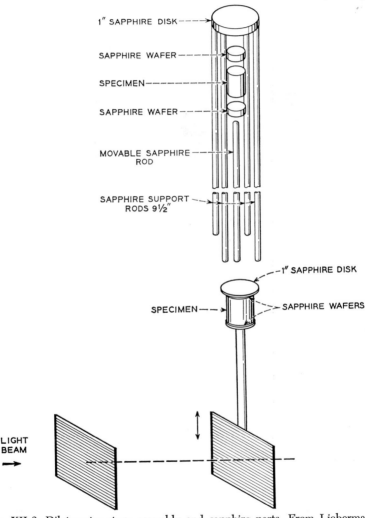

Fig. XII-3. Dilatometer stage assembly and sapphire parts. From Lieberman and Crandall (L7).

The resolution within a half cycle will depend on the collimation of the light and the alignment and quality of the gratings because of their effect on the sharpness of the maxima and minima.

The slight possibility of misinterpretation of the data due to reversal of direction of travel when the intensity happens to be at a maximum or minimum can be avoided; the present author would use a grating with one end shielded so that successive intensity maxima became greater or less as the specimen expanded or contracted. By the time another maximum has passed the actual direction of travel would be unequivocally known.

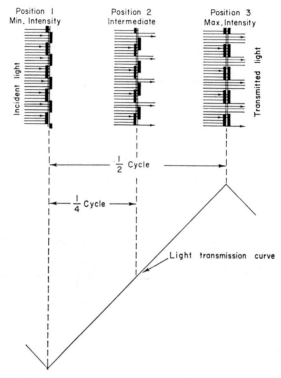

Fig. XII-4. Relation between grating position and light transmission. From Lieberman and Crandall (L7).

Within a half cycle the effect of grating defects is small because the total intensity from a large number of apertures is measured.

Thermal expansion data may also be obtained by X-ray diffraction, but this is ordinarily a static technique (see, for example, Campbell's array of data on magnesium oxide (C5).

Another type of optical recording was used by Dannis (D2). He rested one leg of a tripod carrying a mirror on the specimen and recorded the position of the light beam (Fig. XII-5) in a manner similar to that of Keith and Tuttle (K14). The use of photoresistors is probably more covenient experimentally than the phototube used by Keith and Tuttle. Dannis obtained the curve of Fig. XII-6 using the apparatus. The temperature was recorded from a 38-gauge thermocouple to avoid any extraneous movement due to springiness or differences in thermal expansion of the thermocouple wires (D1).

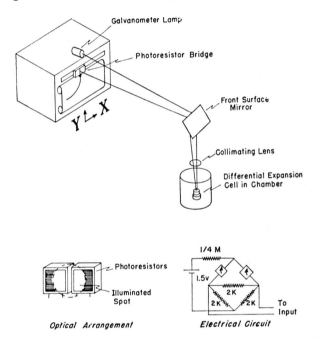

FIG. XII-5. Schematic arrangement of expansion apparatus with details of photo-resistor arrangement. From Dannis (D2).

The expansion or contraction of the specimen displaces the mirror. The pen carriage moves to keep the photoresistor cells in the reflected beam.

12.3. Electrical Measurements

The electrical properties of a solid material can be of use in detecting changes of state. Consider, for example, a well-crystallized ordinary salt or oxide which can undergo a crystallographic phase transformation. In either form the energy levels are well-defined and are properly filled, leaving a very few electrons in the high-energy conduction levels. During a phase transformation, however, an unrest appears. The movement of ions from the one configuration to the other quite necessarily disturbs the order of the system as the valence electrons settle into their new energy states. During this transitory disorder electrons are relatively free to move and, under the influence of an electric field, conduct current.

If we measure the resistance of a pure material as it is heated, then we may expect a decrease in resistance during the time of transition followed by an increase to some not necessarily equal level. The extent of the decrease and the temperature or time interval over which it occurs should be dependent not only on the nature of the material but also—to a lesser degree—on its history.

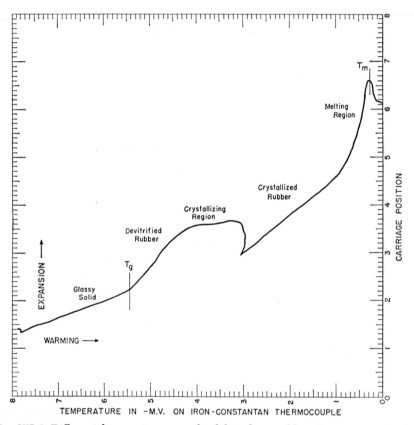

FIG. XII-6. Differential expansion curve of polybutadiene rubber. From Dannis (D2). *Changes in state can be detected by changes in rate of expansion.*

The ease of detection of polymorphic phase changes will depend on the experimental apparatus and technique. Reisman *et al.* (R16) measured the voltage drop across a specimen in series with a known resistance, thereby obtaining actual resistance values. The present author, with Flaschen (G11), preferred to use a resistance bridge and obtain only an indication of change. Neither set of authors used the alternate technique so a critical comparison is not available.

The latter authors (G11) were only able to detect very easily not only the effect due to a drastic phase change (Fig. XII-7a) in a pure material and to the corresponding transition in a solid solution with an isomorphic material (Fig. XII-7b) but even the effect due to the relatively small shift (Fig. XII-7c) during the α-β quartz transition. Melting points (Fig. XII-7d) would present no difficulty even with very simple equipment.

An important virtue of the technique is that highly accurate temperature programming is not needed. The time or temperature range of the deflection should be unaffected by relatively small—but even abrupt—changes in heating rate. The magnitude of the deflection should be affected by the heating rate because at higher heating rates a greater portion of the sample could be expected to be changing at a given time (Fig. XII-8).

The example shown in Fig. XII-8 is unusual in that the resistance increases during the transition. Barium titanate has a positive temperature coefficient of resistance whose range and magnitude depend on the nature and quality of impurities.

The polarizability of a material varies only slowly with temperature in the absence of any change in state. The mobility during a change permits relatively great movement during the time that the ion is in a disordered state so that the dielectric constant increases and subsequently decreases, yielding plots with temperature similar to that of I-13.

12.4. X-Ray Diffraction

A technique only recently approaching its real potentialities in thermal analysis is X-ray diffraction. The analysis of samples at room temperature after heating to some temperature at which the observer believes a given—but no other—reaction has taken place is simple X-ray analysis and need not be treated here. Of substantially greater interest are studies performed on heated samples.

Several authors have reported results using X-ray diffraction on samples held at an elevated constant temperature. These constant-temperature studies are perfectly straightforward for crystal structure measurements, including the detection of crystallographic phase transformations. Ordinary changes in crystal structure can be located on the temperature scale with an accuracy limited by the accuracies of control and measurement of the temperature of the sample. A few diffraction patterns taken at temperature intervals in the vicinity of the suspected transition will narrow the range; a few more will bracket it more closely and the

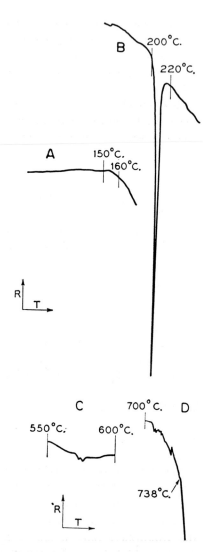

Fig. XII-7. Change of electrical resistance during phase changes for: (a) single crystal of potassium niobate; (b) ceramic of potassium niobate-tantalate (0.90:0.10); (c) single crystal of quartz; and (d) powdered sodium bromide. From Garn and Flaschen (G11).

The indications may be a brief period of disorder (a), *a well-defined change in temperature coefficient* (b), *or sharp discontinuity* (d) *in resistance. In* (d) *the recorder pen went off scale during the deflection starting at 738°C. The earlier minor change is due to premelting.*

transition temperature may then be determined with a preciseness dependent on the accuracy of the apparatus and the diligence of the operator. Similarly, the cell dimensions may be determined at each of a
number of temperatures to determine the thermal expansion coefficient.

For those samples which decompose, especially reversibly, to give off
a gaseous product the arguments previously advanced concerning the
agreement between differential thermal analysis and thermogravimetric
analysis apply. More accurately, the arguments apply with special force
because of the geometry of the specimen. In differential thermal analy-

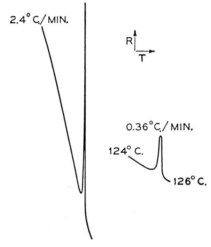

Fig. XII-8. Change of electrical resistance with temperature for barium titanate
single crystal. From Garn and Flaschen (G11).
The transient positive temperature coefficient of resistance occurs over a consider-
able temperature range in ceramic compositions.

sis without a dynamic atmosphere the orthodox sample geometry is a
cylinder exposed to the atmosphere only at one end. The temperatures
of interest are found at some high heating rates. The X-ray sample, on
the other hand, is a tiny cylinder exposed over the whole surface except
for the support end, a small wedge also with most of the surface exposed,
or a rather thin layer with one side (nearly half of the total surface area
of the bulk sample) exposed. This sample is then heated at one temperature for about the same length of time as that during which the
differential thermal analysis sample was heated through its whole
range. If there is another decomposition (reversible) within the next
hundred degrees it is almost certain to take place during these 2 or more

hours. Control of the atmosphere might prevent the unwanted reaction. Solid-state reactions could not be prevented by these controlled atmospheres.

Weiss and Rowland (W12) devised a technique for oscillating the goniometer across a selected X-ray diffraction maximum. This scanning permits repetitive automatic examination of a single diffraction as the sample is heated. Since the limits of travel of the goniometer are known, any excursions of the maximum intensity due to lattice expansion may be measured. The principal objective, however, is the detection of the appearance, disappearance, or sudden shift of position of a diffraction due to a change in state.

The shift in position can be observed readily because the scanning limits are within the background region and have already a moderate

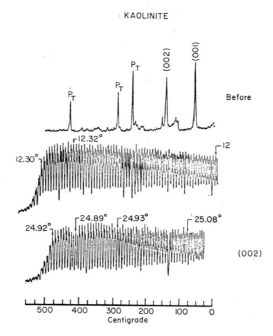

FIG. XII-9. Heating-oscillating patterns of the first and second order of the basal spacing of kaolinite. From Weiss and Rowland (W12).

As the temperature increases, the peak shifts to a higher 2θ due to lattice expansion. This is shown by the increase in intensity at the low-angle limit. In the 475–525°C region, the peak disappears because of the decomposition of the kaolinite. Note that the decomposition of this rather thin film is well under way at 500°C (see Chapters V and VII).

intensity. Since the limits are in regions of fairly high $(dI/d2\theta)$ slope and this slope has opposite signs at either end, a slight shift of the diffraction will cause an increase in the background at one end and a decrease at the other. An example of the data of Weiss and Rowland is shown in Fig. XII-9, with some explanatory additions by the (present) author.

After the room temperature diffraction record is obtained (Fig. XII-9), the goniometer is set to scan as small a range as is practicable. These limits take into account the background slopes and any expected shift in the maximum and obviously depend to a fair degree on the previous experience or knowledge of the operator concerning the specimen. The background intensity limits are preferably equal and of moderate intensity at the beginning. The furnace program is started and the scanning continued automatically. At Weiss and Rowland's 5°C/minute heating rate, the specimen's diffraction peak was scanned at 3°C intervals.

Rowland *et al.* (R35) have reported on a small sample mount, Fig. XII-10, and a program control, Fig. XII-11, designed to drive the sample holder temperature to 1000°C. The tiny heating element is in good contact with the sample so the temperature indication and response to programming should be very satisfactory.

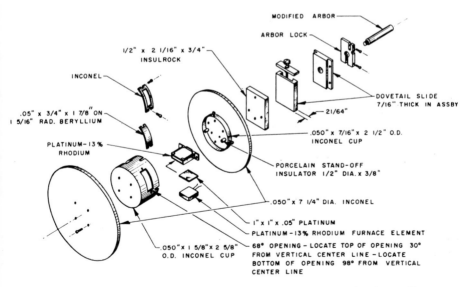

FIG. XII-10. Cutaway drawing of components of specimen holder for oscillating-heating X-ray diffraction studies. From Rowland *et al.* (R35).

The sample is heated from below by the furnace element.

The control system is not well-designed for the heater described, since the control variables are not permitted to operate over their full range. From their description, the furnace element has a hot resistance of 8 ohms and their controller needs to supply no more than 80 watts. Since $E^2/R = P = 80$ watts $= E^2/8$ ohms, E is in the order of 25 volts at maximum power input. With line voltage input, the system should always be operating at 75%, or more, turndown. The control current from the amplifier must necessarily perform with three quarters of its range inaccessible. With this type of furnace, Rowland, Weiss, and Lewis no doubt were able to control well even without proportional band, etc., corrections. The control thermocouple is so close to the heater that response is immediate.

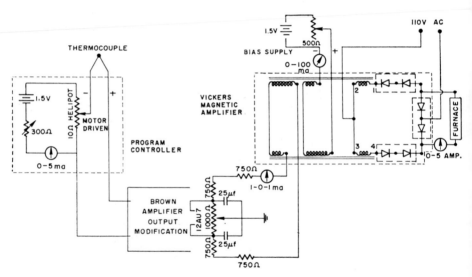

Fig. XII-11. Schematic diagram of program controller. From Rowland *et al.* (R35). *The linear thermocouple output programming provides a somewhat nonlinear temperature program but this is less serious than in differential thermal analysis.*

Examine Rowland, Weiss, and Lewis' data for the decomposition of a sodium montmorillonite-glycol complex (Fig. XII-12). Bear in mind that (1) the descriptive numbers are taken from the goniometer setting and, in accordance with X-ray diffraction practice, are twice the angle that the reflecting plane makes with the beam; (2) since $n\lambda = 2d \sin \theta$, the angle θ and the lattice spacing are inversely related, hence an increasing 2θ implies a diminishing spacing; (3) complexes of this nature formed at room temperature are not necessarily in their most stable state and diminution in size on heating is to be expected; and (4) increase in relative stability is indicated by increased intensity of the peak since the peak intensity is a measure of the order of the system. Rowland *et al.* point out: "Sodium montmorillonite also forms a two-layer glycol complex with a spacing at 5.17° 2θ (17.2 a.u.). As the temperature is increased this complex stabilizes and reaches maximum stability between 50° and 70°C. at a spacing of 5.20° 2θ (17 a.u.). Above 70°C. the intensity begins to decrease and by 80°C. there are remnants of the two-layer complex mixed with a separate one-layer complex. At about 90°C. the one-layer complex begins to stabilize at 6.53° 2θ (13.6 a.u.)

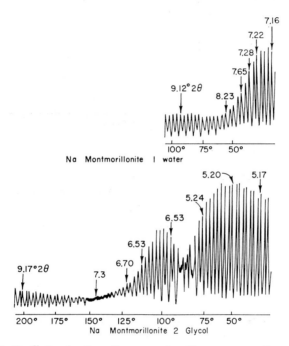

Fɪɢ. XII-12. Oscillating-heating diagrams of sodium montmorillonite with water and with glycol layers. From Rowland *et al.* (R35).

The increasing order of a newly formed species can be observed.

and reaches maximum stability between 100° and 110°C. Thereafter, the intensity begins to decrease and by 120°C. the one-layer complex has collapsed to a spacing of 6.70° 2θ (13.2 a.u.). The remaining glycol is driven off and at 160°C. the spacing is 9.10° 2θ (9.7 a.u.), which represents the collapsed lattice without glycol."

Now let us consider the details of construction of the furnace arrangement used as an example, but with the clear understanding that, since the design elements to be discussed are quite generally used, the criticisms expounded apply equally generally. We will note only briefly the atmosphere effect since that is covered elsewhere. The changing atmosphere will influence decomposition patterns and, since the ease of diffusion in and out of the furnace will vary from one design to another, the temperatures of decomposition will be more or less unique to the apparatus.

An equally serious flaw exists in the heating arrangement. The specimen is in good thermal contact with the heater on one side; the other side is exposed to unheated surfaces. At low temperatures the gradient across the specimen will be relatively small (except during a reaction) but at high temperatures the increasing radiation of heat from particle to particle of the specimen is quite unlikely to compensate for the radiation from the face of the sample which is also increasing.

A high-temperature X-ray specimen could be heated more satisfactorily by radiation from a source not in mechanical contact. (Remember that the X-ray beam only penetrates a few layers.) A thin specimen on an insulating material could be used satisfactorily.

12.5. Thermomicroscopy

Observation of phase changes of bulk samples is perfectly feasible—within narrow limits. Temperature gradients can lead to sizable errors. These same gradients will cause even rapid changes to occur over a large time interval. Polarized light cannot be generally used. For these reasons optical thermal analysis is normally done microscopically and the specimen is heated on a specially designed hot stage. Since microscopists have in effect pre-empted the field, the term thermomicroscopy came into use rather than optical thermal analysis. That convention is followed herein.

We may best consider thermomicroscopy in two parts depending on the temperature range. The lower range comprises all temperatures—above and below room temperature—at which the specimen is not very thermally luminous; the higher range comprises the temperatures at which the sample is thermally luminous. Naturally there is some overlapping since the observations possible at room temperature are not rendered impossible discontinuously as the sample becomes faintly luminous. Let us consider only the more generally applicable lower-temperature thermomicroscopy and further confine our attention to the range from room temperature to a few hundred degrees centigrade. Cold stages are available commercially but the same effects are observed as may be seen in different specimens at more convenient temperatures. The problems involved are roughly the same.

Thermomicroscopy in this range is of rather moderate use in inorganic studies but is an important tool for most organic work. The size and complexity of nearly any organic molecule renders optical isotropy impossible. Polarized light may be used to detect very sharply the growth, disappearance, or rearrangement of crystals. (A major hazard is that such observation is likely to become an avocation.) Since the detailed techniques of thermomicroscopy can properly constitute a separate volume, only basic instruction will be offered herein. The reader may find a more extensive treatment in McCrone's (M25) book, from which the present author has learned much.

The observation of thermal effects is generally done on specimens placed on an ordinary microscope slide, covered with a cover glass, and set on a heating stage. The temperature of the hot-stage block is measured by use of a thermometer inserted in the block. Two problems immediately arise: thermal homogeneity and measuring error.

The thermal homogeneity of the slide is not even assumed ordinarily; instead, an empirically chosen set of conditions is used so that the small area under observation is nearly isothermal. The principal condition is a fairly rigorously controlled slow heating rate. The observed temperature of thermal effect depends strongly on the heating rate.

The measuring error is closely related to the thermal inhomogeneity. Consider a heating stage being heated at some customary rate such as 2°C/minute and assume that the heating has been proceeding for several minutes and a nearly steady-state transfer of heat to the sample prevails. The sample is in a part of the slide not in contact with the block—since we shall want to pass light through the sample; further, the thin cover glass over the specimen is in close proximity to the microscope objective—a fairly large heat sink that does not much exceed room temperature. A significant difference in temperature must therefore exist between the sample and the thermometer.

The first of these sources of error is dependent on heating rate, the second on temperature. The use of prescribed conditions of heating and observation will permit reproducibility—generally—even though there is a real error.

The existence of these difficulties should not cause the reader to shun the technique. One may look with dismay at the temperature measurement without losing sight of the extensive qualitative information which may be derived therefrom.

Thermomicroscopy is generally carried out by visual observation but there is no reason why this observation cannot be mechanized. Reese *et al.* (R11) set up an arrangement (Fig. XII-13) which permits detection of polymorphic phase transformations by measurement (recording) of light intensity. The light is polarized and analyzed by crossed polarizing filters; this has the advantage that melting is detected rather specifically by the drop in intensity of transmitted light. This condition exists because the occurrence of an isotropic organic solid is rare among the materials likely to be studied. The light intensity is adjusted at the start of the run; any change thereafter—excluding ordinary drift—should be relatable to some change in state of the specimen. Figure I-11 shows their results for amobarbital.

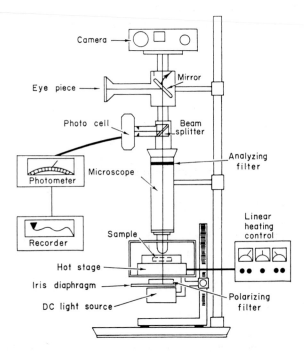

Fig. XII-13. Apparatus for optical detection of phase changes. From Reese *et al.* (R11).

The change in intensity of the polarized light may be detected instrumentally or visually and a photograph taken.

12.6. Thermal Conductivity

Any property which shows a discontinuous change may be used to detect and determine the temperature at which the change occurs, including thermal conductivity, the bête noir of the many derivers of equations for differential thermal analysis. Claussen (C16), who refers to his technique as differential thermal conductivity analysis, studied the shift of the α-γ iron transformation at pressures up to one hundred thousand atmospheres using a nickel reference for the iron piece under study (Fig. XII-14). The furnace arrangement is rather ingenious. The entire assembly is within the pressure device and the heating elements surround the specimens. Claussen provides his temperature gradient by stacking discs of lava against the nickel equalizing disc at one end and alumina discs against the equalizing disc at the other. Since the lava has a higher thermal conductivity than the alumina the disc at that end will be hotter and a gradient will be set up.

Claussen assumes that in the absence of a phase change the temperature at the center of the nickel reference strip ought to be the same as the temperature at the center of the iron specimen because of the

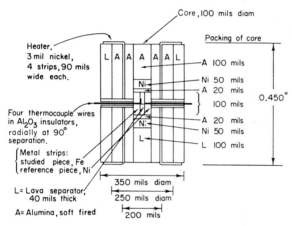

Fig. XII-14. Complete differential thermal conductivity analysis cell design. From Claussen (C16).

A temperature gradient exists between the ends of the strips because of the difference in thermal conductivity between the lava and alumina discs in the ends.

equalizing blocks at the ends. He is then forced to offer a very questionable explanation for the base line drift of the typical curves 2, 3, and 4 of Fig. XII-15. This explanation involves a possible high heat flux between the heater strips and the test strips (across the alumina bushing). He observed also that "more perfect maxima ΔT curves were obtained with cells containing nickel heaters than with Nichrome heaters." He attributes this to heater characteristics: "Nickel would tend to produce a hot spot. Nichrome would produce more even heat."

A more probable reason for the base line drift is the continual change in the temperature gradient. The difference in thermal conductivity of the reference and test specimens (nickel is about twice as good a conductor as iron in the transformation temperature region) would be of no importance if the temperature difference between the equalizer blocks were constant. The central points would be at the same temperature in steady-state heating while no discontinuous change was occuring anywhere in the specimen. On the other hand, if the temperature difference between the equalizer blocks varies, the temperature gradients within the metal specimens will vary over their lengths and the midpoint of neither will necessarily have a temperature halfway between the temperatures of its ends. Further, the two midpoints will not change to the same degree because of the difference in thermal conductivity and its influence on the heat transfer to the specimens. Therefore, if the temperature difference between the equalizer blocks is increasing—or decreasing, for that matter—the ΔT signal will become larger. The drift of curves 2, 3, and 4 is to be expected in this system.

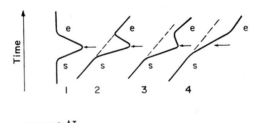

FIG. XII-15. Typical ΔT curves on recorder charts: s = start of transformation; e = end of transformation; → = transformation half-completed. From Claussen (C16).
The marked base line drift could prevent detection of transitions; any more severe drift would render curve 4 quite doubtful.

Claussen shows (Fig. XII-16) a variation in transformation temperature rather different from Strong's (S68) data. Neither cites the purity of the test specimen. Differences in impurities might account for the apparent discrepancy. The differences in results with different heater materials are much more likely due to a change in construction whether planned or inadvertent.

The technique could be improved by providing a reference specimen more nearly like the sample. The material most like the sample would be another specimen of the same material. If two such pieces were used and spacers added to the high-temperature end of one and to the low-temperature end of the other, the gradient within the pieces would be nearly the same but with a geometric and temporal displacement. Now if thermocouples are attached to appropriate points a small differential signal with small drift could be obtained. This near equality of temperature ought to be very significantly disturbed during the traverse of the phase change in the specimens. While there would be small changes in heat flow across the boundary, this initial perturbation as the hotter end of one and then the other specimen began the transformation should be small in comparison to the effects seen as the transition passed one and then the other of the thermocouple locations.

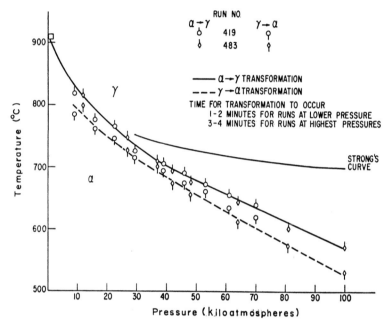

Fig. XII-16. Effect of pressure on α-γ transformation in iron. Pressure calibration is based on the transitions for Bi and Ba, which were assumed to occur at 24,800 and 77,400 atmospheres, respectively. From Claussen (C16).

The difference in temperature of transition on heating and cooling ranges from ca 15 to 04 C.

The more prosaic thermal conductivity measurements, in which the data wanted are actually the values directly obtained, can be done in a multitude of ways. As in most of the techniques described in this monograph no one manner is of general applicability. Kingery (K28) discusses a number of methods including spherical and cylindrical configurations for the sample. His cylindrical test assembly (K27) is shown in Fig. XII-17. Note that the thermocouple junctions are centered along the axis and that the axis is relatively long. A major problem is the avoidance of axial heat flow. This axial heat flow will be least, of course, where the axial temperature distribution is most nearly uniform.

End effects and such are eliminated by use of spherical sample holders but the problems of uniform heating and obtaining precisely concentric sample, containers, and central heater are severe. Beck (B20) has, in effect, inverted the technique; he devised a spherical sample container

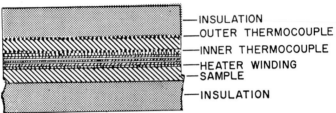

—INSULATION
—OUTER THERMOCOUPLE
—INNER THERMOCOUPLE
—HEATER WINDING
—SAMPLE
—INSULATION

FIG. XII-17. Cross section of cylindrical assembly for measuring thermal conductivity. From Kingery (K27).

The heat dissipated by the electrical resistor must be conducted outward. The temperature difference and dimensions of the sample and the amount of heat dissipated are used to calculate the thermal conductivity.

with only a thermocouple at the center (Fig. XII-18). The containing block was heated and the temperature difference between block and sample measured. The uniformity of packing is questionable indeed, but since Berg was concerned with detection of effects (Fig. XII-19) rather than precise measurement of effects the relative inaccuracy is not important. Note, however, that even a close approach to a real measurement of thermal conductivity is obtained only between thermal effects.

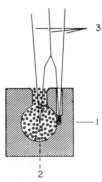

FIG. XII-18. Spherical sample holder for thermal analysis. From Berg and Sidorova (B41).

Although thermal conductivity in nonsteady-state heating could be measured the device is useful for detecting phase changes.

12.7. Calorimetry

The change in temperature of a specimen or system including specimen as heat is added can be related to the heat of reaction. Several approaches are used depending on the information sought. The heating may be stepwise, continuous, a single pulse, or supplied by the sample.

If the heat capacity is of principal interest the calorimetry will generally be done stepwise on moderately large specimens. In such a case a calorimeter of the type shown in Fig. XII-20 may be used. The addition of a known quantity of heat to the central assembly by supplying a

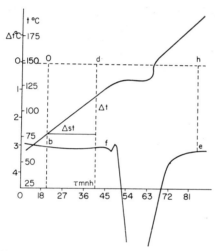

Fɪɢ. XII-19. Thermogram obtained with the sample holder of Fig. XII-18. From Berg and Sidorova (B41).

In essence, the plot yields a differential thermogram with a nonzero base line.

known electric power for a measured time is followed by the diffusion of this heat throughout the specimen. The ensuing steady temperature, when reached, is measured and another quantity of heat added. The empty calorimeter must be calibrated because of the rather substantial mass of the heater and sample holder assembly.

Since at temperatures substantially different from ambient the loss of heat to the surroundings could become a source of significant error, the common practice is to surround the sample holder with a jacket whose temperature is controlled to match the surface of the sample holder (ΔT of Fig. XII-20 is maintained at zero) by the outer heater. This becomes, then, an adiabatic calorimeter. Insulation from the outside condition simplifies control. The temperature of the sample need not be measured at the edge as shown in Fig. XII-20 since the equilibrium temperature is measured, it can be done anywhere.

Heats of reaction can be measured in this type of calorimeter, but if the heat of reaction data are to be referred to room temperature an isothermal calorimeter would more often be used. In this type of apparatus the outside is maintained at some chosen temperature (for relatively imprecise measurements on short-term reactions, moderate insulation from ambient temperature is enough) and the rise or fall of the calorimeter temperature is measured. This rise or fall is deliberately made to

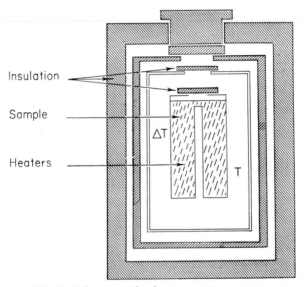

FIG. XII-20. Calorimeter for heat capacity measurements.
From this general plan the more complex design for minimizing mechanical contacts and other sources of heat loss can be evolved.

be of low magnitude so that the actual change in temperature has little influence on the values obtained. A water jacket or other heat sink is generally used.

Much high-temperature calorimetry has been done by the "drop" method, in which a sample is brought to thermal equilibrium at the temperature of interest, a release mechanism is operated, and the sample falls into a calorimeter in which the sample's total heat content difference between the initial and final temperatures is measured. This heat content refers, obviously, to the specimen in whatever form it was at the time it was dropped. Heats of decomposition are not determinable in this manner; some kind of adiabatic system with controlled atmosphere or isothermal system with special provisions would be needed. Foldvari-Vogl and Kliburszky (F12) have constructed an apparatus especially for determining heats of reaction for events occurring at elevated temperatures and have eliminated the possible error involving the heat content of the released gas. Under reasonably favorable conditions, it should be very useful.

Their calorimeter comprises an externally insulated copper vessel containing 200 ml of water, a calorimetric bomb, and a small furnace inside the bomb. This small furnace has an inside winding; the filament is in direct contact with the sample. A thermocouple is centered in the furnace. The bomb has connected to it a capillary tube 50 cm long through which gaseous products escape. This capillary tube is immersed nearly all its length in the water of the calorimeter so that any gas leaving the hot zone gives up its heat before escaping.

In use, the sample is placed in the small furnace and the bomb closed. The system is allowed to come to thermal equilibrium, then a measured current is passed through the heating coils until the indicated temperature of the specimen rises to some point at which the reaction is known to be complete. The furnace is turned off, and the bomb is allowed to cool; the heat is given up to the surrounding water. The temperature rise of the water is measured in the usual manner. By comparison of the heat added electrically and the heat recovered thermally the heat of reaction at ambient temperature may be determined. By substituting appropriate values for the heat capacities of all species involved, the heat of reaction at the elevated temperature may be calculated (see Chapter V).

The rapid heating is a probable source of trouble. The rapid heating insures a temperature lag within the sample that may reach 100°C or more during the 2- or 3-minute heating. If another reaction occurs at a temperature very close to that of the reaction being studied, the user might have to settle for a longer heating time to avoid drastic overshoot. The material in contact with the heater can become very substantially hotter than the inside even when no reaction occurs; this condition is aggravated during any change of state (see Chapter III).

12.8. Summary

Measurement of any of a number of properties can be useful in interpreting the events that occur as a substance is heated. Some of these may be performed simultaneously or in combination with differential thermal or thermogravimetric analysis. These latter techniques are the most used because the returns in information (compared to the effort and expense) are greater.

CHAPTER XIII

Miscellaneous Topics

13.1. Introduction

The description of techniques necessarily included some illustrations of use but these were chosen for their applicability to the discussion, not for their subjective interest. This chapter contains some discussion of applications of thermoanalytical methods of investigation to particular materials or problems. Examples are offered, frequently only reportorially, to show the range of utility of the methods. On the other hand, further discourses on a few topics are presented.

13.2. Polymers

Since the seeming relegation of an important field of science to only a section may arouse the ire of dedicated polymer chemists, let it be clearly understood that much of the book is about polymers—just as much as any other class of materials. Other materials, however, undergo reactions more quickly or otherwise show more clearly the effects associated with the parameters under discussion.

The major differences between polymeric and other materials are

(a) the thermal effects are relatively slow and (b) thermal effects occur at less well-defined temperatures because the material is not really homogeneous. Coupled with these annoyances are those found with organic materials in general, i.e., low heats of transition or fusion and poor thermal conductivity.

Smaller organic molecules or ions have shapes that are complex relative to most inorganic molecules and ions; further, polyfunctionality is common and this may include not only different kinds of functional groups but similar groups with somewhat different reactivities resulting from differences in their structural environment. For these reasons, many organic materials can enter into a multiplicity of crystal structures. Organic materials in general are hence suitable materials for study by thermoanalytical methods and, conversely, thermoanalytical methods will supply considerable information about said organic materials. Now consider the special problems of polymeric materials.

Long-chain molecules moving around in a solution or melt cannot be expected to achieve—on precipitation, evaporation, or cooling—the same degree of order found in smaller organic and in inorganic materials. Polymethylene chains, for example, tend to look about the same all down their lengths. A molecule, finding itself in need of an energetically acceptable resting place on solidification, would have little tendency to seek out an end to end or any other specific relation with its neighbor. Neither would a part of the molecule, entering into the solid phase after another part had already situated itself, check down its own length to ascertain that methylene segments match one for one along the length.

Consider now that the nearest neighbor of some given part of a long-chain molecule is quite likely to be another portion of the same molecule. If these parts are not greatly separated the stability of the solid can be increased (due to interactions) compared to the stability of a pairing with a distant part or with a part of another molecule. Given enough time, the molecule will tend to form a single crystal by folding back on itself so that chain segments lie alongside each other (B51). The length of the typical chain segment may be kinetically or thermodynamically controlled but the actual length of a given segment may be different because of branching. That is, random imperfections will tend to move (with the attached carbon) to the fold, leaving, if necessary, somewhat longer or shorter chain segments in the immediate vicinity.

We have at this point an assembly of chain segments all interconnected. Even assuming that this is truly a single crystal, i.e., having no chains held jointly with another crystal, we have a range of energy states. If we heat this crystal to the onset of rotation it is quite apparent that the chain segments at the edge have a lesser barrier to rotation than the more central segments, hemmed in as they are by their neighbors. Consider also the melting: segments at the edges will gain some freedom at lower energies (and temperatures) than those surrounded by their fellows and the end of the chain, if exposed, will tend also to move freely. In either case these are local differences from strains caused by imperfections and variations in segment length.

Because of all these complications, polymeric materials cannot be expected to show transition points as sharp, as well-defined, as insensitive

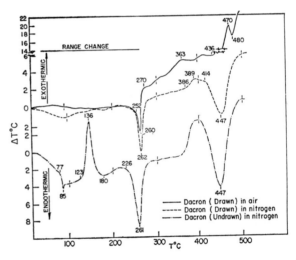

Fig. XIII-1. Differential thermal analysis curves of Dacron. From Schwenker and Beck (S16).
The undrawn fiber shows a second-order transition at 77°C and crystallization at 136°C.

to heating rate and other parameters as can be found in simpler organic materials, let alone inorganics. Nevertheless, differential thermal analysis is a highly useful tool in the study of polymers. This is not because of any particular ease of use but because other methods of investigation also fail to yield clear-cut and reliable answers without considerable effort.

As an identification technique differential thermal analysis is useful as a comparison tool. Some assemblages of curves have been published but these will be of little value unless the thermogram of the material to be identified is obtained on the same type of apparatus. For this reason they are not reviewed. Even assemblages of curves or data on inorganic materials are not likely to show much agreement when different types of apparatus are used (see Chapter II, Sec. 2.1). To expect to sort out the relatively poorly formed peaks of polymeric materials would be unrealistic and to use a particular experimental procedure only in the hope of getting a curve that looks like someone else's is a waste of time. If comparison with the published literature is to be attempted, the proper procedure is to interpret the curves so far as is possible, then to compare the data: temperatures of peaks or second-order transitions, relative peak heights or areas, etc.

In the case of polymers it is especially unwise to plan to make all sorts of important discoveries by dropping a sample into a commercial instrument and pushing a switch (see Chapters III, IV, and VIII). The sample holder must be designed for the experiment. Hay (H8), for example, melts his samples *in situ* and quenches or anneals them. His principal interest is in the intrinsic properties of the polymer. His apparatus would not be suitable for study of drawn or extruded fibers or resin-forming reactions nor does it pretend to be.

Schwenker and Beck (S16), on the other hand, need to use the sample with a minimum of pretreatment since they are concerned with, for example, the effects due to mechanical history (Fig. XIII-1). These effects very likely present one of the most fruitful uses of differential thermal analysis in the study of polymers.

13.3. Mechanical Effects in Polymers

The crystalline form obtained by careful annealing of a polymer is of substantial interest because it is a characteristic of that material and study of the crystal can lead to knowledge of the material. Polymers are not often made just to permit study of their properties. They are formed into usable articles by extrusion, spinning, molding, and similar processes so it is essential that we study their behavior under all this pulling and pushing.

The purpose here is only to point out that the orientations and disorientations due to mechanical treatment—or mechanical strain due to thermal treatment—will necessarily have a heat effect associated with them. This may be reflected in a slow evolution or absorption of heat and hence manifested only by a change in heat capacity. More likely, however, is the occurrence of similar events of the same energy in many parts of the specimen, which regions then evince themselves over a narrow temperature range. This range may be narrow enough so that a well-formed peak is obtained.

An example of the effect of stretching is given in Fig. XIII-1. Ke (K11a) provides an example of the effect of quenching (Fig. XIII-2), showing the thermal effects resulting when the high-temperature form— or something approximating it—is retained by rapid cooling to low temperatures (see Chapter II).

13.4. The "Integral Procedural Decomposition Temperature"

The comparison of polymers on the basis of thermal stability is quite difficult because of the wide variety of possible behaviors. Even disregarding any atmosphere effects such as oxidation, the start of decomposition may be the degradation of a side group while the chain remains

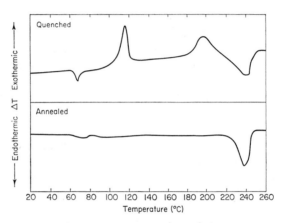

FIG. XIII-2. Thermograms of polyethylene/diethylene terephthalate. From Ke (K11).
The quenched specimen shows crystallization effects well below the melting point.

intact. At some higher temperature further decomposition occurs, eventually affecting the entire material. On the other hand, under identical heating conditions, another substance might degrade completely in a single step and a third decompose in some other manner but leave a residue at the upper limit of heating. Doyle (D14, D15) puts these various behaviors on a common numerical basis by use of an arbitrarily defined "integral procedural decomposition temperature."

This integral procedural decomposition temperature, or *ipdt*, is derived from the weight loss vs temperature plot under rigidly controlled experimental conditions. The weight loss is assigned to a single temperature, the *ipdt*, at which the area under the curve (Fig. XIII-3) could be represented as a rectangle bounded by the residual weight fractions 1.00 and 0.00, 0°C, and T_A. Thus, "in T_A, it is *pretended* that all materials volatilize completely in TGA to 900°C and do so at a single temperature."

This does not really take into account the refractoriness of some materials. Some polymers contain inorganic fragments which may remain at the arbitrary termination of heating. To take account of this, Doyle introduces a correction K^*/K to this area which essentially moves up the base of the rectangle from a residual weight fraction of zero to the actual fraction remaining at 900°C. Without this correction, a material degrading at a low temperature but leaving a substantial residue would have an *ipdt* indicating good stability. As a comparison, Doyle shows the *ipdt*'s (Fig. XIII-4) of a series of polymers, some containing inorganic portions, and relates them to the temperatures of half weight loss.

A set of data such as that obtained by Doyle can be quite useful for comparing polymers as long as the data are obtained in the same manner and probably by the same equipment. Taking a datum from the set for use in another comparison or even taking an *ipdt* as having some physical significance would indeed be risky.

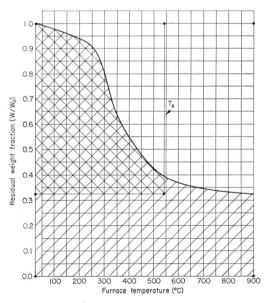

FIG. XIII-3. The thermogravimetric analysis curve areas A^*, ////, and K^*, crosshatching. From Doyle (D15).
   By use of both corrections, account is taken of the residual weight.

13.5. Dolomite and Siderite Decompositions

The decomposition of dolomite has attracted considerable attention because of the quite different nature of the two endothermic peaks. The first peak is quite well-established as being the decomposition of the dolomite structure rather than the decomposition of a magnesium carbonate moiety of a mixed crystal. The decomposition temperature is not significantly affected by the usual change: dilution, subatmospheric

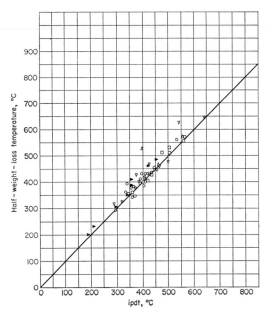

Fig. XIII-4. Half weight loss temperature vs *ipdt* for fifty-four polymers containing: **O**–C, H, N, O; △–F; □–SI: ▲–B, P; ▼–Cu, Fn, Be. From Doyle (D15).
The corrected temperature agrees well with the temperature at which half the weight loss has occurred.

pressure, etc. Strangely enough, an atmosphere of carbon dioxide seems to lower rather than raise the decomposition temperature. Berg (B25a) showed that the presence of alkali-metal compounds could also lower the decomposition temperature but simply washing the sample eliminated the effect. Ivanova and Tatarskii (17) have shown that dilution of dolomite with up to 85% kaolin causes "no substantial and consistent lowering of the decomposition temperature."

The lowering of the dolomite peak temperature in the presence of carbon dioxide is interesting not only because this behavior is contrary to ordinary experience but also because there is an accompanying change in the shape of the peak (Fig. XIII-5). If one considers only the atmosphere effect the van't Hoff relation would be obeyed only in the event of a negative heat of decomposition; admittedly a negative heat of reaction could be obscured by the positive heat of reaction (decomposition) of the magnesium carbonate formed by decomposition of the

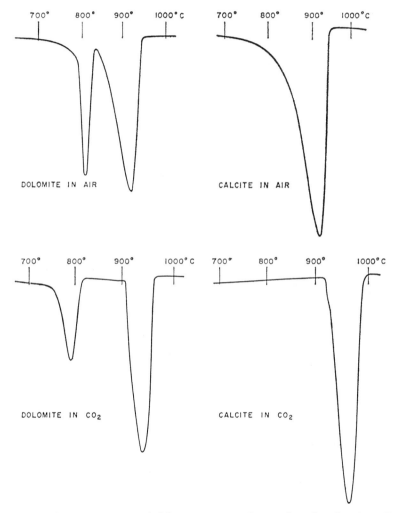

FIG. XIII-5. Decomposition of dolomite in air and in carbon dioxide. From Rowland and Lewis (R34).

The presence of carbon dioxide lowers the decomposition temperature of the dolomite but raises the decomposition temperature of the residual calcium carbonate.

dolomite. The exact behavior would depend on the heat capacities of the various substances as well as on the heats of reaction since $d(\Delta H)/dT = \Delta C_p$.

Take note of the several effects which lower the decomposition temperature: the presence of carbon dioxide, the presence of certain salts. The latter tends to distort the surface of the crystal but another effect must be postulated for the former.

Consider now that dolomite is presumably unstable at temperatures near the decomposition temperature, lacking only the necessary activation energy for decomposition. The soluble salts provide the energy by distortion of the lattice. The carbon dioxide, on the other hand, lowers the activation energy requirement by providing another reaction mechanism—one requiring a lower activation energy. Haul and associates (H7) have demonstrated the exchange of carbon dioxide between calcite and carbon dioxide atmosphere.

The advent of another mechanism could be expected to change even the shape of the curve. In effect, the over-all decomposition changes from a principally temperature effect whose reaction rate is determined by the transport of heat to a kinetic effect whose reaction rate is determined substantially by the interchange with the atmosphere.

The decomposition of siderite or chalybite (natural ferrous carbonate) presents an interesting problem in competing reactions. The ferrous carbonate (Fig. 1-4) will decompose to magnetite and oxides of carbon in a nonoxidizing atmosphere in the vicinity of 500°C; in an oxidizing atmosphere, on the other hand, the ferrous ion moiety will tend to oxidize to ferric in the same region. In air the exothermic response is far greater than the endothermic response if there is a reasonable opportunity for oxidation. From this, it has been concluded that the evolution of carbon dioxide from ferrous carbonate requires little energy compared to that given off by the oxidation of ferrous to ferric oxide.

Careful examination of siderite curves in air or oxygen will disclose a tendency for oxidation to begin before the carbonate decomposition. Examination will also disclose that there is a correspondence between the magnitude of the carbon dioxide evolution endotherm in air and the later oxidation peak ca 840°C.

Let us hypothesize that two quite separate reaction paths exist and that the path taken by any small segment of the specimen is determined only by the presence or absence of oxygen at the instant of change. In the absence of oxygen, the reaction is endothermic, the products being carbon dioxide, carbon monoxide, magnetite, Fe_3O_4, and—apparently under some conditions—ferrous oxide. If oxygen is available, we may hypothesize the oxidation as the first step, but this would yield ferric carbonate—an unstable structure. This unstable material would decompose exothermally to yield ferric and/or ferrosoferric oxide. The major point here is that the carbon dioxide from the oxidation path is not driven off endothermally. Hence, the curve showing both reactions cannot be interpreted by simply considering that the endothermic carbonate decomposition must be going on but the heat of oxidation is so great that the endotherm may be masked. The carbon dioxide evolution that does not take up heat gives off heat instead. The endothermic portion of the curve is only a measure of the amount of lower oxides formed; this is subsequently indicated also by the oxidation peak ca 840°C. Handbook (L1a) values for heats of formation indicate that the endothermic decomposition would show a heat effect not much less than that of the oxidation.

In static oxidizing atmospheres, whether air or oxygen, the oxidation process is self-limiting because the carbon dioxide produced will tend to prevent oxidation of more material but diffusion interchange of gases would enable some continuation except for the other reaction. The material that has no oxygen available when it would otherwise be ready to react will react (possibly several degrees later) by decomposition, also producing carbon dioxide and thus sustaining the condition. Whether or not the thermogram will show any further oxidation will depend on the geometry—including location of the thermocouple—and state of dilution (see Chapter II) of the specimen.

13.6. Study of Metathetical Reactions at Elevated Temperatures

Differential thermal analysis is a useful tool in the observation or study of reactions between solids at elevated temperatures. The extension to include the effect of some materials on the decomposition of others is but a short step.

One interesting application of metathetical reactions in recent years has been the re-examination of the Hedvall effect by Borchardt and Thompson (B70). The Hedvall effect refers to the enhanced reactivity of solid materials during a crystallographic transition.

Borchardt and Thompson repeated the experiment of Hedvall and Heuberger, obtaining the curves of Fig. XIII-6, in which the endothermic peaks in (a) and (c) are good evidence for the formation of barium and strontium carbonates. These were samples that had been exposed to air. On the other hand, if the same starting materials, protected from the atmosphere and well-mixed as before, were heated to substantially above the reaction temperature indicated by the exotherm, the materials retained their identity. Further, both barium and strontium oxides showed endothermic peaks which suggested the possibility of melting of a eutectic oxide-hydroxide system to provide a liquid phase. [Balarew (B3) had suggested that the Hedvall effect appeared because of the formation of a liquid phase which could then provide a low-energy reaction path for the metathesis.]

Borchardt and Thompson (B70) made direct observations on silver nitrate mixtures with the alkaline earth oxides and found that reaction occurred at the appearance of a liquid phase, i.e., melting of silver nitrate (Fig. XIII-7), not at the phase transition about 50°C lower in temperature. These and other data led Borchardt and Thompson to ques-

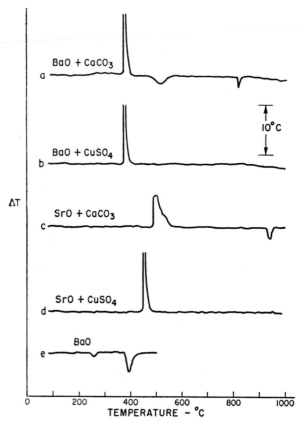

Fɪɢ. XIII-6. Differential thermal analyses of barium oxide and mixtures of barium and strontium oxides with calcium carbonate and with copper sulfate. From Borchardt and Thompson (B68).

The exothermic peaks indicate reaction at fairly low temperatures. The high-temperature endothermic peaks confirm the formation of barium and strontium carbonates.

tion the actual existence of a Hedvall effect, at least in the original narrow sense of an increased reactivity *while* the transformation is taking place.

The effect of impurities in changing the reactivities or even reactions of materials is demonstrated well by Martin's (M17) data on clay-carbonate mixtures, from which Martin concludes that measurement of carbonates in natural soils could possibly miss nearly half of the carbonate present. Lowering of the decomposition temperature of dolomite by

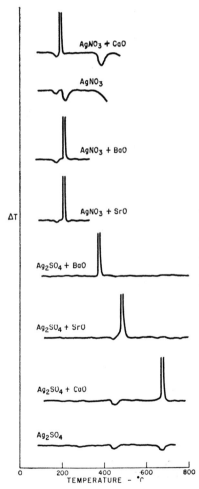

Fig. XIII-7. Differential thermal analysis of binary mixtures with silver nitrate and with silver sulfate. From Borchardt and Thompson (B70).

A liquid phase has apparently facilitated the metathetical reaction.

addition of soluble salts had been demonstrated by Berg (B25a) and
Graf (G38), but dolomite is a rather special case; calcite is relatively
unaffected by such impurities. Nevertheless, the natural soil containing
calcite, curve E of Fig. XIII-8, shows little sign of calcium carbonate although if the soil is washed (curve G) there appears a very pronounced

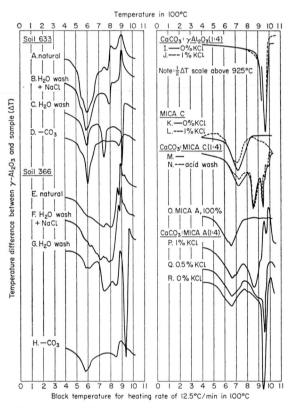

Fɪɢ. XIII-8. Thermograms of natural soils and prepared mixtures showing anomalous carbonate peaks. From Martin (M17).
   *The presence of soluble salts permits interactions which alter the thermogram
quite substantially.*

calcite peak ca 900°C. Now if sodium chloride is added to a suspension
of this water-washed clay and the material is dried, this sample yields a
thermogram (curve F) nearly identical to the original material.
   Note, apropos of the Borchardt and Thompson work, that sodium
chloride melts at 800°C and that thermograms E and F begin an exothermic deflection in this region. This existence of even a relatively small

quantity of liquid phase could bring about the destruction of calcium carbonate by, in effect, precipitation of calcium silicate. The presence of this liquid phase could render the metathesis sufficiently rapid to compete with the decomposition.

13.7. Clay Minerals as a Continuous Series

Keeling (K12) has compared several measurements on clay minerals and suggested that they may be considered to be a continuous series describable in terms of the ratio of combined water to the specific sur-

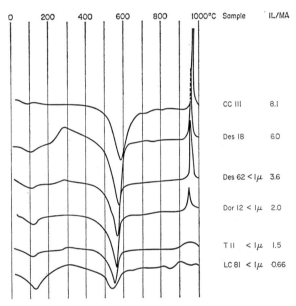

Fig. XIII-9. Differential thermal analyses of clays. From Keeling (K12). *The figures on the right are a measure of the water/area ratio.*

face. Infrared absorption and X-ray diffraction data as well as differential thermal analysis (Fig. XIII-9) show, with a decreasing water/surface ratio, "progressive increase in size and peak temperature of the adsorbed moisture endotherm, a decrease in size and peak temperature of the breakdown [dehydroxylation] endotherm at 500–600°C, and a decrease in definition and peak temperature of the 900–1000°C exotherm." He relates these structural properties to the plasticity and green strength which are important in the ceramic art, but relation to more precisely measurable parameters may sometime be instructive.

13.8. Biological Studies

This section will be limited to the presentation of a few examples of biological samples. The potential range of application is great. Here in particular effluence analysis would be useful.

The thermograms of ankle bone and of hemoglobin, Fig. XIII-10 and XIII-11, show possible use in medical studies while the thermograms of

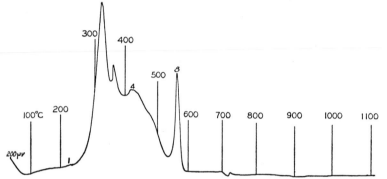

FIG. XIII-10. Thermogram of ankle bone leached in chloroform for 24 hours. (Courtesy of Robert L. Stone Co.)

The residue from the chloroform leaching may be of aid in studying bone composition.

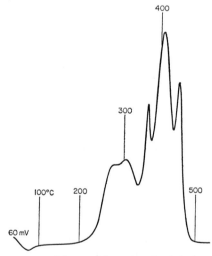

FIG. XIII-11. Thermogram of hemoglobin—70% fetal from cord blood; 1 atm, O_2 (1 wt. H + 7 wt. Al_2O_3). (Courtesy of Robert L. Stone Co.)

Some oxidations occur prior to the combustion. The peaks might provide a quick test for the sources of the blood.

wood and its extracts, Fig. XIII-12, and of plant gums and acids, Fig. XIII-13, suggest possible botanical applications.

13.9. Fractional Thermogravimetric Analysis

The technique devised by Waters (W7) in which some components leaving a sample during decomposition are trapped within the weighed assembly may be very useful in studies in which more than one reaction may be going on simultaneously. Waters constructed his sample holders

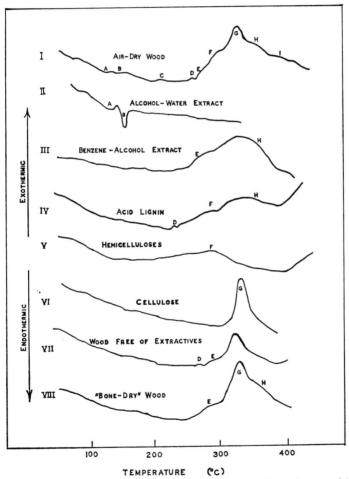

Fig. XIII-12. Thermograms of balsam fir and its extracts. From Arsenan (A14).

The multiplicity of components renders the thermogram of the original material uninterpretable; separation of components by extraction or distillation would be an essential step.

(Fig. XIII-14) such that gases from the sample had to pass through adsorbents to escape.

The study will require a number of runs to learn the manner in which each component is driven off from the sample. Waters used the technique in the study of coals (Fig. XIII-15) in which there are a number

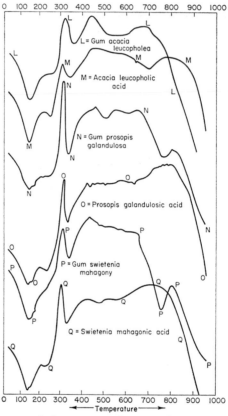

Fig. XIII-13. Thermograms of plant gums and gum acids. From Kulshrestha (K47a). *Effluence analysis would be very helpful in further characterization.*

of each of several types of materials coming off. A more specific effluence analysis (Chapter XIV) would be extremely tedious and very possibly pointless.

13.10. Detection of Formation of Compounds

The present author showed (G14), several years ago, that the product obtained by alkaline hydrolysis of maleate esters was not the same as that obtained by a similar hydrolysis of maleic anhydride. One piece of evidence cited (G12) was a comparison of differential thermal analysis curves of the two materials (Fig. XIII-16). From several pieces of evidence we (G14, G19) advanced the hypothesis that dimerization occurred during hydrolysis of the esters and that the potassium salt of the dimeric acid crystallized as a hemialcoholate. The thermogram of the potassium maleate appears to be that of a well-crystallized material with some very sharply defined reactions. The hemialcoholate, after losing the alcohol, shows a general similarity to the potassium maleate without the good definition of the oxidation of the various parts of the molecule.

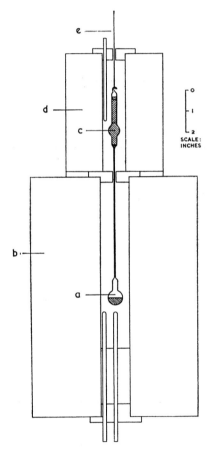

Fɪɢ. XIII-14. Apparatus for fractional thermogravimetric analysis: a sample bulb; b, furnace; c, absorption tubes; d, subsidiary furnace; e, suspension wire to balance. From Waters (W7).

The absorption tube, c. may be packed with several adsorbents or chemisorbents. allowing only selected materials to escape.

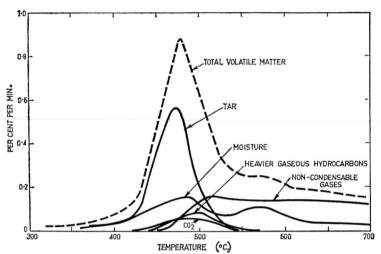

Fig. XIII-15. Fractional thermogravimetric analysis of a coking coal. From Waters (W7).

A quantitative analysis as well as the temperature dependence is obtained.

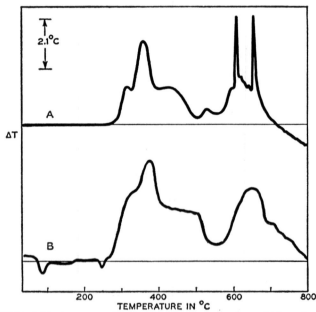

Fig. XIII-16. Thermograms of saponication products from (A) maleic anhydride and (B) diethyl maleate. From Garn and Flaschen (G12).

The general similarity of the exothermic reaction indicates a general similarity of the two potassium salts. The potassium maleate in (A) is more crystalline and would be expected to yield sharper peaks. The initial endotherm in (B) is due to decomposition of an alcoholate.

(Similar curves were published by Rey and Kostomaroff (R18). Since no reference is made to the present author's work, said present author is uncertain whether or not Rey and Kostomaroff have confirmed the observation.)

The subsequent experience of the present author would dictate a rather different approach, permitting a quite conclusive resolution of the problem by techniques within the scope of this monograph. There is, for example, no reason why an atmosphere of ethyl alcohol cannot be used in either differential thermal analysis or thermogravimetric analysis. The expected shift of temperature of the initial decomposition in Fig. XIII-16 would confirm the nature of the alcoholate. Alternatively, effluence analysis could be used to identify the decomposition product. The methods appropriate to structure analysis would still be needed to establish or refute the dimerization.

13.11. Qualitative Identifications

The usual organic identification procedures of mixed melting points or determining the melting points of derivatives can be carried out readily by differential thermal analysis. Chiu (C11) demonstrated the utility of a simple process of derivative formation by heating a mixture of triethylamine and picric acid (Fig. XIII-17) and showing the formation of the

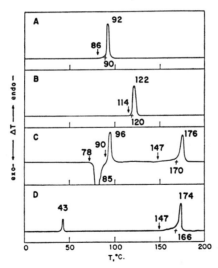

Fig. XIII-17. Thermogram showing formation of triethylamine picrate. From Chiu (C11). (A) triethylamine; (B) picric acid; (C) reaction mixture of triethylamine and picric acid; (D) rerun of residue from C.

The melting point of the derivative is obtained very quickly. A rerun of the residue would be advisable.

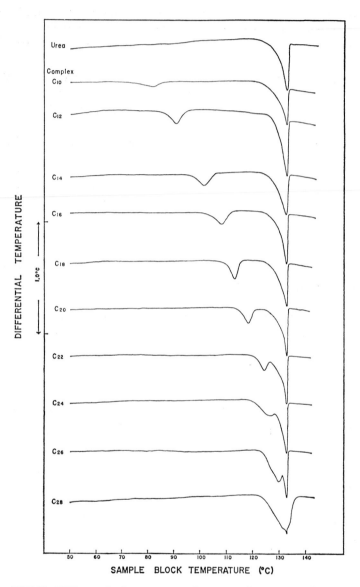

Fɪɢ. XIII-18. Differential thermograms of urea and a series of urea–*n*-paraffin complexes. From McAdie (M23).

The dissociation temperature increases with carbon number up to the melting point of urea.

picrate derivative. The rerun, as shown in Fig. XIII-17d, should be carried out routinely. Thermal effects occurring in the product but below the reaction temperature may be helpful. With nonstoichiometric mixtures some of one reactant may interfere.

Molecular complexes, such as the inclusion complexes of methylnaphthalenes (M33a) or urea (K33a), not only are interesting chemically but also can be useful. The urea complexes of *n*-paraffins were studied by McAdie, who reported the variation (Fig. XIII-18) of decomposition temperature of the complex with the chain length of the adduct.

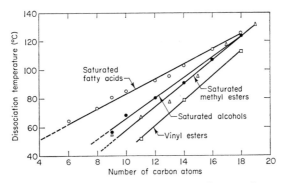

Fig. XIII-19. Dissociation temperatures of urea complexes as functions of number of carbon atoms in the adduct. From Knight *et al.* (K33a).
Several classes of materials vary in similar manners.

Knight *et al.* had found similar variations in other classes of compounds (Fig. XIII-19). The value found should be of help in identifications and differential thermal analysis should be an expeditious manner of finding that value.

13.12. Summary

The uses of thermoanalytical techniques are many and varied. Anomalies may be disclosed and investigation of these will sometimes lead to new knowledge.

CHAPTER XIV

Analysis of Gaseous Decomposition Products

14.1. Introduction

As used herein, effluence analysis is defined as the qualitative and/or quantitative analysis of gaseous products given off during the heating of a specimen. We can study these gases most easily by the types of detectors generally used in gas chromatography. Many analyses of such products have appeared in the literature in contexts not directly related to thermal analysis but since a reader may plan to use similar methods the author feels justified in extending his remarks and evaluations beyond the general scope of this book.

14.2. Heating of Specimens

The solid material being studied has been or can be heated in several manners and for multiple purpose studies as well as specifically for the analysis of the decomposition products. The most common of the multiple determinations would be simultaneous differential thermal analysis and effluence analysis; the effluence from a thermogravimetric analysis could also be analyzed, but this will invariably be accompanied by considerable dilution. In any event, in such simultaneous determinations the heating program and heating conditions are fairly rigidly prescribed by the requirements of the other technique. In those cases in which the sample is heated specifically for analysis of gaseous decomposition products, a fairly wide range of heating conditions can be and have been used. Examples could include slow heating of a rather massive sample to some fixed temperature or, at the other extreme, flash heating by use of a high-intensity source of visible and infrared radiation. A common technique, intermediate between these, is the practice of placing the sample on a heater (wire) or in a heater specially formed, then applying a predetermined voltage to the heater so that the specimen heats in an uncontrolled but approximately reproducible manner. In contrast to this latter, the specimen can be heated in some programmed manner as would be typical in the simultaneous determinations.

14.3. Simultaneous Determinations

Let us use as a starting point the present author's work with some simultaneous determinations; this work has been, of late, generally concerned with problems such that simultaneous differential thermal analysis and effluence analysis would have obvious benefits. In previously reported work, the author (G18) has connected a dynamic-atmosphere differential thermal analysis to various devices for detecting gaseous products and/or establishing the nature of the products.

One arrangement used is shown in Fig. XIV-1. In this arrangement a gas is supplied to the furnace chamber under sufficient pressure to cause a reasonable flow—this flow varies with the type of experiment—downward through the sample and through the reference materials. The gas passing through the reference is used as the reference gas in the thermal conductivity detector and the gas passing through the sample is compared with it. Any gaseous decomposition product whose thermal conductivity, k, is different from that of the "chamber gas" will then produce in the thermal conductivity detector a different cooling effect than the pure chamber gas during the time that the product gas is passing through the detector. The magnitude of the differential signal from such a detector is, at low concentrations, proportional to the quantity of the product gas passing through at the moment, so that integration of the area under a total deflection is a measure of the quantity of the gas evolved, provided the gas is known.

In the arrangement of Fig. XIV-1, the gas which passed through the sample then goes into the gas density detector. This detector has the advantage (over the thermal conductivity detector) that it is not only a quantitative measuring device but also to some extent qualitative. It has a further advantage that the sensitivity of the detection can be adjusted by judicious selection of carrier gas since the density or "apparent molecular weight" is the only property of importance in the measurement. One potential advantage is that some effluent species may be completely blanked out by use of a mixed carrier gas of the same density. A small quantity of some other gas could be detected in the presence of a large mass of the first.

The gas density detector depends for its operation on the effect of minor changes of flow in the vertical column on the total flow in tubes connected to the top and bottom of a vertical column. Let us assume that

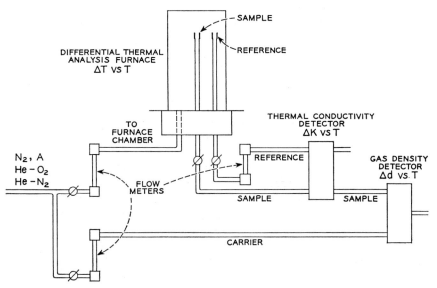

Fig. XIV-1. Combination differential thermal analysis and double effluence analysis.

The transient changes in the sample stream are detected in chromatographic-type analyzers.

in the device shown in Fig. XIV-2 a steady-state flow into the ports both on the right and in the center has been established so that we have a steady-state cooling of the detector elements. Now at some point upstream we inject a small quantity of a product gas, as we might in the normal course of a decomposition in differential thermal analysis. If this product gas is heavier than the carrier gas, the change in density, of course, will be an increase and, hence, the sample plus carrier gas will tend to flow downward to a greater extent than upward. This downward flow will decrease slightly the flow in the lower supply tube (coming from the right) and increase slightly the flow in the upper supply tube; this change in flow in the supply tubes produces a change in the cooling effect on the detector elements, an increase on the upper and a decrease on the lower.

The differential flow at any moment is proportional to the change in density of the sample plus carrier gas from that of the carrier gas alone, permitting, of course, a quantitative measurement of the material passing through—assuming that it is a single gas. Note, however, that the density of the sample plus carrier gas is dependent not only on the quantity of sample but also on the nature of the sample; that is, a gas which, pure, is only slightly heavier than the carrier gas will at a given level of concentration produce some fixed differential flow while a gas

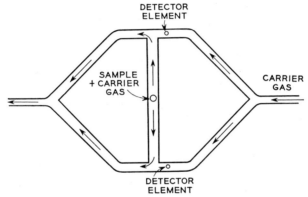

FIG. XIV-2. Gas density detector. From Garn and Kessler (G18).
A change in density of the sample gas produces a greater flow upward or downward. This in turn changes the flow of the reference gas.

substantially heavier than the carrier gas will at the same concentration produce a significantly greater differential flow. Because of this, qualitative as well as quantitative information can be obtained. If the sample gas is unknown, a second experiment with a carrier gas of different density will provide data for calculation of the real or apparent molecular weight of the sample. (If the sample is a mixture of gases, the apparent density will be dependent on their relative proportions and their relative densities in the pure state). If the number of possibilities is quite limited, a simpler identification is possible by bracketing the density of the suspected gas in two runs; for example, if there is reason to believe that the specimen gives off oxygen when heated in an inert atmosphere, an experiment using nitrogen as the carrier gas will show that the sample is more dense while a second experiment using argon will show that the sample gas is less dense, and if necessary direct comparison of the areas will show whether or not the apparent molecular weight of the gas is 32.

The present author has used this type of identification in several cases. Two are cited below. In some studies of cobalt oxalate hydrate the nature of the second step was not known with certainty. Most oxalates decompose in a nonoxidizing atmosphere by loss of carbon monoxide producing the corresponding carbonate. A cobalt oxalate resulting from the heating of the dihydrate decomposed ca. 400 C to yield what appeared to be a finely divided metal. In closed-chamber differential thermal analysis experiments with air as the furnace atmosphere, this metal powder had, around the opening along the support tube, evidence of oxide formation. The question was resolved by effluence analysis with density detection using nitrogen as the carrier gas. Figure XIV-3 shows a temperature-based, simultaneous differential thermal analysis and effluence analysis of cobalt oxalate dihydrate. A curve similar to the lower curve of Fig. XIV-3—but recorded on a time base—was obtained and the areas below and above the two peaks were measured. If a mole of cobalt oxalate dihydrate decomposes directly to the metal, 2 moles of carbon dioxide are released, and since 2 moles of water are also released the areas should be in direct relation to the density difference. The density difference between water and nitrogen, assuming ideal gas, etc., is 28—18 or 10 gm per mole while the difference between carbon dioxide and nitrogen would be 44—28 or 16 gm per mole. The ratio of areas then should be 1.6 if the decomposition is directly to the metal. Within a few per cent, attributable to experimental error, this is the result obtained; thus the gas must be carbon dioxide. Note that in this experiment carbon monoxide, having a molecular weight of 28, would not have shown its presence at all because its density is the same as that of nitrogen.

A case in which nitrogen and argon were used to establish the evolution of oxygen concerned the decomposition of lanthanum oxalate hydrate. Some plots are shown in Fig. XIV-4. We are concerned here with the reaction just above 700°C in which a material heavier than nitrogen but lighter than argon is evolved. From the nature of the system this is obviously oxygen. Note, too, that in the region of 400°C in nitrogen there is a substantial increase in density while in argon there is an increase followed by a sharp but transient decrease. The increase is attributable to the volution of carbon dioxide and the decrease to carbon monoxide, which is also evolved and whose presence would pass unnoticed in the nitrogen experiment.

Figure XIV-5 shows the decomposition of lanthanum oxalate hydrate in oxygen using the arrangement shown in Fig. XIV-1. In the low-temperature region the water loss is shown as a series of endothermic reactions, as a series of increases of the thermal conductivity and decreases in density. In this experiment no carbon monoxide is given off; instead, the carbon monoxide is oxidized to carbon dioxide, accounting both for the sharp increase in density around 350°C and the sharp exotherm in the differential thermal analysis plot. The thermal conductivity decreases. In the 750°C region we again see a decomposition yielding carbon dioxide since the density becomes heavier; the thermal conductivity decreases but the differential temperature first shows evi-

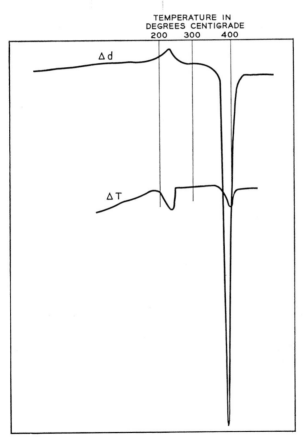

Fig. XIV-3. Differential thermal and effluence density analysis of cobalt oxalate dihydrate: $\Delta d = d$ carrier gas $- d$ effluent gas. From Garn and Kessler (G18).

The areas of the differential density deflection can be related to the mass and concentration of the decomposition product.

dence of an endothermic reaction followed by an exothermic rearrangement of some sort.

While these particular sets of curves were obtained during single runs with all measurements being made simultaneously, this is not by any means a necessary procedure. Separate experiments would be just as instructive and possibly experimentally more convenient as long as they were planned properly.

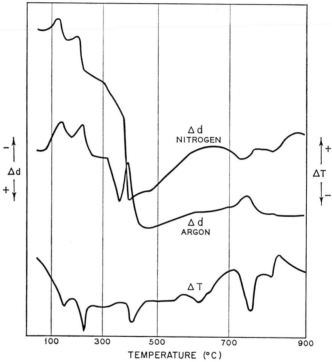

Fig. XIV-4. Identification of gaseous products by use of gas density detector. From Garn and Kessler (G18).

Use of nitrogen and argon discloses evolution of carbon monoxide ca 370°C and oxygen ca 750°C.

14.4. Gas Chromatography

In many cases a more specific identification than described above may be needed because at some stages in the decomposition more than one product may be given off. For such cases the addition of gas chromatography is useful. Gas chromatography as ordinarily practiced would be relatively ineffective; it would measure all the decomposition products up to the time of sampling. Specific identification of the product of a particular reaction requires that the sampling be made for that reaction alone; that is, any reaction products from previous decompositions are already removed from the site of sampling. This can be done readily by an arrangement such as that shown in Fig. XIV-6. In this system a furnace such as that shown in Fig. XIV-1 or Fig. VII-21, is used to carry

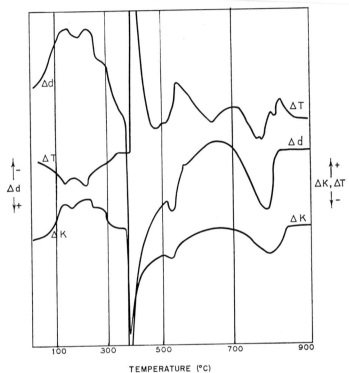

TEMPERATURE (°C)

Fig. XIV-5. Simultaneous measurement of differential temperature (ΔT), density (Δd), and thermal conductivity (Δk) of the effluent gas. From Garn and Kessler (G18).

Fairly precise interpretation of the effects can be made by use of the several curves.

out the thermal decomposition. The carrier gas which passes through the sample may, if desired, be passed through a thermal conductivity cell for a continuous and general survey of decomposition products, but more important, it passes through a pair of sampling valves with, in some cases, an interposed water trap. These sampling valves operate at programmed intervals to withdraw samples of gas from the stream and pass them through chromatographic columns and detectors. The programming is done by trial and error. For the Fluoropak column, and separately for the split column, flow conditions were determined which gave adequate separation. An adjustable cam timer was then connected to the sampling valves so that during each revolution one sampling valve would open for 5 seconds, then close, and after the selected interval of

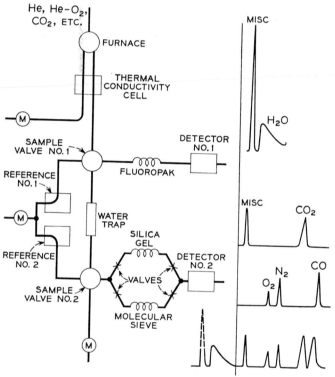

Fɪɢ. XIV-6. Gas train and switching for repetitive dual sampling chromatography. From Garn (G7).

Sample valve No. 1 transfers a 3-ml sample and No. 2 a 5-ml sample. Sampling interruptions have been deleted in copying (see Fig. XIV-7).

time the other valve would open and close. The oven temperature, the flow rates, and the sampling times were chosen for each type of experiment specifically to permit rapid sampling. In effect, each sampling occurs soon after the last expected peak from the previous sampling.

The Fluoropak column, when used, permits all nonpolar and slightly polar materials to run through rapidly but holds up the water long enough to give separation and permit measurement.

The second sampling valve in turn withdraws a specimen from the stream and directs it through a split column and to a second detector. This split column has silica gel in the one side and a molecular sieve in the other, the silica gel holding up the carbon dioxide but passing the other permanent gases through rapidly while the molecular sieve separates the permanent gases. Proper adjustment of the relative flows permits appearance of the carbon dioxide conveniently in the interval of time between the appearance of nitrogen and of carbon monoxide from the molecular sieve. The chromatogram resulting from the presence of all the gases but water is shown at the right for each column and at the bottom for a complete cycle. Figure XIV-7 shows a chart section with a

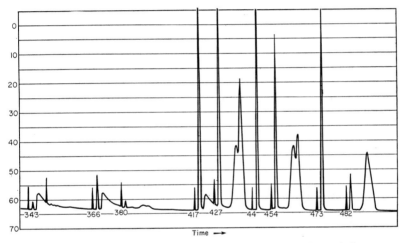

Fig. XIV-7. Chart section showing a number of sampling cycles and the temperature at which the sample was taken. From Garn (G7).

The temperature at the moment of sampling is measured and the reaction occurring at that temperature thus described (see Fig. XIV-6). Alternate samplings, e.g., 417° and 446°C, are into the Flouropak column; the others go through the split-column.

number of cycles, the appearance and disappearance of peaks reflecting the beginning and subsidence of reactions as the specimen material is heated.

Examination of several cycles of the chromatographic analysis permits the following of a single reaction, or, more important, a series of reactions, by the relative heights or areas of peaks. Figure XIV-8 shows such a series. The left-hand set of analyses are solely for water, those to their immediate right are the associated samplings for the permanent gases, and those at the far right a subsequent series of analyses for the perman-

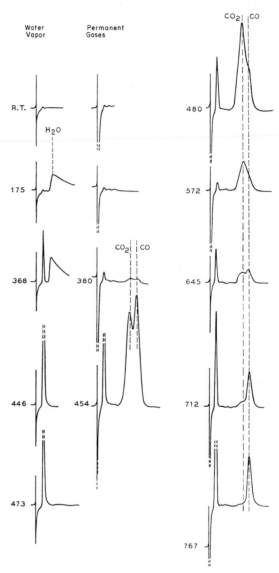

FIG. XIV-8. Reproduction of several chromatographic analyses from the chart of which Fig. XIV-7 showed a part. The temperatures of sampling are indicated. From Garn (G7).

The appearance and disappearance of specific products can be followed easily (see Fig. XIV-6).

ent gases. No water appeared in the later analyses so they are not shown. Note that even in the water analysis an indication of the increasing concentration of other gases was apparent from the growth of the peak just prior to the rather broad water peak. Similarly, even though the carbon dioxide and carbon monoxide peaks run together at high concentrations, the sharp peak shortly after the sampling, due to the permanent gases other than carbon dioxide passing rapidly through the silica gel column, gives an indication of the concentration of carbon monoxide even when the peak is almost obscured by the carbon dioxide. At the higher temperatures carbon dioxide evolution ceases and carbon monoxide is the only product detected.

The data from one run are tabulated in Fig. XIV-9 along with the differential thermal analysis and differential conductivity curves. The water is given off over a rather wide range and the peaks are poorly defined in this dynamic atmosphere of helium; then the decomposition of oxalate occurs very sharply and the interrupted peak on the thermal conductivity curve can be related to the more or less continual evolution of carbon dioxide coupled with the quickly terminated evolution of carbon monoxide. The new appearance of carbon monoxide at higher temperatures is also apparent. The high drift in the differential thermal analysis signal is a result of sintering of the specimen and consequent change in the heat transfer from the side to the center of the specimen. One might conclude from these particular curves that Δk is a more sensitive measurement than ΔT and in some cases this could be justified. Consider, however, that this particular experiment used a helium atmosphere and the thermal conductivity change is at a maximum [a dynamic atmosphere of helium would seldom be picked for differential thermal analysis (see below)]. Further, differential thermal analysis detects changes of state which the thermal conductivity of the gas stream obviously cannot reflect.

Some of the earlier exploratory work with the combination of chromatography with differential thermal analysis shows the hazard of vitiating data from one of the techniques. Figure XIV-10 shows some differential thermal analysis curves for an ocean sediment specimen obtained with air and with helium as dynamic atmospheres. While the analysis in helium was being performed, a technician took chromatographic samples by manual operation of a sampling valve at regular intervals (G15). There is no difficulty following the appearance of carbon monoxide and the appearance and virtual disappearance of carbon dioxide in the decomposition products, but there is significant difficulty in finding related. One may not conclude that combinations of techniques will be any thermal effects in the helium run to which the gas evolution may be necessarily useful. Simultaneous determinations are of benefit only under those conditions in which neither technique is greatly compromised. The planning of separate experiments for each technique will often be more fruitful.

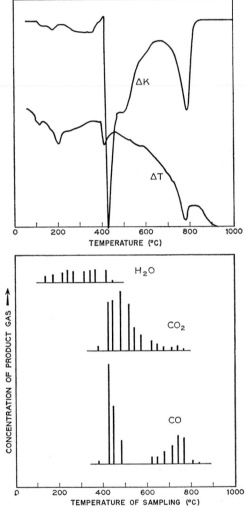

FIG. XIV-9. Tabulated chromatographic peak heights related to the simultaneously obtained differential thermal analysis and thermal conductivity analysis of the effluent stream. From Garn (G7).

The sudden appearance of carbon monoxide and dioxide is indicated also by the plots. The curves, however, give no hint of the relative amounts of CO₂ and CO.

14.5. Critique

With all the experimental problems of simultaneous analysis and the distinct probability that separate experiments could be better controlled or more instructive, nevertheless the simultaneous-determinations technique is generally superior to point-by-point sampling for the same types of analyses. Let us consider the technique devised by Murphy *et al.* (M42) in which a differential thermal analysis was performed of poly(vinyl chloride) in an evacuated vessel which had connections also (Fig. XIV-11) to some previously evacuated sampling tubes for mass spectrometry. The object is, of course, to determine the identity of

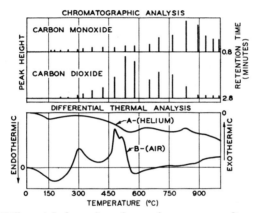

Fig. XIV-10. Differential thermal analyses of an ocean sediment related to the effluence analysis. From Garn (G7).

The appearance and disappearance of the gases can be related to the peaks of curve A but curve B bears no appreciable resemblance because the reactions are quite different.

the gaseous products coming off at various stages of the heating, but consider the required procedure. One must first make a trial run in order to establish the temperatures which may be of interest. After selecting the sampling temperatures a rerun must be made with operator monitoring in order that the selected samples may be taken at the proper time, and finally the gaseous samples taken must be conveyed to the other instrument, in this case a mass spectrometer, and analyzed individually. All of this is perfectly possible and may be justified on the basis of the need for information about a particular sample, but there immediately arises the problem of the need for an operator to make a judgment on probably inadequate data. That is, on a specimen with which the operator is not familiar, a single thermogram is seldom sufficient to establish the identity of a given reaction.

In this technique the choice of sampling points is obviously extremely important, yet the example shown by Murphy *et al.* (M42) in Fig. XIV-12 involves what is apparently an error in choice. They sampled at 300 and 400°C, the lower temperature being at the peak of an endothermic reaction and the higher temperature at what they describe as a flat exotherm. They found, as they expected, hydrogen chloride evolved at 300°C, and we may infer that they had expected similar evolution at 400°C for they reported that no hydrogen chloride was evolved without specifying the presence or absence of any other material. The absence of any material evolved in the 400°C region should not be a surprise; that

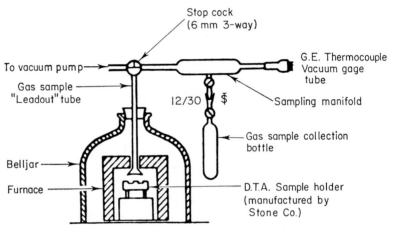

Fɪɢ. XIV-11. Differential thermal analysis with point-by-point sampling. From Murphy *et al.* (M42).

Since the gas samples are analyzed separately a small number would be taken at temperatures selected by the operator.

region is almost certainly not an exotherm or due to any reaction at all. It is far more likely a simple change in base line due to the change in thermal properties of the specimen. The important point here is not that they made an error and their information needs reinterpretation but that such an error is easily possible with point-by-point sampling techniques.

Let us now consider an arrangement in which the gas given off by a heated specimen is swept by a carrier gas into a thermal conductivity detector. In the arrangement described by Ayres and Bens (A19), the sample cells are test tubes set in a metal block as shown in Fig. XIV-13. A differential thermal analysis is performed on the specimen and the plot from the thermal conductivity cell is related to the differential thermal analysis plot. The carrier gas passes through a preheater and then flows over the sample and reference specimens and thence into the detector cell; note that the gas does not pass *through* the specimen, so the atmosphere surrounding the particles will vary depending on the nature of the product gas and the depth of the particle within the total specimen. The upper layers are continually exposed to an atmosphere of essentially pure helium, but during a decomposition the helium will be displaced by the product gas and, especially near the bottom, the particle will experience an enrichment of the product gas concentration.

The effect of the enrichment within the bulk of the specimen will vary depending on the nature of the sample. Reactions having any appreci-

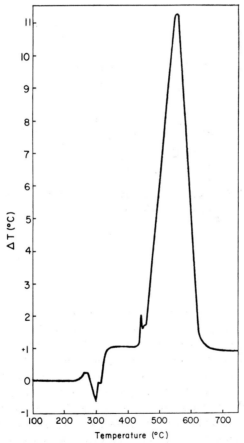

Fɪɢ. XIV-12. Differential thermal analysis of poly(vinyl chloride) showing sampling temperatures. From Murphy *et al.* (M42).

The necessity for operator judgment based on limited information is more subject to error than programmed sampling.

able semblance of reversibility will be spread over a range of temperatures because of the atmosphere effect, yet not to the same extent as
would be the case in the absence of a moving atmosphere because we
can consider any product gas to be diffusing outward into a zero-level
concentration above the specimen (cf. Chapter VII). For a reversible
reaction, then, this technique will yield differential thermal analysis
curves intermediate between those obtained in static atmospheres or in
dynamic atmospheres as cited previously. The effluent gas analysis will

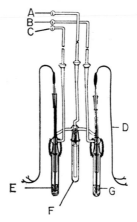

Fig. XIV-13. Differential thermal analysis apparatus providing detection of
evolved gases: (A) sweeping gas inlet; (B) gas train to detector, sample; (C) gas
train to detector, reference: (D) thermocouple probe leads; (E) reference cell with
glass beads; (F) sweeping gas preheater, with glass wool; (G) sample cell, with
sample and glass beads. From Ayres and Bens (A19).
   *The carrier gas sweeps over the sample, carrying toward the detector gases that
diffuse out of the sample.*

closely parallel the differential thermal analysis curve. Irreversible decompositions, such as the perchloric decomposition and many organic
decompositions, will be virtually unaffected by any movement of the
atmosphere because these reactions proceed rapidly when the decomposition temperature is reached regardless of the ambient atmosphere.
The detection of the effluent gas can be expected to agree less well
than in the case of the reversible reactions because a tailing off is essentially certain to follow a rapid exothermic reaction; in addition to the
burst of gaseous products spewed into the carrier stream, these products
displace the carrier gas from the nooks and crannies within the specimen
and some reasonable interval of time will be required for this material
to diffuse out of the specimen and into the gas stream. In reversible

reactions, under this type of conditions, there is very probably a diminution in the rate of formation of the product gases. Their concentration increases and, toward the bottom of the sample vessel, unreacted material may yet exist after the peak temperature difference has passed. The return to the base line will be slow because of this continuing reaction and during the same period these last portions of product gases will be diffusing out of the specimen and into the gas stream in ever-decreasing quantities; the effect in the gas detector is, then, rather similar to the differential thermal analysis peak.

Let us examine the data obtained by Ayres and Bens using ammonium perchlorate; but first we can well review the reactions of ammonium perchlorate under a small variety of conditions. Differential thermal analysis curves in various atmospheres were obtained by Stone (S58); his data are shown in Fig. VII-1 (see also Fig. VII-2). In an ammonia atmosphere the entire decomposition occurs at one temperature because the presence of the ammonia represses the initial decomposition. In any other gas a preliminary decomposition occurs which is only slightly pressure-dependent. The final decomposition temperature remains the same. Note that this initial decomposition is not a *necessary* prelude to the exothermic decomposition. The evidence so far suggests that in the absence of ammonia this initial decomposition comprises the loss of all or part of the ammonia. We might hypothesize either a double salt remaining at this stage or, if all the ammonia is lost, that the perchloric acid vapor pressure has not yet reached one atmosphere.

In vacuum the final decomposition is not exothermic at all. We may infer that the ammonium perchlorate decomposition products from the initial reaction volatilize and the material is swept out before decomposition.

In any case, the curve obtained by Ayres and Bens in helium (Fig. XIV-14) would correspond to the third of Stone's curves, i.e., the one obtained in nitrogen at one atmosphere. The difference in the nature of the flowing or dynamic gas between the two experiments is of no consequence as long as the gas does not enter into any sort of reaction with the specimen. The drawn-out initial decomposition and the tailing off of the gas evolution after the final decomposition can be attributed to the manner of passing the gas across the sample as explained above.

Less volatile products will cause a rather different trouble, but the problem is apparently purely physical and could be corrected by redesign of the apparatus. Ayres and Bens also show decomposition curves for nitroglycerin and a propellant (Fig. XIV-15). Note that at the upper extremes in temperature an evolution of gas appears to take place with no evidence of a thermal effect. This is more likely due to the condensation of a decomposition residue in a cooler part of the glassware and subsequent vaporization of the residue as the heating continues and that part of the glassware reaches a sufficiently high temperature.

Ayres and Bens called attention to the possible troubles due to condensation; the present author's contribution is the delineation of events within the sample.

Another use of simultaneous differential thermal analysis and a form of effluence analysis was of a very special kind; Bussiere and co-workers (B91) constructed an apparatus. (Fig. XIV-16) in which they could si-

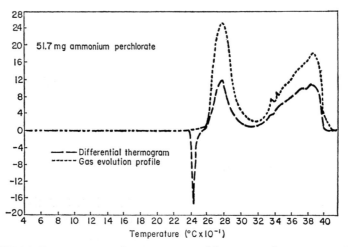

Fig. XIV-14. Decomposition of ammonium perchlorate in a flowing atmosphere of helium. From Ayres and Bens (A19).

The evolved gases do not enter the stream instantaneously so tailing-off can be expected.

multaneously perform differential thermal analysis, thermogravimetric analysis, and a measure of the emanation from thoron. Their work is based on the absorption of thoron along the interfaces between crystallites. The sample used was thorium oxalate hydrate. The radioactive decay of thorium produces (also radioactive) thoron, part of which escapes and part of which is trapped in the interfaces or interstices and, at best, moves slowly to the particle surface. When, however, the material undergoes a change of state, the disruption of the crystals permits more ready escape of the thoron from among the crystallites.

Bussiere *et al.* (B91) passed a gas stream across their specimen and into a detector in which the radioactivity of this gas stream (due to the thoron) was measured. The data of Fig. XIV-17 are not easily interpreted at first sight. The first dehydration is unambiguous; each of the measurements demonstrates an effect which we can accept as decomposition to the dehydrate as stated by Bussiere and associates. The second weight loss and accompanying endotherm are clear enough, but there is no corresponding event in the emanation measurement. Further,

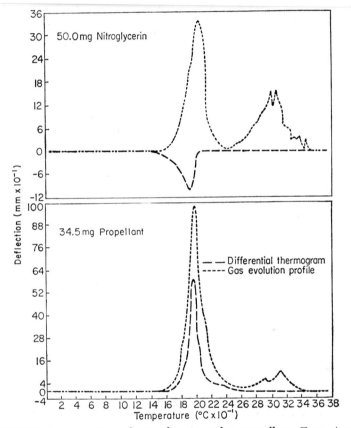

FIG. XIV-15. Decomposition of nitroglycerin and a propellant. From Ayres and Bens (A19).
The comparatively nonvolatile residues apparently condense and are driven slowly toward the detector.

in the final decomposition, not only does the thermogravimetric curve indicate a single, smooth weight loss while the differential thermal analysis curve shows a pair of reactions, but the emanation curve even shows a decrease rather than the predicted increase.

The two-step final endotherm shown by the differential thermal anal-

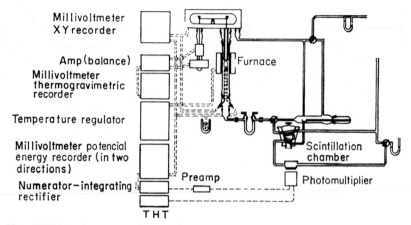

Millivoltmeter
XY recorder

Amp(balance)   Furnace
Millivoltmeter
thermogravimetric
recorder

Temperature regulator

Millivoltmeter potencial   Scintillation
energy recorder (in two   chamber
directions)
                          Preamp   Photomultiplier
Numerator−integrating
rectifier

T H T

FIG. XIV-16. Apparatus for simultaneous differential thermal analysis, thermo-gravimetric analysis, and radioactive emanation detection. From Bussiere *et al.* (B91).

The radioactive gas is a decay product of thorium. Dilution and delay could be important problems.

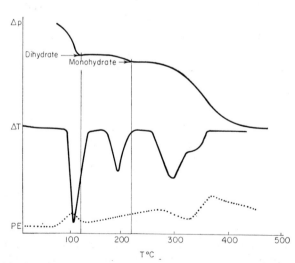

FIG. XIV-17. Simultaneous measurement of weight loss, thermal effects, and emanation of thorium oxalate hydrate. From Bussiere *et al.* (B91).

The weight loss curve does not show the double thermal effect ca 300°C nor can the emanation curve be related prima facie *to either.*

ysis could be the decomposition of the oxalate first to the carbonate and subsequently to the oxide. On moderately large specimens and with no useful atmosphere control, these two decompositions will or at least can overlap enough to give a single thermogravimetric weight loss. The present author will not attempt to explain the slow rise in the emanation between about 120 and 250°C. The decrease in the region of 300°C may possibly be due to dilution; the evolution of the other gases may become such a significant part of the total gas flow that the flow through the counter is increased and the quantity of thoron present in the counter at any moment consequently decreased. As the rapid evolution diminishes the increased concentration is again apparent. The method is interesting and may be particularly useful in special cases. As a general technique, it suffers from the disadvantages that it does not provide a complete and unambiguous response to events in the specimen and, further, that it requires the presence of thorium or some other radioactive material producing a radioactive gas with a short half-life.

14.6. Determination of Gaseous Products Only

Let us now consider some experiments in which the gathering of information was confined to study of the gaseous products of decompositions. These range from systems in which only the event is of interest to systems in which the products are measured quite specifically both qualitatively and quantitatively. One of the former type is that of Rogers and associates (R27) in which (Fig. XIV-18) the specimen was pyrolyzed in a stream of helium. The organic vapors from the pyrolysis chamber are oxidized to water and carbon dioxide in the combustion tube to avoid condensation as well as to enhance sensitivity. (The conversion of a molecule of some fairly complex organic material to many molecules of

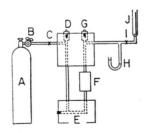

Fɪɢ. XIV-18. Schematic drawing of pyrolysis apparatus: A, carrier gas supply; B, pressure regulator; C, flow-control needle valve; D, reference thermal conductivity; E, pyrolysis chamber F, combustion tube; G, active cell; H, monometer; I, pressure-control needle valve; J, rotameter.

The oxidation of the products in the combustion tube avoids the condensation encountered by Ayres and Bens (A19).

carbon dioxide and water will quite naturally enhance the signal obtained in passing through the thermal conductivity cell.) [Bohon (B60)
has used this type of pyrolysis chamber without the combustion tube; in
this way he was able to collect the combustion products.] The pyrolysis
block (Fig. XIV-19) is heated by commerical cartridge heaters through
a temperature program. The data gained from the thermal conductivity
measurements are simple indications of decompositions without identification (Fig. XIV-20) except, in some cases, by the temperature at which

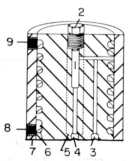

FIG. XIV-19. Pyrolysis block: 1, pyrolysis chamber; 2, nickel plug; 3, carrier gas
inlet; 4, carrier gas outlet; 5, cartridge heater wells (two); 6, helical threads cut
in inner body of block; 7, outer shell of block; 8, cooling jacket inlet; 9, cooling
jacket outlet.

Because of the high temperatures, the inlet and outlet are sealed by use of
model airplane spark plug gaskets or dead-soft copper washers.

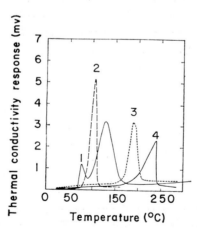

FIG. XIV-20. Pyrolysis curves: 1, 10 mg NaHCO$_2$ contaminated with Na$_2$CO$_3$•H$_2$O;
2, 10 mg CaSO$_4$•2H$_2$O; 3, 10 mg tetryl; 4, 10 mg hexanitrosobenzene.

The decomposition reaction must be inferred since no specific identification is ob-
tained.

the decomposition occurs. This apparatus has the advantage over the Ayres and Bens apparatus that the conversion to carbon dioxide and water rids the system of easily condensable materials which might later vaporize and give a false signal.

These simple indications of decompositions are useful principally in establishing temperatures of decomposition, but with known products the technique can also be used as a quantitative measure with the same confidence as gas chromatography since the same type of detector is used. The user must know the product gases very specifically, or at least know that the same material containing the same proportions of carbon and hydrogen will come off from each sample tested. If this knowledge is not available with certainty, more detailed analyses may be in order. It is necessary only to substitute a technique for analysis instead of, or as well as, detection of the gaseous products. There is no reason why programming of the temperature is not still possible. The most generally useful technique for analysis of these effluent gases is gas chromatography; in the reported work seen by the present author, these sample materials have been vaporized into the carrier gas stream and carried immediately into the chromatographic column.

14.7. Qualitative Identification of Decomposition Products

In general, the direct injection of the decomposition product gases into the chromatograph is done by rapidly heating the material in the gas stream, the means of heating being usually the sample container as well. Experimenters principally interested in the chromatographic analysis can very easily overlook the importance of the manner of heating, and, indeed, this is a common occurrence. The specimens are heated rapidly so that the product gases appear in the chromatograph as a single pulse of gases; identification of the gases given off at intermediate temperatures is not attempted.

The transfer of heat from the heater wire to the sample material is a source of variation and error with specimens of appreciable thickness. Jennings and Dimick (J5) avoided the heat-transfer problem by evaportating the specimen on the heater wire using aqueous phosphoric acid to supply hydrogen and oxygen for the decomposition reaction. Their sampling apparatus is shown in Fig. XIV-21. They examined the effect of temperatures from 550 to 1100°C, finding that for thymine there was no appreciable difference in the pyrolysis pattern, that is, the identities and relative quantities of products. An example of their work is shown in Fig. XIV-22 where the lower plot gives by integration a measure of the volatile components. The first composite peak is likely to be permanent gases. These data show their reproducibility on repetition of the experiment as indicated in Table XIV-1. This is not the sort of reproducibility one would expect from an ordinary chromatographic analysis so the deviation or irreproducibility must be related to the pyrolysis technique. The nonlinearity in Jennings and Dimick's calibration data may still possibly be a heat-transfer problem; the thin specimens with good exposure to the atmosphere may partly volatilize without decomposition while the thicker specimens being heated from the inside may be subject only to the same absolute quantity of vaporization and hence a smaller percentage effect. The probability that the thicker specimens

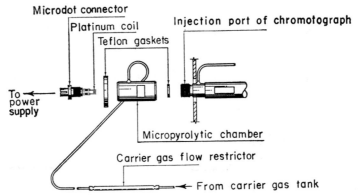

Fɪɢ. XIV-21. Exploded view of pyrolytic accessory. From Jennings and Dimick (J5).

Evaporation of a thin layer of sample onto the heater wire leads to good thermal contact and comparatively uniform heating.

reach higher temperatures locally may also lead to some variation in the relative quantities of the several products even though the identities of the products remain the same. Jennings and Dimick were also able to distinguish quite clearly between positional isomers; cytosine and isocytosine showed quite different proportions of products under similar pyrolysis conditions.

Quite different heating conditions were used by Strassburger *et al.* (S62); these authors used a much lower-temperature pyrolysis in their studies of methyl methacrylate copolymers. They heated their pyrolysis coil, shown in Fig. XIV-23, to about 450°C with 10 to 15 mg of specimen contained therein. At that temperature and in the absence of oxygen and hydrogen a relatively nonvolatile residue is formed. The reactions causing the formation of the residue also introduce distinct nonlinearities into the calibration for quantitative measurements so that, for example, the sample weight-to-peak area ratio varies by a factor of 2 in the methyl methacrylate–ethylene dimethacrylate copolymer.

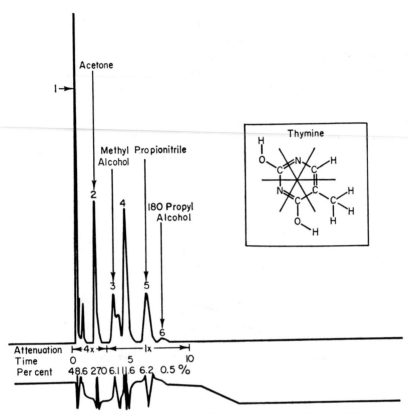

Fig. XIV-22. Pyrolysis of thymine. From Jennings and Dimick (J5).
The relative quantities of products are determined by the manner of splitting of the molecule and recombinations of the fragments.

TABLE XIV-1

COMPOSITION OF THYMINE PYROLYSIS PRODUCTS (J5)

Peak No.	RRT[a]	Per cent	Standard deviation
1	b	45.8	3.6
2	0.28	31.7	4.4
3	0.49	5.6	1.1
4	0.64	10.5	1.7
5	0.88	3.8	2.5
6	1.04	1.1	0.7

[a]RRT refers to relative retention time to benzene (7.2 minutes) on Hallcomid M-18 at 62°C.
[b]Represents a group of peaks.

14.8. Dependence of Products on Conditions of Their Formation

While some of the authors cited indicate that the pyrolysis products are the same over a wide range of pyrolysis conditions, to assume this happy circumstance for any given material to be studied would be exceedingly optimistic. A thin layer of material in contact with a heating element or other form of hot surface at a temperature approximating the ultimate decomposition temperature of the material may transmit heat rapidly enough to permit the entire film to decompose at essentially the same time and more or less at the same temperature. The material in contact with the heated surface does not necessarily rise in temperature greatly above the surface of the film. If this heated surface were several hundred degrees, say, above the ultimate decomposition temperature, rapid decomposition of the inner portion of the film could

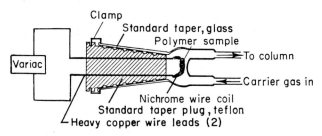

Fɪɢ. XIV-23. Sample introduction system. From Strassburger *et al.* (S62). *Solid pieces of material were placed in the heater coil.*

change the conditions of heat transfer substantially. With very thin specimens the problem will arise only in the extreme cases because the heating of the surface is not instanteous; the heat capacity of the wire itself will cause some delay in reaching the final temperature, permitting a similar smooth rise by the specimen material.

If a thick sample is placed in contact with a heating element and the heating element is supplied with a sudden application of an electric current, the relatively low thermal conductivity of the typical organic specimen will permit the establishment of a high (and not necessarily continuous) temperature gradient through the specimen. The over-all effect will depend on the nature of the sample holding system. If the material has been deposited on a wire or other surface by evaporation of a solvent so that there is a continuous layer on the heating surface, the material next to the heating surface may well be heated slowly enough so that low-temperature decomposition products might form, but these decomposition products cannot escape and will consequently be subject to further decomposition. If particles are merely laid upon the heating surface the portion of the surface initially in contact may be heated slowly enough to undergo a low-temperature decomposition, but the new layers of material subsequently touching the heated surface are being subjected to a progressively hotter surface bringing about the possibility of a different decomposition mechanism.

The change in products obtained with change of pyrolysis conditions has been demonstrated by Martin and Ramstad (M18) who used flash pyrolysis to decompose cellulose in the sample chamber of a two-stage column. They separated the permanent gases on a gas-solid absorption column using polypropylene glycol. The specimen was heated by flash photolysis; that is, intense radiation from a flash tube or arc source was directed on the specimen for a short length of time, the temperature reached depending both on the intensity and the time of exposure. They induced momentary temperatures in the sample in excess of 600°C with intense radiation of a millisecond duration and compared the results with a slower pyrolysis in the 250 to 350°C range induced by less intense radiation lasting for several seconds. The plots are shown in Fig. XIV-24.

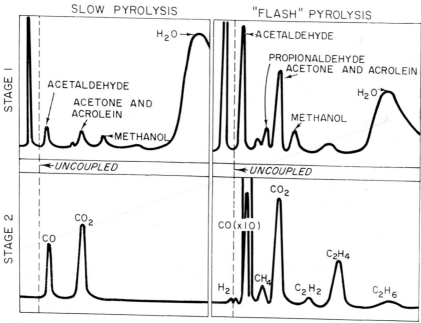

Fig. XIV-24. Chromatograms of cellulose pyrolysis products. From Martin and Ramstad (M18).

The manner of splitting and recombination is decidedly temperature-dependent.

The decomposition products are carried into the polypropylene glycol column where the permanent gases are impeded only slightly. These are led from the glycol column into the activated charcoal column where the gases are separated, the columns being uncoupled immediately after passage of the permanent gases from stage 1 into stage 2. The slow pyrolysis produces only carbon monoxide and carbon dioxide among the permanent gases while the flash pyrolysis produces significant quantities of the lighter hydrocarbons. The principal feature of the partition column curves is the greatly diminished water relative to the other components in the flash pyrolysis. While it is the major component, two of the other peaks at least surpass it in height. Note, too, that the magnitude of the carbon monoxide peak in the flash pyrolysis is more than ten times that of the carbon dioxide peak while in the slow pyrolysis it is somewhat smaller. Explanation of these variations would require further knowledge of the system, but a safe general conclusion can be stated: variations in the rate of heating of an organic specimen may cause different products or different relative quantities of products.

14.9. Other Possibilities

Now let us consider some of the extensions of effluence analysis; first of all, changes in the carrier gas used with the intention of encouraging or inhibiting some particular reaction. The use of helium-oxygen and helium-nitrogen mixtures has already been discussed in relation to determining the steps of an inorganic reaction. In this case, the helium-oxygen mixture permitted the oxidation of carbon monoxide while the absence of the oxygen brought about decomposition without oxidation. Similarly, small quantities of oxygen in the carrier gas stream would permit oxidation or partial oxidation of the specimen or the presence of hydrogen might permit saturation of organic carbon chains. This is not being recommended as a general technique but as a modification of procedure which might yield useful information. Repetitive sampling into the column in the manner practiced by the present author (see above) would yield successive lots of decomposition products as the temperature was increased.

Repetitive sampling for chromatography need not be an intermittent withdrawal of a portion of a gas stream. An alternative procedure, having some substantial advantages, is repetitive instanteous heating to successively higher temperatures. This may be done by extending Martin and Ramstad's (R18) technique to a *programmed* flash pyrolysis.

In this procedure the sample is within the gas stream at all times. At selected time intervals—depending on the nature of the columns and products—and flow conditions, light flashes of progressively higher intensity are directed at the sample. The heat generated within the sample due to optical absorption raises the temperature to a degree determined by the heat capacity and nature and quantity of the specimen. Some measure of the thermal effects may be obtained by relaxation time measurements as discussed later. The temperature can sooner or later be raised to a temperature at which some decomposition will occur. The millisecond—or less—pulse brings about a sudden expulsion of gas into the chromatographic gas stream. This sudden sampling inserts a very small "slug" of the gaseous products which means, in turn, comparatively narrow peaks as the components pass through the detector.

The major problem is the usual one of temperature inhomogeneity. The possibility of momentary temperature differences of hundreds of degrees across the sample forces the use of thin samples—essentially a monolayer of particles. Even so, the illuminated side of a particle may be completely decomposed while portions of the dark side are yet in the original state.

The enforced use of a very small sample is not such a handicap as it might appear *prima facie*. Since the sampling consists of heating the entire sample briefly to each of the successively higher temperatures the entire effluence is injected into the chromatographic column—rather than a comparatively small fraction as in repetitive sampling from a gas stream. This represents a gain of 30 to 100 to compensate for the diminution in sample size.

Measurement of the temperature could be done with a high-speed, probably oscillographic, recorder. Relaxation time studies of the variation of temperature after each flash are potentially of considerable use in investigation of thermal properties and behavior of freshly formed and freshly disrupted surfaces and crystals. Conversely, programmed flashing could be used to induce reaction of a solid—or liquid—specimen with the atmosphere. A reaction which is not strongly exothermic could be carried out using a multitude of low-energy and/or short pulses and some information on relative activities of surface regions gained.

Decompositions of specimens can be carried out directly in the sampling locations of other analytical instruments as well as chromatographs or chromatographic type of detectors, and similarly the decompositions can be programmed either stepwise or continuously. Two types of analyzers are of particular promise, optical and mass spectrometers. Decomposition into say, an infrared absorption spectrometer sample tube would be of particular interest if a particular compound or functional group were being monitored. Fairly high resolution would be required to obtain unambiguous reults. There is the advantage, however, that the appearance of the product could be followed during the entire decomposition, and if the decomposition is programmed some measure of the temperatures of appearance of various products may be obtained.

Of the mass spectrometers, the time-of-flight spectrometer would be of special interest because of the high frequency of repetitive sampling possible. Decomposition in a chamber connected to the spectrometer by an appropriate orifice would make possible the gathering of kinetic data on decompositions.

Relating the events recorded by these various techniques needs to be done with great care. Bussiere *et al.* (B91) compared curves obtained by their simultaneous determinations (see above) with those obtained on other (apparently single purpose) apparatus. An example is the pair of differential thermal analysis plots of Fig. XIV-25. Bussiere *et al.* conclude that it is preferable to make all the measurements simultaneously to obtain agreement in the interpretation of a given reaction. This is a fairly

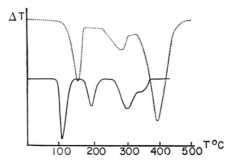

Fɪɢ. XIV-25. Comparison of differential thermal analyses of $Th(C_2O_4)_2 \cdot 6H_2O$: _____, simultaneous with thermogravimetric and emanation analyses; . . . . . ., in a separate apparatus. From Bussiere *et al.* (B91).

Differences in both the temperatures and the manners of the decompositions are apparent.

common attitude. The present author has contended (G4)—and still contends—that, unless the data from each technique have some real significance, attempts to relate them are seldom gainful even when apparently successful. The agreement that is almost unavoidable in simultaneous determinations can give the observer an entirely unwarranted confidence in whatever he chooses the curves to mean.

14.10. Summary

When a gas is given off during a thermal decomposition it is no longer necessary to speculate on its identity to describe the reaction. Gases can be identified quite easily, directly or indirectly. The specificity of the analysis should be chosen to fit the problem at hand.

Simultaneous meaasurements may be very helpful but proper care in design of the experiment is important.

When a sample is degraded thermally with the intent of only analyzing the gases, the problems incident to heating of the sample have not lost their importance. Pyrolysis products from even mildly complex organic molecules can be different under different heating conditions.

Programmed pyrolyses should provide more significant data.

CHAPTER XV

Recording, Control, and Power Equipment

15.1. General

Since nearly all recording of differential thermal analysis data will be done by the use of strip chart recording potentiometers, a reasonably complete description of their operation is appropriate. A nonhistorical survey of other techniques will be found later in the chapter.

Strip chart recording potentiometers may be X vs t or X vs. Y. In the latter case the Y signal either moves the chart back and forth under the X pen support or moves the carriage supporting the X pen back and forth as needed. In either case, the position of the pen with respect to the chart indicates the value of the Y signal.

15.2. Recording Potentiometers

Recording potentiometers are of special value in differential thermal analysis because of their null balance characteristic; i.e., no current is drawn from the measuring elements except when their potential is changing, and even during a process of change the currents drawn are negligibly small. In essence, the potential from the thermocouple or amplifier is compared with the potential of a moving contact on a slide-wire (Fig. XV-1). The comparison circuit includes an amplifier and motor arranged so that if an unbalance in potential does exist this unbalance is amplified and supplied to the motor. The motor moves the contact on the slide-wire to a position at which the unbalance signal is returned to zero. A recording pen is connected mechanically to the slide-wire contact shaft, so that movement of the contact resulting from a changing input potential leaves a record on the moving chart paper.

The signal from the thermocouple or differential thermocouple is, of course, a direct current potential. In order to amplify the unbalance potential to a sufficient voltage to drive a motor, the signal must be converted to a nonsteady, e.g., pulsating, potential. In standard commercial recorders, the usual procedure is to convert the direct potential to a non-

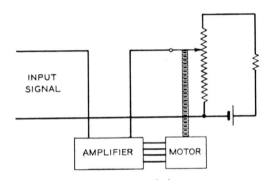

Fɪɢ. XV-1. Potentiometer balancing system.
The amplifier detects any difference between the slide-wire contact and the input potential and causes the motor to drive the slide-wire to eliminate the difference.

sinusoidal alternating potential by means of a "chopper." This chopper applies the potential to a pair of primary transformer windings alternately by mechanical switching. These windings are so connected that the secondary winding has induced in it a series of pulses, each opposed to the last (Fig. XV-2). The result is a potential which is alternating at a frequency determined by the rapidity of the mechanical switching. The wave is sufficiently pure that it can be amplified and used to drive the balancing motor with a moderate amount of filtering of harmonics.

The mechanical switching is commonly synchronous with the supply frequency so that the amplified frequency on a 60-cps supply voltage is also 60 cps. This condition will normally cause an inquiry by the neophyte because of the obvious possibility of electrical pickup from dozens of nearby sources; the choice of frequency must be justified in some manner. The principal reason for the choice is the customary one—saving of money.

The amplified voltage fed into the grid of the output stage of the amplifier being an alternating current of known frequency, the plates of a push-pull output stage can be fed with an alternating voltage of the same frequency (Fig. XV-3) rather than with a direct current supply. This permits the elimination of a fair-sized rectifier and filter for the plate

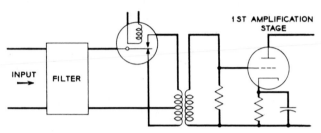

Fɪɢ. XV-2. Amplifier input.
The amplifier dc input is "chopped" by the vibrating contacts to send the current alternately through each of the two halves of the transformer primary winding.

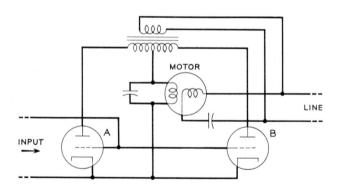

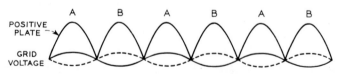

Fɪɢ. XV-3. Push-pull output to motor.
The grids of tubes A and B follow the driver signal together but only one plate at a time is positive. In the diagram at the bottom the plate in tube A is positive while the grids are positive (solid line) so the tube conducts. When the plate of tube B is positive the grids have gone negative and the tube does not conduct. If the input signal were reversed, the grid voltage would follow the dotted line and tube B would conduct.

supply. Interference from electrical pickup is avoided by filtering the input.

In circuits like that of Fig. XV-3, the electron tubes are acting essentially as switches. A positive signal on the grid while the plate is positive allows a current to flow. The phase of the grid signal is in phase—or 180° out of phase—with the plate potential so that the presence of a grid signal means that either tube A or tube B will conduct. The motor will move rapidly toward the rebalancing position. Zero signal on the grids will permit some current to flow each half cycle, causing a tendency for the motor to rotate in each direction in turn and hence a noticeable "jitter." A capacitor across the motor leads provides some damping by smoothing the pulsations somewhat, introducing thereby a dc component.

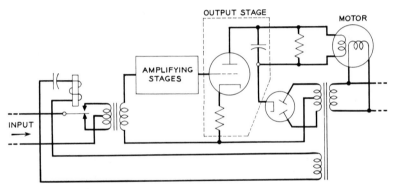

Fig. XV-4. Output stage with motor as the plate load.
The phase shift in the amplifier plus that caused by the capacitor in the chopper-drive circuit equals 90°.

With an amplifier output of the supply frequency a relatively small alternating current motor may be used to obtain bidirectional drive since one field can be supplied directly from the line. Any frequency other than line frequency would require a power supply large enough to drive the entire measuring system.

More elegant systems supply the output plate with a direct (but not heavily filtered) current (Fig. XV-4). The motor winding is the plate load. A moderate direct current flows all the time applying some continuous damping on the motor movement. Zero signal on the grid allows a direct current flow to damp motor movement completely. The phase shift (90°) necessary to provide direction of control is supplied principally by operating the converter (chopper) out of phase, taking into account the small phase shift through the amplifier.

15.3. Phase Shift

The phase shift in either case performs the same general function as the capacitor in an ordinary split-phase motor. This type of motor has no electrical connection between rotor and stator; it depends on an induced field arising from sets of adjacent coils; these coils obviously cannot be supplied with currents all in phase with each other or there would be no net effect. The phase shift need not be 90° for unidirectional drive but it must be quite specifically 90° for most reversible motor applications; any sizable deviation will cause a difference in power in the two directions—an obviously pointless condition.

Whether this phase shift causes a "lag" or "lead" of the control-winding current in relation to the line-winding current depends on the polarity of the input voltage to the amplifier. Since the direction of the motor rotation depends on whether it sees a "lag" or "lead," it, too, reflects the polarity of the input signal and is thus able to move in the proper direction to drive the error signal back to zero.

15.4. Input Impedance

Since the chopper amplifier does have a transformer input stage, a real—though small—electric current must flow when an off-balance condition exists. Design and construction for high input signal strength is obviously simpler than for low signal strength. For this reason recording potentiometers are most readily available for signal strength of 400–1000 ohms input impedance. Thermocouples are well below this level (0–15 ohms) so that a base-metal thermocouple can be connected directly to a fairly sensitive (−0.5 to +0.5 mv) recording potentiometer and reasonably good thermograms obtained. This span represents ca. ± 11°C for a Chromel-Alumel thermocouple.

Some thermistors and strain gauges may exceed the upper limits of input impedance. In this case the recording potentiometer must be selected partly on the basis of its input impedance. Commercial recorders are available with input impedance greater than one megohm.

15.5. Recording Potentiometer as a Signal Follower

The normal function of a strip chart recording potentiometer is to measure and record a potential, but the possibility of otherwise using its circuitry should not be overlooked. The author, for example, has used a second slide-wire, mounted on the same shaft as the ordinary slide-wire contact, to follow the movements of the chain of an automatic balance (G3). Before the days of Zener diodes, one had a choice of manual, semiautomatic, or automatic standardization of measuring slide-wires.

Essentially this required a very stable battery or cell in the recorder or else the appearance—at regular intervals—of standardization resets. In addition, if a movement was to be followed by converting that movement into an electrical signal, that circuit likewise had to be especially stable.

Consider now a circuit in which the same voltage supply is fed to two slide-wires adjusted to match electrically (Fig. XV-5). If the moving contacts are in such a position that no voltage difference exists between them, a change in the voltage at the source will change the voltage of either moving contact with respect to any reference except the other moving contact. This voltage difference remains zero. If this potential between the two moving contacts is amplified and used to drive one of the contacts back to the balance point, the result is a servo system which is insensitive to changes in supply voltage.

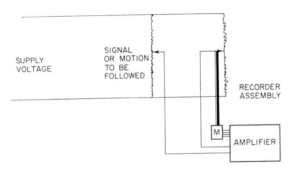

Fig. XV-5. Recorder amplifier used to follow rather than measure a signal. *Since the two slide-wires are fed from the same voltage, the system is insensitive to ordinary voltage changes.*

In the application cited, a potentiometer was mounted on the shaft from which the balance chain was driven. This potentiometer was fed from the same electrical source as the second slide-wire on the recorder shaft. The intrinsic slide-wire was disconnected from the recorder amplifier. The difference signal from the moving contacts was fed into this amplifier. When a difference existed, the recorder shaft was moved by the motor to return the difference signal to zero. Since the pen is driven by the same shaft, the pen provided a continuous indication of the position of the potentiometer and hence the chain. Since the chain was itself actuated by an independent circuit which kept the balance continuously at null, a weight change record could be obtained overnight or over other intervals too long for reliable voltage supplies.

15.6. Recording Potentiometer as Position Follower

Another use of a recorder as a position indicator was more direct (Fig. IV-8). Keith and Tuttle (K14) mounted a split photocell on the pen carriage of a recording potentiometer. The recorder amplifier was fed from the photocell circuit so that the pen carriage moved in the direction of more intense illumination. When the light flow on the two sides of the photocell was equal, the carriage remained at rest.

Keith and Tuttle connected their (DTA) differential thermocouple to a mirror galvanometer so that the light beam fell on the path of the photocell. The pen then followed the galvanometer light beam to give the ΔT plot. A reasonably long light path and a sensitive galvanometer will yield a quite satisfactory optical amplification. The "noise" in this case would be mechanical in origin. See also Dannis (D2).

15.7. Recording Potentiometer as Position Adjuster

The servo features in strip chart recorders have been used to provide direct balancing in thermogravimetry. Ewald (E8) used the recorder shaft to pay out or take up chain. The pen position indicated the amount of chain paid out.

Ordinary single-pen recording potentiometers are available in ranges suitable for temperature measurement as well as for much of the differential temperature measurement. The multitude of available types permits a great latitude of choice of input signals for thermogravimetric analysis.

15.8. Special Types of Recorders

For thermal analysis studies, in which some other quantity must be related to the temperature, comparison of T from one strip chart with $f(T)$ from another is inconvenient and unnecessary. Reference marking or "pipping" indicators will be described later. Modern design generally calls for simultaneous recording on a single chart. The principal types of recorders for this purpose are X vs Y, multipen, multipoint, and multichannel.

An X-Y recorder is frequently used to obtain a direct plot of $f(T)$ vs T. Plotting of weight loss vs time in thermogravimetry is a reasonably satisfactory technique because variations in the rate of heating are relatively insignificant compared to differential thermal analysis.

For differential thermal analysis, however, the maintenance of an essentially constant rate of heating is essential. To use an X-Y recorder with no monitoring apparatus is to place complete faith in an unsupervised control system. A failure or defect in the programming will appear as a spurious thermal effect which may not be recognized. X-Y recorders are often used in differential thermal analysis with motor-driven auto-transformer power supplies. The nonlinear temperature increase is concealed by the ΔT vs T plot. An X-Y recorder is useful but the temperature should be separately monitored. A relatively inexpensive galvanometer recorder with an independent thermocouple is sufficient.

Multipen recorders provide independent measuring circuits, each operating over the entire range of the chart. There is necessarily a displacement of one record with respect to the other since the pens must be able to pass one another. The author makes use of several two-pen recorders including one whose chart movement depends on temperature rather than time, that is, an X_1, X_2 vs Y recorder.

A multipoint recorder is one in which a simple measuring circuit scans, repetitively and in sequence, a number of input signals; the number may be as high as a few dozen. These recorders have quite limited use in thermal analysis because of their noncontinuous plotting; their principal use would be in multiple differential thermal analysis. In general, one would be constrained to do studies involving gross samples so that a reading every 4 to 24 seconds is adequate. The more serious limitation is the fact that all circuits to be measured must have the same range. Putting a number of ΔT signals on one chart is really no great problem, nor is putting a number of temperature signals, but to try to put a temperature signal and a difference signal on the same multipoint recorder means that one signal has to be given one or two extra treatments. Specifically one needs to amplify or attenuate one signal so that it agrees in span magnitude with the other and, in addition, a bias must be inserted to shift the zero. By this time, enough equipment and effort are used up so that a multipen recorder would have been cheaper. Nevertheless, it can be done.

Kauffman and Dilling (K8), in the early days of electronic recording, converted a 0–10 mv multipoint potentiometric recorder to a 0–0.4 mv instrument so that temperature differences could be measured directly, then they fed the temperature signal (from the reference couple) into a voltage divider, R10 and R11 of Fig. XV-6. Since they were recording three thermograms they added a different bias to each of the three differential signals, accomplishing the double purpose of separating the traces and establishing the zero line at a more convenient place than at the recorder zero at the right-hand edge of the chart.

Both temperature and differential temperature were recorded by a single pen in the arrangement used by Keavney and Eberlin (K11b). At a preset interval the input was switched from ΔT by a timing switch long enough to allow a suitable measurement of T. The peaks for T in

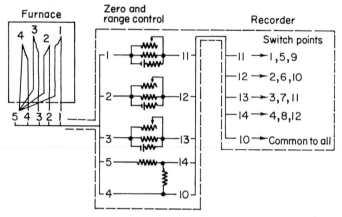

FIG. XV-6. Multipoint potentiometer to record both T and ΔT. From Kauffman and Dilling (K8).

The recording circuit is switched successively to each of twelve sets of contacts, in this case paralleled in four sets of three each. The fourth set records a fraction of the thermocouple electromotive force.

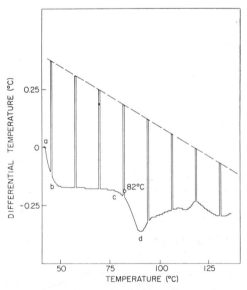

FIG. XV-7. Temperature and differential temperature of the glass transition in polystyrene. From Keavney and Eberlin (K11b).

The recording technique is economical but a large recorder dead zone results.

Fig. XV-7 can be interpolated easily to give the value at any point. Quite good data were obtained but note that Keavney and Eberlin had to set their recorder sensitivity to a low value to avoid a very messy record (because of the sudden large pen movements). The low sensitivity causes the stepping in the record. This particular nuisance could be avoided by addition of a damping resistor on the motor drive and a time-delay relay so that the movement would be damped heavily as the pen changes but the damping resistor is shorted during normal operation.

A multichannel recorder provides (generally two) side-by-side measuring systems each with limited chart travel. While they lack the readability of multipen recorders, there is a more or less compensating gain in that the two signals may be related more accurately by reading across —with reference to the printed chart lines—than by measuring the pen displacement.

15.9. Galvanometer Recorders

In addition to the recording potentiometer, a number of types of galvanometer recorders are available. These are meter movements generally equipped with some low-friction means of marking the position on the moving chart paper. Alternatively, the meter arm may be periodically arrested and pressed against the chart. The low-friction marking may be properly extended to the zero-friction devices using optical or thermal methods.

In general, these galvanometric measuring devices are less expensive than recording potentiometers and require less maintenance. Operationally, they are somewhat inferior to recording potentiometers because they draw current and hence the heat source must do some work on the thermocouple. The withdrawal of this energy changes the temperature distribution in the region of the thermocouple. Also, the current drawn from the thermocouple produces a voltage drop across the resistance of the thermocouple leads. This voltage subtracts from the voltage produced by the thermocouple, and its magnitude changes with change in resistance of the leads due to aging and ambient temperature variations. The change in thermal gradient is of little importance when the thermocouple and meter are being used for measurement or control near the furnace windings or in a heavy sample block but in work needing high sensitivity a recording potentiometer must be used.

15.10. Miscellaneous Notes on Recording

Here we must differentiate between recording potentiometers and recorders with a potentiometric circuit. A recording potentiometer compares the full magnitude of an incoming signal directly with a signal from a slide-wire or equivalent; a recorder with a potentiometric measuring circuit has instead a tapped resistance in which the *voltage drop* across a portion of the resistance is measured—with a potentiometric circuit. The requirement that there be a voltage drop to measure implies a current flow, which is precisely what a recording potentiometer avoids. These recorders with potentiometric circuits are characterized in general by a multitude of ranges.

For most purposes, including more general temperature measurements, this type of recording is satisfactory. Even for differential thermal analysis they present no disadvantage if the furnace or block temperature is being measured or if sample sizes are large. The moment one attempts to measure directly the temperature of small specimens, sample or reference, from or near the differential thermocouple, the work drawn from the specimen to maintain the required current flow will upset the temperature distribution and cause a smoothly increasing (with temperature) base line (see Chapters III and IV). The differential signal, however, can be fed into such a recorder after amplification because this small current drawn from the output of the amplifier will not affect the input circuit and because the work drawn would be very, very small. Remember that measurements of T are with reference to ambient temperature or a fixed reference temperature while ΔT is measured with reference to a junction at nearly the same temperature.

The function of the amplifier-motor combination was performed on some early recorders by a galvanometer and a mechanical linkage from the chart drive motor. The unbalance between the slide-wire and input signal was supplied to the galvanometer. Periodically (ca every 2 seconds) the galvanometer movement would be arrested and the deflection of the pointer arm would determine the action of a clutch. The clutch could drive the slide-wire either way with a limit of nearly an inch per operation. This sort of movement is satisfactory for monitoring differential thermal analysis furnace temperatures but not for programming or for recording the differential temperature itself. It would be suitable for use in programming a low-speed thermogravimetry furnace.

A rather different approach to the comparison-signal problem involves the use of strain gauges as a replacement for the slide-wire. The strain gauge is a device whose electrical resistance is changed by mechanical strain.

The input signal is treated in the same manner as in a slide-wire potentiometer. The motor drive responds to a difference signal to increase and decrease strain to restore the unbalance to zero. The advantages are the infinite resolution and the lack of moving electrical contacts. The first is of only moderate interest since the resolution of a slide-wire, i.e., the voltage increment per turn, is one of the lesser problems. The instruments having accuracies of $\frac{1}{4}\%$ of full scale have three or more turns within their error tolerance; the existence of ten times this number would be of little benefit. The moving-contact avoidance is of real value. The range of movement of the strain gauges is so small that nonlinearity constitutes no problem.

15.11. Power Supplies

The means of controlling the temperature of a furnace—even before one attempts to program it—are so varied that a complete separation of topics is not practicable. In general we shall consider first the power supplies—ranging from switches through thyratrons—as the physical method of limiting at the will of the operator the power input to the furnace. We shall then consider control systems—to the extent that they are separable—as the means by which the operator indicates his wishes to the power supply. We shall subsequently examine programming techniques by which the user—prior to the beginning of an operation—gives the control system all instructions required to carry out said operation.

During the discussion it will be expedient to refer to combinations of power supplies, controllers, and even programming in a manner intended for over-all clarity. The author has been unable to consign each type of unit to a separate paragraph or two and still offer a hope for a general understanding of the whole exposition, but, as far as is practicable, the various devices will be described separately.

15.12. Variable Autotransformer

A simple and popular power supply device is the variable autotransformer. (In this day and age, the use of a variable resistance is almost inconceivable.) An autotransformer comprises a single winding with a number of connections for input and output voltages (Fig. XV-8). As a step-down transformer, it is the inductance analog to a resistance-type voltage divider. Alternating currents may be stepped up as well as down. A variable autotransformer, then, is a device with provision for changing the output in a large number of small steps. In commercial practice, this variable autotransformer normally takes the form of a toroidal winding of several dozen to a few hundred turns arranged so that a wiping contact may sweep around to make electrical connection with any turn. Actually two or three turns are touching the wiping arm at the same time; this multiple contact avoids momentary open circuits and arcing. The number of turns and the size of the wire is dependent on the voltage supply and the current rating. The flux density within the core is determined by the current input and the number of turns. An autotransformer may be used for lower than rated input voltage but not for higher. This rated input voltage should not be exceeded significantly since the core would become overloaded, i.e., magnetically saturated. The autotransformer may also be operated in reverse, but, since the output voltage is then something approximating an ordinary supply voltage, the advantages of this arrangement are generally trivial.

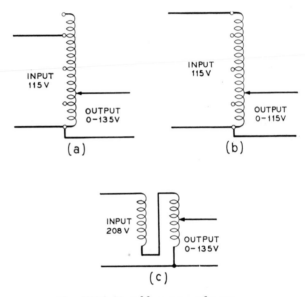

Fɪɢ. XV-8. Variable autotransformers.

When power is supplied to less than the full winding but may be taken from the full winding (a), a voltage step-up can be obtained. Applying power to the entire winding (b) permits variation only up to supply voltage. If power can be taken from less turns than it is applied to (c), there is a voltage step-down.

The variable—or adjustable—autotransformer can increase or decrease the furnace power to bring the temperature back to the set point. It has two advantages over the saturable-core rector (see below): it may be selected to match the largest load, yet will perform in the same manner for smaller loads (except see below) and it has a zero turndown. On the other hand, the adjustment action is by no means stepless. Unless the control system is adjusted so that it is on the verge of "hunting," adjusting action may change the input voltage several volts. A few seconds later, a reverse change nearly as great may take place. On very rapid-response heating systems, the time constant of the motor-driven transformer may approach that of the system resulting in an unstable control which will continually oscillate. On a very rapid-response differential thermal analysis or differential calorimetry furnace, the result may be a scalloped base line. For other systems, nothing is lost by having a slower-response furnace. The reader may argue that a control system should ordinarily be adjusted so that it is on the verge of "hunting"; this is correct—ordinarily. Operation of a rapid-response furnace in this manner is quite satisfactory as long as nothing is changed. Let a sample block be used in place of cups or a ceramic block in place of nickel and the control system may go into oscillation. This is normally a problem only on very rapid-response furnaces.

15.13. Saturable-Core Reactor

A saturable-core reactor comprises a laminated iron transformer core with a power and a control winding (Fig. XV-9). To understand its operation, it is necessary to review the role of the iron core in transformers and chokes.

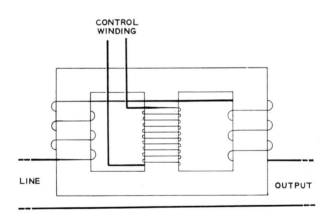

Fɪɢ. XV-9. Saturable-core reactor.
Supply of part of the flux density from the control coil decreases the impedance to alternating current.

As the voltage in a coil increases, the magnetic field in the coil increases. In the absence of a material of high permeability, the region within the coil is quickly saturated, i.e., reaches its maximum flux density, and little impedance is offered at power frequencies. If an iron core is now inserted into the coil, the possible flux density is much greater. The work necessary to build up a field is consequently much larger and a sizable impedance to alternating current is offered.

The impedance offered by the winding depends, then, on the flux density which the current through the winding must generate. Movement of an iron core in and out of the coil is a possible but not practical means of control. An easier way to limit the flux density in the core is to provide some portion of the possible density in some other way. This may be done readily from another (control) winding on the same core. If this second coil should now supply 80% of the saturation flux density, the first (power) coil would now supply only the other 20% and the winding would offer only one-fifth of the maximum inductive impedance to the flow of alternating current. The control coil uses a low direct current, e.g., 0–5 ma, but a relatively very large number of turns makes it able to supply a saturation flux density.

The current through the control winding can be varied readily, rapidly, and continuously so that the saturable-core reactor has an advantage over the position-adjusting system, i.e., continuous variation within its range as well as nearly instantaneous response. There are also some disadvantages: nonzero turndown and the necessity of designing or selecting for the particular load.

The nonzero turndown is simply the result of having a continuous circuit at all times. Even at maximum impedance, some current will flow. A characteristic value of this current is 3% of full load. The selection requirement is, in part, related to the nonzero turndown. If, for example, a 0.5-kw load were connected to a 2.0-kw reactor, not only would the turndown current tend to be about four times too high, but also the higher resistance load would become a more significant portion of the voltage drop and the voltage on the furnace might be 15% or more of the supply voltage. Obviously, control at low temperatures would be out of the question with an oversized reactor.

The other reason that a saturable-core reactor must be matched to its load is simply the dc resistance of the winding. At full saturation by the control winding, the reactor appears only as a resistive load. Its resistance must be low enough and the windings large enough to permit dissipation of the rated power in the load.

As in the ON-OFF control, the furnace input is varied to keep the temperature at or near the set point—with an immense difference. Since the voltage drop across the reactor can be varied in an infinite number of steps, the power dissipated in the furnace can likewise be varied in an infinite number of steps. If one supplies a control signal which can be varied similarly, one may control without anything resembling the discrete increases and decreases found with ON-OFF controllers; instead, as the temperature drops below the set point, the power input increases in a stepless manner to bring the furnace back up in temperature. As the temperature rises, the power input is cut back.

This and other current—or voltage—adjusting controllers benefit greatly from proportional band, rate time, and reset action. These devices are outlined in a later section.

15.14. Controlled Rectifier

The ordinary form of the controlled rectifier at the power levels of interest here is the thyratron. This may be an electron tube or, more recently, a solid-state device—in essence, a king-size transistor.

The electron tube thyratron is a gas-filled tube with a heater and three, or more, working electrodes. As in ordinary electron tubes connected as amplifiers, electrons are emitted from the heated cathode (Fig. XV-10) but their flow toward the positively charged anode is inhibited

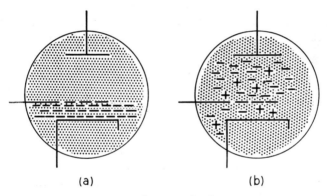

(a)   (b)

Fig. XV-10. Electron tube thyratron.

While the bridge is kept sufficiently negative (a) the tube does not conduct; if the grid permits flow (b) the movement of electrons toward the plate will ionize the gas and the positive ions will prevent the grid from regaining control until the conduction is stopped externally.

or prevented by the negatively charged grid. Like an amplifier, for a given grid voltage some anode potential will be sufficient to draw some electrons past the grid and toward the anode. Unlike the amplifier, once the flow has started the grid no longer can control it. The current through the tube either is zero or is limited by the load and the anode dissipation. This lack of control is the result of ionization of the gas within the tube. An electron accelerated toward the anode collides with gas atoms with sufficient energy to ionize a few before reaching the anode. This supplies not only more electrons but also positive ions. These latter are attracted not only to the cathode but also to the more negatively charged grid. Since current flow in the grid circuit is limited by a resistor to a small value, these positive ions tend simply to depolarize the grid. [If the current were not limited, the grid would supply electrons to the positive ions, thereby acting as a second (cold) cathode and losing control anyway.]

The thyratron discharge ends only when the anode voltage is not sufficient to sustain the flow, i.e., when an electron is not accelerated rapidly enough to ionize gas particles. When this occurs, no positive ions are formed to depolarize the grid and the grid discharges the ions near it, becomes negative, and rather abruptly shuts off the flow of electrons to the anode.

For most applications, the thyratron is supplied with an alternating potential so that the anode voltage drops to zero each cycle. During the following half cycle, the anode is less positive than the grid so that the tube could not conduct anyway. Typical operation characteristic of a thyratron is shown in Fig. XV-11.

The current flow through a thyratron is controlled by varying the grid voltage and thus limiting the fraction of the half cycle during which the tube conducts. The control signal may be an alternating potential whose phase angle (with respect to the anode supply) is shifted so that it is more negative than the control characteristic (Fig. XV-11) until the proper time of firing. A controlled-rectifier system for furnace program control would more generally make use of a direct current control supply, which adjusts the phase angle of the alternating current grid potential as a function of its magnitude. The same control signal used in saturable-core reactor systems can be used in some controlled-rectifier systems.

A solid-state thyratron has similar over-all performance even though it functions rather differently.

15.15 Ignitron

The ignitron is a controlled rectifier used to supply greater amounts of power than are common in thermal analysis. Its operation is generally similar to that of a thyratron.

15.16. Control System

Furnaces with constant rates of heating with either constant or linearly increasing voltage input have not yet been constructed. Further, reproducibility of response from one furnace to another is poor. The need or desire for a reasonably constant heating rate over the full temperature range or from one furnace to another leads directly to temperature control.

Consider first static control, i.e., setting of a control point to a given temperature or condition representing a given temperature, comparing

this set point to the actual temperature, and from the difference determining the voltage input to the furnace. A simple case is an ON-OFF
regulator of the bimetallic strip type. There are a multitude of ways of
adjusting the voltage input, a number of ways in which the off-balance
signal is detected, and a few corrections which may be added to more
sophisticated systems. These may well be discussed before approaching
the problem of moving the set point.

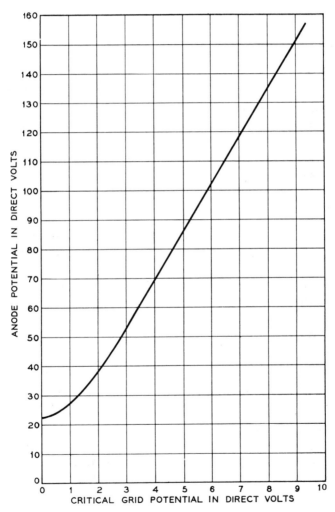

Fig. XV-11. An example of control characteristics of a thyratron.
*The instantaneous anode cathode voltage must exceed that shown at the instanta-
neous grid cathode (negative) potential. Both values may be continuously changing.*

15.17. ON-OFF Control

The increase in temperature to above the set point opens a switch or de-energizes a relay and removes power from the furnace. Voltage input is, then, either zero or a set voltage. This set voltage may be the line voltage or may be the output from an autotransformer. With an autotransformer an additional safety feature is available; i.e., the supply voltage may be that which will just barely bring the furnace to the maximum temperature at the desired heating rate. It cannot then go far above that temperature even with a constant supply voltage.

15.18. HIGH-LOW Control

The ON-OFF control may be changed easily to a HIGH-LOW control such that when the sensing point in the furnace reaches or exceeds the control temperature the electric power is not switched OFF but to a lower voltage—a voltage known to be too low to maintain the control temperature. This may be done in several ways; for example a load in series with the furnace might be short-circuited when the furnace is below the control point, the control switch opening up the short circuit as the control point is reached so that a portion of the voltage drop is dissipated in this load. By close adjustment of the HIGH-LOW inputs not only can the temperature fluctuations be made small but the cycle time can be made long. The essential condition is that under all operating conditions the higher voltage is sufficient to keep the furnace at or above the control point and the lower voltage is under no conditions sufficient to maintain the furnace at the control point.

An autotransformer can be switched to perform nearly the same function. The switching arrangement will depend partly on the power requirements. If the voltage output needed is somewhere close to the maximum, switching of the output is feasible (Fig. XV-12a) if there is no objection to having the furnace winding ca 20 volts above ground potential at the lowest point. This switching will add or subtract 17 or 20 volts depending on the input connection. If the output voltage requirement is low, say in the order of 30 volts average, switching between 20 and 40 volts is a considerable change. For such cases input switching (Fig. XV-12b) is better. Now, regardless of position of the moving contact, the output voltage will increase by about 17% when the control operates, and in the example cited the switching can be between $27\frac{1}{2}$ and $32\frac{1}{2}$ volts, giving both longer cycle time and lower variation than the arrangement in Fig. XV-12a. With the generally low-current requirements (< 20 amp) of modern thermal analysis apparatus switching on the primary is quite satisfactory. For very high currents the surge that occurs if the switching occurs at the peak of the voltage cycle might cause mechanical damage.

Any HIGH-LOW switching must be based on certain knowledge that the furnace requirements will always lie between the two positions; otherwise the system can go out of control.

The ON-OFF or HIGH-LOW control may also be used with the other power supplies in which case their only advantage is in avoiding switching the relatively high furnace current. With either the saturable-core reactor or the controlled rectifier, a HIGH-LOW control system could be set up easily with a dc supply and a few resistors.

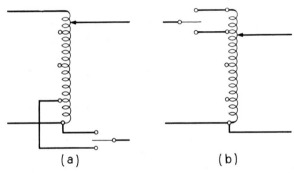

(a)   (b)

Fig. XV-12. Autotransformer connections for HIGH-LOW control. *Switching the output (a) adds or subtracts a fixed voltage while switching the input (b) changes the output by a fixed percentage.*

An even more nearly constant temperature can be obtained by attaching a reversible drive motor to an adjustable autotransformer and connecting the sensing element so that the autotransformer output is slowly increased while the furnace temperature is below the control point and slowly decreased while the furnace temperature is above the control point. Now the controller and power supply combination has a complete range of inputs. In event of a sudden increase in load the autotransformer will move until the control point is again reached. (The slow drive is to avoid serious overheating in just such a case.) For steady-state heating the autotransformer will necessarily cycle up and down through a small voltage range because of the constant driving one way or the other.

This system has a wider range of control than the HIGH-LOW and a smoother control with less tendency to overheat than the ON-OFF. The drive speed is necessarily a compromise between the high speed the operator might wish to use for rapid adjustment for large changes and the low speed required to avoid serious overshoot or large-amplitude cycling.

Again, such a control system could use a saturable-core reactor or a controlled rectifier by driving a potentiometer to vary the control signal. Under almost steady-state conditions the control will be quite superior to the ON-OFF or HIGH-LOW, but there is, nevertheless, a built-in cycling that can be objectionable and almost certainly will be objectionable in low-lag furnaces. (The reader must bear in mind that each step in improvement must be made at some cost in dollars or the equivalent.) The next step is the introduction of proportioning control.

15.19. Proportioning Control

The comparison of the temperature of the furnace with the desired temperature and adjustment of the voltage or current input according to the magnitude of the deviation is proportioning control. It differs from the reversible-drive autotransformer and related systems in that the change or rate of change in furnace input is principally a function of displacement or deviation rather than of time. The simplest form of proportioning control would comprise a device which independently interrupts the furnace input to a greater and greater degree as the furnace temperature increases in the region of the control point. This can be done on optical systems by moving a shutter back and forth such that it does not interrupt the light beam when it is far below the control point (large galvanometer deflection) but because of its sinusoidal motion interrupts for longer and longer periods as the temperature increases. The temperature reaches a steady-state position at which the electric power is supplied to the furnace at the right proportion of the time to maintain that temperature. The actual control temperature will deviate from the set point by an amount which varies slightly and regularly over the range of the instrument.

Electric meter (millivoltmeter) indicator-controllers can be equipped with a similar function. When the indicating pointer moves below the control point an electric impulse is supplied that drives the meter movement upscale so that if the temperature is only slightly below the control point the indicator will pass it and the power will be shut off. Since the impulse to the movement is also discontinued the pointer will drift back toward the control point. The impulse is rather small so the power will remain on except when the furnace temperature is within a few degrees of the control point and will be shut off an increasing percentage of the time until the temperature exceeds the control point.

Electronic controllers not making use of mechanical inertia have other means of modifying response in order to avoid cycling. Electronic circuits, fortunately, are not limited by the need to move parts, so, while their action must often be tempered to cope with a slow reacting system, these moderating influences can be adjusted to suit the individual needs. These are dynamic corrections based on the actual deviation or the rate of change of deviation. Their function is to bring about a very rapid return to the control point without serious overshooting. The corrections are: proportional band, rate of approach or reset, and rate time. The first two can be used with proportioning control systems; since the last is closely related the description of all is postponed until after the introduction of feedback control.

15.20. Feedback Control

Up to this point, we have considered systems whose power input to the process was related in a simple manner to the deviation of the temperature signal from a set point. The controller (Fig. XV-13a) compares the temperature signal with the temperature signal it has been instructed (set) to maintain and adjusts its signal to the power supply in such a manner as to correct or reduce the error. This action occurs and continues without regard for recent history or for possible future events. A controller without feedback must have capabilities suited specifically to its function; otherwise there is a risk of loss of control and possible damage to the process or apparatus. As an example, an autotransformer

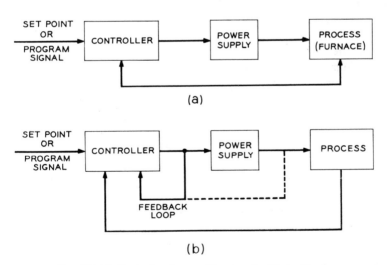

Fig. XV-13. Control systems without and with feedback.

A simple control system as in (a) recognizes and acts on the instantaneous condition of the process; introduction of a feedback loop (b) permits modification of the action according to amount and rate of change of error.

driven in one direction or another by a HIGH-LOW switching controller might be set to driving upward due to some temporary cooling (furnace door opened) and at the cessation of the demand be in a position that could bring the temperature far above the control point, yet it would still drive upward until the furnace did reach the set temperature because the controller had no information about the position of the autotransformer. Providing such information will permit a more flexible control system; i.e., it can adjust the process input to correct for a greater degree and a greater variety of processes unbalances. This arrangement by which the controller is supplied with information describing the input to the process so that it may adjust this input not only from temperature signal set point comparison but also from present input and rate of change of input is feedback control.

Figure XV-13b shows the full control loop with the added feedback loop. Whether the information comes from the input to or the output from the power supply depends generally on the nature of the power supply. If an adjustable autotransformer is used, the feedback information must be the output or position; if a saturable-core reactor or a controlled rectifier is used, the input signal can be used just as easily.

Now we have a control device supplied with three signals: the control or set point signal, the furnace temperature signal, and the furnace input signal. The controller can not only relate the temperature to the set point but also make use of the furnace input signal to monitor and modify its action. With electronic rather than mechanical information, greater flexibility is possible because modifying actions may be obtained very readily. These actions may be made to operate over wide ranges and at adjustable speeds, so that a single control unit can—with changes in instructions by resetting of dial knobs—control a small laboratory furnace or a room-size furnace, perhaps even with the same power unit. Rate time and reset are secondary modifying actions; the primary action is *proportional band*.

15.21. Proportional Band

Adjustment of the proportional band expands or contracts the portion of the full range over which proportioning of any kind occurs. If the deviation is beyond this range the controller should turn the power supply full ON or full OFF. For very slow response systems proportioning action may be required over 50% of full range; i.e., if the control unit range is 1000°C, a 500°C interval about the control point is within the proportioning zone (Fig. XV-14). With a control point of 600°C and a cold furnace full power would be applied until the sensing point reached ca 350°C at which time turndown or time proportioning would begin. If this furnace should "line out" at 600°C and then be reset down to 200°C the control unit would turn down or off until the furnace temperature dropped to ca 450°C and would then apply larger and larger quantities of power until the furnace "lined out" at the new temperature.

Rapidly responding systems could be operated with a proportional band of a few per cent so that with the same range (1000°C) the furnace would heat or cool at full rate until the temperature was within 20–40°C of the control point.

While the proportioning control helps in quickly regaining the control point region, it operates over the entire proportional band region without discrimination; i.e., the furnace will reach some temperature within the proportioning region such that the power input—under the influence of proportional band operation—is just sufficient to maintain that tempera-

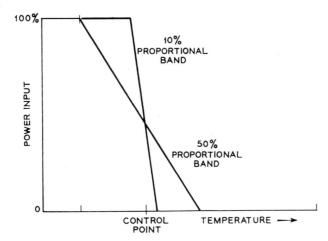

Fig. XV-14. Variation of power input with deviation (of temperature) from control point.
A smaller proportional band accentuates the response to small deviations.

ture. This temperature has no fixed relation to the control point because proportional band operation alone has no way to recognize the control point. For control point recognition *reset action* is added.

15.22. Reset Action

Consider that due to a process unbalance of some sort the temperature is displaced from the control point. Reset action modifies the proportional band action at a rate proportional to this displacement and the length of time away from control point. This modification is in effect an electrical shifting of the proportional band region up- or downscale to increase or decrease the power input. The rate of this shift can be modified so that the proportional band is shifted downscale or upscale from several per cent per minute to several minutes per per cent.

This reset action is the only part of the circuit which knows when to stop, but the nature of its action dictates that it cannot stop without overshoot unless its action is very slow.

Let us assume a large (because we need a door) electric muffle on control. Let us open the door for half a minute to put in a specimen. During this half minute the furnace cools somewhat and the recorder pen moves downscale. Reset action moves slowly to aid by shifting the proportional band position—thus accentuating the effect—and the temperature moves back toward the control point. During all this time reset action has been pushing the proportional band region further upscale. When the temperature reaches the control point the proportional band has been shifted enough to maintain a furnace temperature higher than the control point, so the temperature must necessarily overshoot. During the overshoot the proportional band is shifted downscale again so that with proper adjustment for that sort of demand change the furnace will be on control after a cycle or two. The possibility of serious overshoot after a large demand change leads to the need for *rate action.*

15.23. Rate Action

Rate action acts in a manner similar to reset action in that it, too, shifts the proportional band range; the difference is in the source of the control signal. While reset action is proportional to displacement of the recorder pen from the control point, rate action is proportional to the rate of change of displacement, i.e., the speed, irrespective of position, at which the pen is moving. Rate time thereby tends to slow down the pen motion by shifting the proportional band in the proper direction. In the case of the opened door the first action is the upscale shift of proportional band partly because of reset but mostly because of rate action. When the temperature has dropped as low as it will the rate action stops, but immediately begins to bring the proportional band region downscale again as the temperature starts to climb. Now it competes with reset action, but, for the furnaces common in thermal analysis, rate action should have the greater influence here. As the temperature approaches the control point it slows down its rate of approach and reaches the control point with no overshoot (in a carefully adjusted system).

15.24. Moving Control Point

The description of the various features of feedback control referred to a set control point, applicable to steady-state heating. The same elements will behave in essentially the same manner with a driven set point (Fig. XV-15). Consider the usual case—a linear (with time) heating rate. The control point is being driven upscale at a constant rate. The proportional band region is following at a rate modified by the other actions. Since we are trying to heat at a linear rate the recorder pen is moving at a nearly constant rate so the proportional band is shifted upscale by a nearly constant amount. Variations in the rate action are a small part of the total rate action in fairly rapid heating (several degrees per minute), so the over-all effect of properly adjusted rate action is to move the proportional band region upscale an amount dependent on the heating rate so that reset action can maintain close control. Reset action should now be able to move the proportional band up and down to maintain even the moving control temperature.

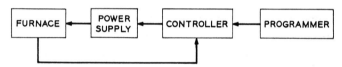

Fig. XV-15. Programmed control system.
The introduction of a program unit permits the operator to give time-based instructions to the control unit.

The author's experience is that settings derived from static heating are satisfactory for linear heating and cycling at linear rates. The author's power programming and control system comprise—at the time of writing —an L & N Series 60 Current Adjusting Type controller, a retransmitting slide-wire on the temperature pen of an X_1, X_2 vs t recorder, a cam-driven slide-wire programmer, and a silicon controlled rectifier. Since the temperature range is 0–1500°C or 0–1200°C, the initial position of the cam calls for a temperature below ambient; thus at the start of a program there is a brief time with no action, but the temperature pen eventually starts upscale forming an angle with the room-temperature portion of the trace rather than a curve. Similarly when the preset limit is reached, the furnace temperature begins dropping within a few seconds. When the programmer is set for cycling between preset limits, the temperature trace plots from one limit to the other at a uniform rate, cutting sharply back toward the other limit yet repeating these limits within ca 3°C over as many as eight cycles.

15.25. Programming

The imposition of the desired time-temperature cycle on the furnace and/or sample is called programming. Programming may range from the trivial but sometimes useful case of application of a constant—for example, line—voltage on a furnace designed to reach a particular temperature in a particular time to a multiple-step raising of the temperature with adjustable hold times and separately adjustable heating rates. The choice will be dictated by requirements and available funds.

The programming device comprises the parts and/or units necessary to retain and carry out the instructions of the operator. The degrees of complexity will depend on the flexibility desired for the program and the control accuracy needed.

The common devices are motor-driven adjustable autotransformers and cam-driven or screw-driven set point controllers. The first is simplest. Each of the others has features contributing to greater flexibility as well as some limitations. The performance of a programming unit is obviously tied quite closely to the controller and/or power supply.

15.26 Motor-Driven Adjustable Autotransformer

The adjustable autotransformer is the most widely used technique for controlling and varying the voltage input to furnaces. The simplest technique offering fair control, linear voltage programming, comprises the variable autotransformer driven at a selected but constant rate by an electric motor. The nearness to linearity of the temperature rise will depend on the furnace winding and construction. An approach to linearity over a portion of the range is all that a linear increase of voltage input can afford (Fig. XV-16).

The power input to a furnace with a purely resistive load is determined by $W = E^2/R$.

The heat losses from a furnace are by a variety of mechanisms, none of them proportional to the square of the voltage input. Radiation losses are a function of the fourth power of the absolute temperature while thermal conduction is proportional to the difference in temperature between the hot and the heating body. We may expect, then, a slow initial rise in temperature following, more or less, the E^2 relation because heat loss is not yet very rapid. As the temperature increases so does the heat loss, but because of the T^4 dependence of the radiative loss the heating rate not only stops increasing but will decrease. The only region approaching a linear rate of heating is that in which the conductive and convective heat losses and the radiative heat loss are changing in a manner approximating the changing power input so that net power input is fairly steady for an extensive period of time.

The heating of the base metal-wound furnace (Fig. XV-16) demonstrates the problem. At the slow driving rate the heating rate increases, maintains an almost steady state, and eventually begins to decrease. The heating rate ca 900°C is 50% greater than at 200°C. If we choose arbitrary criteria of performance we can conclude that a heating rate range with no more than 20% variation extends from ca 350 to 1100 C, but if we wish no more than 10% variation the most extensive range is from ca 400 to ca 850 C.

At the faster driving the rate has not yet started to decrease at 1100°C. A nearly constant range extends from ca 600 to 1100°C. The rate in the

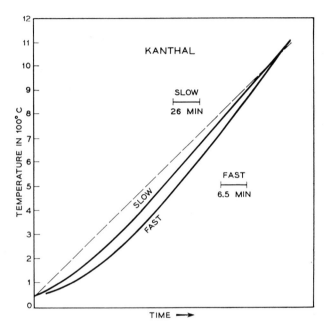

TIME →

Fig. XV-16. Temperature vs time for a linear increase of voltage input to a base metal-wound furnace.

A very slow rise at first results from relatively poor thermal conductivity at low temperatures. The rapid increase in power ($W = E^2/R$) *causes an increasing heating rate.*

900–1100°C range, however, is twice that at 150°C. If we apply the same criteria as before, the 20% variation range is from ca 400 to 1100°C and the 10% variation range from ca 600 to 1100°C. Other base metal windings would perform similarly.

The variation of heating rate is not so pronounced for platinum-wound furnaces because the resistance increases with temperature. The power input consequently is a function of a nonintegral ($1 < n < 2$) power of E and therefore of time. At the slower heating rate, the slowdown of heating (Fig. XV-17) due to radiation losses is quite apparent. Nevertheless, the 20% variation range extends from ca 200 to at least 1400°C. The longest 10% variation range is from ca 200 to 850°C.

In the faster heating, the slowing is less than 10%, so the 20% variation range extends from ca 350 to over 1400°C and the longest 10% range from ca 625 to over 1400°C.

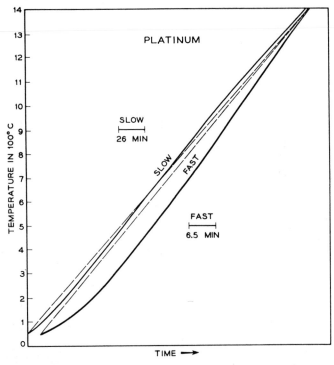

Fig. XV-17. Temperature vs time for a linear increase of voltage input to a platinum-wound furnace.

The increasing (with temperature) resistance of the winding tends to diminish the power input so that a nearly linear heating rate is maintained for a substantial range.

In these experiments the heating was stopped (automatically) well below the operational limits of the two furnaces because of the high heating rates. The temperature measured was, of course, the interior temperature. The windings would be substantially hotter—and possibly approaching their melting points—at the high heating rates. A furnace offering a nearly linear temperature increase when driven by a linearly increasing voltage is little more than fortuitous. Nevertheless, a variable autotransformer driven by a constant-speed motor through a set of gears will provide a fairly reproducible heating program rather economically, provided conditions are essentially the same each run.

The sameness of conditions will very definitely include the initial temperature. In well-insulated furnaces the ambient temperature is not very important (within the ordinary laboratory ranges) but lightly insulated furnaces may heat at somewhat different rates from day to day depending on the temperature and humidity. To even hope for reproducibility, the operator must permit the furnace to cool to the ambient temperature before reuse.

15.27. Motor-Driven Set Point: ON-OFF Controllers

In general, the use of ON-OFF controllers for differential thermal analysis work must be approached with considerable caution. The imposition or sudden removal of a substantial voltage will, with most furnace arrangements, show a definite pickup in the thermocouple circuit. In addition, the very real cycling of temperature in the furnace may be observed. Here, especially, one must pay careful attention to the relative positions of heater control point and sample. An ON-OFF control will obviously introduce cycling at the control point. This control point, equally obviously, must be at a point close to the heater, and preferably between the heater and the sample. The geometry should be such that the path for conduction of the heat is shorter from heater to control point than from control point on to the sample. In this manner, the sharp cycling unavoidable with ON-OFF controllers will be, or may be, damped sufficiently that the oscillation has no apparent effect on the time-temperature relation at the sample point.

The ON-OFF switching might be used to operate an autotransformer drive so that when the temperature is below the control point a motor drives the autotransformer but when the temperature overtakes the control point the autotransformer remains stationary. This technique would avoid nearly all the undesirable consequences of use of ON-OFF programming.

The most probable consequence of this technique is a saw-toothed heating curve if the autotransformer drive is very much faster than the programming needs; in this use the drive should be on most of the time. This would require different drive speeds for significantly different heating rates.

In general, the motor-driven set point controllers comprise arrangements by which a control point is moved across the face of an indicating meter or recorder, and the unbalance or difference between the control point and the indicated actual temperature actuates electrical circuitry to produce some more involved type of control than simple ON-OFF switching.

15.28. Cam-Driven Set Point

A cam programmer comprises a motor-driven cam (Fig. XV-18a) which changes the position of a set point as a function of time. The cam may be cut for linear rise (Fig. XV-18a) as well as for linear rise and

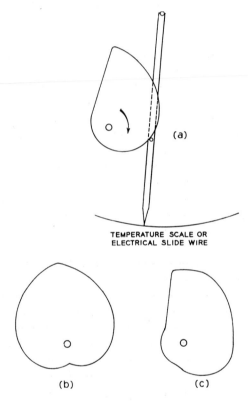

TEMPERATURE SCALE OR
ELECTRICAL SLIDE WIRE

(a)

(b) (c)

Fig. XV-18. Cam programmer
The rotation of the cam moves a contact or set point according to a fixed pattern.

fall (Fig. XV-18b) or nonlinear rise (Fig. XV-18c) of temperature. It may contain one hold time or several, depending on the needs of the system. The rates of heating or cooling may vary from step to step in a complex program.

On the other hand, the program time is limited to one revolution of the cam. The existence, then, of a long hold time might mean that a heating step would be such a small part of the total rotation that accurate cutting of the cam would be difficult. While the total rotation time might be extended by the use of percentage timers (Chapter XVI), the problem is unchanged because the relative—rather than actual—times are the controlling factors.

The turning of the cam displaces the riding arm a greater or lesser distance or angle from the axis. The arm is mechanically coupled to a slide-wire or other device which permits a comparison of positions of the set point and the actual temperature indicator. The error signal is sent along to the control unit for appropriate action.

By the cam method the temperature rise may be made very nearly linear with time if special precautions are taken. These precautions comprise ways of compensating for the nonlinearity of thermocouple electromotive force (emf) with temperature. One technique is the "linearized" slide-wire for the temperature measurement. The "linearization" may be accomplished by tapping (electrically) the slide-wire at several points and shunting these several sections with resistors selected to keep the rate of angular displacement, $d\theta/dT$, of the new shaft (Chapter XVI) very nearly constant over the recorder span. The set point drive may then be linear with time. The nearness of approach to linearity is obviously dependent on the number of taps. The greater the number of taps, properly placed and shunted, the less the deviation from linearity. Since the slide-wire must first be tapped and then the shunting resistances calculated and installed, construction of a linearized slide-wire with very small deviation (less than 0.5%) becomes expensive. This increasing cost might—if only very minute deviations can be tolerated—justify a tapered slide-wire. The tapered slide-wire is nonuniformly wound and by the variation in windings compensates for the nonlinearity of the thermal emf. (Where dE/dT is high, the turns are close together; i.e., $dE/d\theta$ is high, so that $d\theta/dT$ is constant.)

Cam-driven set points may use compensated cams for the same purpose. The cam is cut so that the set point variation is similar to the emf variation. In this case, the temperature slide-wire may be uniform, i.e., $dE/d\theta$ constant; the chart paper should be compensated. The corresponding arrangement on the motor-driven set point (across the recorder scale) is a nonlinear drive. The worm in which the set point rides may have a nonuniform cut so that the set point travels faster in the region where dE/dt is larger.

An approximation to a linearly increasing temperature is often obtained by use of a linear drive over a millivolt, i.e., nonlinearized, temperature scale. This is less expensive than the other techniques and hence will often be used in conjunction with galvanometer indication or recording. The error in temperature will be as high a 3% in a 0-1000°C range using Chromel-Alumel thermocouples. The heating rate based on this system would vary by over 15%.

15.29. Screw-Driven Set Point

Screw-driven set points comprise a recorder or indicator, a set point which may be moved across the scale, a drive system, and an error-detecting system. This system has a distinct advantage in programming in that times—including relative times—are not rigidly circumscribed. If, for example, one wished to observe cooling curves after driving the sample up in temperature at some given rate and then holding at a constant temperature for varying times, the only limit on the "soak" time would be the range of the timer available. The heating and cooling rates would be practically independent.

A number of adjustable switches can be provided on some programmers. These permit the user to modify the program when the indicator reaches the preset temperature. He might, for example, heat a furnace very rapidly to some given temperature, then introduce a percentage timer or the drive to cut the drive speed to the desired rate for the continued heating.

The screw-driven set point can be as reproducible in heating rate as the cam-driven set point assuming full time (no percentage timers) in each case. The temperature limits will not be so reproducible on the screw-driven set point, nor will multiple heating rates, because of the difficulty of resetting the switch or timer positions precisely.

The linearity or nonlinearity of heating rate will depend on the recording or indicating system. A nonlinearized system will have the errors described in the previous section. One could supply a nonuniform cut on the driving worm but the expense would be difficult to justify. The best arrangement currently available would use a linearized slide-wire.

15.30. Eccentrically Driven Potentiometer

Another approach to the problem of approximating a linear temperature rise was taken by Satava and Trousil. They positioned their comparison potentiometer off-center (Fig. XV-19) so that the steady driving of the potentiometer would produce a reference potential (for their furnace control thermocouple) which would rise at a rate corresponding closely to that of the Pt vs Pt-Rh thermocouple. The agreement (Fig. XV-20) can be quite good, certainly a far better approximation than the straight-line variation pretended in simple programming devices.

15.31. Summary

Null balance potentiometers perform best for recording thermoanalytical data. The recording potentiometer may be used as part of a servo loop as well as an ordinary measuring device.

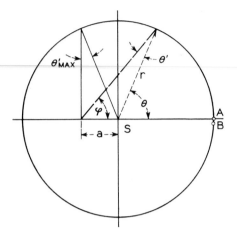

FIG. XV-19. Eccentric positioning of the programming potentiometer to obtain nonlinear time dependence of potential (S5).

The fact that different arcs are swept out by a given angle at different positions provides a curved E vs t dependence.

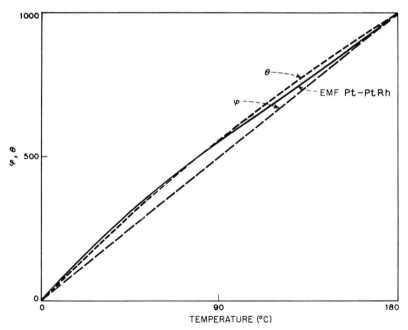

FIG. XV-20. Comparison of the angular position of the potentiometer, the potential at the contact, and the potential of a Pt vs Pt-Rh thermocouple (S5).

The shift in the axis produces good approximation of the thermoelectric potential curve with a simple cam modification.

For complete and unchanging systems the saturable-core reactor permits good stepless control, but where different types of experiments will be done the controlled rectifier is superior because it can control a wide range of loads.

The control unit should provide a continuous, stepless signal to the power supply and this signal should be modified by proportional band, rate, and reset action.

The choice between cam- and screw-driven (or otherwise driven) set points depends on the general nature of the work planned. Cam programmers give high reproducibility at the price of relative inflexibility of operation.

CHAPTER XVI

Miscellaneous Apparatus and Information

16.1. Thermocouples

The usual method of measuring temperature and change of temperature in thermal analysis is by use of thermocouples; these are junctions of dissimilar metals or alloys welded, soldered, swaged, or otherwise held in contact. The relative electronic energy levels give rise to a potential between the two. If the two materials are connected electrically at some other point so that a complete circuit is made, a similar potential will be established at that junction. If both junctions are at the same temperature the potentials are equal but, since these potentials are temperature-dependent, if the two junctions are at different temperatures the potentials will be different in the two and electric current can flow. This is the Seebeck effect. If one of the two materials is now opened (electrically speaking) the potential difference between the two ends can be measured and used to determine the temperature difference between the junctions. (The flow of current can also be made to do useful work but this is not within our immediate interest.) Unfortunately

487

this potential is not a linear function of temperature difference; on the other hand, some combinations of metals have a variation with temperature which is close enough to being linear to permit use of linear measuring circuits with fair accuracy.

From this point on the discussion will assume the materials to be in the form of wires, for the simple reason that a wire form is the one most commonly used; the reader should understand that a wire of one material secured to a surface of another metal or alloy can be used to measure the temperature at the point of contact.

The thermoelectric effect obeys certain laws:

(1) No thermoelectric potential is established in a homogeneous electrical conductor regardless of temperature gradient along the wire.

This statement implies that wires may be led from hot furnaces to measuring apparatus at room temperature without loss of accuracy.

(2) If one of the dissimilar wires is cut and each end joined to a wire of a third material and both of these latter junctions are at the same temperature, the thermoelectric potential is not affected.

This statement follows from the first by applying the earlier stated law to the third material. It implies that connection may be made to other kinds of wires and hence to measuring apparatus without any effect. It is only necessary to keep these junctions at the same—but not necessarily steady—temperature.

(3) The observed thermoelectric potential is the sum of the potentials characteristic of each junction at its temperature.

This statement implies that one may keep all junctions save one at some uniform temperature and, knowing this temperature, determine the temperature of the other junction. Similarly, if two junctions are at temperatures different from the rest, the thermoelectric potential will be the sum of or the difference between (depending on how they are connected) the individual potentials with respect to the potential at the temperature of the remaining junctions. A multiple-junction array can be assembled into a thermopile. A given difference in potential, in turn, represents a given difference in temperature from that reference temperature. The nonlinearity (Fig. XVI-1) of the thermoelectric potential with temperature precludes any other inference except as an approximation.

While any combination of dissimilar metals and alloys could be used to obtain a thermoelectric potential, only a few are in practical use; the principal considerations are the magnitude of the thermoelectric potentials, the reproducibility of potential from one thermocouple to another, and the stability of the combination in use. Table XVI-1 shows the commonly used thermocouples, their useful ranges, and the potential difference for an arbitrarily selected interval. Tables of thermoelectric potentials are given in Appendix II.

The maximum temperatures shown are not absolute limits; they are the temperatures at which extrapolated values reach an arbitrarily selected uncertainty. Calibrations are obtainable for somewhat higher temperatures but the user should realize that the possible error is becoming substantial.

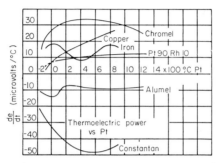

Fig. XVI-1. Thermoelectric powers of common thermocouple elements against Pt. From Finch (F7).

None of the combinations have a linear or even linearly changing response to temperature.

TABLE XVI-1

Thermocouples in Common Use with Their Usual and Maximum Service Temperatures and a Measure of Their Sensitivities.

Thermocouple pair	Temperature range (°C)		$E_{300°C} - E_{200°C}$
	Usual	Maximum	
Platinum vs platinum-10% rhodium	0 to +1450	1700	0.880
Chromel vs Alumel	−190 to +1100	1350	4.08
Iron vs constantan	−190 to + 760	1000	5.55
Copper vs constantan	−190 to + 300	600	5.58

There are several techniques for joining thermocouple wires; the important criterion is whether or not a joint is small enough that it will itself contain no temperature gradients under the conditions used. From there on, sturdiness, sensitivity, ease of handling, and external circuitry must be considered.

Sturdiness calls for large sizes, sensitivity for small, while ease of handling calls for moderation in size. Since the present author customarily reads temperatures by true (recording) potentiometers, wire sizes from 0.0015 to 0.030 inches in diameter have presented no problems in measurement (see Chapter XV).

Thermocouple wires can be jointed by electric arc, flame heating, soldering, or pressure. When a butt-welded junction is needed it is generally formed by use of a dc carbon arc.

Parallel-wire or twisted-wire junctions can be made by forming the junction, moistening with a flux, and arc-welding, flame-welding, or soldering. The arc-welding can be done by carbon or mercury arc simply and easily. The process requires a melting together of the two wires. This is done by connecting one lead from a power source to one or both thermocouple wires and the other to an electrode and touching the junction to the electrode. The author presently uses a mercury arc apparatus comprising a pool of mercury covered with a layer of tricresyl phosphate. The tricresyl phosphate serves as a flux (D3) so that no preparation of the wires other than skinning and twisting is required. The mercury pool cannot be used with copper so connection to the mercury pool in the author's apparatus is by a carbon rod. Copper-constantan junctions are made by touching the junction to the carbon rod under the surface of the tricresyl phosphate.

Arc-welding by electrical discharge is often useful. By this technique a bank of capacitors is charged to some chosen voltage and this charge is subsequently dissipated to form the thermocouple by use of a carbon rod to produce a carbon arc by direct welding of the wires or by welding a wire to an object of the other thermocouple material (see Fig. VIII-2). This technique has the advantage that completed thermocouples can also be joined to surfaces, e.g., sample cups or crucibles as well as the tubes of Fig. VIII-34.

Soldering is frequently used for low-temperature work. The thermocouple wires are twisted or simply held against each other and silver solder applied using a torch (and flux) or soft solder may be applied with an iron. Only a short length should be soldered so that temperature homogeneity will not be in doubt.

16.2. Recording of Temperature—Millivolt Recorder

Since thermocouple wires will show a thermal emf with the copper conductors ordinarily used in measuring apparatus it is necessary to make the connections properly to avoid or compensate for the effect. Whether to avoid or compensate depends on the measuring system; some recorders have built-in compensation, but let us consider first measurement of temperature with a millivolt recorder, a potentiometer, or a galvanometer. If a thermocouple is connected directly to the terminals of any of these devices with no precaution whatever, the potential measured depends on the difference between the thermojunction temperature and that of the terminals of the measuring device. This is clearly an unsuitable condition for continuously measuring temperatures; room temperatures change and recorders warm up. A convenient solution for short times is the insertion of the junctions to copper in an ice bath. An ice bath has the advantages of being easily prepared and being already a temperature reference (0.0 . . .°C). Now the potential measured is dependent on the difference between the thermojunction temperature and 0°C, obviously quite a convenient arrangement. Since only a little care is needed in preparation of an ice bath it is a very popular system for providing a cold junction.

Unfortunately, the ice bath depends for its constancy of temperature on melting of the ice so these baths—even in Dewar flasks—require occasional attention. The ice must be replenished and firmly packed and water must be drawn off, so for protracted measurements other reference points may be more convenient. The other major reference temperature is the boiling point of water, achieved readily and steadily by immersion of the reference junction in a refluxing water bath. With a good condensing system the loss of water vapor is inappreciable so measurements extending over several days can be made. The only trouble with a boiling water bath as a reference junction thermostat is that setting it up is a nuisance.

16.3. Recording of Temperature—Compensated Recorders

To enable the customer to avoid the need for preparing a reference junction of any sort, makers of recording potentiometers supply built-in compensation for temperature ranges. This compensation comprises a temperature-sensitive resistance which shifts the scale slightly (Fig. XVI-2) but, because of the circuit arrangement, changes the zero-potential position markedly.

Assume a 0–1000°C scale and the entire system initially at a room temperature of 25C°. We then wish the recorder pen to indicate 25°C even though no thermal emf exists so the slide-wire zero must be $25/1000$ upscale. This is a simple matter: resistors R_1 and R_2 establish the reference point by their relative magnitudes. (The actual resistance is of no great concern in this discussion.) Now let the thermojunction be at some elevated temperature, T; the potential difference measured by the recorder is $T - 25°C$ but since the zero potential is shifted upscale the temperature shown is $T°C$.

Note in Fig. XVI-2 that the thermocouple leads join the copper recorder leads in the vicinity of R_1; in some recorders the connections are actually enclosed by the resistor, in others they are merely close by. Since the resistance of R_1 is temperature-sensitive, if the temperature should change the potential drop across R_1 would change; the potential at point P therefore changes and the zero-potential point on the slide-wire shifts from point O toward A if the temperature rises and toward B if it falls. The actual temperature error due to use of a compensator instead of a thermostatted reference junction is small.

Whether a reference junction or a compensator is used the thermocouple materials or properly chosen equivalent must lead from the thermojunction to the reference junction or the recorder terminals. For the base metal thermocouples the common practice is to use thermocouple wire even if the run is fairly long but for noble metal thermocouples special extension wires are often used for reasons of economy. These extension wires are alloys chosen or made to give very low thermoelectric potentials with the thermocouple wires. This nonsensitivity to temperature must apply for a range from the reference temperature to the actual temperature of the junction between extension and thermocouple wires.

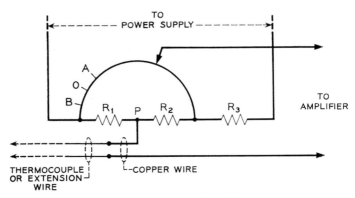

Fig. XVI-2. Recording potentiometer with cold junction compensation.
Temperature-sensitive resistance changes zero point toward A if the temperature rises and toward B if it falls.

Note that connection of sets of dissimilar wires may take place through another conductor without effect as long as the temperatures at the actual points of connection are the same. This permits the use of connector blocks whether or not the wires are held in actual contact with each other. Note, too, that a differential thermocouple need not be connected through any sort of reference junction. Assuming that two like wires are connected together and no other connection is made to them, the other two like wires—from which the differential signal is measured—may be connected directly to copper at any convenient point.

The present author generally—but by no means always—uses lead wire alloy plugs for interconnections. For millivolt recorders, an arrangement such as that used by Vassallo and Harden (V3) is perfectly satisfactory (Fig. XVI-3). The only precaution necessary in changing to copper leads is that, within each set of terminals, the temperature must be uniform; this is not difficult within usually acceptable limits of error. The apparatus more recently assembled uses spring clip terminals to hold wires together. These terminals are enclosed by a metal block which serves to keep the temperature *uniform; constant* temperature is unnecessary.

Recording potentiometers provided with temperature ranges will normally be equipped with the appropriate extension or thermocouple wire from the terminals to the cold junction. These recorders may be

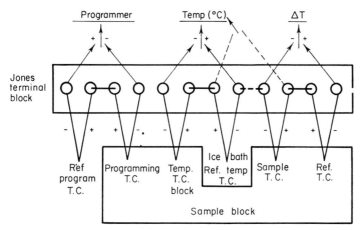

Fɪɢ. XVI-3. Thermocouple junctions for temperature programming, temperature, and differential temperature measurements. From Vassallo and Harden (V3).

A connector block (at a uniform temperature) permits convenient change or replacement of individual thermocouples.

ordinary millivolt recorders, they may be ordinary millivolt recorders designed for nonlinear scales and chart paper, or they may have a "linearized" slide-wire. The choice of scales depends on the need, with appropriate attention to cost.

If one is only recording temperature the second choice is the best. The cost is only slightly more than the ordinary millivolt recorder. If a two-pen recorder is used and the other variable is not temperature one of the other choices is more appropriate. Presumably the other variable can be measured best on linear paper, as, for example, weight change or differential temperature. An ordinary millivolt recorder will require correction for the less than linear E vs T relation; for a few hundred dollars more this correction can be made negligible by use of a linearized slide-wire.

Recall that in a recording potentiometer the range is determined (Fig. XVI-4) by the relation between R_A and the resistance, R_{eq}, equivalent to the slide-wire R_S and its parallel resistors R_B and R_C, i.e.,

$$\text{measuring range} = E_x \, \frac{R_{eq}}{R_A + R_{eq}}.$$

The zero is established by the relative magnitudes of R_B and R_C and the slide-wire contact position can supply a linearly varying portion of the potential drop across $R_B + R_C$. This slide-wire can be made to supply an approximation to a thermocouple output by tapping it at a number of points and shunting it with several resistors instead of two (Fig. XVI-4b). Now the slide-wire can supply a varying portion of the potential drop across $R_B + R_D + R_E + R_J$, but this potential will

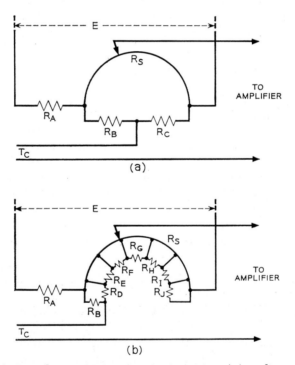

Fig. XVI-4. Recording potentiometer circuits giving (a) a linear measure of thermal emf and (b) a nearly linear measurement of temperature. R_B is the temperature-compensation resistor.

R_C *is replaced in* (b) *by shunt resistors whose number and values are selected according to the type of thermocouple. Another possible arrangement would comprise a complete set of linearizing resistors shunted by* R_B *and* R_C.

vary in a series of linear segments designed to give a good approximation to the actual thermocouple output. With the linearized slide-wire
the temperature may be recorded on the same linear chart as another
variable without much error in reading the temperature.

In any case, if a highly accurate temperature reading is needed a
potentiometer may be used to reproduce the pen position and the correct
temperature determined from the potentiometer reading.

16.4. Photocells

A common method of obtaining a signal related to the degree of unbalance in thermogravimetry is by use of a photocell so arranged that
movement of the balance beam permits more or less light on the sensitive
region. This method is useful for general purpose displacement measuring of moderate sensitivity and for sensing in pseudonull balance
systems. The photocell comprises one or two light-sensitive elements
whose resistance varies inversely with the amount of light impinging
upon them. This change in voltage drop due to the change in resistance
can be amplified and measured or used to control a power input or
a balancing device.

16.5. Capacitance Detection

The electrical capacitance of a pair of neighboring plates or other conductors is governed, among other things, by their separation. If one is
free to move with respect to the other, the capacitance will change. By
suitable equipment, this capacity change can be measured or used to
initiate some operation. The displacement detector used in the pseudo-
null balance of van der Breggen and Wouterlood (B74), shown in Fig.
XIV-5, detects the increase of one capacitance and consequent decrease
of the other as the center plate, attached to a balance beam, moves. The
circuit ought to be more sensitive if the resistors and diode rectifiers

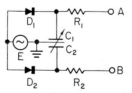

Fɪɢ. XVI-5. Differential capacitance detector. From van der Breggen and Wouterlood (B74).

*Change in position of the central plate changes the voltage of A relative to B. (D_1,
D_2 = OA72; R_1, R_2 = 470 kohm, 0.5 watt, high stability.) This signal controls the
restoring force of a magnet.*

were interchanged; the continuous flow of the alternating current and reading-off of the resulting voltage drops would provide a better response than reading the current flow between the plates.

A capacitance measurement of this type will be approximately linear over only a narrow range. Since the capacitance varies inversely with the square of the distance, only in the center will an increment of displacement in one direction have an effect equal (in absolute magnitude) to a similar displacement in the other. The rapidly increasing increments of signal at greater displacements might make the detector useful in a true or force-restored null balance.

16.6. Strain Gauges

The stretching of a wire brings about a small change in its electrical resistance simply because of dimensional changes. Some metal alloys have special characteristics so that the resistance of a wire under strain provides a stable and reproducible measure of the elongation. Wires of such alloys are assembled into conveniently used units so that the user may attach them to material under strain.

The gauges may be connected in any standard resistance measuring circuit but the customary arrangement is a bridge. This bridge may have two gauges as in Fig. XVI-6, in which the second gauge is unstrained

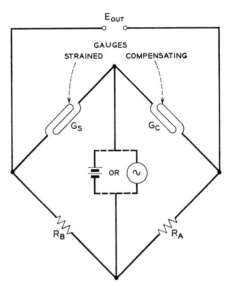

Fig. XVI-6. Strain gauge circuit using compensating gauge.
R_A and R_B could be replaced by another G_S and G_C, respectively, to double the sensitivity.

and merely compensates for temperature variations. Note that if the strained and compensating gauges (G_s and G_c, respectively) both change in resistance by the same fraction the potentials at points s and c change by very nearly the same amount and the output voltage E_{out} is virtually unaffected.

A strain gauge can be applied to a strip of spring steel or to a drill rod or to any material which is elastically deformed. (A primary requirement is, of course, that the material on which the gauge is mounted will respond reproducibly to strain.) A sample can then be supported in a manner such that a change in weight (or length) can be detected and measured.

16.7. Variable Differential Transformers

A variable differential transformer comprises three windings and a movable core; an example is given in Fig. XVI-7. This is specifically a

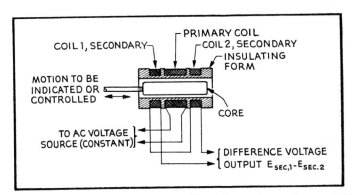

Fig. XVI-7. Operation of the linear variable differential transformer (LVDT). *Movement of the core changes the relative inductive couplings of the two secondaries with the primary.*

linear variable differential transformer because the motion detected is along the axis of the transformer. (Rotary variable differential transformers may be used to measure angular displacement, but the linear variety is of more interest here.) As long as the core is symmetrically located with respect to the two secondaries, the outputs are equal and, if properly connected, opposite in phase. There is essentially no net voltage; a quite small residual voltage is still present because of the phase angle shift in the transformer but for most applications this is not important.

Let us move the core toward the left, toward point A in Fig. XVI-8, and let us measure the instantaneous output from the secondaries at some constant point on the alternating current wave. When the core is at point A, a voltage will appear which will diminish as the core is moved toward the center because the inductive coupling between the primary and the left-hand secondary is decreasing while that between the primary and the right-hand secondary is increasing. As the core moves past the center O and toward B, the output from the right-hand secondary becomes greater than that from the left-hand secondary and the instantaneous voltage changes sign.

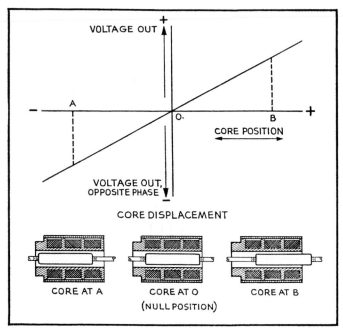

Fɪɢ. XVI-8. LVDT output voltage and phase as function of core position, linear graph.

Both magnitude and direction of displacement can be measured.

The important features are: (1) as the core passes the center (null) position, there is a phase shift of 180°; and (2) the output voltage varies linearly with displacement. The first feature makes possible null-seeking systems, and the second permits measurement of displacement or servo systems to follow displacement. Some linear variable differential trans-formers are single-ended, i.e., designed to measure only displacement.

Since a current is passing through the primary, it follows that there will be some tendency for the transformer to act as a solenoid, pulling on the core to bring it to the center or null position. The force varies with displacement and inversely with excitation frequency. This force must be taken into account in displacement-measuring balances, but in null-seeking devices the effect can be eliminated by adjustment so that the magnetic null coincides with the mechanical null of the balance (see Chapter X).

16.8. Electrical Differentiation

A measure of the rate of change of a direct electric current can be obtained easily by the circuit shown in Fig. XVI-9. Under steady-state conditions the potential across capacitor C is equal to the potential drop across R, i.e., $E_C = i_1 R_1 = E$. If the potential drop should increase, electrons would flow through R_2 until $E_C = E$, resulting in a

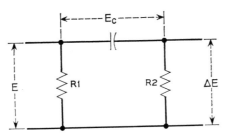

FIG. XVI-9. Differentiating circuit.

When a change in E occurs, the capacitor must charge or discharge to return E_C to zero. The voltage drop across R_2 gives a measure of the rate of change of E.

transient potential drop, $i_2 R_2$, across R_2. This potential drop is proportional to the difference between E and E_C, i.e., the effective charging voltage; the capacitance of C and the resistance R.

A high capacitance will obviously need a large quantity of electricity to charge it; therefore, at some given current i_2 the time needed to change a capacitor will vary with the capacitance. Similarly, a given capacitor can be charged (or discharged) more rapidly at a high current (low resistance) than at a low; the time required for a capacitor to charge or discharge will vary with the resistance in series with it.

For some instantaneous change in E, E_C will approach E at a rate determined by the magnitude of the change and by R and C. Specifically, the approach follows a first-order reaction (radioactive decay) relation, i.e.,

$$\frac{dx}{dt} = -kx,$$

for this particular case,

$$\frac{d\Delta E}{dt} = \frac{-\Delta E}{RC}.$$

Instead of the half-life of the reaction, the commonly used measure of such a circuit is the time constant, $R \cdot C$, which gives the time required for the voltage to decay to $1/2.3$ of its original value.

Now it is apparent that if a circuit is constructed with a long time constant and the potential is changed by some increment, the approach of E_C to its new value will be slow. A measurable ΔE will persist for a considerable time. Such a condition has limited utility; the measurement of ΔE will fail to show much more than the grosser features of successive changes of E. If, on the other hand, a very small time constant circuit is used the capacitor will approach its new potential so rapidly that the ΔE signal cannot be measured conveniently. With a small time constant the value of E_C is never far different from E except in the case of instantaneous changes; the measured ΔE will more closely approach the true value of dE/dt than with a large time constant circuit. The selection of a differentiating circuit is based principally on the rapidity of variation of the signal and on the speed of response of the measuring apparatus.

Consider two quite different cases, (I) a thermogravimetric apparatus which supplies a signal proportional to the sample weight and (II) a differential thermal analysis apparatus operating under rather ordinary conditions. In case I the signal will be slow to change compared to case II. If the same derivative circuit were used the time constant suitable for differential thermal analysis would be too small for thermogravimetric analysis and as a result the ΔE signal would be unnecessarily and inconveniently small. On the other hand, a large time constant giving acceptable results for following thermogravimetric measurements would obscure any rapid variations in differential thermal analysis signals.

The choice of circuitry must be a compromise between high signal strength and reasonably accurate following of the dE/dt signal. If one is recording the signal, there is no real need or value to have a time constant smaller than the balancing time of the recording system. From this minimum time constant one makes whatever increase he finds necessary to obtain a useful (both measurable and meaningful) ΔE vs t plot. Since the voltage across R_2 is the quantity usually measured, the value of this resistor should be equal to the maximum permissible input impedance of the measuring apparatus; this will permit use of only as much capacitance as may be needed and will enable the closest practicable following of dE/dt.

If the differentiating circuit is supplying other electric or electronic circuitry, the time constants are generally much smaller simply because the absence of mechanical motion removes the greatest obstacle to close following of the potential E.

16.9. Electrical Filtering

The occasional need for conversion of an alternating or pulsating current to a direct current raises immediately the problem of filtering. The charging and discharging of a capacitor through a resistor was described briefly in the previous section. The possibility of spreading out the change of potential over a substantial period of time was pointed out there as something to avoid; under different circumstances it is highly desirable. In each case, one must consider how much filtering needs to be supplied; too much will slow any response to change as well as being extra trouble to supply while too little may give erratic response and irreproducible and inaccurate results. The amount of this filtering is not highly critical; a factor of two or three has little effect, but only a little thoughtlessness is needed to throw in one hundred-fold too much filtering.

The R part of the time constant is often beyond the direct control of the user. The load to be supplied makes certain requirements which have to be met. Power supply filtering is just a special case in which a very appreciable current needs to be smoothed.

Let us consider a case in which a 60-cps differential transformer output is to be measured on a direct current recording potentiometer. If the transformer output is supplied to a full-wave rectifier (Fig. XVI-10a) a pulsating current of 120 cps is obtained. Let us assume that our recording potentiometer has an input impedance maximum of 400 ohms and that the signal we need to measure will drive the recorder approximately full-scale (no voltage divider is needed). Let us put in a capacitor with a capacitance of 25 μf. The time constant is 400 ohms $\times$ 25 $\times$ 10^{-6} farads or 0.01 second. From the decay relation this means that the capacitor will discharge more than half of its stored energy before it is charged by the next pulse.

If the time constant were increased by about two orders of magnitude the capacitor would discharge less than 1% of its stored energy before being charged by the next pulse. This is a rather convenient rate. (Note that if the input signal drops suddenly the capacitor will follow at this less than 1% per cycle rate because the input potential would have no effect until the capacitor potential dropped below it; on the other hand, an increase in potential will be followed at a rate determined by the time constant of the rectifier-capacitor system.)

We can make this one hundred-fold increase in the time constant most easily by increasing the total resistance (Fig. XVI-10b) but this means that if the proper input resistance is maintained the signal drops proportionately. The alternative would be to increase the capacitance, but

2500 µf consumes both space and funds. (The apparently simple expedient of using electrolytic capacitors is unwise because these devices often develop spurious voltages.)

In the event that the entire signal is needed a stage of amplification may be the best solution; a high-impedance recorder is another possibility. Whatever solution is used the circuit will be a compromise between the speed of response that accompanies the low time constant and the higher signal level that goes with a higher time constant. Whatever the

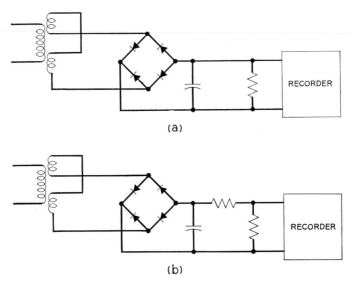

(a)

(b)

Fig. XVI-10. Transformer rectifier circuit with filter.

The signal appearing at the recorder in (a) will reach slightly less than the peak voltage and will vary sinusoidally by a magnitude determined by R•C. Attenuation by inserting the additional resistor in (b) will decrease the magnitude of the signal but will decrease the sinusoidal variation additionally by increasing the time constant.

frequency, the time ought to fall in the 5–20 cycle range as a first approximation. For higher frequencies this might be extended to, say, 0.05–0.2 second. For special cases, further extensions in either direction may be desirable.

Filtering of a signal which is part of a servo loop is a special case in which a fairly long time constant is desirable. Consider the same type of signal as before except that now it will be fed into an amplifier which operates a motor which in turn brings the signal back to zero. We cannot use a full-wave rectifier because we could then drive in only one direction; instead, we oppose two half-wave rectifiers (Fig. XVI-11). (We are assuming here that there is good reason to use a dc input amplifier as part of the servo system.) Even though both signals may be—and usually are—rather high, the servo amplifier sees only the difference. Since the capacitors will be charged up to nearly peak voltage at each cycle, each must maintain its voltage essentially undiminished during the next half cycle while the other is being charged. Too rapid a discharge would cause the servomotor to tend to drive in opposite directions each half cycle so that it would sit and hum. Worse, it would impose a condition by which the amplifier would see enough of a signal to actually get the motor turning only when a substantial difference existed; the sensitivity would be lowered. An extremely high time constant might possibly cause hunting because of the persistence of the signal.

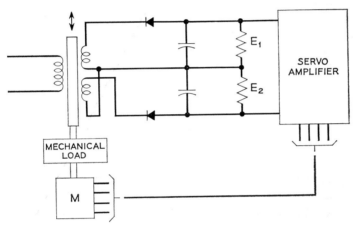

Fig. XVI-11. Servo systems using rectification and filtering.
The servo amplifier drives in the direction indicated by the sign of $E_1 - E_2$.

16.10. Phase Relations

Filtering in the servo system described above is a necessary companion to expediency. If the signal could be applied to the amplifier with the proper phase relation no filtering at all would be needed.

The author has done this sort of thing but instead of supplying the unbalance signal to the normal input he supplied it directly to the input transformer (see Chapter X). The only provision for phasing was to make certain that the motor drove in the proper direction. Correct phasing would have been fortuitous; the amplifier is probably quite heavily overloaded.

Proper phasing could be obtained by proper selection of a series capacitor but an easier solution is to smooth the output. Bear in mind that the only function of the ΔE is, essentially, to destroy itself. We are not interested in its magnitude but we are interested in following changes rapidly. A substantial time constant means overshoot and hunting but an inadequate filtering might permit the potential to drop off while the amplifier needs the maximum signal. A time constant of only a couple of cycles would maintain a readable signal without serious impairment of the response time.

16.11. Impedance Matching

One may find, in appropriate texts, evidence that maximum power can be transferred electrically when the output impedance of the supply circuit is equal to the input impedance of the receiving circuit. A complete discussion is outside the scope of this book, but a few selected applications may be described.

In furnace power circuits one may generally feed a high-impedance load from a low-impedance source; e.g., a furnace drawing a maximum of 8 amp may be fed from a 20- or 50-amp autotransformer without trouble. The major exception is due to loss of control sensitivity as with a saturable-core reactor rated for low load impedance feeding a high-resistance load. The opposite is not practical. Supplying a low-impedance load from a high-impedance source will have results ranging from nonfunctioning of the apparatus to damage to the source.

In electronic gear the same general considerations hold, including the possibility of damage to the source if moderate powers can be drawn. In these cases, the impedance matching must be considered simply for protection of apparatus. At still lower power levels, i.e., where the actual amount of power is insignificant, the penalty for mismatch of impedance is loss of sensitivity, failure of the receiving circuit to respond.

The impedance (resistance) of a thermocouple will range from less than 1 ohm to 70 or 100 ohms. This is a low resistance and a thermocouple can thence supply essentially any ordinary electronic circuit, amplifier, recorder, etc. (The higher-resistance thermocouples may not be able to supply galvanometer recorders or indicators.) We do encounter the problem of amplifying thermistor bridge or other high-resistance bridge circuit signals.

In essence, stable amplification of a direct current signal requires that a small current flows. Similarly, a recording potentiometer will require current flow during any unbalance. (In a true recording potentiometer there is no drain on the measured circuit except after a change and until balance is restored.) In the case of the dc amplifier the current flow across the input grid resistor must be enough to establish the proper grid bias voltage. If the output impedance from the source is excessive, the current flow will set up a sizable voltage drop in the source circuit, detracting thereby from the input voltage in the amplifier. The amplified signal will not reflect accurately the voltage it is ostensibly measuring.

The recording potentiometer will show a different effect. In this case, some minimum voltage drop must appear across the input stage grid resistor before the output stage can supply enough energy to start the motor. A reasonably common set of values might be 1000 ohms nominal input impedance with 1 μv sensitivity. This means that a source of no more than 1000 ohms and having a net unbalance of 1 μv will supply enough voltage drop to start the balancing motor. Higher source impedances may require several microvolts, open circuit, to be able to supply 1 μv, closed circuit. This results in a range of voltages on each side of the balance voltage within which not enough power can be supplied to the recorder amplifier to cause it to operate; this is a "dead zone." The symptom of a large dead zone on the record is a "stepping" of the recorded signal.

One can operate outside the rated impedance limits of recorders or amplifiers when it is expedient. The penalties are severe only if they are unrecognized, the principal effect being slower speed or response. Habitual operation beyond the limits recommended by the maker is unwise. The author indulges in the practice only when testing of a hypothesis would otherwise have to await acquisition of a suitable instrument. If there is need for continued use of the new system, proper instrumentation is bought or otherwise acquired.

16.12. Noninductive Furnaces

The ordinary helical winding on a furnace tube sets up an electric field. The effect of this field on differential thermal analysis apparatus is not really well-known. (In thermogravimetric analysis it requires use of a nonmagnetic sample holder.) The present author used noninductively wound furnaces for a short time. These were wound by bending the wire around a pin at one end of the zone and applying two windings (i.e., from the midpoint of the piece of resistance wire out toward both ends) side by side. This resulted in the entire input voltage being applied across an insulation-filled gap not much more than a millimeter wide. When the furnace became hot the insulation broke down and the platinum-rhodium furnace winding followed suit.

Noninductive windings can be applied as two separate coils. The essential features are that they have very nearly the same number of turns, pass very nearly the same amount of current, and are quite close to each other. One winding can be of a good conductor and serve only as a compensator.

The author subsequently eliminated noise by inserting a grounded platinum shield inside the furnace tube. In recent work shielding has ordinarily been needed only for temperatures above 1000°C, when using base thermocouple wires. The author is not absolutely convinced that noninductive furnaces are useful but he is performing some experiments on a hopefully better way of applying a noninductive winding on a ceramic tube furnace.

16.13. Induced Currents and Noise

Recall that when a steady direct current is flowing through a conductor a magnetic field exists around that conductor. If that current should increase or decrease, so would the field. Similarly, if a magnetic field encompasses a conductor and the magnetic field changes in strength, an emf is induced in the conductor.

If an alternating current is flowing, the field is constantly increasing, decreasing, reversing, etc. This smooth change may be a source of interference, i.e., hum spurious steady signals, etc., but filtering and simple shielding are usually sufficient protection for any single major component. To avoid the effects of induced emf's of different levels in different parts, the chassis or frames of the several components are grounded. This is often done by grounding each frame or chassis separately to a metal cabinet but is better done by connecting all the frames together by a ground lead. Each component with very much metal, i.e., recorder, furnace base, program unit, etc., should be grounded to a common point with separate wires.

In severe cases, stray currents may be induced in metal cabinets. Two components grounded to each other as well as each to the cabinet will constitute a "ground loop" such that current may flow. (This situation is analogous to the grounding of a circuit at two points which are not supposed to be at the same potential.) The author avoids the problem by mounting the several components in a wooden cabinet and grounding them individually to a common point.

When a discontinuous change of current occurs in a conductor the field increases or decreases sharply and seldom smoothly. The making or breaking of a switch, for example, sets up a field quite irregularly so that a multitude of frequencies will be induced in nearby conductors. Loose contacts will often have the same effects. These spurious signals in the very low-level differential temperature signal may cause pips, jitter, and other forms of noise in the thermogram.

Thermoelectric noise in the furnace winding may cause a high-level "hash" at temperatures in the vicinity of 800°C. Symmetry of conductors appears to be of great help here. The author had considerable noise in an early horizontal furnace (G12). It was eliminated by use of a grounded platinum cylinder inside the furnace tube. The vertical furnaces the author presently uses do not appear to be subject to this type of noise. If such noise should appear, the proper procedure is to (1) check connections very carefully, (2) ground any component that can be grounded, and (3) shield any suspected source.

In some cases a component exposed to induce noise cannot be grounded; this is often the case with thermocouples which feed amplifiers which are already grounded. Assuming a dc signal, as in a thermocouple, ac noise can be bypassed to ground by use of large nonelectrolytic capacitors. In severe cases a choke input to the amplifier may be needed along with the capacitors.

16.14. Summary

Thermoelectric potentials result when dissimilar metals are in contact. Connection of other wires to thermocouple wires must be at a known, constant, or compensated temperature for a measuring thermocouple; for differential temperatures, the connections must only be at the same, though perhaps not steady, temperature. Variations in photoelectric effects, capacitance, resistance, and magnetic effects are often used in thermogravimetric and other apparatus.

Electrical techniques and problems are described.

CHAPTER XVII

Apparatus Design

17.1. General

The design of an apparatus can be a reasonably simple affair, provided one has (1) the performance requirements for the final assembly clearly in mind, (2) a reasonably thorough knowledge of available components and their characteristics, and (3) several years of experience. For the rest of us, periods of indecision and uncertainty, occasional compromise, and frequent revision must be expected and considered routine. One gains experience only by doing and to a lesser degree one can establish performance requirements only from experience. The other aid in design, knowledge of components, is part of one's collateral education gained sometimes by experience but more often by diligent study at the time of need.

The material presented in the accompanying sections is intended to diminish the uncertainty and indecision. The need for compromise may be alleviated by a clearer understanding of performance requirements. The need for revision may possibly be lessened for the same reason, but new techniques, new components, new problems, plus the awareness of ways to meet the new requirements might bring about fairly frequent revision even for an experienced user. Cognition of the possibility of modifying or adapting a commercially available apparatus may tip the balance in favor of purchase rather than construction, particularly for the neophyte. The final sections describe, purely as examples, assemblies designed by the author.

The experimenter must keep in mind at all times that the means of handling the sample is of prime importance. Once an experimental procedure has been selected the design problem becomes quite general. For example, when the type of sample holder and furnace for a differential thermal study has been chosen, the programming and recording system will likely be very like some other assembly. This is all to the good; if a different type of problem arises, another furnace and/or sample holder can be substituted.

17.2. To Design or Not to Design

A person experienced in thermal analysis and who needs new apparatus will probably design it; he is convinced that commercially available equipment does not fill his needs; to a considerable degree he is right.

Apparatus manufactured for general sale is constrained to nonspecificity; in order that it may serve the needs of many reasonably well the maker must shun the features which improve it for only limited purposes and which limit its utility for other purposes or increase its cost unnecessarily. One experienced in the art can immediately see disadvantages in any given commercial apparatus. Whether the new requirements of the user can be met better by purchase and modifications or by construction according to the user's own design is a question not always answered objectively.

The neophyte has a quite different problem; he does not even know to what degree the commercial apparatus will satisfy his needs; he must evaluate the conflicting advice of various authorities; he can foresee obstacles to obtaining funds for design of an apparatus at any short interval after purchase of a complete apparatus. Only the most enlightened management is likely to understand that even good scientists are not always able to invade new fields without error. Perhaps the course of action can best be decided by evaluation of one's own attitude. He who wants a tool to get an answer and who cares not how it happens must settle for the available apparatus. He who is ready and willing to study the technique and apparatus critically can well undertake the problem of modifying or designing to suit his special needs.

The author places himself squarely with the norm in his response to an apparatus problem. A few years ago an apparently expensive packaged apparatus was put on the market. The author was investigating such apparatus for his own use. He rejected the commercial ready-to-use apparatus in favor of design and construction around a commercially available principal component. The final apparatus was significantly more expensive than the commercial unit but had the quality of filling —after several further modifications—the special needs of the author; yet the author has recommended the commercial unit for those who had not had the experience essential for such design or who had no needs beyond its capabilities.

Unfortunately one may expect little aid, comfort, or encouragement from manufacturers of materials. If the designer of a furnace should follow strictly the conditions recommended by these manufacturers and was still able to construct the furnace, it would certainly have a life expectancy of 30 years, far more than the useful life of the rest of the apparatus. A maker of platinum wire, for example, points out that platinum windings should not be cycled up and down in temperature; crystallization of the wire would shorten the life of the winding. The author has cycled such a furnace several hundred times with no evidence that it was near failure. The furnace was taken out of service because of obsolescence, a much greater hazard in this work.

17.3. To Design

The previous question having been settled, consideration of the real problem may begin. Assume now that a differential thermal analysis apparatus of an orthodox type is to be constructed for use to 1500°C at a heating rate not less than 10°C/minute and that only the furnace and programming apparatus are under consideration. The first problem is obviously the size and nature of the furnace. The temperature range will narrow the choice of windings to platinum or an alloy for the ordinary tube furnace.

Design of the windings, i.e., size and quantity of wire, will depend on the size and construction of the furnace and the voltage supply. All of the furnace parameters are interrelated. This requires an attempt at simultaneous consideration of ease and quality of control, degree of insulation, size of heated chamber, rate of heating, etc.

A furnace with plenty of insulating material around it does not necessarily require less power to heat it than a similar furnace with less insulation. The insulating material must be heated, too. The heavily insulated furnace is less subject to minor fluctuations in temperature. Because of its mass, changes in input voltage are less immediately apparent as changes in temperature. This means that rather simple programming apparatus will give a smooth nondiscontinuous heating curve. The reader should not infer a linear or even a highly reproducible heating rate. These both may require good control equipment. (A heavily lagged furnace driven by a voltage increasing at a fixed rate should have a fairly reproducible heating rate; if this voltage input is programmed the heating rate can be reasonably close to linear. Both statements assume that the furnace is essentially at room temperature at the start of the program.) One quality is certain. The furnace will take a long time to cool. Another run can be made the following day.

A lightly insulated furnace will be more affected by changes in supply voltage; it will require sensitive and quick-acting control apparatus to maintain a programmed temperature rise; good apparatus can program the furnace with good precision because of the rapid response; the furnace will cool quickly.

Returning now to the problem of heating to 1500°C, one may select a power input on the basis of experience when possible. Otherwise a reasonably safe estimate is 1500 watts. This is a beginning.

Consider next the type of voltage or current control. Assuming the supply voltage is 115 volts ac, one has available 115 volts with an ON-OFF controller (included only for information; an ON-OFF program would not be used with a platinum winding; see Chapter XIV), 115 or 135 volts with an adjustable or driven autotransformer, about 105 volts with a properly loaded saturable-core reactor, and about 110 volts with a solid-state controlled rectifier. This maximum voltage is needed to calculate the furnace resistance (see the following section). Choose, for the purpose of this discussion, an autotransformer. (The other cases are even simpler.) If the transformer is connected to give 0–135 volts, the relation is $P = E^2/R = 1500$ watts $= (135 \text{ volts})^2/R = 1.7 \times 10^4/R$ and $R = 11^+$ ohms. If the autotransformer is connected to deliver 0–115 volts, $R = 9^-$ ohms. The windings then must have a resistance of 9^- or 11^+ ohms at a temperature somewhat above 1500°C. This last is important since platinum has a relatively high-temperature coefficient or resistance.

Choosing the 11^+ ohms for this problem and assuming the winding may reach 1600°C the electrical resistance must be about 4.5 ohms at room temperature. (Platinum and platinum alloys have high positive temperature coefficients of resistance which must be taken into account. The high-temperature resistance is used in calculating the amount of wire.) This 4.5 ohms must obviously be a long length of fairly thick wire rather than a short length of fine wire, but since the cost of the winding for a given power dissipation varies as the fourth power of the diameter, i.e., $\$ = kd^4$, a compromise must be made. The author has generally used 0.032-inch wire in this power range. The oldest furnace was in use for about 7 years before removal from service. It has not shown any signs of deterioration.

There must be enough turns on a tube furnace (probably no less than six turns per inch) so that no noticeable image of the winding shows through the tube to the heated chamber. The total number will now depend partly on the use of the furnace. A horizontal furnace will need a sizable constant-temperature zone so the winding will occupy 6 to 8 inches for a differential thermal analysis furnace. In a vertical furnace the same wire can be distributed along 4 to 5 inches since gradients are going to exist anyway. In vertical furnaces, we rely on symmetry. At the same distance from the axis at any given height the temperature should be the same. If a high-conductivity block is used to contain the sample, temperature differences at symmetric points will be very small.

Horizontal furnaces are subject to "end effects," i.e., greater heat loss at the end of the wound portion simply because the adjacent region in the one direction is not heated. The furnace designer will generally compensate for this by doubling the number of turns in the last inch on either end (Fig. XVII-1). This is an arbitrary choice. Very close compen-

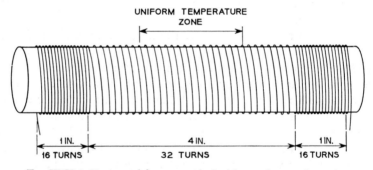

Fɪɢ. XVII-1. Horizontal furnace with double winding at the ends.
The additional heat at the ends will provide a nearly uniform temperature zone in the center section because heat loss to the ends is avoided.

sation over any sizable temperature range is neither likely nor often expected. The object of this and winding is to present to the uniformly wound center section an adjoining region at nearly the same temperature so that finally the center region of the center section has a temperature gradient within it sufficiently low that it can be considered as a uniform temperature region.

17.4. Power Supply

The selection of a power supply for differential thermal analysis depends on the funds available and the demands to be placed on it. A simple ON-OFF supply is out of the question for any but very heavily lagged furnaces; even on these the induced emf'ts may introduce serious noise. For lighter, quick-response furnaces an ON-OFF control will show clearly in the record of any but the most precisely balanced sample and thermocouple assemblies; this objection would not apply to thermogravimetric furnaces. The application of line voltage to a cold winding is generally without serious consequences to the winding, but the sudden heating of this winding may very well cause other troubles. A winding directly on a ceramic tube, for example, may crack the tube after repeated use of an ON-OFF controller. Once the furnace is hot this problem ceases to exist. When the tube is already hot the sudden heating of an area a couple of hundred degrees is not serious, but the sudden heating of a small area to a thousand degrees higher than the neighboring area causes severe strains in any material.

A platinum or platinum alloy furnace winding would also rule out a simple ON-OFF control because of the high-temperature coefficient of resistance. A winding designed to dissipate 1000 watts at 1500°C will dissipate roughly 2500 watts at room temperature. One may safely assume that somewhere along the winding there will be a point at which the rapidly heating wire cannot dissipate heat to its surroundings rapidly enough to keep the wire temperature below its melting point. In a matter of a few seconds the winding burns out.

Another result which will arise in differential thermal analysis but not in thermogravimetric analysis from the use of an ON-OFF controller is electrical interference. Switching of currents in the 5–20 amp range in the general vicinity of a system measuring a few tens of microvolts is an invitation to trouble on two counts. If the power supply and the recording system are fed from the same supply line there is likely to be a very decidedly noticeable change in line voltage. This will affect recorders which are not strictly null balance potentiometers or moving-coil galvanometers. Specifically it can and generally will affect recorders which measure voltage drop across a resistor. The other source of electrical interference is electromagnetic radiation; i.e., the making and breaking of the contacts with the incident sparking transmits a damped wave which has fairly high intensity close by. [The author has had interference from a percentage timer on a cam-drive motor (½ amp) in spite of shielded thermocouples, a null balance recording potentiometer, and a regulated and isolated power supply.] This radio-frequency wave can be picked up as a very high-level noise signal within the recorder-amplifier circuit where the input filter has no effect.

To summarize, ON-OFF controllers are generally not suitable for thermal analysis. They should certainly not be used in any system in which low-level electrical signals are to be measured. They should not be used with a furnace having a helical winding directly on a ceramic tube. Since they are inexpensive and will for this reason be considered in design of apparatus, a positive set of limitations is in order. ON-OFF controllers may be used in a slow-response system where the temperature fluctuations of the winding are not felt appreciably at the sample. They may be used when the measurement does not make use of a low-level electrical signal or when this signal is measured on a galvanometer or similar instrument; hence they may be used for thermogravimetry with most recording systems, or high-temperature X-ray diffraction or the like, or even for differential thermal analysis if one is using samples gross enough to permit direct recording from base metal differential thermocouples.

If the designer of an apparatus decides that an ON-OFF supply cannot be used he still has several possible systems of varying the furnace power. The next simplest is an adjustable autotransformer. The adjustable autotransformer is nearly as versatile as the ON-OFF controller; i.e., it needs to fit the largest demand but will supply smaller currents equally well. It can be used very satisfactorily on much more rapidly responding systems than the ON-OFF controller since the voltage output will change no more than a few volts at a time. It is far less likely to cause electrical interference because the moving of the contact from one turn to the next only exchanges a shorted turn for a lesser but significant load, or vice versa. The only disadvantage of the adjustable autotransformer is the discrete increments of voltage and this disadvantage manifests itself only on rapid-response systems. The effect on rapid-response systems will be to cause a wavy base line when a low-level signal is being measured and if there is some thermal asymmetry in the sample block. In summary, the adjustable autotransformer is a good general purpose power supply which may be used with any but very rapid-response systems.

We will use the adjustable autotransformer as the general example in this chapter partly because it is a useful device and partly because the planning of cam drives for other power supplies is rather similar.

The adjustable autotransformer must be compared with two continuously adjustable systems, the thyratron and the saturable-core reactor. These three systems have a wide enough range of applicability that for many applications any one of the three is quite satisfactory.

The thyratron may be turned down to zero output like the adjustable autotransformer but it cannot step up the voltage as the autotransformer can; in fact there is a loss of a few volts at maximum power and this must be taken into account when designing the furnace. The voltage variation is continuous rather than in discrete steps. It may be selected on the basis of maximum demand without sacrifice of performance at lower powers. The author's experience is that a silicon controlled rectifier (solid-state thyratron) power supply is an excellent power supply.

The saturable-core reactor is similar to the thyratron in that the voltage variation is continuous and there is a small voltage drop at maximum power. It has two interrelated disadvantages, the nonzero turndown and its need to be matched to the load to provide suitable control. This means that if one uses a significantly different furnace than the reactor was designed to supply one must replace the reactor or make other adaptations. This adaptation would usually take the form of a dummy load, just a resistor dissipating the difference between the actual and the rated load. If the new furnace requires a greater power input than the reactor can control, a new reactor is obviously required; a reactor wound to control a 500-watt load and having a 10-volt internal drop would have a drop nearly three times as large if a 1500-watt load were substituted. The dissipation within the reactor would be about eight times as large and the reactor windings would likely burn out the first time the control system called for full power.

In summary, the saturable-core reactor is a perfectly good control system for apparatus in which the heating requirements are not likely to be changed greatly and in which the nonzero turndown is of no consequence. For research instrumentation, in which different sized loads may be used, its use is ill-advised.

For most purposes the designer of an apparatus should by now have a reasonably firm concept of the right controller for his particular system. If special problems do not lead to special ways of heating (Chapter VIII) one of the systems discussed above should perform quite satisfactorily. For a general purpose research apparatus the author favors the solid-state thyratron. The author is well-aware that in the assembly of an apparatus it is sometimes expedient to compromise for reasons of price, delivery, and availability of packaged subassemblies. Such a compromise may now be made with some fairly accurate knowledge of the consequences.

17.5. Program Controllers

Several general modes of control are used: linear (with time) voltage increase, programmed voltage increase, programmed temperature increase, linear (with time) temperature increase, and variations approximating the last.

The first-named program control is generally a motor and gear train attached to an adjustable autotransformer. The gears are selected and arranged to drive the autotransformer at a speed calculated to reach maximum voltage (end of travel) not long after the temperature limit is reached. These are interdependent quantities and must be guessed ahead of time with some provision for closer approximation after the system is tested. Since the designer can only estimate his power requirements for any reasonably fast heating rate, he has presumably left a margin of safety and expects to reach his maximum planned temperature at the desired heating rate when the voltage output is 120–125 volts out of the possible 135 volts. He must now plan his autotransformer drive to reach 120–125 volts at the time his furnace is supposed to reach the temperature limit, with some provision for adjustment after trial. This adjustment will be a gear change for precise and reproducible changes but may be a proportional timer for approximations. The rate of heating may be varied in the same ways—reproducible changes by gear changes, approximation with a percentage timer.

A programmed voltage increase would generally take the form of a nonuniformly driven autotransformer, i.e., $d\theta/dT \neq$ constant. The variable rate of adjustment of the shaft angle, θ, may be the deliberate imposition of grossly nonuniform heating or it may be an attempt to obtain a constant temperature rise with a simple program and control system.

Since the dissipated power, W, is equal to E^2/R, a uniform rate of voltage increase will give a nonuniform power increase. On the other hand the conduction losses are roughly proportional to the temperature, so this effect modifies the nonlinearity of temperature rise which the first effect causes. With furnaces having hot outside walls the radiation loss (proportional to T^4) will have a further modifying effect at high temperature. Obviously, a furnace and a uniformly ($d\theta/dT =$ constant) driven autotransformer which yield a linearly (with time) increasing temperature within the furnace is a purely fortuitous combination. For this reason the rate of drive of the autotransformer may need to be modified to compensate for those effects.

Any modification of the drive speed must be established for a given type of furnace. Any given modification is likely to be impractical if two or more types of furnaces must be driven from the same program controller. The deliberate gross modification, such as a discontinuous change in heating rate, is quite practical.

The programmed or linearly driven autotransformer supplies power to a furnace at a rate not directly related to the temperature within that furnace. There must necessarily be a means of cutting off power unless the furnace can operate indefinitely at the maximum supply voltage. Two limiting devices may immediately be suggested: an adjustable limit on the travel of the autotransformer or, preferably, an adjustable limit switch on the temperature recorder.

In summary, both kinds of voltage drive have the serious disadvantage that their action is not related to the quantity (temperature) being changed. They can provide a nondiscontinuous rise in temperature with smooth changes in heating rate, except for very low-lag furnaces. A simple motor-driven autotransformer is the least expensive system by which a reasonable and somewhat nearly reproducible heating rate may be obtained. It is extremely sensitive to line voltage fluctuations, as can be seen from the derivative, $dW/dE = 2E/R$.

An infrequently occurring source of error with these controls is long-term supply voltage fluctuation. Commercial power systems should be quite stable; a few institutional systems with large daily variations may remain. [One university had a system so heavily overloaded that a graduate student is reported to have had to make measurements only in the early Sunday morning hours (before 6 o'clock) because this was the only time the voltage was reasonably nearly constant.]

Programmed temperature increase and linear (with time) temperature increase are generally accomplished with driven set points or variations on the latter. A common form of the driven set point is the temperature indicator or strip chart recorder with an additional index pen. This index pen is driven across the scale according to a schedule and its position is constantly compared with that of the temperature pen. Their relative positions determine the signal sent to the controller and hence the signal to the power supply.

Consider a case in which the designer of the apparatus expects to need 1100°C maximum and a heating rate of 10°C/minute. Assume that he knows that the voltage input to his furnace must be 120 volts at the time the sample reaches 1100°C at an average rate of 10°C/minute. Since this is slightly higher than ordinary line voltage, the usual 115 volt input, 0–135 volt output connections will be used. The transformer must travel eight-ninths of its span in 110 minutes but its span is about 320° or eight-ninths of a full circle. The autotransformer must then turn

$$\frac{8 \text{ revolutions}}{9} \times \frac{120 \text{ volts}}{135 \text{ volts}} \times \frac{1}{110 \text{ minutes}},$$

1 revolution/140 minutes.

Low-speed motors are large and expensive; gears are easily selected and used. The designer selects a set of gears to reduce the, say, 1800 revolutions/minute to 140 minutes/revolution. This 250,000 : 1 reduction is done in several steps, possibly including a commercial gear box or starting with a motor already geared down. This is the simplest arrangement. From this point, the designer begins to add features intended for protection of apparatus, for increased versatility, or for convenience in operation.

17.6. Auxiliary Components or Functions

These added features may include a number of the following as well as some others the author has not thought of.

SLIP CLUTCH

The slip clutch is a standard feature. It permits manual adjustment or reset of the variable autotransformer or any driven component.

POWER RELAY

The power relay is a useful device for enabling shutdown of power from a number of points and thus permits more flexible circuitry. A small current flow in the relay winding controls a much larger current through the contacts.

LIMIT SWITCH

The limit switch is one device used for terminating or changing the cycle. It may operate to stop the autotransformer drive, reverse the drive (see below), shut off all power, change the drive speed, or start a timer.

REVERSIBLE MOTOR

The reversible motor is useful generally in differential thermal analysis but has only occasional value in thermogravimetry. The programmed decrease in temperature would be instituted on operation of the limit switch (see above). A pair of limit switches could be arranged to cause the reversible motor to drive repeatedly up and down, providing a cycling between the preset limits.

PILOT OR INDICATOR LIGHTS

Indicator lights in various colors can serve a multitude of useful purposes. Essentially, they tell the operator—at a glance—what parts of the apparatus are or should be functioning. For example, in a simple system, lights on (1) the main switch, (2) the motor circuit, and (3) the furnace power circuit would immediately indicate (1) whether or not anything should be happening, (2) whether or not the programmer has reached its limit, and (3) whether or not there should be power supplied to the furnace.

Whether or not any of this information is trivial or superfluous depends on the circuit.

Temperature Limit Switch

Temperature-actuated adjustable switches may be obtained on many recorders. These may be used to shut off the furnace as a protection feature or used in place of the limit switches on the autotransformer drive.

Internal Timer

The timer may be used in place of the limit switch where protection is not an important requirement. The timer may also be used to shut down the apparatus when it is to be left unattended for long periods.

Function Switches

A few switches wired to modify operation rather than only to turn it on or off can be very useful. A switch permitting the furnace either to remain hot or to cool when the program limit is reached, and one short-circuiting timer contacts or manually reversing the drive motor can add considerably to the utility of the apparatus.

Percentage Timer

The percentage timer comprises a clock motor and a cam-operated switch designed so that the "closed time" of the switch is adjustable from a few per cent to 100% of the time. It is used generally to adjust heating rates or chart speeds, by opening and closing the motor circuit (Fig. XVII-3). It should not be used to control directly current flows more than a few tenths of an ampere in the vicinity of low-level signals such as in differential thermal analysis.

Gear Change

If the same program controller is used for several purposes, a gear change arrangement is essential. The operation of a percentage timer to slow down a driver motor is reasonably good, but for any high degree of reproducibility of a lower drive speed a known gear change is far superior and avoids an important source of noise.

Meters

A voltmeter to show that the controller is supplying a voltage and an ammeter to show that the furnace is using it will generally be enough.

With some control systems, the control signal may be shown instead. Saturable-core reactor and solid-state thyratron systems generally show only the control current.

RELAYS

Large furnace currents may require large switches. These switches may be so large that their presence on a control panel is inconvenient. The furnace power is better switched by use of a relay which in turn may be operated by use of a small switch. Use of a relay permits all sorts of switching devices to turn on or off the furnace power under specified conditions. Relay control of the operating power likewise permits a high degree of automatic control and, hence, untended operation.

For special circumstances, slow-acting or slow-releasing relays might be applicable. A more useful special type would be the time-delay relay which closes or opens a circuit after preset periods of time, less than 1 second on up.

THERMOCOUPLE BREAK PROTECTION

Occasionally thermocouples will fail and occasionally operators will fail to make proper connections. If the thermocouple involved is a control thermocouple, the system will call for heat with no indication when the control point is reached or exceeded. The usual result is a burned-out furnace.

To protect the equipment from such a mishap, a thermocouple break protection circuit is used. In essence, this circuit provides a false signal when a break occurs tending to drive the temperature indication upscale so that the control system will shut down the power. The break protection circuit (Fig. XVII–2) comprises, in its simplest form, a dry cell and a limiting resistor. The limiting resistor is so chosen that (a) the voltage drop across the indicating galvanometer will exceed the range of the meter or (b) the voltage drop across the amplifier input is sufficient to cause the motor to drive the slide-wire.

A galvanometer-type control unit will suffer a slight offset in its ordinary operation because the circuit must be capable of supplying, e.g., 10 to 50 mv to the meter. Through the comparatively low-resistance thermocouple, however, the drop is considerably smaller, so that the offset will generally be only a few degrees. Since the protection circuit only needs to supply a few microvolts to a potentiometric circuit, the presence of the circuit is unnoticeable. Note that any low-impedance connection across the thermocouple terminals renders the protection circuit inoperative. This means, first, that a short-circuited thermocouple or extension will still permit furnace burnout and, second, that connection of another measuring device to the same thermocouple will inactivate the protection.

The present author has found it expedient to add this protection circuit to his control equipment.

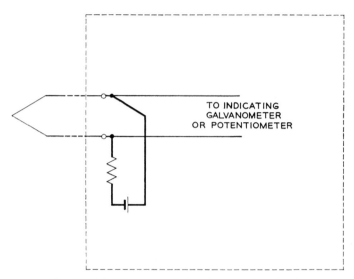

Fig. XVII-2. Thermocouple break protection circuit.

In event of an open circuit outside the controller the low current from the battery circuit is sufficient to drive the temperature indication upscale to the limit. No protection against short-circuited thermocouples is provided.

17.7. Complete Assemblies

The various apparatus designed completely or partly by the author are described herein, not in a spirit of advocacy but as a reference or point of departure for a would-be designer. The reasons for the components will be offered so that the reader may pick and choose as fits his need or fancy. With the exception of the first thermobalance, each apparatus has been packaged in a metal (or, most recently, wood) cabinet designed specifically for that apparatus. The reader may suggest that this operation decreases the versatility of the several parts of the assembly. The author does not admit this to be a handicap. The "versatility" phase of the author's career ended when some interesting differential thermal analyses had to be postponed while some rather long thermogravimetric analyses were completed, the thermogravimetric and differential thermal analysis apparatus sharing the program controller and recorder at that time.

The design of an apparatus to do a multitude of operations is an eternal and personal challenge. Success would probably bring deep satisfaction. The result of such an attempt may be little more than a monument to the designer's conceit; it is per se an admission that there is not a potential significant need for any one of the several manifestations of the creation. The author prefers to assemble an apparatus to perform a particular function; if some additions can be made without interfering with its principal function and the additions extend its utility, well and good—as long as there is no compromise on its performance of its principal task. If the special characteristics of an apparatus are such that some portion can be used to great advantage in another type of apparatus, the author would choose an opportune time and convert the one apparatus to the other—to the extent of dismantling the first if necessary. If the second apparatus is successful, the question of reconverting or replacing components in the first can be argued on tenable grounds. The author is at the time of writing awaiting such a strategic moment to metamorphose an apparatus currently in his custody.

17.8. Thermobalance

The second thermobalance constructed by the author was, like the first (G3), a null balance driven chain instrument. The heater power is supplied through a motor-driven adjustable autotransformer. The control circuitry is shown in Fig. XVII-3. Since platinum-wound furnaces are used most of the time, the possibility of inadvertently supplying line voltage to the furnace must be avoided. This is done by use of a microswitch operated by a cam on the autotransformer shaft. The cam is positioned so that the microswitch is operated only while the output voltage is no more than about 4 volts. This switch closes the furnace relay circuit and, since a hold circuit is incorporated therein, the autotransformer may be turned up. The function of this arrangement is to require the operator to turn back the autotransformer manually before a supply voltage is available to the furnace. From then on the operator may adjust the voltage manually—the autotransformer being fitted with a slip clutch and the drive motor with a switch—or it may be increased at any of four standard speeds by use of two sets of gears. Any of these speeds may be further decreased, in a less reproducible manner, by setting of the percentage timer in the motor circuit.

In the absence of operator intervention the autotransformer is driven to higher voltage output until the adjustable limit on the temperature pen shaft is reached. The motor will stop driving or the entire furnace circuit will shut down at this point, depending on the position of the HEAT ONLY–HEAT AND HOLD switch. (Since this limit switch is the only device which automatically stops the autotransformer, the recorder is wired so that it is on at any time the furnace is on. It may also be turned on separately.)

On very extended runs, at heating rates, for example, of less than

1°C per minute, the strip chart record may be inconveniently long, so the chart drive is equipped with a percentage time to slow it down. For runs in which no record is necessary or in which there is an extended heating period with no weight loss the chart drive can be shut off completely.

The balance may be operated independently of the recorder since the recording circuit has no bearing on the balance operation. Since the recorder amplifier would tend to drive the weight-change pen off scale if no signal were applied, the recording circuit is supplied from the recorder rather than from the balance. The weight-change pen always reproduces the chain position whether or not the balance is operating.

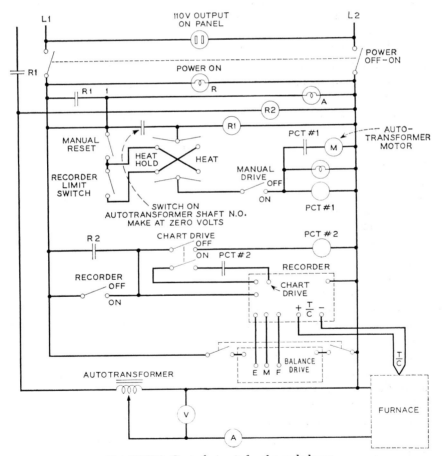

Fɪɢ. XVII-3. Control circuit for thermobalance.

A reasonably extensive choice of operations is available by the addition of a few components.

The chain-drive motor may also be shut off for occasional checking of the balance. A dummy load is substituted to avoid damage to the servo amplifier.

The entire unit is packaged in a metal cabinet fabricated for it. It comprises a box 36 inches high including the casters and resembles the cabinet of Fig. XVII-5. Of the 4-foot length slightly more than half is clear working space for the balance; the remainder is occupied by a permanently mounted box which contains the recorder, the switching, the electrical connections to the balance, and a drawer for storage of gears, sample holders, etc. Beneath this box are the autotransformer and its drive, the balance amplifier and adjusting potentiometer, the adjusting potentiometers for the recording circuit, and two percentage timers (autotransformer and chart). The speed change gear shafts for the autotransformer extend out the front of the cabinet. A hinged cover encloses the gears. This section of the cabinet is thermally insulated internally from the other side. The section under the balance contains the furnaces and their supports. These are small, well-insulated tube furnaces which hang from supports positioned beneath the balance pan hooks. The support wires for the sample holders pass through $\frac{1}{4}$-inch holes in the balance pans, the floor of the balance case, the base on which the balancing mechanism is mounted, and the top of the cabinet.

Access to the furnace compartment is by a door, latched at the top and hinged on rollers at the bottom, which may be swung down and pushed back to recess below the furnace compartment. Access to the other compartment and to the control and recording compartment above is by lift-out panels at the side and rear, respectively.

17.9. Differential Thermal Analysis Apparatus

The present differential thermal analysis equipment is an example of evolution of an apparatus. It began its existence in 1953 (G12) as a reasonably advanced design. The control and programming system (Fig. XVII-4) performed very well with the furnace used. For some time, the programming and recording equipment served a dual purpose since conversion of thermogravimetric use required physical addition only of an auxiliary slide-wire on the 5–0–5 millivolt pen shaft.

To use the apparatus for thermogravimetry the operator needed to: (a) plug in the thermogravimetric furnace in place of the differential thermal analysis furnace; (b) change gears to program at a lower rate; and (c) remove the amplifier input plug and substitute two single-lead plugs.

Similarly, when electrical resistance monitoring (G11) was more useful than thermal measurements, a resistance ratio bridge with supply voltage and adjustable resistances was packaged in a small box and attached to one side of the control panel. This could be put to use by (a) changing furnace leads and (b) replacing the differential thermocouple lead (at the amplifier input) with the output from the bridge. A zero-adjusting circuit was added at the comparatively high signal level between the amplifier and recorder. (This is feasible because the linear range of the amplifier extends well beyond its working range and this type of monitoring could use even the nonlinear range still further out.) (See Chapter IV, Sec. 4.3.)

At one point a copper-constantan range was added on the temperature pen to permit measurements below room temperature. This has sub-

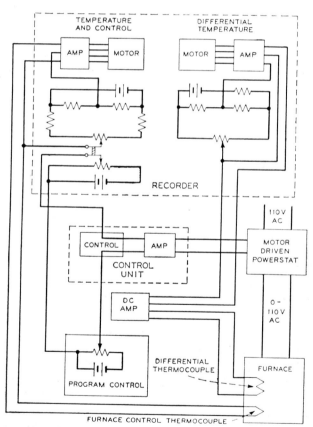

Fig. XVII-4. Block diagrams of control and recording apparatus for differential thermal analysis (G12).

The furnace control signal is also the recorded temperature signal.

sequently been changed to a Chromel-Alumel range so that the recorder now has a 0–1500°C Pt vs Pt-10% Rh range and a 0–1200°C Chromel vs Alumel range (selected by a switch) on one pen and a 5–0–5 millivolt range on the other pen. The reason for having two ranges so close together is not so much to gain accuracy in temperature measurement as to permit measurement from one of the differential thermojunctions whether base metal or Pt vs Pt-Rh couples were being used.

The apparatus was repackaged in a metal cabinet at about this point. An *X–Y* recorder was added for some special work. The cabinet provided a reasonably centralized control system with at least as convenient access to the various components as before. It also provided a work area directly associated with the furnaces. This was concurrent with the change to the Lodding–Hammell (L10) type of furnace so that a relatively small table-top area was sufficient.

The advent of effluence analysis—made practicable by the Lodding–Hammell technique—brought new needs and, hence, new instrumentation. It is clearly inconvenient and a source of error to measure two dependent variables on two separate recorders and subsequently relate both records to temperature; further, repetitive gas chromatography of the effluence was planned, and this has distinctly different chart speed requirements. To permit simultaneous recording from differential thermocouples and a gas density detector, a Leeds and Northrup two-pen *X–Y* recorder was added in place of the single-pen *X–Y* recorder. This X_1, X_2 vs Y recorder plots, when needed, both the differential temperature and the differential gas density against temperature. The temperature drive has a fixed 0–1500°C Pt vs Pt–10% Rh range and a second range governed by a range-change card similar to that used by Leeds and Northrup in their Speedomax Model H. The two X ranges are 1 and 10 mv with live end point, both slide-wires being equipped with switches to center the zero point or move it to the left margin.

To make room for this recorder, the amplifier disappeared into the cabinet (Fig. XVII-5) where it is set on its side in such a position that the range switch may be operated conveniently by use of a jointed rod connecting the knob on the front with the switch on the chassis. The range-change switch operates at low signal levels and should be left encased in the amplifier chassis. The output switch could be removed easily from its panel position so it is mounted directly on the cabinet. The *X–Y* recorder was completely removed from service with this differential thermal analysis apparatus.

The removal of these two units provided space not only for the new recorder but also for a drawer. This drawer is a very worthwhile addition to the apparatus. It is used to store change gears for recorder or

Fɪɢ. XVII-5. Differential thermal analysis apparatus.
The lower recorder can record ΔT *and another function vs* T. *The upper recorder plots* ΔT *and* T *against time.*

programmer, pen cleaners, sample holders, sample blocks, thermo-couples, thermocouple extension leads, a pencil, spare nuts and O-rings, as well as miscellaneous items. Another useful addition was an electrical outlet for using soldering irons or an electronic voltohmmeter.

A connector panel was added more recently—after changing to fre-quent use of commercial shielded thermocouples. This is wired to permit connection of the differential thermocouples to the control and recording circuits when desired. The plugs in the center row are connected to the sample and reference plugs below so that patch cords can be plugged into center and top rows, thus connecting reference and sample thermo-couples with control and recording circuits. This is by no means a neces-sary condition, since most of the furnaces have or can be fitted with thermocouples in special wells near the winding and several of the fur-nace bases have a third thermocouple. (The term "most of the furnaces" can be taken literally. Obviously, when one is experienced in the art, furnaces can be designed and wound cheaply. Experimenting with fur-nace design is therefore not only possible but practical. On the other hand, acquiring this degree of experience can be expensive.) The sev-eral furnace bases represent two adapted from the Lodding–Hammell concept and various experimental special purpose types. The one shown in Fig. XVII-6 is used for closed-chamber differential thermal analysis of small samples (Fig. VIII-5). These special purpose bases are essentially devices for holding one or more ceramic tubes so that one or two sample holders can be positioned in the hot zone. In the example given, two stainless steel–shielded thermocouples with exposed #36 Chromel-Alumel junctions are led through a two-hole, $\frac{1}{4}$ inches OD, $\frac{3}{32}$ inches ID, alumina tube. This tube is held by the base so that the samples are held at the selected level in the furnace. The sample and reference ma-terials are placed in tubes (closed at one end) which fit rather snugly over the thermocouple shield. These are slid over the thermocouples—lifting the base from its stand and tilting the assembly to avoid spilling—so that the thermocouple bead is buried in the sample or reference ma-terial (see Chapter VIII). For some work, a block—resembling an in-verted sample block—is set on top to equalize temperatures as much as possible.

The control connection on the thermocouple panel goes to the senior recorder for a very good reason: the temperature pen shaft of that re-corder is equipped with a slide-wire which is a basic part of the con-trol system (see above). The author considers a time-based temperature recorder to be a necessary part of any differential thermal analysis ap-paratus (see Chapters V & XVI). The second pen of this recorder may be used with the chromatograph so that, when repetitive chromatography is being done on the effluent gas from a furnace, the qualitiative data may be referred to the temperature at the time of sampling, thus permitting better identification of the reaction products with the thermal effect (see Chapter XV).

The most recent important change in the apparatus has been in the control system. The adoption of rapid-response furnaces led to a troublesome cycling effect on the temperature difference signal when some special techniques—and high amplification—were used. This is a natural occurrence for control systems using adjustable autotransformers since the voltage changes are necessarily discrete. A new control unit and a solid-state thyratron power supply were substituted for the old unit and the adjustable autotransformer. The program unit and the recorder were unchanged. Since all the furnaces had been designed for 0–135 volt operation, some would not heat satisfactorily at 0–115 volts. The 115-volt supply had to be led into an autotransformer and the stepped-up voltage (135 volts) fed into the power supply. This power supply is far more rapid in response and, with the present furnaces, gives a much more nearly linear heating rate than the adjustable autotransformer.

Since the photograph was made an adjustable-zero circuit has been added, along with switching to permit recording the amplifier output on the X,X vs Y, the X,X vs t, or both recorders while shorting the input of either recorder not in use. This arrangement permits recording of the differential signal as a function of temperature, time, or both. Also, a thermoelectric device which gives a small direct current indication of an alternating current or voltage was connected to the output of the power supply. This provides a convenient method of recording power input to the furnace.

17.10. Controlled Atmosphere Thermobalance

Because of the frequent need for controlled atmosphere thermogravimetry another thermobalance was constructed. Basically it was a commercial automatic recording balance (Ainsworth RV-AU2) fitted with a pair of furnaces (Fig. XVII-6). The balance was purchased as a semimicrobalance but the behavior was initially so erratic—apparently due to convection—in any appreciable atmospheres that it was converted to ordinary analytical range operation. The problem of significant convection currents was diminished by introduction of a series of plates between the hot zone and the balance chamber. These served both as barriers to passage of streams of hot or cold gases (convection) and as radiation shields in vacuum operation. The support wire passed through a $\frac{1}{4}$-inch hole in the center of each.

The arrangement was suitable for rather limited work but for general

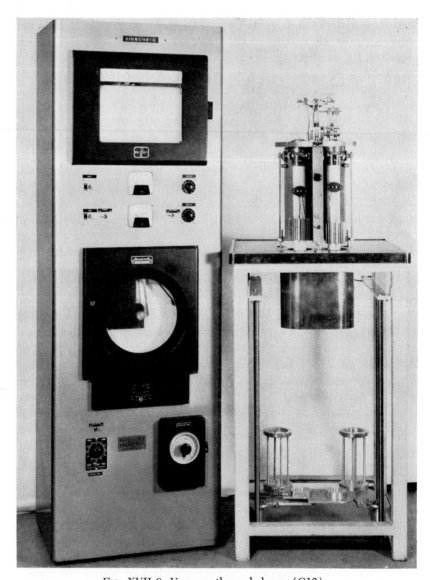

Fig. XVII-6. Vacuum thermobalance (G13).
The furnace support arrangement permitted easy operation of the balance even with the long furnace tubes. The apparatus was subsequently converted to a top-loading arrangement.

high-temperature work at near-atmospheric pressure its operation was "noisy" so the assembly has subsequently been converted very successfully to top-loading (see Chapter IX). A metal dome was formed and fitted to receive furnaces rather similar to the differential thermal analysis furnaces. A 12-inch metal ring was grooved to take an O-ring on each side and so provide a vacuum seal between the dome and the base. Two counterweighted support tubes were hung from the beam; the lower ends hanging in brass tubes were connected to the furnace openings in the base. The upper ends were ceramic tubes; thermocouple wires were led through one of the tubes and joined at the top and so that the sample holder sat directly on the bead. Connection is made to these thermocouple wires in the manner used by Reisman (R12) (see Chapter X). The sample temperature is recorded and occasionally programmed (see Chapter XV); generally the furnace is programmed.

The control power is supplied through the contacts of relay No.1 (Fig. XVII-7). This relay winding is wired through another set of contacts to provide a "hold" circuit. Any momentary break in the relay circuit will permit the relay to "drop out" and remain in the nonoperated condition until the operator again pushes the Main Power ON button. This momentary contact button is in parallel with the hold contacts and so completes the relay winding circuit. The circuit may be interrupted and the power shut off by the Main Power OFF button or by opening all four parallel sets of contacts in the "lockup" mechanism in such a manner that they are all open at the same time. This is discussed later. (A limit switch was later added on the temperature pen shaft.)

With the main power on, the balance and furnace may be turned on. The interval and percentage timer motors and the cam driver in the program unit are now supplied with power. The program and control units are left on simply because electronic equipment will normally function better if left on. This is not done with all equipment because of the problem of attacking components internally to separate the functions which must be shut off from those which may remain on.

The furnace relay switches on the moving contact of the variable autotransformer rather than on the primary supply to avoid the surges of power that occur when line voltage is suddenly connected to a transformer which has a sizable load on its secondary. The voltmeter and ammeter monitor only one of the two furnaces with the expectation that the other similarly wound furnace will differ only negligibly. The principal function of the second furnace is to permit buoyancy compensation so the temperature need only be approximately the same. If differential thermogravimetry were to be attempted, a second controller would be used (see Chapter X).

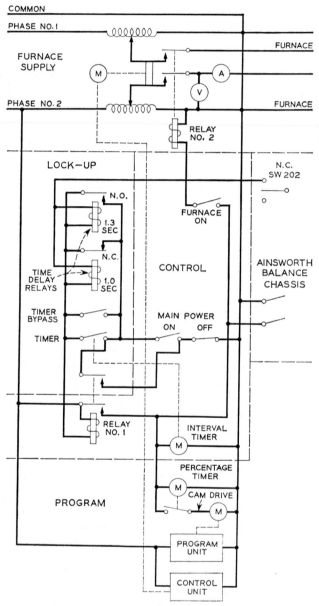

Fɪɢ. XVII-7. Circuit diagram for control system. From Garn *et al.* (G13).
The lockup circuit permits extensive unattended operation. The program could be
terminated by a temperature limit switch as well as by the timer.

The automatic lockup mechanism of the balance operates to lift the beam from the knife edges and reset it, compensating for any displacement due to building vibration. The present author devised a way to use this mechanism to assist in timed automatic shutdown.

The lockup, in addition to the parts of the manual lockup and the timing mechanism, comprises a motor geared to a wheel fitted with an eccentric pin which slides a shaft which, in turn, operates the manual lockup. The beam is lifted about 0.8 second after the start of the cycle and is released again about 1.8 seconds after the start of the cycle. The electrical impulse which initiates the lockup cycle remains on for about 15 seconds. These conditions require that shutdown occur during—and only during—this 1-second interval. This is done with a pair of electronic time-delay relays and a hold circuit on the power relay. The relay may be released from the main power switch or the shutdown circuit.

When the shutdown circuit is not in use the time-delay relays are bypassed by the timer bypass switch. When the timer circuit is in use the time-delay relays are bypassed by the timer contacts until the expiration of the preset time. When the timer contacts open the relay hold current passes through the time-delay relay contacts so that when they are next activated the thermobalance is shut down with the balance beam locked up.

The time-delay relay circuit opens the hold circuit 1.0 second and closes it 1.3 seconds after the lockup cycle is initiated. The circuit closure is necessary to avoid shutdown while the initiating signal is still on (15 seconds) but the beam has been restored to its operating position. Runs of a couple of days duration have been terminated—generally on a weekend—without operator attention.

17.11. Another Differential Thermal Analysis Apparatus

The apparatus in use by the author at the time of publication is similar in many ways to the previous design. It has a cam-programmed silicon controlled rectifier power supply, but the Leeds and Northrup Series 60 control unit has with it a Speedomax H recorder, so the control system is independent of the recording system. As first choice, a two-pen X_1, X_2 vs T recorder was used.

If long-duration experiments are needed, an X–Y recorder will be installed. The use of a ΔT vs T plot is now feasible since the temperature program is being monitored independently. The programming thermocouple would be moved nearer the sample and the *proportional band* and the *rate* and *reset* actions of the controller readjusted; the change of thermocouple position would provide a better measure of the sample temperature and the readjustment would be necessary because the furnace temperature—at the point of measurement—would not be responding as quickly as before.

The temperature pen shaft of the recorder is equipped with a switch by which the chart only moves when the pen is *on-scale*. This permits the substitution of a small millivolt range and biasing the temperature signal *off-scale*. This, in turn, allows measurement of a small part of a long run, conserving paper and space, without sacrificing the advantages of time-based recording. One use planned for this arrangement involves the study of an inorganic reaction in the 900°C range. A 5.0-mv range card would provide a span of about 125°C full scale. Biasing the measuring circuit with 37 mv would permit recording from just below 900°C to slightly above 1000°C. With a moderately fast chart speed, good peak area measurements can be obtained.

The amplifier is connected directly to the line and left on. This minimizes drift which would be most marked during warm-up.

A rectifier and voltage-dividing potentiometer are wired to an independent manual input control for the power supply. This permits the setting of a repeatable voltage input to the furnace quite separate from the normal control functions.

Two pressure gauges and a regulator are mounted on the panel and some flowmeters will be added. These are interconnected with polyethylene and /or nylon tubing with fittings which allow easy interchange of connections. The interchange of connecting tubing is not quite as easy as manipulating a number of valves but this approach consumes less space and design time and presents a lesser number of places which may leak.

The controlling recorder has two switches operated by the pen shaft. One is used as a limit switch. It is wired into the *hold* circuit of the main relay so that if the switch opens the whole apparatus quietly ceases to operate. This switch is normally set at the furnace limit but may be set at some lower value to prevent—for example—the melting of certain kinds of samples. The second switch is used as a function switch and may be set to stop the program drive and hold the temperature, to reverse the drive to allow the furnace to cool, to shut off the furnace while leaving the recorder on, or to shut down the whole apparatus.

The electrical and plumbing gear are all mounted in a plywood cabinet (stained to match the laboratory furniture) and the furnace assembly is fastened to the side. The several connections are brought out at positions which allow easy connection to whatever furnace assembly is in use. The wooden box not only presents an electrical advantage but also makes possible very easy modification. New components can be added without the aid of a machinist. The whole apparatus is mounted on casters.

A gas density detector is being added for effluence detection and analysis (Chapter XIV). If repetitive chromatographic analyses are undertaken, most of that equipment will be housed separately.

17.12. Summary

The design of an experimental apparatus requires a background of experience and knowledge gained principally firsthand (as by the author) or vicariously (as by the reader). Once the small nucleus has been chosen with the help of the first fourteen chapters, these last three will aid in design of the portion greater in bulk and cost.

Two thermobalances and two differential thermal analysis assemblies are described, along with miscellaneous parts or functions that may be of use.

References

(A1) Adler, H. H., and Puig, J. A., Thermal behavior of brannerite. *Am. Mineralogist* **46**, 1086–1096 (1961).

(A2) Agafonoff, V., Mineralogical study of soil. *Trans. 3rd Intern. Congr. Soil Sci., Oxford* pp. 74–78 (1935).

(A3) Aliev, B. D., and Aliev, G. M., Effect of the addition of cadmium on the thermal and electrical conductivity of selenium. *Izv. Akad. Nauk Azerb. SSR, Ser. Fiz.-Mat. i Tekhn. Nauk* **5**, 85–90 (1960).

(A4) Allison, E. B., Quantitative thermal analysis of clay minerals. *Clay Minerals Bull.* **2**, 242–254 (1955).

(A5) Anderson, A. C., Salinger, G. L., and Steyert, W. A., Specific heat and thermal boundary resistance of liquid helium-3. *Phys. Rev. Letters* **6**, 331–334 (1961).

(A6) Anderson, D. A., and Freeman, E. S., Characterization of saturated polyesters by differential thermal analysis. *Anal. Chem.* **31**, 1697–1700 (1959).

(A7) Anderson, D. A., and Freeman, E. S., Differential thermal analysis of potassium per chlorate. *Nature* **195**, No. 4848; **196**, No. 4849, p. 1297 (1962).

(A8) Anderson, H. C., Differential thermal analysis of epoxide reactions. *Anal. Chem.* **32**, 1592–1595 (1960).

(A9) Anderson, H. C., Differential thermogravimetry versus differential thermometry in studying the pyrolysis of polymers. *Nature* **191**, 1088–1089 (1961).

(A10) Andrianov, K. A., and Manucharova, I. F., Study of polyorgano siloxanes and polyorgano elemento siloxanes thermostability using the method of differential thermal analysis. *Izv. Akad. Nauk SSSR, Otd. Khim. Nauk* No. 3, pp. 420–424 (1962).

(A11) Anikin, A. G., and Dugacheva, G. M., Determination of small heat effects by a thermographic method at temperatures below 0-deg. *Dokl. Akad. Nauk SSSR* **135**, 634–637 (1960).

(A12) Arens, P. L., "A Study of the Differential Thermal Analysis of Clays and Clay Minerals." Excelsiors Foto-Offsets, 1951.

(A13) Ariesan, V., Ionescu, C., Tilinca, A., Cojocaru, Z., and Pitea, M., Application of the micro thermal method in the study of certain binary barbiturate-alkaloid systems. *Farmacia (Bucharest)* **9**, 65–73 (1961).

(A14) Arsenan, D. F., The differential thermal analysis of wood. *Can. J. Chem.* **39**, 1915–1919 (1961).

(A15) Arutiunova, L. B., and Ravich, G. B., Combined micro thermal and spectroscopic investigation of polymorphism among higher fatty acids. *Dokl. Akad. Nauk SSSR* **135**, 837–839 (1960).

(A16) Asaba, T., and Hikita, T., Thermal decomposition of lithium perchlorate. *Kogyo Kagaku Zasshi* **63**, 1890–1893 (1960).

(A17) Ashby, G. E., and Kellagher, R. C., An apparatus for the study of thermoluminescence from minerals. *Am. Mineralogist* **43**, 695–706 (1958).

(A18) Austin, J. B., Thermal expansion of nonmetallic crystals. *J. Am. Ceram. Soc.* **35**, 243–253 (1952).

(A19) Ayres, W. M., and Bens, E. M., Differential thermal studies with simultaneous gas evolution profiles. *Anal. Chem.* **33**, 568–572 (1961).

(B1) Bachelet, M., and Christen, M., Effect of renewing the atmosphere on the thermal decomposition of calcium carbonate. *Compt. Rend.* **251**, 2961–2963 (1960).

(B2) Balandin, A. A., Tolstopyatova, A. A., and Kokenko, I. R., Catalytic conversion of iso propyl alcohol and hydrocarbons on titanium di oxide (anatase) using differential thermocouple. *Izv. Akad. Nauk SSSR, Otd. Khim. Nauk* pp. 2096–2102 (1960).

(B3) Balarew, D., *Z. Anorg. Chem.* **160**, 92 (1927).

(B4) Balygin, I. E., Transformation of amorphous quartz into crystalline during thermal diffusion of silver. *Kristallografiya* **6**, 727–732 (1961).

(B5) Barney, J. E., Remote operation of single-pan balance for weighing in inert atmospheres. *Anal. Chem.* **33**, 1294–1295 (1961).

(B6) Barnier, Y., Pauthenet, R., and Rimet, G., Thermal variation of the anisotropy constants and the spontaneous magnetization of cobalt in the hexagonal phase. *Compt. Rend.* **252**, 2839–2841 (1961).

(B7) Barrall, E. M., and Rogers, L. B., Differential thermal analysis of organic samples. Effects of geometry and operating variables. *Anal. Chem.* **34**, No. 9, 1101–1105 (1962).

(B8) Barrall, E. M., and Rogers, L. B., Differential thermal analysis of organic compounds. Effects of diluting agents. *Anal. Chem.* **34**, No. 9, 1106–1110 (1962).

(B9) Barshad, I., Temperature and heat of reaction calibration of the differential thermal analysis apparatus. *Am. Mineralogist* **37**, 667–694 (1952).

(B10) Bartenev, G. M., and Kongarov, G. S., Dilatometric determination of polymer compatibility. *Vysokomolekul. Soedin.* **2**, 1692–1697 (1960).

(B11) Barthomeuf, D., Perrin, M., and Trambouze, Y., Study of the exothermal phenomenon detected in silica-alumina gels during their thermal evolution. Test of the generalization. *Compt. Rend.* **252**, 4154–4156 (1961).

(B12) Bartlett, E. S., and Williams, D. N., Continuous recording laboratory thermobalance. *Rev. Sci. Instr.* **28**, 919–921 (1957).

(B13) Barton, C. J., Friedman, H. A., Grimes, W. R., Insley, H., Moore, R. E., and Thoma, R. E., Phase equilibriums in the alkali fluoride-uranium tetrafluoride fused salt systems. I. The systems $LiF–UF_4$ and $NaF–UF_4$. *J. Am. Ceram. Soc.* **41**, 63–69 (1958).

(B14) Basden, K. S., Fluidized bed differential thermal analysis. *Fuel* **39**, 270–272 (1960).

(B15) Basden, K. S., Low temperature reactions in fluidized-bed coal pyrolysis. *Fuel* **39**, 359–360 (1960.)

(B16) Bates, L. F., and Barnard, R. D., Electrical resistivities and magnetic suscepti-bilities of some stable and metastable uranium-molybdenum alloys. *Proc. Phys. Soc.* (*London*) **77**, 691–699 (1961).

(B17) Baumann, E. W., Thermal decomposition of amberlite IRA-400. *J. Chem. Eng. Data* **5**, 376–382 (1960).

(B18) Bayliss, P., and Warne, S. S. J., Effects of the controllable variables on dif-ferential thermal analysis. *Am. Mineralogist* **47**, 775–778 (1962).

(B19) Beams, J. W., Hulburt, C. W., Lotz, W. E., Jr., and Montague, R. M., Jr., Magnetic suspension balance. *Rev. Sci. Instr.* **26**, 1181 (1955).

(B20) Beck, C. W., Differential thermal analysis curves of carbonate minerals. *Am. Mineralogist* **35**, 985–1013 (1950).

(B21) Beckett, R., and Winfield, M. E., The thermal decomposition of thorium oxalate. *Australian J. Sci. Res.* **A4**, 644–650 (1951).

(B22) Beech, D. G., and Holdridge, D. A., Testing clays for the pottery industry. *Trans. Brit. Ceram. Soc.* **53**, 103–133 (1954).

(B23) Behl, W. K., and Gaur, H. C., Differential thermal analysis of magnesium chloride hydrates. *Proc. Natl. Inst. Sci. India* **27A**, 33–37 (1961).

(B23a) Belcher, R., Erdey, L., Paulik, F., and Liptay, G., A derivatographic study of potassium hydrogen phthalate. *Talanta* **5**, 53–57 (1960).

(B24) Belov, K. P., and Nikitin, S. A., Low-temperature transformation in the crys-tal of manganese ferrite. *Kristallografiya* **5**, 726–731 (1960).

(B25) Beretka, J., Differential thermal analysis of yttrium iron garnet. *Phys. Chem. Solids* **24**, 169–170 (1963).

(B25a) Berg, L. G., Influence of salt admixtures upon dissociation of dolomite. *Compt. Rend. Acad. Sci. URSS* **38**, 24–27 (1943).

(B26) Berg, L. G., On area measurements in thermogram for quantitative estima-tion and the determination of heats of reaction. *Compt. Rend. Acad. Sci. URSS* **49**, 648–51 (1945).

(B27) Berg, L. G., New method of physicochemical investigation of phases in mix-tures. *Izv. Sek. Fiz.-Khim. Anal., Inst. Obshch. i Neorg. Khim. Akad. Nauk SSSR* **19**, 249–255 (1949).

(B28) Berg, L. G., Thermographic determination of the heat of phase transitions. *Tr. Pervogo Sov. Termogr. Kazan* pp. 59–66 (1953).

(B29) Berg, L. G., The thermographic investigation of some dehydration processes. *Izv. Kazan Filiala Akad. Nauk SSSR, Ser. Khim. Nauk* No. 4, 133–139 (1957); see *Chem. Abstr.* **54**, 6282 (1960).

(B30) Berg, L. G., and Burmistrova, N. P., Thermographic analysis of salts with simultaneous determination of temperature effects and electrical conductivity. *Zh. Neorg. Khim.* **5**, 676–683 (1960); see *Chem. Abstr.* **55**, 3261 (1961).

(B31) Berg, L. G., and Ganelina, S. G., Calcination of dolomite. *Izv. Kazan Filiala Akad. Nauk SSR, Ser. Khim. Nauk*, pp. 83–89 (1955); see *Chem. Abstr.* **51**, 18499 (1957).

(B32) Berg, L. G., Ganelina, S. G., Rassonskaya, I. S., and Teitel'baum, B. Ya., Improvements of methods of thermographic investigation. *Tr. Pervogo Sov. Termogr. Kazan* pp. 42–47 (1953).

(B33) Berg, L. G., Gromakov, S. D., and Zoroatskaya, I. V., An accelerated method of study of diagrams of state by means of thermography., *Dok. Akad. Nauk SSSR* **125**, 78–79 (1959).

(B34) Berg, L. G., Leperhkov, I. N., and Rassonskaya, I. S., Thermographic analysis of salts. *Tr. Pervogo Sov. Termogr. Kazan* pp. 171–181 (1953).

(B35) Berg, L. G., Mochalov, K. N., Kurenkova, P. A., and Amoshina, N. P., Thermogravimetric study of bromoplatnic acid. *Izv. Kazan Filial Akad. Nauk SSSR, Ser. Khim. Nauk* No. 4, 127–132 (1957); see *Chem. Abstr.* **54**, 5312 (1960).

(B36) Berg, L. G., and Rassonskaya, I. S., Rapid thermal analysis. *Dokl. Akad. Nauk SSSR* **73**, 113–115 (1950).

(B37) Berg, L. G., and Rassonskaya, I. S., Thermographic method of determination of dissociation pressure. *Izv. Sekt. Fiz.-Khim. Anal., Inst. Obshch. i Neorg. Khim. Akad. Nauk SSSR* **22**, 140–154 (1953); see *Chem. Abstr.* **52**, 3497 (1958).

(B38) Berg, L. G., Rassonskaya, I. S., and Buris, E. V., The thermographic dissociation pressure of some salts. *Izv. Sekt. Fiz.-Khim. Anal., Inst. Obshch. i Neorg. Khim. Akad. Nauk SSSR* **27**, 239–250 (1956); see *Chem. Abstr.* **50**, 15195 (1956).

(B39) Berg, L. G., and Yagfarov, M. Sh., The effect of some factors on the character of thermographic recording. *Tr. Pervogo Sov. Termogr. Kazan* pp. 53–58 (1953).

(B40) Berg, L. G., and Rassonskaya, I. S., Thermographic analysis at high pressures. *Dokl. Akad. Nauk SSSR* **81**, 855–858 (1951).

(B41) Berg, L. G., and Sidorova, E. E., Temperature conductivity determination by using the method of the differential thermal analysis with applications. *Bul. Inst. Politehn. Iasi* **5**, No. 9, 95–102 (1959).

(B42) Berg, P. W., Influence of the fine and coarse fractions of a clay on the results of differential thermal analysis. *Ber. Deut. Keram. Ges.* **30**, 231–235 (1953); see *Ceram. Abstr.* p. 133 (1954).

(B43) Berg, P. W., The influence of the size of the particles of clay on the results of the differential thermal analysis. *Kemisk* **34**, 49–54 (1953).

(B44) Bergeron, C. G., Russell, C. K., and Friedberg, A. L., Thermal analysis of lead borate glasses during crystallization. *J. Am. Ceram. Soc.* **46**, 246–247 (1963).

(B45) Bergstein, A., and Vintera, J., Thermal decomposition of manganese (II) carbonate. *Chem. Listy* **50**, 1530–1539 (1956).

(B46) Berkelhamer, L. H., An apparatus for differential thermal analysis. *U. S. Bur. Mines, Tech. Paper* **664**, 38–55; *U. S. Bur. Mines, Rept. Invest.* **3762** (1944).

(B47) Berlin, A., and Robinson, R. J., Thermo gravimetric determination of magnesium, potassium and lead by precipitation with dilituric acid. *Anal. Chim. Acta* **24**, 224–234 (1961).

(B48) Berlin, A., and Robinson, R. J., Thermo gravimetric determination of ethylene DI amine and quinine with dilituric acid solubilities of some poly methylene DI amine diliturates. *Anal. Chim. Acta* **24**, 319–328 (1961).

(B49) Berlin, A., and Robinson, R. J., Thermogravimetric analysis. Temperature limits and rate of heating. *Anal. Chim. Acta* **27**, 50–57 (1962).

(B50) Bernstein, L., and Beals, R. J., Thermal expansion and related bonding problems of some (III-V) compound semiconductors. *J. Appl. Phys.* **32**, 122–123 (1961).

(B50a) Biermann, W. J., and Heinrichs, M., A simple thermobalance for studies over a pressure range of 0 to 60 atmospheres. *Can. J. Chem.* **40**, 1361–1367 (1962).

(B51) Billmeyer, F. W., Jr., "Textbook of Polymer Science." Wiley (Interscience), New York, 1962.

(B52) Binnington, D. S., and Geddes, W. F., An automatic recording balance. *Ind. Eng. Chem., Anal. Ed.* **8,** 76–79 (1936).

(B53) Bishui, B. M., and Dhar, R. N., Indian mica. Effect of dry grinding on differential thermal analysis. *Central Glass Ceram. Res. Inst. (India) Bull.* **8,** 15–22 (1961).

(B54) Blau, M., and Carlin, J. R., Industrial applications of radioactivity. *Electronics* **21,** 78–82 (1948).

(B55) Blazek, A., *Silikaty* **1,** 158–163 (1957).

(B56) Blazek, A., Electronic thermobalance with simultaneous registration of differential thermal analysis curves and of curves of decomposition gas product analysis. *Hutnicke Listy* **12,** 1096–1102 (1957).

(B57) Blum, S. L., Paladino, A. E., and Rubin, L. G., Differential thermal analysis technique for determining Curie points. *Am. Ceram. Soc. Bull.* **36,** 175–177 (1957).

(B58) Boersma, S. L., A theory of differential thermal analysis and new methods of measurement and interpretation. *J. Am. Ceram. Soc.* **38,** 281–284 (1955).

(B59) Bohon, R. L., Differential thermal analysis of explosives and propellants under controlled atmospheres. *Anal. Chem.* **33,** 1451–1453 (1961).

(B60) Bohon, R. L., Approximate heats of explosion using differential thermal analysis. *Anal. Chem.* **35,** 1845–1852 (1963).

(B61) Bohon, R. L., Private communication (1964).

(B62) Bollin, E. M., Dunne, J. A., and Kerr, P. F., Differential thermal study of pyrosynthesis. *Science* **131** 661–662 (1960).

(B63) Bollmann, W., Phase transformation of cobalt., *Acta Met.* **9,** 972–974 (1961).

(B64) Bondarenko, A. V., Kiselev, V. F., and Krasil'nikov, K. G., Thermal dehydration of silica and certain properties of its surface. *Dokl. Akad. Nauk SSSR* **136,** 1133–1136 (1961).

(B65) Borchardt, H. J., Differential thermal analysis. An experiment for the physical chemistry laboratory. *J. Chem. Educ.* **33,** 103–107 (1956).

(B66) Borchardt, H. J., Initial reaction rates from differential thermal analysis. *J. Inorg. Nucl. Chem.* **12,** 252–254 (1960).

(B67) Borchardt, H. J., and Daniels, F., Application of differential thermal analysis to the study of reaction kinetics. *J. Am. Chem. Soc.* **79,** 41–46 (1957).

(B68) Borchardt, H. J., and Thompson, B. A., Reactions of solid alkaline earth oxides. I. BaO and SrO. *J. Am. Chem. Soc.* **81,** 4182 (1959).

(B69) Borchardt, H. J., and Thompson, B. A., Reactions of solid alkaline earth oxides. II. CaO and MgO. *J. Am. Chem. Soc.* **82,** 355–357 (1960).

(B70) Borchardt, H. J., and Thompson, B. A., Reactions of alkaline earth oxides. III. A re-examination of the Hedvall effect. *J. Am. Chem. Soc.* **82,** 5630–5632 (1960).

(B71) Bowen, C. H., Data for interpretation of differential thermal curves. *Eng. Expt. Sta. Ohio State Univ., Circ.* **56** (1954).

(B72) Bradley, W. F., Burst, J. F., and Graf, D. L., Crystal chemistry and differential thermal effects of dolomite. *Am. Mineralogist* **38,** 207–217 (1953).

(B73) Bragg, W. L., "Atomic Structure of Minerals." Cornell Univ. Press, Ithaca, New York, 1937.

(B74) van der Breggen, J. C., and Wouterlood, H. J., Novel displacement detector and its application in a recording thermobalance. *J. Sci. Instr.* **37**, 297 (1960).

(B75) Bretsznajder, S., Leyko, J., and Blum, A., Rate of nuclei formation of a new solid phase in the course of thermal dissociation of magnesium carbonate. *Bull. Acad. Polon. Sci., Ser. Sci. Chim.* **8**, 605–608 (1960).

(B76) Brewer, L., and Greene, F. T., Differential thermal analysis of the Si-SiO$_2$ system. *Phys. Chem. Solids* **2**, 2868 (1957).

(B77) Brewer, L., and Savitsamos, P., A study of the Ge–GeO$_2$ system by an inductively heated DTA apparatus. *Phys. Chem. Solids* **2**, 284–285 (1957).

(B78) Brindley, G. W., "The Kaolin Minerals: X-ray Identification and Crystal Structures of Clay Minerals," pp. 32–75. Mineral. Soc., London, 1951.

(B79) Brindley, G. W., and Nakahira, M., The kaolinite-mullite reaction series: III, the high-temperature phases. *J. Am. Ceram. Soc.* **42**, 319–324 (1959).

(B80) Brindley, G. W., and Nakahira, M., X-ray diffraction and gravimetric study of the dehydration reactions of gibbsite. *Z. Krist.* **112**, 136 (1959).

(B81) Brockdorff, U. V., and Kirsch, K., *Electrotech. Z.* **71**, 611 (1950).

(B82) Brokaw, R. S., Thermal conductivity and chemical kinetics. *J. Chem. Phys.* **35**, 1569–1580 (1961).

(B83) Brown, F. E., Loomis, T. C., Peabody, R. C., and Woods, J. D., The design construction and some uses of an automatic recording balance. *Proc. Iowa Acad. Sci.* **59**, 159–169 (1952).

(B84) Brown, F. H., Jr., and Duwez, P., The systems zirconia-lanthana and zirconia-neodymia. *J. Am. Ceram. Soc.* **38**, 95–101 (1955).

(B85) deBruijn, C. M. A., and van der Marel, H. W., Mineralogical analysis of soil clays: I. Introduction and differential thermal analysis; II. Example of mineral analysis by X-ray diffraction and differential thermal analysis. *Geol. Mijnbouw* [N.S.] **16**, 69–83 and 407–428 (1954).

(B86) Bulgakova, T. I., and Zaitsev, O. S., Thermogravimetric investigation of the reaction of formation of a nickel-magnesium ferrite. *Vestn. Moskov. Univ., Ser. II: Khim.* **16**, No. 4, 33–35 (1961).

(B87) Bundy, F. P., Effect of pressure on EMF of thermocouples. *J. Appl. Phys.* **32**, 483–488 (1961).

(B88) Burriel-Marti, F., and Garcia-Clavel, M. E., Reactions between solids. Application of thermogravimetric analysis to the study of reactions between alkaline earth hydroxides and sulfates. *Anales Real. Soc. Espan. Fis. Quim.* (*Madrid*) **B57**, 99–104 (1961).

(B89) Burriel-Marti, F., and Garcia-Clavel, M. E., Application of the thermogravimetric method to dehydration problems. Hydrates of strontium and barium hydroxides. *Anales Real. Soc. Espan. Fis. Quim.* (*Madrid*) **B57**, 111–116 (1961).

(B90) Burriel-Marti, F., and Garcia-Clavel, M. E., New technique for the determination of the percentage of the reaction between two substances in the solid state. *Anales Real. Soc. Espan. Fis. Quim.* (*Madrid*) **B57**, 105–110 (1961).

(B91) Bussiere, P., Claudel, B., Renouf, J. P., Trambouze, Y., and Prettre, M., Study of solid phases by simultaneous use of thermogravimetry, differential thermal analysis, and the emanation method. *J. Chem. Phys.* **58**, 668–674 (1961).

(C1) Cabane, J., and Bernard, J., Role of diffusion in the thermal decomposition of alkali per chlorates. *Bull. Soc. Chim. France* pp. 36–40 (1961).

(C2) Caillère, S., and Hénin, S., Thermal analysis and its interpretation. *Trans. Intern. Ceram. Congr.*, **1948** pp. 137–150 (1948).

(C2a) Caillère, S., and Hénin, S., *in* "The Differential Thermal Investigation of Clays" (R. C. Mackenzie, ed.), pp. 207–230. Mineral. Soc., London, 1957.

(C3) Calvert, E., A new compensated differential microcalorimeter. *Compt. Rend.* **226**, 1702–1704 (1948).

(C4) Campbell, C., Gordon, S., and Smith, C. L., Derivative thermoanalytical techniques. *Anal. Chem.* **31**, 1188–1191 (1959).

(C5) Campbell, W. J., Thermal expansion of magnesium oxide—An interlaboratory study. *U. S. Bur. Mines, Rept. Invest.* **6115** (1962).

(C6) Caro, P., and Loriers, J., Thermolysis curves of some oxalates of rare earths. *J. Recherches Centre Natl. Recherche Sci. Lab. Bellevue* (*Paris*) **39**, 107–118 (1957).

(C7) Carpeni, G., Hamann, Y., Haladjian, J., and Perinet, G., Isohydric point. Isohydric polygermanate containing two potassium, five germanium, and eleven oxygens. Irreversible transformation of the solid phase in aqueous solutions. Electrometry, thermogravimetry, and X-rays. *Bull. Soc. Chim. France* pp. 1093–1908 (1960).

(C8) Cecil, O. B., and Koerner, W. E., Gas and heat evolution from thermally unstable materials. *Ind. Eng. Chem.* **53**, 475–478 (1961).

(C9) Chaly, V. P., and Shor, O. G., Thermographic investigation of the hydroxides of certain metals. Binary systems of hydroxides. *Ukr. Khim. Zh.* **27**, 7–11 (1961).

(C10) Chaly, V. P., Shor, O. G., and Rozhenko, S. P., Thermographic investigation of the hydroxides of certain metals. Binary systems of hydroxides. *Ukr. Khim. Zh.* **27**, 3–6 (1961).

(C10a) Chanh, Nguyen-BA, Thermal diagram of the solid state of the ternary system constituted of sodium, potassium, chloride, and bromide. *J. Chim. Phys.* **58**, 500–505 (1961).

(C10b) Chiu, J. Identification of organic compounds by differential thermal dynamic analysis. *Anal. Chem.* **34**, 1841–1843 (1962).

(C11) Chiu, J., Visual observation in differential thermal analysis. *Anal. Chem.* **35**, 933 (1963).

(C11a) Cholak, J., The nature of atmospheric pollution in a number of industrial communities. *Proc. 2d Natl. Air Pollution Symp., 6–15 Stanford Res. Inst., Los Angeles, 1952*.

(C12) Chughtai, A. R., and Badaruddin, Thermal decomposition of alkaline earth sulphates. *Pakistan J. Sci. Ind. Res.* **3**, 52–56 (1960).

(C13) Churchill, R. V., "Operational Mathematics." McGraw-Hill, New York, 1958.

(C14) Cimino, A., and Parry, G. S., Interdomain symmetry in the reversible phase transformation of potassium cyanide. *Nuovo Cimento* [10] **19**, 971–980 (1961).

(C15) Claudel, B., Perrin, M., and Trambouze, Y., Nature of reactions observed by differential thermal analysis. *Compt. Rend.* **252**, 107–109 (1961).

(C16) Claussen, W. F., Detection of the $a - \gamma$ iron phase transition by differential thermal conductivity analysis. *Rev. Sci. Instr.* **31**, 878–881 (1960).

(C17) Cochran, C. N., Automatic recording vacuum microbalance. *Rev. Sci. Instr.* **29**, 1135–8 (1958).

(C18) Coffeen, W., Private communication (1952).

(C19) Cola, M., and Castellani-Bisi, C., Thermal decomposition of metallic sulfites. *Gazz. Chim. Ital.* **91**, 173–186 (1961).

(C20) Cole, W. F., and Rowland, N. M., Abnormal effect in differential thermal analysis of clay minerals. *Am. Mineralogist* **46**, 304–312 (1961).

(C21) Collins, G. A., and Swan, A. G., Differential thermal analysis of minerals. *Can. Mining Met. Bull.* **508**, 533–538 (1954).

(C22) Comeforo, J. E., Fischer, R. B., and Bradley, W. F., Mullitization of kaolinite. *J. Am. Ceram. Soc.* **31**, 254–259 (1948).

(C23) Costa, D., and Costa, G., Thermal differential analysis. I. Decomposition of amides of cellulose. *Chim. e Ind.* (*Milan*) **33**, 71–76 (1951).

(C24) Costa, D., and Costa, G., Application of differential thermal analysis to the determination of characteristic temperature. II. Thermal decomposition of several sugars. *Chim. e Ind.* (*Milan*) **33**, 708–711 (1951).

(C25) Crandall, W. B., and West, R. R., An oxidation study of cobalt-alumina mixtures. *Am. Ceram. Soc. Bull.* **35**, 66–70 (1956).

(C26) Cremer, E., and Nitsch, W., The kinetics of the thermal decomposition of calcium carbonate. *In* "Science of Ceramics," Proc. 1961 conf. (G. H. Stewart, ed.), pp. 295–303. Academic Press, New York, 1962.

(C27) Crouthamel, C. E., and Johnson, C. E., Thermogravimetric decomposition of thorium 8-hydroxy quinolate. *Talanta* **8**, 377–380 (1961).

(C28) Cuthbert, F. L., and Rowland, R. A., Differential thermal analysis of some carbonate minerals. *Am. Mineralogist* **32**, 111–116 (1947).

(C29) Cuthbert, F. L., and Rowland, R. A., *Am. Mineralogist* **32**, 591 (1947).

(D1) Dannis, M. L., Thermal expansion measurements and transition temperatures. *J. Appl. Polymer Sci.* **1**, 121 (1959).

(D2) Dannis, M. L., Thermal expansion measurements and transition temperatures. II. An automatic recording system. *J. Appl. Polymer Sci.* **4**, 249–250 (1960).

(D3) Dannis, M. L., Private communication (1964).

(D4) Danusso, F., and Polizzotti, G., Application of differential thermal analysis to isotactic polymers of substituted styrenes. *Makromol. Chem.* **61**, No. 1, 157–163 (1963).

(D5) Das, I. S. S., Differential thermal analysis in ceramic research and industry. *Indian Ceram.* **1**, 167–176 (1954).

(D6) Das, I. S. S., Differential thermal analysis in ceramic research and industry. *Indian Ceram.* **1**, 207–215 (1954).

(D7) Das, I. S. S., Differential thermal analysis in ceramic research and industry. *Indian Ceram.* **1**, 289 (1954).

(D8) Dean, L. A., Differential thermal analysis of Hawaiian soils. *Soil Sci.* **63**, 95–105 (1947).

(D9) Deeg, E., Basis for theoretical treatment of differential thermal analysis. Conclusions for practice. *Ber. Deut. Keram. Ges.* **33**, 321–329 (1956).

(D10) Dempster, P. B., and Ritchie, P. D., Surface of finely ground silica. *Nature* **169**, 538–539 (1952).

(D11) Deshpande, V. T., and Sirdeshmukh, D. B., Thermal expansion of tetragonal tin. *Acta Cryst.* **14**, 355–356 (1961).

(D11a) Dilaktorskii, N. L., and Arkhangel'skaja, L. S., The thermal analysis method. *Proc. 5th Conf. Exptl. Mineral. and Petrogr., Moscow, 1956* pp. 88–96. Acad. Sci. USSR, Moscow, 1958.

(D12) Dollimore, D., Griffiths, D. L., and Nicholson, D., Thermal decomposition of oxalates. Thermo gravimetric analysis of various oxalates in air and in nitrogen. *J. Chem. Soc.* pp. 2617–2622 (1963).

(D13) Dollimore, D., and Nicholson, D., Thermo-gravimetric analysis of some complex oxalates. *J. Inorg. Nucl. Chem.* **25**, 738–740 (1963).

(D14) Doyle, C. D., Evaluation of experimental polymers. *WADD Tech. Rept.* No. 60–283 (1960).

(D15) Doyle, C. D., Estimating thermal stability of experimental polymers by empirical thermo gravimetric analysis. *Anal. Chem.* **33**, 77–78 (1961).

(D16) Doyle, C. D., Kinetic analysis of thermogravimetric data. *J. Appl. Polymer Sci.* **5**, 285–292 (1961).

(D17) Dunne, J. A., and Kerr, P. F., Differential thermal analysis of galena and clausthalite. *Am. Mineralogist* **46**, 1–11 (1961).

(D18) Duval, C., "Inorganic Thermogravimetric Analysis." Elsevier, Amsterdam, 1953.

(D18a) Duval, C., Remarks to article by W. W. Wendlandt: Thermolysis of ammonium 12-molybdophosphate. *Anal. Chim. Acta* **20**, 270 (1959).

(D19) Duval, C. Use of thermogravimetry and of infrared spectrophotometry for following solid-state reactions. *Acta Chim. Acad. Sci. Hung.* **32**, 281–293 (1962).

(D20) Duval, C., History of the development of thermogravimetry. *Chim. Anal.* (*Paris*) **44**, No. 5, 191–194 (1962).

(D21) Duwez, P., and Martens, H., Dilatometric study of sintering of metal powders compacts. *Trans. AIME* **185**, 571–577 (1949).

(E1) Ellis, B. G., and Mortland, M. M., Comparison of two methods of determining heats of reaction by differential thermal analysis. *Am. Mineralogist* **47**, 371–378 (1962).

(E2) Erdey, L., and Paulik, F., Thermal study of precipitates. I. Metal oxalate precipitates. *Magy. Tud. Akad. Kem. Tud. Oszt. Kozlemen.* **5**, 461–476 (1955).

(E3) Erdey, L., and Paulik, F., Thermal study of precipitates. II. Aluminum hydroxide precipitates. *Magy. Tud. Akad. Kem. Tud. Oszt. Kozlemen.* **5**, 477–487 (1955).

(E4) Erdey, L., Paulik, F., and Paulik, J., Differential thermogravimetry. *Nature* 174, 885–886 (1954).

(E5) Eriksson, E., Problems of heat flow in differential thermal analysis. *Kgl. Lantbruks-Hogskol. Ann.* **20**, 117–123 (1953) (in English).

(E6) Ern, V., Differential thermal analysis of a cubic modification of barium titanate. *J. Am. Ceram. Soc.* **46**, 295–296 (1963).

(E7) Escoffier, P., and Gauthier, J., Thermo-magnetic study of some inorganic neutral and basic salts of copper. *Compt. Rend.* **252**, 271–272 (1961).

(E8) Ewald, P., Recording automatic balance. *Ind. Eng. Chem., Anal. Ed.* **14**, 66–67 (1942).

(E9) Eyraud, I., Automatic absorption balance. *J. Chim. Phys.* **47**, 106 (1950).

(E10) Eyraud, C., and Goton, R., Theoretical and experimental considerations in differential heat analysis. *Compt. Rend.* **240**, 423–425 (1955).

(E11) Eyraud, C., Goton, R., and Prettre, M., A study of the dehydration of gibbsite by the simultaneous use of thermogravimetry under reduced pressure and differential thermal analysis. *Compt. Rend.* **240**, 1082–1084 (1955).

(E12) Eyraud, C., Goton, R., Trambouze, Y., The, T. H., and Prettre, M., The decomposition of alumina hydrates by differential enthalpy analysis. *Compt. Rend.* **240**, 862–864 (1955).

(F1) Faust, G. T., Differentiation of aragonite from calcite by differential thermal analysis. *Science* **110**, 402–403 (1949).

(F2) Faust, G. T., Thermal analysis studies on carbonates: I. Aragonite and calcite. *Am. Mineralogist* **35**, 207–224 (1950).

(F3) Fedulov, S. A., Venevtsev, U. N., Zhdanov, G. S., and Smazhevskaya, E. G., high temperature X-ray and thermographic studies of bismuth ferrite. *Kristallografiya* **6**, 795–796 (1961).

(F4) Felix, W. D., McDowall, M. A., and Eyring, H., Differential thermal analysis of natural and modified wool and mohair. *Textile Res. J.* **33**, 465–470 (1963).

(F5) Feurer, I., Radioactive electronic detector. *Anal. Chem.* **20**, 1231–1237 (1948).

(F6) Fialkov, A. S., a д Davidovich, Y. G., Linear thermal expansion of materials consisting of graphite and other coal products. *Zh. Prikl. Khim.* **34**, 300–306 (1961).

(F7) Finch, D. I., "General Principles of Thermoelectric Thermometry," Tech. Publ. ENS2(1). Leeds & Northrup Co., Philadelphia, Pennsylvania, 1962.

(F8) Fischer, W., and Abendroth, H. J., Thermal analysis by the plotting of the piston-sink curve. Melting diagram of the sodium chloride–sodium oxide system. *Z. Anorg. Allgem. Chem.* **308**, 98–104 (1961).

(F9) Flanagan, T. B., Effect of the conditions of dehydration upon the subsequent thermal decomposition of lead styphnate. *Trans. Faraday Soc.* **57**, 797–808 (1961).

(F9a) Fleck, W. E. P., Jones, M. H., Kuntae, R. H., and McAdie, H. G., The differential thermal analysis of natural and synthetic hydrates of calcium sulfate. *Can. J. Chem.* **38**, 936–943 (1960).

(F10) Flom, D. G., Dynamic mechanical spectrometry by means of rolling friction measurements. *Anal. Chem.* **32**, 1550–1554 (1960).

(F11) Foldvari-Vogl, M., and Kliburszky, B., New viewpoints on the theory and practice of differential thermal analysis. *Acta Geol. Acad. Sci. Hung.* **2**, 215–229 (1954) (in German).

(F12) Foldvari-Vogl, M., and Kliburszky, B., On the determination of heats of dissociation of minerals. *Acta Geol.* (*Budapest*) **5**, 187–195 (1958).

(F13) Frederickson, A. F., Derived differential thermal curves. *Am. Mineralogist* **38**, 1023–1025 (1954).

(F14) Freeman, E. S., and Carroll, B., The application of thermoanalytical techniques to reaction kinetics. The thermogravimetric evaluation of the kinetics of the decomposition of calcium oxalate monohydrate. *J. Phys. Chem.* **62**, 394–397 (1958).

(F15) Freeman, E. S., and Edelman, D., Simple method for derivative differential thermal analysis. *Anal. Chem.* **31**, 624–625 (1959).

(F16) Freeman, E. S., and Gordon, S., The application of the absolute rate theory to the ignition of propagatively reacting systems. The thermal ignition of the systems lithium nitrate-magnesium, sodium nitrate-magnesium. *J. Phys. Chem.* **60**, 867–871 (1956).

(G1) Gadzhiev, S. N., and Sharifov, K. A., Use of thermistors in calorimetry. *Zh. Fiz. Khim.* **35**, 1147–1149 (1961).

(G2) Gafner, G., Thermal aspects of the growth of thin films by vacuum sublimation. *Phil. Mag.* [8] **5**, 1041–1048 (1960).

(G3) Garn, P. D., Automatic recording balance. *Anal. Chem.* **29**, 839–841 (1957).

(G4) Garn, P. D., Thermal analysis—A critique. *Anal. Chem.* **33**, 1247–1251 (1961).

(G5) Garn, P. D., Thermal analysis of small samples. *Proc. Intern. Symp. Microchem. Techniques, State College, Pennsylvania, 1961* (N. D. Cheronis, ed.), pp. 1105–1109. Wiley (Interscience), New York, 1962.

(G6) Garn, P. D., Thermal detection of Curie temperatures. Presented at *140th Meeting Am. Chem. Soc.* (*Div. Anal. Chem.*), *Washington, D. C.* (1962).

(G7) Garn, P. D., Some problems in the analysis of gaseous decomposition products. *Talanta* 11, 1417–1432 (1964).

(G8) Garn, P. D., Differential thermal analysis using self-generated atmospheres at sub- and supra-atmospheric pressures. *Anal. Chem.* 37, 77–78 (1965).

(G9) Garn, P. D., Comparison of sample holder materials for differential thermal analysis. *J. Am. Ceram. Soc.* in press (1964).

(G10) Garn, P. D., and Flaschen, S. S., Unpublished measurements (1956).

(G11) Garn, P. D., and Flaschen, S. S., Detection of polymorphic phase transformations by continuous measurement of electrical resistance. *Anal. Chem.* 29, 268–271 (1957).

(G12) Garn, P. D., and Flaschen, S. S., Analytical applications of a differential thermal analysis apparatus. *Anal. Chem.* 29, 271–275 (1957).

(G13) Garn, P. D., Geith, C. R., and DeBala, S., Furnace mounting and control system for Ainsworth vacuum automatic recording balance. *Rev. Sci. Instr.* 33, 293–297 (1962).

(G14) Garn, P. D., and Gilroy, H. M., Determination of maleic anhydride in polyesters. *Anal. Chem.* 30, 1663–1665 (1958).

(G15) Garn, P. D., and Kessler, J. E., Unpublished measurements (1960).

(G16) Garn, P. D., and Kessler, J. E., Thermogravimetry in self-generated atmospheres. *Anal. Chem.* 32, 1563–1565 (1960).

(G17) Garn, P. D., and Kessler, J. E., Free diffusion sample holder. *Anal. Chem.* 32, 1900 (1960).

(G18) Garn, P. D., and Kessler, J. E., Effluence analysis as an aid to thermal analysis. *Anal. Chem.* 33, 952–954 (1961).

(G19) Garn, P. D., Vincent, S. M., and Gilroy, H. M., Unpublished measurements (1956).

(G20) Geller, R. F., and Yavorsky, P. J., Effects of some oxide additions on thermal length changes of zirconia. *J. Res. Natl. Bur. Std.* 35, 87–110 (1945).

(G21) Gerard-Hirne, J., and Lamy, C., Identification of clays by differential thermal analysis. *Bull. Soc. Franc. Ceram.* pp. 26–40 (1951); see *Ceram. Abstr.* p. 93 (1952).

(G22) Gerdanian, P., and Dode, M., Use of a Eyraud-Ugine thermobalance. *Bull. Soc. Chim. France* pp. 1348–1351 (1961).

(G23) Gheith, M. A., Differential thermal analysis of certain iron oxides and oxide hydrates. *Am. J. Sci.* 250, 677–685 (1952).

(G24) Gibaud, M., and Gelosa, M. M., Application of the thermobalance to the determination of mixtures of chalk, magnesium calcium carbonate and dolomite. *Chim. Anal.* (*Paris*) 36, 153 (1954).

(G25) Glasner, A., and Steinberg, M., Thermal decomposition of lanthanum oxalate. *J. Inorg. Nucl. Chem.* 16, 279–289 (1961).

(G26) Glass, H. D., High-temperature phases from kaolinite and halloysite. *Am. Mineralogist* 39, 193–207 (1954).

(G27) Goldsmith, A., Waterman, T. E., and Hirschhorn, H. V., "Handbook of Thermophysical Properties of Solid Materials." Macmillan, New York, 1961.

(G28) Golubenko, A. N., and Rezukhina, T. N., Application of the method of hydrostatic weighing to the study of heterogeneous equilibria. *Zh. Neorg. Khim.* **6**,
674–678 (1961).

(G29) Goodkin, J., Solomons, C., and Janz, G. J. Calorimeter for heats of fusion
of inorganic compounds. *Rev. Sci. Instr.* **29** 105 (1958).

(G30) Gordon, B. E., and Denisov, A. M., Thermal decomposition of crystal hydrates obtained by crystallization of metastable and of labile supersaturated
solutions. *Ukr. Khim. Zh.* **19**, 368–371 (1953).

(G31) Gordon, M., Recent advances in the theory of thermal degradation of hetero-
disperse polymers. *Soc. Chem. Ind.* (*London*) *Monograph* **13**, 163–83 (1961).

(G32) Gordon, S., and Campbell, C., Differential thermal analysis of inorganic oxi-
dants: Nitrates. *U. S. Govt. Res. Rept.* No. PB-116622 (1954).

(G33) Gordon, S., and Campbell, C., Synchronizing and reference marking of
photoelectric and potentiometric recorder curves. *Am. Ceram. Soc. Bull.* **34**,
372–374 (1954); see *Ceram. Abstr.* p. 25 (1956).

(G34) Gordon, S., and Campbell, C., Differential thermal analysis of inorganic
compounds. Nitrates and perchlorates of the alkali and alkaline earth groups
and their subgroups. *Anal. Chem.* **27**, 1102–1109 (1955).

(G35) Gordon, S., and Campbell, C., Automatic and recording balances (Review).
Anal. Chem. **32**, 271–289R 1960).

(G36) Goubeau, J., and Walter, K., Thermal decomposition and the infrared spec-
tra of beryllium dimethyl. *Z. Anorg. Allgem. Chem.* **322**, 58–70 (1963).

(G37) Govorov, A. A., and Granovskii, I. G., Apparatus for the complex thermal
analysis. *Zavodskaya Lab.* **27**, 115–116 (1961).

(G38) Graf, D. L., Variations in differential thermal curves of low-iron dolomites.
Am. Mineralogist **37**, 1–27 (1952).

(G39) Grant, D. H., and Grassie, N., Thermal decomposition of poly (*t*-Butyl
methacrylate). *Polymer* **1**, 445–455 (1960).

(G40) Grauerman, L. A., Karantsevich, L. G., Ul'yanova, T. S., Use of differential
dilatometric curves for the investigation of fats and fat mixtures. *Maslob.-
Zhir. Prom.* **26**, No. 11, 13–18 (1960).

(G41) Gray, T. V., Detwiler, D. P., Rase, D. E., Lawrence, W. G., West, R. R.,
and Vennings, T. C., "The Defect Solid State." Wiley (Interscience), New
York, 1957.

(G42) Gregg, S. V., Parker, T. W., and Stephens, M. J., The grinding of kaolinite.
II. A more detailed study. *J. Appl. Chem.* **4**, 666–674 (1957).

(G43) Griffith, E. J., Thermogravimetric analysis of complex mixtures of hydrates.
Anal. Chem. **29**, 198–202 (1957).

(G44) Grim, R. E., Differential thermal analysis of prepared mixture of clay minerals. *Am. Mineralogist* **32**, 493–501 (1947).

(G45) Greenwood, C. T., Knox, J. H., and Milne, E., Analysis of thermal decomposition products of carbohydrates by gas chromatography. *Chem. & Ind.*
(*London*) pp. 1878–1879 (1961).

(G46) Grimshaw, R. W., The quantitative estimation of silica minerals. *Clay
Minerals Bull.* **2**, 2–7 (1950).

(G47) Groot, C., and Troutner, V. H., Automatic recording thermobalance. *Anal.
Chem.* **29**, 835–839 (1957).

(G48) Gruver, R. M., Differential thermal analysis studies of ceramic materials:
I. Characteristic heat effects of some carbonates. *J. Am. Ceram. Soc.* **33**,
96–101 (1950).

(G49) Gruver, R. M., Differential thermal analysis studies of ceramic materials: II. Transition of aragonite to calcite. *J. Am. Ceram. Soc.* **33**, 171–174 (1950).

(G50) Gubergrits, M., Influence of heating conditions on the distribution of oil shale thermal decomposition products. *Izv. Akad. Nauk Eston. SSR, Ser. Fiz.-Mat. i Tekhn. Nauk* **9**, 343–357 (1960).

(G51) Guichard, M. M., Continuous study of dehydration by means of a hydrostatic compensation balance. *Bull. Soc. Chim. France* **37**, 251–253 (1925).

(G52) Guichard, M. M., A hydrostatic compensation balance. *Bull. Soc. Chim. France* **39**, 1113–1115 (1926).

(G53) Guiochon, G., Thermogravimetric measurements. *Anal. Chem.* **33**, 1124–1125 (1961).

(H1) Haase, R., Hoch, K., and Schoenert, H., Thermo-elements. Evaluation of measurements. *Z. Physik. Chem. (Frankfurt)* [N.S.] **27**, 421–438 (1961).

(H2) Harmelin, M., Study of chromium sulfate by thermogravimetry and infrared absorption spectroscopy. *Compt. Rend.* **252**, 4142–4144 (1961).

(H3) Hasegawa, H., Precipitated calcium carbonates with thermal balance. *Yakugaku Zasshi* **80**, 1739–1742 (1960).

(H4) Hashimoto, H., Thermal decomposition of calcium carbonate—annealing process and electric conductivity. *Kogyo Kagaku Zasshi* **64**, 250–255 (1961).

(H5) Hashimoto, H., and Itoo, M., Recording microthermobalance. *Kogyo Kagaku Zasshi* **64**, 1515–1517 (1961).

(H6) Haul, R. A. W., and Heystek, H., Differential thermal analysis of the dolomite decomposition. *Am. Mineralogist* **37**, 166–179 (1952).

(H7) Haul, R. A. W., Stein, L. H., and Louro, J. D., Exchange of carbon-13 dioxide between solid carbonates and gaseous carbon dioxide. *Nature* **167**, 241–242 (1951).

(H8) Hay, A. W., Private communication (1963).

(H9) Hedvall, J. A., Einführung in die Festkörper Chemie. Vieweg, Braunschweig, 1952.

(H10) Hedvall, J A., Thermal decomposition of dolomite. *Z. Anorg. Allgem. Chem.* **272**, 22–24 (1953).

(H11) Hegedus, A. J., Sasvari, K., and Neugebauer, J., Thermal and X-ray analytical investigation of the reaction of tunsten trioxide and carbon monoxide. *Acta Chim. Acad. Sci. Hung.* **26**, 113–128 (1961).

(H12) Hermodi (Morovky), A., and Salmon, A., Thermal decomposition of ammonium per chlorate in the presence of magnesium oxide. *Bull. Res. Council Israel* **9A**, 206–207 (1960).

(H13) Hill, J. A., and Murphy, C. B., Infrared heating applied to differential thermal analysis. *Anal. Chem.* **31**, 1443–1444 (1959).

(H14) Hill J. A., Murphy, C. B., and Schacher G. P., Thermal decompositions of copper (II) acetate monohydrate. *Anal. Chim. Acta* **24**, 496–497 (1961).

(H15) Hirone, T., Maeda, S., and Tsuza, N., *Rev. Sci. Instr.* **25**, 516–517 (1954).

(H16) Hirota, M., Kitakaze, H., and Seki, K., Automatic recording apparatus for the compound thermal analysis. *Yogyo Kyokai Shi* **69**, 97–102 (1961).

(H17) Hock, C. W., and Arbogast, V. F., Measuring melting points and rates of crystallization of polymers by recording changes in birefringence. *Anal. Chem.* **33**, 462–465 (1961).

(H18) Hogan, V. D., and Gordon, S., A thermoanalytical study of the binary oxidant system potassium perchborate-barium nitrate. *J. Phys. Chem.* **62**, 1433 (1958).

(H19) Hogan, V. D., and Gordon, S., Thermoanalytical study of the reciprocal system $2KNO_3 + BACL_2 \rightarrow 2KCL + BA(NO_3)_2$. *J. Phys. Chem.* **64,** 172–173 (1960.

(H20) Hogan, V. D., and Gordon, S., Apparatus for observing physical changes at elevated temperatures. *Anal. Chem.* **32,** 573–574 (1960).

(H21) Hogan, V. D., Gordon, S., and Campbell, C., Differential thermal analysis and thermogravimetry applied to potassium perchlorate-aluminum-barium nitrate mixtures. *Anal. Chem.* **29,** 306–310 (1957).

(H22) Holt, J., Cutler, I. B., and Wadsworth, M. E., Rate of thermal dehydration of kaolinite in vacuum. *J. Am. Ceram. Soc.* **45,** 133–136 (1962).

(H23) Hooley, J. G., Recording vacuum thermobalance. *Can. J. Chem.* **35,** 374 (1957).

(H24) Horton, G. K., Thermal expansion of metals at low temperatures. *Can. J. Phys.* **39,** 263–271 (1961).

(H25) Houldsworth, H. S., and Cobb, J. W., The behavior of fireclays, bauxites, etc., on heating. *Trans. Brit. Ceram. Soc.* **22,** 111–137 and 344–348 (1923).

(H26) Howard, W. H., The glass temperatures of polyacrylonitrite and acrylonitrite-vinyl acetate copolymers. *J. Appl. Polymer Sci.* **5,** 303–307 (1961).

(H27) Hummel, F. A., Properties of some substances isostructural with silica. *J. Am. Ceram. Soc.* **32,** 320–326 (1949).

(H28) Hummel, F. A., Significant aspects of certain binary compounds and solid solutions. *J. Am. Ceram. Soc.* **35,** 64–66 (1952).

(H29) Huzan, E., Abbiss, C. P., and Jones, G. O., Thermal expansion of aluminum at low temperatures. *Phil. Mag.* [8] **6,** 277–285 (1961).

(H30) Hyatt, E. P., Cutler, I. B., and Wadsworth, M. E., Apparatus for thermogravimetric analysis. *Bull. Am. Ceram. Soc.* **35,** 180–181 (1956).

(H31) Hyatt, E. P., Cutler, I. B., and Wadsworth, M. E., Calcium carbonate decomposition in carbon dioxide atmosphere. *J. Am. Ceram. Soc.* **41,** 70–74 (1958).

(I1) Iida, Y., Sintering of high purity nickel. Dilatometry. *J. Am. Ceram. Soc.* **41,** 397–409 (1958).

(I2) Inoue, M., and Saito, T., Application of differential thermal analysis. Application to polymorphism. *Yakugaku Zasshi* **81,** 615 (1961).

(I3) Intrater, J., Dilatometric investigation of vacuum-melted zircaloy-2. *Trans. Met. Soc. AIME* **221,** 567–572 (1961).

(I4) Ivanov, O. S., The use of N. S. Kurnakov's pyrometer for differential thermal analysis and calorimetric studies of microsamples. *Izv. Sekt. Fiz.-Khim. Anal. Inst. Obshch. i Neorg. Khim. Akad. Nauk SSSR* **25,** 26–40 (1954).

(I5) Ivanov, V. E., Shapoval, B. I., and Amonenko, V. M., Inner friction method for the study of phase transformation in zirconium and beryllium. *Fiz. Metal. i Metalloved.* **11,** No. 1, 52–58 (1961).

(I6) Ivanova, L. I., Relation between the heat capacity of solids and the phase transition temperature. *Zh. Fiz. Khim.* **35,** 2120 (1961).

(I7) Ivanova, V. P., and Tatarskii, V. B., Thermograms of mixtures of dolomite and kaolin. *Dokl. Akad. Nauk SSSR* **73,** 341–343 (1950).

(J1) Jacobs, P. W. M., and Kureishy, A. R. T., Thermal decomposition of nickel oxalate dihydrate. *Trans. Faraday Soc.* **58,** Pt. 3, 551–560 (1962).

(J2) Jacque, L., Guiochon, G., and Gendrel, P., Applications of kinetics to thermogravimetry. *Bull. Soc. Chim. France* pp. 1061–1069 (1961).

(J3) Jaffray, J., and Viloteau, J., The thermal and dilatometric analysis of chromic oxide. *Compt. Rend.* **226,** 1701–1702 (1948).

(J4) Janz, G. J., and Lorenz, M. R., A dynamic method for the dissociation pressures of carbonates. *Rensselaer Polytech. Inst. Project* No. 441.35, *Tech. Rept.* No. 6 (1960).

(J5) Jennings, E. C., Jr., and Dimick, K. P., Gas chromatography of pyrolytic products of purines and pyrimidines. *Anal. Chem.* **34**, 1543–1547 (1962).

(J6) Johns, I. B., Mcelhill, E. A., and Smith, J. O., Thermal stability of organic compounds *Ind. Eng. Chem., Prod. Res. & Develop.* **1**, No. 1, 2–6 (1962).

(J7) Johnson, G. B., Hess, P. H., and Miron, R. R., Relative degree of cure in unsaturated polyester–styrene copolymer as determined by differential thermal analysis. *J. Appl. Polymer Sci.* **6**, 195–205 (1962).

(J8) Johnson, N. M., and Daniels, F., Luminescence during annealing and phase change in crystals. *J. Chem. Phys.* **34**, 1434–1439 (1961).

(J9) de Jong, G., Verification of use of peak area for quantitative differential thermal analysis. *J. Am. Ceram. Soc.* **40**, 42–49 (1957).

(J10) Joyner, T. B., and Verhoek, F. H., Products of the thermal decomposition of some cobalt ammine azides. *J. Am. Chem. Soc.* **83**, 1069–1072 (1961).

(K1) Kadlets, O., and Dubinin, M. M., Kinetics of thermal decomposition of solid substances. Thermal decomposition of silver carbonate. *Izv. Akad. Nauk SSSR, Otd. Khim. Nauk* pp. 390–396 (1961).

(K2) Kalinina, A. M., Conversion of silica during high-temperature reactions of synthetic kaolinite. *Zh. Neorg. Khim.* **6**, 2109–2119 (1961).

(K3) Kalinkina, B. A., Kozlova, N. I., Nikolaev, I. N., and Stepanchikov, A. A., Thermal decomposition of coals and their mixtures. *Izv. Akad. Nauk SSSR, Otd. Tekhn. Nauk, Met. i Toplivo* No. 6, 156–160 (1960).

(K4) Kamecki, J., and Trau, J., Thermal and thermogravimetric analysis of hydrated cupric chloride. *Bull. Acad. Polon. Sci., Cl. III* **3**, No. 2, 111–115 (1955) (in English).

(K5) Karan, C., Barium titanate-potassium fluoride phase diagram. *J. Chem. Phys.* **22**, 957 (1954).

(K6) Karan, C., and Skinner, B. J., BaTiO₃-KF phase diagram. *J. Chem. Phys.* **21**, 2225 (1953).

(K7) Kasner, B., and Hartwig, K. Differential thermogravimetric analysis. *Tonind.-Ztg. Keram. Rundschau* **84**, 471–475 (1960).

(K8) Kauffman, A. V., Jr., and Dilling, E. D., Differential thermal curves of certain hydrous and anhydrous minerals, with a description of the apparatus used. *Econ. Geol.* **45**, 222–224 (1950).

(K9) Kaurkovskii, V. I., Automatic thermoregulation with a thermocontrol element. *J. Appl. Chem. USSR (English Transl.)* **25**, 743–747 (1952).

(K10) Ke, B., Differential thermal analysis of high polymers. Poly amides. *J. Polymer Sci.* **50**, 87–98 (1961).

(K11) Ke, B., Differential thermal analysis of high polymers. Some low-temperature transitions. *J. Polymer Sci.*, Part B, Vol. 1, 167–170 (1963).

(K11a) Ke, B., Differential thermal analysis of high polymers. IV. Saturated linear polyesters. *J. Appl. Polymer Sci.* **6**, 624–628 (1962).

(K11b) Keavney, J. J., and Eberlin, E. C., The determination of glass transition temperatures by differential thermal analysis. *J. Appl. Polymer Sci.* **3**, 47–53 (1960).

(K12) Keeling, P. S., The common clay minerals as a continuous series. *In* "Science of Ceramics," Proc. 1961 Conf. (G. H. Stewart, ed.), Vol. 1. Academic Press, New York, 1962.

(K13) Keena, A. G., Differential thermal analysis of the thermal decomposition of ammonium nitrate. *J. Am. Chem. Soc.* **77**, 1379–1380 (1955).

(K14) Keith, M. L., and Tuttle, O. F., Significance of variation in the high-low inversion of quartz. *Am. J. Sci.*, Bowen Vol., Pt. 1, 203–252 (1952).

(K15) Kelly, H. J., and Harris, H. M., An automatically recording thermal-expansion apparatus. *J. Am. Ceram. Soc.* **39**, 344–348 (1956).

(K16) Kelly, W. C., Application of differential thermal analysis to identification of the natural hydrous ferric oxides. *Am. Mineralogist* **41**, 353–355 (1956).

(K17) Kerr, P. F., and Kulp, J. L., Differential thermal analysis of siderite. *Am. Mineralogist* **32**, 678–680 (1947).

(K18) Kertzmann, J., Presented at *130th Meeting Am. Chem. Soc. (Div. Anal. Chem.), Atlantic City, N. J.* (1956).

(K19) Kessler, M. F., and Romovackova, H., Experiences with differential thermal analysis of coal and coke. *Fuel* **40**, 161–170 (1961).

(K20) Ketov, A. N., Pechkovskii, V. V., Varskoi, B. N., and Starkov, N. P., Thermal decomposition of copper sulfate. *Zh. Prikl. Khim.* **34**, 517–521 (1961).

(K21) de Keyser, W. L., A study of kaolin and some Belgian clays. III. Discussion of results. *Ann. Mines Belg.* **40**, 357–429 and 711–806 (1939).

(K22) de Keyser, W. L., Differential thermobalance—new tool of research., *Bull. Soc. Franc. Ceram.* pp. 2–5 (1953).

(K23) de Keyser, W. L., The thermal behavior of kaolin and of clay minerals. *Silicates Ind.* **24**, 117–123 and 190–196 (1959).

(K24) Khu, C. T., and Novoselova, A. V., Thermal analysis of the potassium fluoride–lanthanum fluoride–potassium fluoberyllate system. *Zh. Neorg. Khim.* **6**, 2148–2157 (1961).

(K25) Khutsaidze, A. L., Apparatus for thermal analysis with a programmed regime. *Soobshch. Akad. Nauk Gruz. SSR* **26**, 681–686 (1961).

(K26) Kirillova, E. I., Matveeva, E. N., Potapenko, T. G., Rachinskii, F. Y., and Slovachevskaya, N. M., Effect of organic compounds on thermal decomposition of poly vinyl butyral. *Plasticheskie Massy* No. 5, 15–19 (1961).

(K27) Kingery, W. D., Thermal conductivity. VI. Determination of conductivity of aluminum oxide by spherical envelope and cylinder methods. *J. Am. Ceram. Soc.* **37**, 88 (1954).

(K28) Kingery, W. D., "Property Measurements at High Temperatures." Wiley, New York, 1959.

(K29) Kissinger, H. E., Variation of peak temperature with heating rate in differential thermal analysis. *J. Res. Natl. Bur. Std.* **57**, 217–221 (1956) (Res. Paper No. 2712).

(K30) Kissinger, H. E., Reaction kinetics in differential thermal analysis. *Anal. Chem.* **29**, 1702–1706 (1957).

(K31) Kissinger, H. E., McMurdie, H. F., and Simpson, B. S., Thermal decomposition of manganous and ferrous carbonates. *J. Am. Ceram. Soc.* **39**, 168–172 (1956).

(K32) Kitamura, N., Kashiwase, Y., Harada, J., and Honjo, G., Electron diffraction study of the phase transition of hydrogen sulfide at −170-Deg.-C. *Acta Cryst.* **14**, 687–688 (1961).

(K33) Kleber, W., and Noack, H., Dielectric measurements on powdered minerals with comparative differential thermal analysis determinations. *Chem. Erde* **21**, 5–23 (1961).

(K33a) Knight, H. B.; Witnauer, L. P.; Coleman, J. E.; Noble, W. R., Jr.; Swern, D. Dissociation temperatures of urea complexes of long-chain fatty acids, esters and alcohols. *Anal. Chem.*, **24**, 1331–4 (1952).

(K34) Kobayashi, I., Thermal decomposition and air-oxidation of some uranium compounds. *Rika Gaku Kenkyushu Hokoku* **36**, 710–713 (1960).

(K35) Kofler, A., Microthermal analysis of the system $NaNO_3$–KNO_3. *Monatsh.* **86**, 643–652 (1955).

(K36) Kopp, O. C., and Kerr, P. F., Differential thermal analysis of pyrite and marcasite. *Am. Mineralogist* **43**, 679–697 (1958).

(K37) Kopp, O. C., and Kerr, P. F., Differential thermal analysis of sphalerite. *Am. Mineralogists* **43**, 732–748 (1958).

(K38) Kornienko, V. P., Kinetics and chemical mechanism of thermal decomposition of formates and oxalates. *Sb. Nauch. Rabot Akad. Nauk Beloruss. SSR, Inst. Khim.* No. 5, 92–99 (1956); see *Chem. Abstr.* **52**, 6906 (1958).

(K39) Kornienko, V. P., Effect of the nature of the cation on the thermal decomposition of oxalates. *Ukrain. Khim. Zh.* **23**, 159–167 (1957); see *Chem. Abstr.* **51**, 12617 (1957).

(K40) Krogmann, K., Thermal decomposition of nickel formate. *Z. Anorg. Allgem. Chem.* **308**, 226–241 (1961).

(K41) Krueger, J. E., and Bryden, J. G., Apparatus for combined thermogravimetric and differential thermal analysis. *J. Sci. Instr.* **40**, 178–182 (1963).

(K42) Kulp, J. L., Kent, P., and Kerr, P. F., Thermal study of the Ca–Mg–Fe carbonate minerals. *Am. Mineralogist* **36**, 643–670 (1951).

(K43) Kulp, J. L., and Kerr, P. F., Multiple thermal analysis. *Science* **105**, 413 (1947).

(K44) Kulp, J. L., and Kerr, P. F., Improved differential thermal apparatus. *Am. Mineralogist* **34**, 839–845 (1949).

(K45) Kulp, J. L., and Trites, A. F., Differential thermal analysis of natural hydrous ferric oxides. *Am. Mineralogist* **36**, 23–44 (1951).

(K46) Kulp, J. L., Wright, H. D., and Holmes, R. J., Thermal study of rhodochrosite. *Am. Mineralogist* **34**, 195–219 and 285 (1949).

(K47) Kulp, J. L., Volchok, H. L., and Holland, H. S., Age from metamict minerals., *Am. Mineralogist* **37**, 709–718 (1952).

(K47a) Kulshrestha, V. K., Differential thermal studies on plant gums. *J. Polymer Sci.* **58**, 791–808 (1962).

(K48) Kuntze, R. A., Determination of small amounts of gypsum in calcium sulfate hemi hydrate by differential thermal analysis. *Mater. Res. Std.* **2**, 640–642 (1962).

(L1) Lambert, A., A recording electronic balance for the study of sedimentation or thermogravimetry. *Bull. Soc. Franc. Ceram.* **45**, 19 (1959).

(L1a) Lange, N. A., "Handbook of Chemistry" Handbook Publishers, Sandusky, Ohio, 1956.

(L2) Larson, H. V., Myers, I. T., and LeBlanc, W. H., Method of linearizing thermistor thermometer data in calorimetry. *J. Sci. Instr.* **38**, 400–401 (1961).

(L3) Laval, J., Thermal expansion of crystalline media. *J. Phys. Radium* **22**, 451–458 (1961).

(L3a) *Leeds & Northrup (Phila.) Bull.* ND46–33(107) (1962).

(L4) Le Floch, G., Le Montagner, S., and Rousselot, M. M., Apparatus for differential thermal analysis. *J. Phys. Radium* **23**, 959–960 (1962).

(L5) Leicester, J., and Redman, M. J., Thermal decomposition of the nickel and cobalt salts of aliphatic acids. *J. Appl. Chem. (London)* **12**, 357–365 (1962).

(L6) Li, Y. S., Thermal and tensimetric analysis of the aluminum chloride-ammonium chloride system. *Zh. Neorg. Khim.* **5**, 2804–2807 (1960).

(L7) Lieberman, A., and Crandall, W. B., Design and construction of a self-calibrating dialatometer for high-temperature use. *J. Am. Ceram. Soc.* **35**, 304–308 (1952).

(L8) Lloyd, S. V., and Murray, J. R., A simple, automatic high-temperature thermal analysis apparatus. *J. Sci. Instr.* **35**, 252–254 (1958).

(L9) Loasby, R. G., A simple volumenometer. *J. Sci. Instr.* **38**, 306 (1961).

(L10) Lodding, W., and Hammell, L., High temperature pressure-vacuum furnace. *Rev. Sci. Instr.* **30**, 885–886 (1959).

(L11) Lodding, W., and Hammell, L., Differential thermal analysis of hydroxides in reducing atmospheres. *Anal. Chem.* **32**, 657–662 (1960).

(L12) Lodding, W., and Sturm, E., A new method of differential thermal analysis employing multiple thermocouples. *Am. Mineralogist* **42**, 78–82 (1957).

(L13) Lohmann, I. W., An electronic recording analytical balance. *J. Sci. Instr.* **21**, 999–1002 (1950).

(L14) Longuet-Escar, Mme. V., Reactions in the solid state at low temperatures in the presence of water. *Bull. Soc. Chim. France* p. 153 (1949).

(L15) Longwell, P. A., and Sage, B. H., Thermal decomposition of N-hexane at high pressures. *J. Chem. Eng. Data* **5**, 322–330 (1960).

(L16) Lowell, T. L., Thermal expansion of alpha-uranium single crystals. *J. Nucl. Mater.* **3**, 67–71 (1961).

(L17) Lukaszewski, G. M., Accuracy in thermogravimetric analysis. *Nature* **194**, 959–961 (1962).

(M1) Macarovici, C. G., and Macarovici, D., Thermogravimetric study and X-ray study of the dehydration and thermal decomposition of a basic carbonate of magnesium. *Acad. Rep. Populare Romine, Filiala Cluj, Studii Cercetari Chem.* **11**, 281–288 (1960).

(M2) Mackenzie, R. C., Differential thermal analysis apparatus. *Anales Edafol. Fisiol. Vegetal (Madrid)* **11**, 159–184 (1952).

(M3) Mackenzie, R. C., "The Differential Thermal Investigation of Clays." Mineral. Soc., London, 1957.

(M4) Mackenzie, R. C., "Scifax Differential Thermal Analysis Data Index." Cleaver-Hume Press, London, 1962.

(M5) Mackenzie, R. C., and Farmer, V. C., Notes on Arens' theory of differential thermal analysis. *Clay Minerals Bull.* **1**, 262–266 (1952).

(M6) Mackenzie, R. C., and Farquharson, K. R., Standardization of differential thermal analysis technique. *Proc. 19th Session Intern. Geol. Congr., Algiers, 1952* pp. 183–200 (1953).

(M7) Majumdar, A. J., and Roy R., System $CaO-Al_2O_3-H_2O$. *J. Am. Ceram. Soc.* **39**, 434–442 (1956).

(M8) Makarov, S. Z., Arnold, T. I., Stasevich, N. N., and Shorina, E. V., Systems having concentrated hydrogen per oxide. Thermal analysis of copper per oxide compounds *Izv. Akad. Nauk SSSR, Otd. Khim. Nauk* pp. 2090–2095 (1960).

(M9) Malard, C., Thermal decomposition of simple and double selenates of cobalt and of potassium, rubidium, and cesium. *Compt. Rend.* **252**, 2238–2240 (1961).

(M10) Mallya, R. M., and Murthy, A. R. V., Hydrated basic nickel carbonates. Potentiometric study of precipitation. Preparation of basic nickel carbonates and their differential thermal analysis. *J. Indian Inst. Sci.* **43**, 65–96 (1961).

(M11) Mallya, R. M., and Murthy, A. R. V., Basic carbonates of nickel. Thermo-gravimetric behavior of basic nickel carbonates. Thermal decomposition of basic nickel carbonates in vacuum and the nature of the surfaces. Formation and configurations of basic nickel carbonates. *J. Indian Inst. Sci.* **43**, 131–157 (1961).

(M12) van der Marel, H. W., Quantitative differential thermal analysis of clay and other minerals. *Am. Mineralogist* **41**, 222–244 (1956).

(M13) Markin, T. L., Thermal decomposition of americium (III) oxalate. *J. Inorg. Nucl. Chem.* **7**, 290–291 (1958).

(M14) Markov, P. J., and Peschew, P. D., Study of the kinetics of the reaction between N-butyl iodide and magnesium by differential thermal analysis. *Compt. Rend. Acad. Bulgare Sci.* **14**, 175–178 (1961).

(M15) Martin, A. J., and Edwards, K. L., Linear voltage temperature furnace for thermal analysis. *J. Sci. Instr.* **36**, 170–172 (1959).

(M16) Martin, A. J., and Moore, A., The structure of beryllium, with particular reference to temperatures above 1200°C. *J. Less-Common Metals* **1**, 85–93 (1959).

(M17) Martin, R. T., Clay-carbonate-soluble salt interaction during differential thermal analysis. *Am. Mineralogist* **43**, 649–655 (1958).

(M18) Martin, S. B., and Ramstad, R. W., Compact two-stage gas chromatograph for flash pyrolysis studies. *Anal. Chem.* **33**, 982–985 (1961).

(M19) Martinez, E., The effect of particle size on the thermal properties of serpentine minerals. *Am. Mineralogist* **46**, 901–912 (1961).

(M20) Mauer, F. A., Analytical balance for recording rapid change in weight. *Rev. Sci. Instr.* **25**, 598–602 (1954).

(M21) Mazières, C., Differential thermal microanalysis, physical-chemical applications. *Bull. Soc. Chim. France* pp. 1695–701 (1961).

(M22) Mazières, C., Microsamples, thermal phenomena that are connected with structural transformations. *Ann. Chim.* (*Paris*) **6**, 575–622 (1961).

(M23) McAdie, H. G., Thermal decomposition of molecular complexes. 1. Urea–n-paraffin inclusion compounds. *Can. J. Chem.* **40**, 2195–2203 (1962).

(M24) McAdie, H. G., Simultaneous thermal analysis using the open pan type of sample holder. *Anal. Chem.* **35**, 1840–1844 (1963).

(M25) McCrone, W. C., "Fusion Methods in Chemical Microscopy." Wiley (Interscience), New York, 1957.

(M26) McKeand, I. J., and Hursh, R. K., A tungsten coil furnace for high-temperature X-ray diffraction investigations. *J. Am. Ceram. Soc.* **38**, 63–65 (1955).

(M27) McLaughlin, R. J. W., Quantitative differential thermal analysis. *Am. J. Sci.* **252**, 555–566 (1954).

(M28) McLaughlin, R. J. W., Effects of grinding on dickite. *Clay Minerals Bull.* **2**, 309–317 (1955).

(M29) McLaughlin, R. J. W., Differential thermal analysis of kaolinite-illite mixtures. *Trans. Brit. Ceram. Soc.* **59**, 178–187 (1960).

(M30) McLaughlin, R. J. W., Effect of dilution on the shape of differential thermal curves of kaolinite. *Trans. Brit. Ceram. Soc.* **60**, 177–189 (1961).

(M31) McLaughlin, R. J. W., Geochemistry of some kaolinitic clays. *Geochim. et Cosmochim. Acta* **17**, 11–16 (1959).

(M32) Medlin, W. L., The preparation of synthetic dolomite. *Am. Mineralogist* **44**, 979–986 (1959).

(M33) Middlehurst, J., Mercury switch for establishing the true electrical zero in precise thermocouple measurements. *J. Sci. Instr.* **38**, 165 (1961).

(M33a) Milgrom, J., Inclusion complexes of methylnaphthalenes *J. Phys. Chem.* **63**, 1843–1848 (1959).

(M34) Misra, M. L., Gipta, M. M., and Upadhyaya, V. G., Assam and Rewa sillimanite-dehydration, DTA, and thermal expansion study. *Refractories J.* **31**, 399–401 (1955).

(M35) Mitchell, B. D., and Mackenzie, R. C., An apparatus for differential thermal analysis under controlled atmosphere conditions. *Clay Minerals Bull.* **4**, No. 21, 31 (1959).

(M36) Morita, H., and Rice, H., Characterization of organic substances by differential thermal analysis. *Anal. Chem.* **27**, 336–339 (1955).

(M37) Morrison, R. D., and Lachenmayer, R. R., Thin film thermocouples for substrate temperature measurement. *Rev. Sci. Instr.* **34**, 106–107 (1963).

(M38) Muan, A., and Somiya, S., Phase equilibrium studies in the system $CaO-FeO-Fe_2O_3-SiO_2$. *J. Am. Ceram. Soc.* **42**, 603–613 (1959).

(M39) Muller, R. H., Instrumentation. *Anal. Chem.* **32**, No. 13, 107A (1960).

(M40) Muller, R. H., and Garman, R. L., Electronic recording analytical balance. *Ind. Eng. Chem., Anal. Ed.* **10**, 436–440 (1938).

(M41) Muller, N. W., and Peck, R. E., Simple automatic and recording balance. *Ind. Eng. Chem., Anal. Ed.* **15**, 46–48 (1943).

(M42) Murphy, C. B., Hill, J. A., and Schacher, G. P., Differential thermal analysis and simultaneous gas analysis. *Anal. Chem.* **32**, 1374–1375 (1960).

(M43) Murray, J. A., Fischer, H. C., and Shade, R. W., M.I.T. Fellowship Report. *Proc. Natl. Lime Assoc.* (*Wash., D. C.*) **49**, 95–116 (1951).

(M44) Murray, P., and Allison, E. B., The monoclinic to tetragonal phase transformation in zirconia. *Trans. Brit. Ceram. Soc.* **53**, 335–361 (1954).

(M45) Murray, P., and White, J., The kinetics of clay decomposition. *Trans. Brit. Ceram. Soc.* **48**, 187–206 (1949).

(M46) Murray, P., and White, J., Kinetics of the thermal dehydration of clays. IV. Interpretation of the differential thermal analysis of the clay minerals. *Trans. Brit. Ceram. Soc.* **54**, 204–238 (1955).

(N1) Nakai, Y., Powdered preparations. Theoretical consideration of tablet disintegration process by thermal analysis. *Chem. Pharm. Bull.* (*Tokyo*) **9**, 796–800 (1961).

(N2) Nakamura, Y., Differential thermal analysis of phenol- form aldehyde resin. *Kogyo Kagaku Zasshi* **64**, 392–395 (1961).

(N3) Narsimhan, G., Thermal decomposition of calcium carbonate. *Chem. Eng. Sci.* **16**, 21–30 (1961).

(N4) Nechitailo, N. A., Tolchinskii, N. M., and Sanin, P. I., Thermal analysis in the study of polymer destruction. *Plasticheskie Massy* No. 11, 54–57 (1960).

(N5) Newkirk, A. E., Thermogravimetric measurements. *Anal. Chem.* **32**, 1559–1563 (1960).

(N6) Newkirk, A. E., and Laware, R., Thermogravimetric analysis of potassium hydrogen phthalate *Talanta* **9**, 169–173 (1962).

(N7) Newkirk, T. F., Differential thermal analysis above 1200°. *J. Am. Ceram. Soc.* **41**, 409–414 (1958).

(N8) Newman, P. C., Phase changes in In_2Se_3. *Z. anorg. allgem. Chem.* **299**, 158–159 (1959) (in English).

(N9) Nikitina, E. A., and Buris, E. V., Thermographic investigation of important saturated heteropolyacids. *J. Gen. Chem. USSR* (*English transl.*) **26**, 717–720 (1956).

(N10) Nikolaev, A. V., and Shubina, S. M., Differential thermal microanalysis. *Vopr. Petrog. i Mineral. Akad. Nauk SSSR* **2**, 427–432 (1953).

(N11) Nishiyama, Z., Shimizu, K., and Sugino, K., Martensite transformation in thin foils. *Acta Met.* **9**, 620–622 (1961).

(N12) Norin, R., The decomposition products of kaolinite. *Geol. Foren. Stockholm Forh.* **66**, 15–8 (1944).

(N13) Norton, F. H., Hydrothermal formation of clay minerals in the laboratory. *Am. Mineralogist* **24**, 1–17 (1939).

(N14) Notz, K. J., and Jaffe, H. H., Correlation of TGA and DTA temperatures in decomposition reactions. *J. Am. Ceram. Soc.* **43**, 53–54 (1960).

(N15) Nozaki, F., and Morikawa, K., Surface composition and chemical properties of the supported nickel catalysts X-ray analysis, infrared spectrum analysis and differential thermal analysis. *Kogyo Kagaku Zasshi* **64**, 1568–1573 (1961).

(N16) Nutting, P. G., Some standard thermal dehydration curves. *U. S. Geol. Surv. Profess. Papers* **197E**, 197–217 (1943).

(O1) O'Connor, J. R., Use of thermo electric effects during crystal growth. *J. Electrochem. Soc.* **108**, 713–715 (1961).

(O2) Oetting, F. L., and Gregory, N. W., Heat capacity of and a transition in iron(II) iodide above room temperature., *J. Phys. Chem.* **65**, 173–175 (1961).

(O3) Ogimachi, N. N., Corcoran, J. M., and Kruse, H. W., Thermal analysis of systems of hydrazine with propyl alcohol, isopropyl alcohol, and allyl alcohol. *J. Chem. Eng. Data* **6**, 238–239 (1961).

(O4) Okada, Y, and Ameniya, A., Effect of atmosphere on radiation-induced cross-linking of polyethylene. *J. Polymer Sci.* **50**, S22–S24 (1961).

(O5) Okuda, H., Kato, S., and Iga, T., Formation of mullite from kaolin minerals at the temperatures lower than 900. *Yogyo Kyokai Shi* **69**, 149–160 (1961).

(O6) Orcel, J., and Caillère, S., Differential thermal analysis of clays and montmorillonites *Compt. Rend.* **197**, 774 (1933).

(O7) Oriani, R. A., and Murphy, W. K., Differential calorimeter for heats of formation of alloys. *J. Phys. Chem.* **62**, 303 (1958).

(O8) O'Shaughnessy, M. T., Fundamental ideas of polymer chemistry. (Contract AF-04(695)-69) Report No. TDR-69(2240–54)TN-1, DCAS-TDR-62-118.

(O9) Osipov, A. I., Infringement of Boltzmann's distribution in the process of thermal dissociation of molecules. *Dokl. Akad. Nauk SSSR* **137**, 833–835 (1961).

(O10) Otsubo, Y., and Yamaguchi, K., Thermochemical properties and reaction processes of alkali carbonate–iron(III) oxide systems as investigated by means of differential thermal method. Lithium carbonate–iron(III) oxide system. Sodium carbonate–iron(III) oxide system. *Nippon Kagaku Zasshi* **82**, 557–562 (1961).

(P1) Paciorek, K. L., Lajiness, W. G., and Lenk, C. T. Differential thermal analysis of fluoro-elastomer systems. *J. Polymer Sci.* **60**, 141–148 (1962).

(P2) Paciorek, K. L., Lajiness, W. G., Spain, R. G., and Lenk, C. T., Differential thermal analysis of fluorinated polymers. *J. Polymer Sci.* **61**, 415–435 (1962).

(P3) Padmanabhan, V. M., Saraiya, S. C., and Sundaram, A. K., Thermal decomposition of oxalates, *J. Inorg. Nucl. Chem.* **12**, 356–359 (1960).

(P4) Pakulak, J. M., Jr., and Leonard, G. W., Thermistorized apparatus for differential thermal analysis. *Anal. Chem.* **31**, 1037–1039 (1959).

(P5) Palei, P. N., Sentyurin, I. G., and Skylreiko, I. S., Application of thermogravimetry in analytical chemistry. *Zh. Anal. Khim.* **12**, 318 (1957).

(P5a) Papailhau, J., Apparatus for simultaneous thermogravimetric and differential thermal analysis. *Bull. Soc. Franc. Mineral. Crist.* **82**, 367–373 (1959).

(P6) Parker, C. J., Hathaway, J. C., and Blackmon, P. D., Some curves from a portable differential thermal analysis unit. *U. S. Geol. Surv. Bull.* **1021G**, (1956).

(P7) Partridge, E. P., Hicks, V., and Smith, G. W., A thermal, microscopic, and X-ray study of the system $NaPO_3$–$Na_4P_2O_7$. *J. Am. Chem. Soc.* **63**, 454–466 (1941).

(P8) Pask, J. A., and Warner, M. F., Fundamental studies of talc. I. Constitution of talcs. *J. Am. Ceram. Soc.* **37**, 118–128 (1954).

(P9) Pask, J. A., and Warner, M. F., Differential thermal analysis methods and techniques. *Am. Ceram. Soc. Bull.* **33**, 168–175 (1954).

(P10) Paulik, F., Paulik, J., and Erdey, L., Derivatograph. *Z. Anal. Chem.* **160**, 241–252 (1958).

(P11) Paulik, F., Paulik, J., and Erdey, L., Effect of the atmosphere which is formed within the sample on the case of derivatographic investigations. *Acta. Chim. Acad. Sci. Hung.* **26**, 143–148 (1961).

(P12) Pavel, L., and Fojtik, L., New method of thermal analysis of clay minerals—rapid derivative thermal analysis. *Sb. Cesk. Akad. Zemedel. Ved, Rostlinna Vyroba* **4**, 863 (1958).

(P13) Pearce, J. H., and Mardon, P. G., Apparatus for combined thermal analysis and dilatometry. *J. Sci. Instr.* **36**, 457 (1959).

(P14) Peco, G., Differential thermal analysis of clays. *Ceramica* (Milan) [N.S.] **7**, 48–52 (1952).

(P15) Pedregal, J. D., and Aparicio-Arroyo, E., Fluoride-based ceramics. *In* "Science of Ceramics," Proc. 1961 Conf. (G. H. Stewart, ed.), Vol. 1. Academic Press, New York, 1962.

(P16) Pegolotti, J. A., and Young, W. G., Allylic rearrangements. Reactions of A- and gamma-trifluoromethyl allyl alcohols with thionyl chloride and thermal decomposition of the chlorosulfinate intermediates. Displacement reactions in trifluoromethyl allyl systems. *J. Am. Chem. Soc.* **83**, 3251–3261 (1961).

(P17) Penther, C. J., Abrams, S. T., and Stross, E. H., Semiautomatic thermal analysis apparatus. *Anal. Chem.* **23**, 1459–1466 (1951).

(P18) Perlin, S. M., Gilman, T. P., and Leites, A. Z., Degree of consolidation of unsaturated polyester resins by the dilatometric method. *Plasticheskie Massy* No 10, 64–68 (1960).

(P19) Peters, H., and Wiedemann, H. G., Thermalbalance of high accuracy and wide application. *Z. Anorg. Allgem. Chem.* **298**, 202–211 (1959).

(P20) Peters, H., and Wiedemann, H. G., Thermal decomposition of calcium oxalate and calcium carbonate on a thermobalance of high accuracy. *Z. Anorg. Allgem. Chem.* **300**, 142–51 (1959).

(P21) Peterson, A. H., Analytical balance $+$ differential transformer $+$ recording potentiometer $=$ recording microbalance. *Instr. Automation* **28**, 1104–1106 (1955).

(P22) Phillips, B., and Muan, A., Stability relationship of calcium ferrites: Phase equilibria in the system 2 CaO–Fe_2O_3–$FeO \cdot Fe_2O_3$–Fe_2O_3 above $1135°C$. *Trans. Met. Soc. AIME* **218**, 1112–1118 (1960).

(P23) Phillips, N. D., and Wagoner, C. L., Use of differential thermal analysis in exploring minimum temperature limits of oil-ash corrosion. *Corrosion* **17**, 396T–400T (1961).

(P24) Pietri, A., Haladjian, J., Perinet, G., and Carpeni, G., Isohydric Point. Hydrated germanium dioxide, preparation, thermogravimetry, and X-rays. *Bull. Soc. Chim. France* pp. 1909–1913 (1960).

(P25) Pirisi, R., and Mattu, F., Differential thermal analysis of sodium and ammonium oxalates. *Chimica (Milan)* **8**, 283–287 (1953).

(P26) Polizzotti, G., X-ray and differential thermal analyses on a Sicilian montmorillonitic clay. *Chim. Ind. (Milan)* **43**, 154–158 (1961).

(P27) Primak, W., Fuchs, L. H., and Day, P., Effects of nuclear reactor exposure on same properties of vitreous silica and quartz. *J. Am. Ceram. Soc.* **38**, 135–139 (1955).

(P28) Proks, I., and Siske, V., Study of $CaCO_3 \rightleftharpoons CaO + CO_2$ reaction by differential thermal analysis. *Chem. Zvesti* **12**, 275–283 (1958).

(P29) Proks, I., and Siske, V., Apparatus for the performance of differential thermal analysis at low temperatures. *Chem. Zvesti* **15**, 309–314 (1961).

(R1) Rabatin, J. G., and Card, C. S., Simple recording thermobalance for vacuum and pressure studies. *Anal. Chem.* **31**, 1689–1692 (1959).

(R2) Radchenko, O. A., and Koperina, V. V., Thermal analysis applied to the study of dispersed organic matter of rocks. *Dokl. Akad. Nauk SSSR* **135**, 713–716 (1960).

(R3) Radzikovskaya, S. V., and Samsonov, G. V., Vacuum thermal method of preparation of cerium and lanthanum mono sulfides. *Zh. Prikl. Khim.* **34**, 671–672 (1961).

(R4) Ralls, J. W., and Elliger, C. A., Thermal transformations of O-alkyl-lactims. *Chem. & Ind. (London)* p. 20 (1961).

(R5) Rao, C. N. R., Yoganarasimhan, S. R., and Faeth, P. A., Brookite-rutile transformation. *Trans. Faraday Soc.* **57**, 504–510 (1961).

(R6) Rao, K. V., Dielectric loss and thermal bleaching of calcite irradiated by X-rays. *Phys. Chem. Solids* **20**, 193–196 (1961).

(R7) Rase, D. E., and Roy, R., Phase equilibria in the system $BaO–TiO_2$. *J. Am. Ceram. Soc.* **38**, 102–113 (1955).

(R8) Raudsepp, I. Y., Instrument for differential recording of electro conductivity changes in polythermal analysis. *Zh. Fiz. Khim.* **35**, 665–668 (1961).

(R9) Ravich, G. B., and Burtsev, U. N., Effect of polymorphism on thermal conductivity. *Dokl. Akad. Nauk SSSR* **137**, 1155–1157 (1961).

(R10) Razuvaev, G. A., Terman, L. M., and Petukhov, G. G., Mechanism underlying the thermal decomposition of percarbonates in solution. *Dokl. Akad. Nauk SSSR* **136**, 628–630 (1961).

(R11) Reese, D. R., Nordberg, P. N., Eriksen, S. P., and Swintosky, J. V., Technique for studying thermally induced phase transitions. *J. Pharm. Sci.* **50**, 177–178 (1961).

(R12) Reisman, A., Isobaric dissociation studies of alkali-metal carbonatehydrate using simultaneous differential thermal analysis–thermogravimetric analysis. *Anal. Chem.* **32**, 1566–1574 (1960).

(R13) Reisman, A., and Holtzberg, F., Phase equilibria in the system potassium carbonate-niobium pentoxide by the method of differential thermal analysis. *J. Am. Chem. Soc.* **77**, 2115–2119 (1955).

References 559

(R14) Reisman, A., Holtzberg, F., Berkenblit, M., and Berry, M., Reactions of the group VB pentoxides with alkali oxides and carbonates. III. Thermal and X-ray phase diagrams of the system K_2O and K_2CO_3 with Ta_2O_5. *J. Chem. Soc.* **78**, 4514–4520 (1956).

(R15) Reisman, A., and Karlak, J., Observations on the differential thermal analysis of copper sulfate pentahydrate. *J. Am. Chem. Soc.* **80**, 6500 (1958).

(R16) Reisman, A., Triebwasser, S., and Holtzberg, F., Phase diagram of the system potassium niobate–potassium tantalate by the methods of differential-thermal and resistance analysis. *J. Am. Chem. Soc.* **77**, 4228–4230 (1955).

(R17) Remizova, A. A., and Tamarin, A. A., Effect of admixtures on the anomaly of thermal expansion near the melting points. *Izv. Vysshikh Uchebn. Zavedenii, Fiz.* No. 6, 152–156 (1960).

(R18) Rey, M., and Kostomaroff, V., Physico-chemical interpretation of differential thermal analysis. *Silicates Ind.* **24**, 603 (1959).

(R19) Richer, A., and Vallet, P., On the method of study of chemical systems by variation of the mass during linearly increasing temperature, its application to the pyrolysis of calcium carbonate in netrogen and carbon dioxide and to the study of gravimetric methods. *Bull. Soc. Chim. France* pp. 148–151 (1953).

(R20) Richmond, J. C., and Stewart, J. E., Spectral emittance of ceramic-coated and uncoated specimens of incaved and stainless steel. *J. Am. Ceram. Soc.* **42**, 633–640 (1959).

(R21) Ringwood, A. E., Aspects of the thermal evolution of the earth. *Geochim. Cosmochim. Acta* **20**, 241–259 (1960).

(R22) Roberts, A. L., and Brindley, G. W., A review of clay mineral research in the University of Leeds. *Clay Minerals Bull* **1**, No. 1, 15–17 (1952).

(R23) Roberts, A. L., and Grimshaw, R. W., The quantitative determination of minerals by thermal analysis. *Trans. 2nd Intern. Ceram. Congr., 1950* p. 71 (1950).

(R24) Robertson, R. H. S., Thermal decomposition of dolomite. *Nature* **172**, 998–1001 (1953).

(R25) Rodot, M., Thermomagnetic ambielectronic effects and mechanism of the electronic relaxation in semiconductors of groups III and V. *Compt. Rend.* **252**, 2526–2528 (1961).

(R26) Rogers, R. N., Simple microscale differential thermal analysis of explosives. *Microchem. J.* **5**, 91–99 (1961).

(R27) Rogers, R. N., Yasuda, S. K., and Zinn, V., Pyrolysis as an analytical tool. *Anal. Chem.* **32**, 672–678 (1960).

(R28) Rogers, S. S., and Mandelkern, L., *J. Phys. Chem.* **61**, 985 (1957).

(R29) Romo, P. C., and Lynch, T. W., U. S. Patent 2,705,418 (1955). Differential thermal analysis of minerals.

(R30) Ropp, R. C., and Aia, M. A., Thermal analysis of phosphor raw materials. *Anal. Chem.* **34**, 1288–1291 (1962).

(R31) Rosenthal, G., A study of the plasticity of mono-ionic clays. "Science of Ceramics," Proc. 1961 Conf. (G. H. Stewart, ed.), Vol. 1. Academic Press, New York, 1962.

(R32) Rowland, R. A., and Beck, C. W., Determination of small quantities of dolomite by differential thermal analysis. *Am. Mineralogist* **37**, 76–82 (1952).

(R33) Rowland, R. A., and Jonas, E. C., Variations in differential thermal analysis curves of siderite. *Am. Mineralogist* **34**, 550–558 (1949).

(R34) Rowland, R. A., and Lewis, D. R., Furnace-atmosphere control in differential thermal analysis. *Am. Mineralogist* **36**, 80–91 (1951).

(R35) Rowland, R. A., Weiss, E. V., and Lewis, D. R., Apparatus for the oscillating-heating method of X-ray powder diffraction. *J. Am. Ceram. Soc.* **42**, 133–138 (1959).

(R36) Rubin, T., Johnston, H. L., and Altman, H. W., Thermal expansion of rock salt. *J. Phys. Chem.* **65**, 65–67 (1961).

(R37) Rudin, A., Schreiber, H. P., and Waldman, M. H., Measurement of polyethylene oxidation by differential thermal analysis. *Ind. Eng. Chem.* **55**, 137–140 (1961).

(S1) Sabatier, G., Effect of the dimensions of chlorite crystals on their thermal differential analysis curves. *Bull. Soc. Franc. Mineral.* **73**, 43–48 (1950).

(S2) Sabatier, G., Determination of heats of transformation by differential thermal analysis. *Bull. Soc. Franc. Mineral.* **77**, 953–968 and 1077–1083 (1954).

(S3) Saibova, M. T., and Berg, L. G., Thermographic phase analysis of certain salt mixtures. *Uzbeksk. Khim. Zh.* No. 1, 15–22 (1961).

(S4) Sastry, B. S. R., and Hummel, F. A., Studies in lithium oxide systems. V. $Li_2O–Li_2O \cdot B_2O_3$. *J. Am. Ceram. Soc.* **42**, 216–218 (1959).

(S5) Satava, V., and Trousil, Z., Simple construction of an apparatus for automatic DTA. *Silikaty* **4**, 272–277 (1960).

(S6) Saunders, H. L., and Giedroyc, V., Differential thermal analysis in controlled atmosphere. *Trans. Brit. Ceram. Soc.* **49**, 365–374 (1950).

(S7) Sauer, H. A., "An Experimental Dilatometer." To be published, 1964.

(S8) Schaller, W. T., and Vlisidis, A. C., Spontaneous oxidation of a sample of powdered siderite. *Am. Mineralogist* **44**, 433–435 (1959).

(S9) Schawlow, A. L., and Garn, P. D., Unpublished measurements (1958).

(S10) Schnitzer, M., and Hoffman, I., Thermogravimetry of the organic matter of a podzol soil. *Chem. & Ind. (London)* pp. 1397–1398 (1961).

(S11) Schnitzer, M., Wright, J. R., and Hoffman, I., High temperature thermogravimetry of chlorides and sulphates. A study of the application to soils. *Anal. Chim. Acta* **26**, 371–377 (1962).

(S12) Schnitzer, M., Wright, V. X., and Hoffman, I., Use of the thermobalance in the analysis of soils and clays., *Anal. Chem.* **31**, 440–444 (1959).

(S13) Schroeder, J., and Stanik, T., Automatic apparatus for differential thermoanalysis. General description and results of check measurements. *Chem. Stosowana* **4**, 397–406 (1960).

(S14) Schuele, W. J., Preparation of fine particles from bimetal oxalates. *J. Phys. Chem.* **63**, 83–86 (1959).

(S15) Schweite, H. E., and Ziegler, G., Principles and applications of the method of dynamic differential calorimetry. *Ber. Deut. Keram Ges.* **35**, 193–204 (1952).

(S16) Schwenker, R. F., Jr., and Beck, L. R., Jr. The differential thermal analysis of textile and other high polymeric materials. *Textile Res. J.* **30**, 624–626 (1960).

(S17) Sekine, Y., Mechanism of thermal decomposition of urea–formaldehyde resin. *Kogyo Kagaku Zasshi* **63**, 1657–1659 (1960).

(S18) Seto, J., Study on amino acids by using a thermobalance. *Bunseki Kagaku* **9**, 939–945 (1960).

(S19) Sewell, E. C., The consequences for differential thermal analysis of assuming a reaction to be first order. *Clay Minerals Bull.* **2**, 233–241 (1955).

(S19a) Sewell, E. C., and Honeyborne, D. B., *in* "The Differential Thermal Investigation of Clays" (R. C. Mackenzie, ed.), pp. 65–97. Mineral. Soc., London, 1957.

(S20) Shiba, S., Differential thermal analysis of the systems aluminum soap–hydrocarbon. *Bull. Chem. Soc. Japan* **34**, 809–816 (1961).

(S21) Shiba, S., Differential thermal analysis of aluminum soaps. *Bull. Chem. Soc. Japan* **34**, 804–808 (1961).

(S22) Shiloss, J. C., Thermal analysis of the $CrCb_2$–NaCl system. *J. Phys. Chem.* **64**, 1566–1567 (1960).

(S23) Sidorovich, A. V., and Juyshinskii, E. V., Specific features of the thermal expansion of polyethylene terephthalate crystallized after preliminary stretching. *Vysokomolekul. Soedin.* **3**, 161–163 (1961).

(S24) Simchen, A. E., Application of the kinetics of phase transformation to the thermal decomposition of potassium chlorate and potassium per maganate. *J. Chim. Phys.* **58**, 596–601 (1961).

(S25) Simchen, A. E., Fusion point and the thermal decomposition of potassium perchlorate. *J. Phys. Chem.* **65**, 1093–1095 (1961).

(S26) Simons, E. L., Newkirk, A. E., and Aliferis, I., Performance of a pen recording chevenard thermobalance. *Anal. Chem.* **29**, 48–54 (1957).

(S27) Simons, J. H., Scheirer, C. L., Jr., and Ritter, H. L., Magnetic weighing and gas density balances. *Rev. Sci. Instr.* **24**, 36–42 (1953).

(S28) Siske, V., and Proks, I., New arrangement for differential thermal analysis. *Chem. Zvesti* **12**, 185 (1958).

(S29) Siske, V., and Proks, I., Differential thermal analysis of carbonates in carbon dioxide current. *Chem. Zvesti* **12**, 201–208 (1958).

(S30) Sklyarenko, I. S., and Chubukova, T. M., Analytical applications of thermo gravimetry. Thermogravimetric study of plutonium compounds. *Zhur. Anal. Khim.* **15**, 706–710 (1960).

(S31) Sklyarenko, U. S., Sklyarenko, I. S., and Chubukova, T. M., Thermogravimetry in analytical chemistry. Thermogravimetric study of lanthanum carbonate. *Zhur. Anal. Khim.* **16**, 417–421 (1961).

(S32) Skorik, A. I., and Boldyrev, V. V., Arrangement for investigating the kinetics of thermal degradation of solids during irradiation. *Zh. Fiz. Khim.* **35**, 1370–1371 (1961).

(S33) Smith, C. S., A simple method of thermal analysis permitting quantitative measurements of specific and latent heats. *Am. Inst. Mining Met. Engrs., Inst. Metals Div., Tech. Publ.* **1100**, 9 pp. (1939).

(S34) Smith, W., The thermal conductivity of dry soils. *Soil Sci.* **53**, 453–460 (1942).

(S35) Smyth, F. H., and Adams, L. H., The system calcium oxide–carbon dioxide. *J. Am. Chem. Soc.* **45**, 1167 (1923).

(S36) Smyth, H. T., Temperature distribution during mineral inversion and its significance in differential thermal analysis. *J. Am. Ceram. Soc.* **34**, 221–224 (1951).

(S37) Somiya, T., and Hirano, S., Thermal decomposition of oxalates and of nitrates of lanthanum, cerium, praseodymium, neodymium and samarium in the atmosphere of carbon dioxide. *J. Soc. Chem. Ind. Japan* **34**, 495–613 (1931).

(S38) Sosman, R. B., "Properties of Silica," Am. Chem. Soc. Monogr. No. 37. Chem. Catalog Co., New York, 1927.

(S38a) Soulen, J. R., Calculation of thermogravimetric data by electronic digital computer. *Anal. Chem.* **34**, 136–137 (1962).

(S38b) Soulen, J. R., and Mockrin, I., Improved methods of using the thermobalance to determine thermal stabilities. *Anal. Chem.* **33**, 1909–1912 (1961).

(S39) Spatz, S. M., Thermal decarboxylation of diaryl fumarates to stilbenes. *J. Org. Chem.* **26**, 4158–4160 (1961).

(S40) Speil, S., Berkelhamer, L. H., Pask, J. A., and Davies, B., Differential thermal analysis. Its application to clays and other aluminous materials. *U.S. Bur. Mines, Tech. Paper* **664** (1945).

(S41) Speros, D. M., and Woodhouse, R. L., Quantitative differential thermal analysis. Heats and rates of solid-liquid transitions. *Nature* **197**, 1261–1262 (1963).

(S42) Spinedi, P., and Franciosi, O., Thermodifferential precision analysis. *Ricerca Sci.* **22**, 2323–39 (1952).

(S43) Splitek, R., Automatically operated apparatus for differential and gravimetric thermoanalysis. *Hutnicke Listy* **13**, 697 (1958).

(S44) Sriraman, S., and Shanmugasundaram, V., Thermomagnetic study of mercury and dilute amalgams of sodium and potassium. *Bull. Chem. Soc. Japan* **34**, 1288–1290 (1961).

(S45) Srivastava, O. K., and Murthy, A. R. V., Thermal decomposition of cerous oxalate in vacuum. *J. Sci. Ind. Res. (India)* **208**, 96–101 (1961).

(S46) Srivastava, O. K., and Vasudevamurthy, A. R., Thermo gravimetric behavior of lanthanum, thorium and cerium oxalates in an atmosphere of carbon dioxide. *Current Sci. (India)* **29**, 470 (1960).

(S47) Stegmüller, L., Differential thermalanalysis apparatus. *Sprechsaal Keram.* **86**, 1–8 (1953).

(S48) Stephenson, J. L., Smith, G. W., and Trantham, H. V., Automatic recording of weight and temperature for vacuum-sublimation studies. *Rev. Sci. Instr.* **28**, 381–382 (1957).

(S49) Stepko, I. I., Romanova, G. P., and Chmel, N. G., Effect of thermal treatment on gas evolution from a germanium surface. *Ukr. Fiz. Zh.* **5**, 705–707 (1960).

(S50) Stone, R. L., Differential thermal analysis of clay materials under controlled thermodynamic conditions. *Ohio State Univ. Stud. Eng. Expt. Sta. Bull.* **146** (1951).

(S51) Stone, R. L., Apparatus for differential thermal analysis under controlled partial pressures of water, carbon dioxide, other gases. *J. Am. Ceram. Soc.* **35**, 76–82 (1952).

(S52) Stone, R. L., Differential thermal analysis of kaolin-group minerals under controlled partial pressures of water. *J. Am. Ceram. Soc.* **35**, 90–99 (1952).

(S53) Stone, R. L., Preliminary study of the effects of water vapor pressure on thermograms of kaolinitic soils. *Proc. 2nd Natl. Conf. Clays and Clay Minerals, 1953* pp. 315–323. Natl. Acad. Sci.–Natl. Res. Council (Publ. No. 327), Washington, D. C., 1954.

(S54) Stone, R. L., Thermal analysis of magnesite at carbon dioxide pressures up to six atmospheres. *J. Am. Ceram. Soc.* **37**, 46–47 (1954).

(S55) Stone, R. L., Effect of water vapor pressure on thermograms of kaolinitic soils. *Proc. 2nd Natl. Conf. Clays and Clay Minerals, 1953* pp. 315–323. Natl. Acad. Sci.–Natl. Res. Council (Publ. No. 327) Washington, D. C., 1954.

(S56) Stone, R. L., Determinative tests of aid in the design of driers and kilns. *Am. Ceram. Soc. Bull.* **36**, 1–5 (1957).

(S57) Stone, R. L., Laboratory tests on the oxidation characteristics of a Texas shale. *Am. Ceram. Soc. Bull.* **36**, 172–173 (1957).

(S58) Stone, R. L., Differential thermal analysis by the dynamic gas technique. *Anal. Chem.* **32**, 1582–1588 (1960).

(S58a) Stone, R. L., Private communication (1962).

(S59) Stone, R. L., and Rase, H. F., Differential thermal analysis. New techniques for testing silica-alumina catalysts. *Anal. Chem.* **29**, 1273–1277 (1957).

(S60) Stone, R. L., and Rowland, R. A., DTA of kaolinite and montmorillonite under water-vapor pressures up to six atmospheres. *Proc. 3rd Natl. Conf. Clays and Clay Minerals, 1954* pp. 103–117. Natl. Acad. Sci.–Natl. Res. Council (Publ. No. 395), Washington, D. C., 1955.

(S61) Stone, R. L., and Weiss, E. J., Examination of four coarsely crystalline chlorites by X-ray and high-pressure differential thermal analysis techniques. *Clay Minerals Bull.* **2**, 214–222 (1955).

(S62) Strassburger, J., Brauer, G. M., Tryon, M., and Forziati, A. F., Analysis of methyl methacrylate copolymers by gas chromatography. *Anal. Chem.* **32**, 454–457 (1960).

(S63) Straus, S., and Madorsky, S. L., Thermal stability of poly di vinyl benzene and of copolymers of styrene with di vinyl benzene and with trivinyl benzene. *J. Res. Natl. Bur. Std.* **65A**, 243–248 (1961).

(S64) Strekalovskii, V. N., Bessonov, A. V., Vlasov, V. G., and Sidorenko, F. A., Phase transformation during reduction and oxidation of uranium oxides. *Fiz. Metal. i Metalloved.* **11**, 400–403.

(S65) Strella, S., Differential thermal analysis of polymers. 1. The glass transition. *J. Appl. Polymer Sci.* **7**, 569–579 (1963).

(S66) Strella, S., Differential thermal analysis of polymers. II. Melting. *J. Appl. Polymer Sci.* **7**, 1281–1289 (1963).

(S67) Strizhkov, B. V., Lapitskii, A. V., and Vlasov, L. G., Preparation and thermographic study of barium, lead, and strontium titanyl oxalates. *Zh. Prikl. Khim.* **34**, 673–674 (1961).

(S68) Strong H. M., The experimental fusion curve of iron to 96,000 atmospheres. *J. Geophys. Res.* **64**, 653 (1959).

(S69) Stross, E. H., and Abrams, S. T., The phase behavior of the system sodium stearate-cethane. *J. Am. Chem. Soc.* **72**, 3309–3310 (1950).

(S70) Sturm, E., Quantitative differential thermal analysis by controlled heating rates. *J. Phys. Chem.* **65**, 1935–1936.

(S71) Suga, H., Chihara, H., and Seki, S., Crystallochemical study by the differential thermal analysis. Device of automatic recording and program control for the differential thermal analysis. *Nippon Kagaku Zasshi* **82**, 24–29 (1961).

(S72) Suga, H., Nakatusuka, K., Shinoda, T., and Seki, S., Crystallochemical study by the differential thermal analysis. Detection of phase transition. *Nippon Kagaku Zasshi* **82**, 29–32 (1961).

(S73) Suleimanov, A. S., The nature of exothermic effect in magnesium carbonates. *Tr. Pervogo Sov. Termagr. Kazan* pp. 200–204 (1953).

(S74) Sun, M. S., Differential thermal analysis of shattuckite. *Am. Mineralogist* **46**, 67–77 (1961).

(S75) Sundquist, B. E., and Mondolfo, L. F., Heterogeneous nucleation in the liquid-to-solid transformation in alloys. *Trans. Met. Soc. AIME* **215**, 157–164 (1961).

(T1) Taft, R. W., Evidence for phenyl cation with an odd number of pi electrons from the aqueous thermal decomposition of the diazonium ion. *J. Am. Chem. Soc.* **83**, 3350 (1961).

(T2) Takakura, E., and Yasoshima, Y., Thermal decomposition of potassium titanyl sulfate. *Kogyo Kagaku Zasshi* **63**, 1569–1570 (1960).

(T3) Teitel 'baum, B. Ya., and Berg, L. G., Thermal analysis of registration of the volume of evolved gases. *Zh. Anal. Khim.* **8**, 152–157 (1953).

(T4) Teitel 'baum, B. Ya., and Dianov, M. P., Method of recording thermomechanical curves of polymers. *Vysokomolekul. Soedin.* **3**, 594–601 (1961).

(T5) Teitel 'baum, B. Ya., Iagfarova, T. A., Dianov, M. P., and Gubanov, E. F., Thermal transformations of certain rubbers as investigated by the method of thermomechanical curves. *Dokl. Akad. Nauk SSSR* **140**, 1132–1135 (1961).

(T6) Templeton, L. K., and Pask, J. A., Formation of $BaTiO_3$ from $BaCO_3$ and TiO_2 in air and CO_2. *J. Am. Ceram. Soc.* **42**, 212 (1959).

(T7) Thall, E., An automatic recording balance. *Can. Mining Met. Bull.* No. 145, 663–670 (1946).

(T7a) Thomasson, C. V., and Wilburn, F. W., The application of differential thermal analysis and thermogravimetric analysis to the study of reactions between glass-making materials. Part 2. The sodium carbonate-silica system with minor batch additions. *Phys. Chem. Glasses* **1**, 52–69 (1960).

(T8) Torkar, K., and Bertsch, L., Aluminum oxide and aluminum hydroxide. Effect of sodium ions on the formation and the thermal decomposition of bayerite. Effect of small amounts of sodium on the thermal decomposition of boehmite. *Monatsh.* **92**, 525–33 and 746–755 (1961).

(T9) Torkar, K., and Egghart, H., Aluminum oxide and aluminum hydroxide. Effect of hydrolysis conditions on the formation of aluminum hydroxide from aluminum ethylate. *Monatsh.* **92**, 755–768 (1961).

(T10) Torkar, K., Egghart, H., Krischner, H., and Worel, H., Aluminum oxide and aluminum hydroxide. Thermal decomposition of very pure aluminum hydroxide. *Monatsh.* **92**, 512–525 (1961).

(T11) Treloar, F. E., Measurement of polymerization kinetics by dilatometry. *Polymer* **1**, 513–514 (1960).

(T12) Tryhorn, F. G., and Wyatt, W. F., A recording hydrostatic balance of simple design. *Trans. Faraday Soc.* **23**, 238–242 (1927).

(T13) Tsurinov, G. G., "Pyrometer of N. S. Kurnakov." Acad. Sci. USSR, Moscow, 1953.

(T14) Turner, R. C., Hoffman, I., and Chen, D., Thermogravimetry of the dehydration of magnesium hydroxide. *Can. J. Chem.* **41**, 243–251 (1963).

(U1) Ugai, Ya. A., Thermographic investigation of the decomposition of bivalent metal oxalates. *Zh. Obshch. Khim.* **24**, 1315–1321 (1954).

(U2) Ukai, Y., Thermal investigation of mineral by means of dielectric behavior. *Mem. Coll. Sci. Univ. Kyoto, Ser. B* **22**, 185–198 (1955) (in English).

(U3) Ukai, Y., Korekawa, M., and Mochida, Y., The dielectric behavior and the X-ray investigation on some metamict minerals. *Kobutsugaku Zasshi* **2**, 252–262 (1955).

(U3a) U. S. Weather Bur., Private communication (1964).

(U4) Urbanski, T., Semenczuk, A., and Gorski, W., Thermal analysis of the system 1-chloro-2,4-dinitrobenzene–picryl chloride. *Bull. Acad. Polon. Sci., Ser. Sci. Chim.* **8**, 487–488 (1960) (in English).

(V1) Vainstein, E. E., and Kotlar, B. I., Fine structure of the X-ray telluride within the range of antiferromagnetic transformation temperatures. *Dokl. Akad. Nauk SSSR* **136**, 133–135 (1961).

(V2) Vand-Der-Lugt, W., and Poulis, N. J., Magnetic phase transitions of cobalt chloride. *Physica* **26**, 917–921 (1960).

(V3) Vassallo, D. A., and Harden, J. C., Precise phase transition measurements of organic materials by differential thermal analysis. *Anal. Chem.* **34**, 132–135 (1961).

(V4) Venkateswarlu, K., and Sriraman, S., Diamagnetic susceptibility of oxalate, tartrate, and citrate ions. *Trans. Faraday Soc.* **53**, 438–441 (1957).

(V5) Vickery, R. C., and Muir, H. M., Anomalous thermo-electric properties of gadolinium selenide. *Nature* **190**, 336–337 (1961).

(V6) Vieweg, R., and Gast, T., Recording microbalance for the measurements of diffusion through plastic membranes. *Kunstostoffe* **34**, 117–119 (1944).

(V7) Vinogradova, E. N., Vasil'eva, L. N., Use of differential thermocouple during ebullioscopic determination of molecular weight of oil products. *Khim. i Tekhnol. Topliv i Masel* **6**, No. 1, 57–61 (1961).

(V8) Vlasov, A. Y., and Antonov, I. V., Thermal magnetic hysteresis and thermal hysteresis of the magnetostriction of nickel-copper alloys. *Izv. Sibirsk. Otd. Akad. Nauk SSSR* No. 8, 121–124 (1961).

(V9) Vlasov, L. G., Lapitskii, A. V., and Strizhkov, B. V., Thermographic and thermogravimetric study of oxalato niobates. *Vestn. Mosk. Univ., Ser. II, Khim.* **16**, No. 1, 57–58 (1961).

(V10) Vold, M. J., Differential thermal analysis. *Anal. Chem.* **21**, 683–688 (1949).

(V11) Vold, M. J., and Vold, R. D., The phase behavior of lithium stearate in cetane and in decahydronaphthalene. *J. Colloid Sci.* **5**, 1–19 (1950).

(V12) Vold, R. D., Grandine, J. D., and Vold, M. J., *Polymorphic transformations* of calcium stearate and calcium stearate monohydrate. *J. Colloid Sci.* **3**, 339–361 (1948).

(V13) Vratny, F., Kern, S., and Guliotta, F., Thermal decomposition of cerium(III) nitrate hydrate. *J. Inorg. Nucl. Chem.* **17**, 281–285 (1961).

(V14) Vyrodov, I. P., Differential thermal analysis of the ternary system. Magnesium oxide-magnesium chloride-water. *Zh. Prikl. Khim.* **34**, 1208–1218 (1961).

(W1) Wada, G., Rapid evaluation of the activation energy of chemical reactions in solutions by differential thermal analysis. *Nippon Kagaku Zasshi* **81**, 1656–1661 (1960).

(W2) Wahl, F. M., Grim, R. E., and Graf, R. B., Phase transformations in silica as examined by continuous X-ray diffraction. *Am. Mineralogist* **46**, 196–208 (1961).

(W3) Walton, J. D., Jr., New method of preparing clay samples for differential thermal analysis. *J. Am. Ceram. Soc.* **38**, 438–443 (1955).

(W4) Warne, S. S. J., Differential thermal analysis of siderite. *Bull. Soc. Franc. Mineral. Crist.* **84**, 234–237 (1961).

(W5) Warne, S. S. J., and Bayliss, P., Differential thermal analysis of cerussite. *Am. Mineralogist* **47**, 1011–1023 (1962).

(W6) Waterbury, G. R., Douglass, R. M., and Metz, C. F., Thermogravimetric behavior of plutonium metal, nitrate, sulfate, and oxalate. *Anal. Chem.* **33**, 1018–1023 (1961).

(W7) Waters, P. L., Recording differential thermogravimetric balances. *Nature* **178,** 324–326 (1956).

(W8) Waters, P. L., New types of recording differential thermobalances. *J. Sci. Instr.* **35,** 41–46 (1958).

(W9) Waters, P. L., Fractional thermogravimetric analysis. *Anal. Chem.* **32,** 852–858 (1960).

(W10) Webb, T. L., Comparative performance of nickel and porous alumina sample holders for differential thermal analysis. *Nature* **174,** 686–688 (1954).

(W11) Webb, T. L., and Heystek, H., *in* "The Differential Thermal Analysis of Clays" (R. C. Mackenzie, ed.), pp. 329–363. Mineral. Soc., London, 1957.

(W12) Weiss, E. J., and Rowland, R. A., Oscillating reacting X-ray diffractometer studies of clay mineral dehydroxylation. *Am. Mineralogist* **41,** 117–126 (1956).

(W13) Weltner, M., Derivatographic analysis of the thermal decomposition of coal. *Brennstoff-Chem.* **42,** 40–46 (1961).

(W14) Wendlandt, W. W., Inexpensive automatic-recording thermobalance. *Anal. Chem.* **30,** 56–58 (1958).

(W15) Wendlandt, J. J., Thermal decomposition of scandium, yttrium and rare earth metal oxalates. *Anal. Chem.* **30,** 58–61 (1958).

(W16) Wendlandt, W. W., Thermal decomposition of the rare earth metal oxalates. *Anal. Chem.* **31,** 408–410 (1959).

(W17) Wendlandt, W. W., An inexpensive differential-thermal-analysis apparatus. *J. Chem. Educ.* **37,** 94–96 (1960).

(W18) Wendlandt, W. W., Reaction kinetics by differential thermal analysis. *J. Chem. Educ.* **38,** 571–573 (1961).

(W19) Wendlandt, W. W., A controlled atmosphere thermobalance. *J. Chem. Educ.* **38,** 556–558 (1961).

(W20) Wendlandt, W. W., A new apparatus for simultaneous differential thermal analysis and gas evolution analysis. *Anal. Chim. Acta* **27,** 309–314 (1962).

(W21) Wendlandt, W. W., Automatic digital recording thermobalance. *Anal. Chem.* **34,** 1726–1727 (1962).

(W22) Wendlandt, W. W., George, T. D., and Horton, G. R., Thermal decomposition of thorium(IV), uranium(IV), and the rare-earth metal(III) oxalate hydrates. Differential hermal analysis and weight-loss studies. *J. Inorg. Nucl. Chem.* **17,** 273–280 (1961).

(W23) Werner, P. E., Kierkegaard, P., and Magneli, A., Note on the thermal expansion of the tungsten bronzes of potassium, rubidium and cesium. *Acta Chem. Scand.* **15,** 427–428 (1961).

(W24) West, R. R., High-temperature reactions in kaolin-type clays. *Am. Ceram. Soc. Bull.* **36,** 55–58 (1957); see *Ceram. Abstr.* p. 96 (1957).

(W25) West, S. F., and Audrieth, L. F., Differential thermal analysis of some heteropoly acids of molybdenum and tungsten. *J. Phys. Chem.* **59,** 1069–1072 (1955).

(W26) Westman, S., Phase transition in vanadium(IV) oxide. *Acta Chem. Scand.* **15,** 217 (1961).

(W27) White, G. K., Anomalous thermal expansion of chromium. *Australian J. Phys.* **14,** 359–367 (1961).

(W28) White, T. R., Melting behavior of crystalline polymer fibers. *Nature* **175,** 895–896 (1955).

(W29) Whitehead, W. L., The vacuum differential thermal analysis of coals. *Conf. Origin and Constitution of Coal, Crystal Cliffs, Canada, 1950* pp. 100–105. Nova Scotia Dept. Mines, Nova Scotia Res. Found., 1950.

(W30) Whitehead, W. L., and Breger, I. A., Vacuum differential thermal analysis. *Science* 111, 279–281 (1950).

(W31) Whittemore, O. V., Jr., and Ault, N. N., Thermal expansion of various ceramic materials to 1500°C. *J. Am. Ceram. Soc.* 39, 443–444 (1956).

(W32) Wijk, H. F. Van, Impurity determination by thermal analysis. Melting curve of a quickly frozen sample. *Anal. Chim. Acta* 24, 41–45 (1960).

(W33) Wijk, H. F. Van, and Smit, W. M., Impurity determination by thermal analysis. Melting curve of a gradually frozen sample. *Anal. Chim. Acta* 23, 545–551 (1960).

(W34) Wilburn, F. W., and Thomasson, C. V., Application of differential thermal analysis and thermogravimetric analysis to the study of reactions between glass-making materials. Calcium carbonate-silica system. *Phys. Chem. Glasses* 2, 126–131 (1961).

(W35) Wittels, M., The differential thermal analyzer as a microcalorimeter. *Am. Mineralogist* 36, 615–621 (1951).

(W36) Wittels, M., Some aspects of mineral calorimetry. *Am. Mineralogist* 36, 760–767 (1951).

(W37) Woerner, P. F., and Wakefield, G. F., High temperature thermobalance. *Rev. Sci. Instr.* 33, 1456–1457 (1962).

(W38) Wolk, B., Relationship between thermal decomposition and microstructure of alkaline earth carbonates. *J. Electrochem. Soc.* 105, 89 (1958).

(W39) Wolski, W., Formation of ferrites at low temperatures. *Roczniki Chem.* 34, 1815–1818 (1960).

(W40) Wood, E. A., The question of a phase transition in silicon. *J. Phys. Chem.* 60, 508–509 (1956).

(Y1) Yagfarov, M. Sh., New method of quantitative thermography. *Zh. Neorg. Khim.* 6, 2440–2443 (1961).

(Y2) Yamaguchi, S., Thermo magnetic analysis of cobalt with an electron beam. *Z. Metallk.* 52, 284–285 (1961).

(Y3) Yamaguchi, T., Amagasa, M., and Uchiyama, S., Studies on thermal degradation of polyvinyl alcohol with thermobalance. *Kobunshi Kagaku* 18, 406–410 (1961).

(Y4) Yankwich, P. E., and Copeland, J. L., Pyrolysis of lead oxalate; isotope effects and product composition. *J. Am. Chem. Soc.* 79, 2081–2086 (1957).

(Y5) Yasuda, Toshio, and Araki, Y., Effect of pressure on the room-temperature transition of poly(tetrafluoroethylene) and its heat of transition. *J. Appl. Polymer Sci.* 5, 331–336 (1961).

(Z1) Zenz, F. A., and Othmer, D. F., "Fluidization and Fluid Particle Systems." Reinhold, New York, 1960.

(Z2) Zinov'ev, A. A., and Babaeva, V. P., Thermal decomposition of perchloric acid. *Zh. Neorg. Khim.* 6, 271–282 (1961).

(Z3) Zarnoretschki, O. S., and Peschew, P. D., Differential thermal analysis of the raw materials for preparing hard magnetic oxide materials. *Compt. Rend. Acad. Bulgare Sci.* 13, 559–562 (1960).

General References

"A Study of the Differential Thermal Analysis of Clays and Clay Minerals," by P. Laurent Arens. Excelsiors Foto-Offset, Gravenhage, 1951.

"Inorganic Thermogravimetric Analysis," by C. Duval. Elsevier, Amsterdam, 1953.

"The Differential Thermal Investigation of Clays," edited by Robert C. Mackenzie. Mineral. Soc., London, 1957.

"Differential Thermal Analysis: Theory and Practice," by W. J. Smothers and Y. Chiang. Chem. Publ. Co., New York, 1958.

"Automatic Recording Balances" (Review), by S. Gordon and C. Campbell. *Anal. Chem.* **32**, 271–289R (1960).

"Analytical Chemistry of Polymers," edited by Gordon M. Kline: chapter by H. E. Kissinger and S. B. Newman in Part II. Wiley (Interscience), New York, 1962.

"Differential Thermal Analysis" (Review), by C. B. Murphy, *Anal. Chem.* **34**, 298–301R (1962).

"Thermal Analysis" (Review), by C. B. Murphy, *Anal. Chem.* **36**, 347–354R (1964).

"Thermal Analysis Review" (Series), edited by J. P. Redfern. Stanton Instruments, Ltd., London. (A continuing series started in 1962.)

APPENDIX I

The listed firms supply thermoanalytical apparatus in the U.S.A. In each case the method is indicated by "DTA" for differential thermal analysis, "Dil" for dilatometry, or "TGA" for thermogravimetry. Equipment for simultaneous measurements is simply indicated by both classes. Accessory equipment or component apparatus (such as furnaces or balances) are not listed unless the item is specifically for one or more of the fields covered, for example, shielded thermocouples are made for other purposes as are amplifiers and programmers. A borderline case would be the Ainsworth Vacuum Recording Balance, around which the author has built thermobalance assemblies. Differential calorimeters are classed with differential thermal analysis apparatus.

Since new firms frequently enter the field, the prospective purchaser should also look in recent "Buyers Guides" or similar listings. The author does not guarantee completeness.

American Instrument Co. 8030 Georgia Ave. Silver Spring, Md.	DTA TGA	Wm. J. Hacker and Co. P. O. Box 646 West Caldwell, New Jersey	DTA TGA Dil
Apparatus Manufacturers, Inc. P. O. Box 184 Kent, Ohio	DTA TGA	Harrop Precision Furnace Co. 3470 E. Fifth Ave. Columbus 19, Ohio	DTA TGA Dil
C. W. Brabender Instruments, Inc. 50 E. Wesley St. So. Hackensack, New Jersey	TGA	Metrimpex Nader—U 21 Budapest, V., Hungary	DTA TGA
Brinkmann Instruments, Inc. Cantiague Rd. Westbury, L. I., New York	Dil	Mettler Instrument Corp. 20 Nassau St. Princeton, New Jersey	DTA TGA
Burrell Corporation 2223 Fifth Avenue Pittsburgh 19, Penna.	DTA TGA	The Perkin-Elmer Corp. 750 Main Ave. Norwalk, Conn.	DTA
Cahn Instrument Co. 15505 Minnesota Ave. Paramount, California	TGA	Schuco Scientific 250 W. 18th St. New York 11, New York	DTA TGA
E. I. duPont de Nemours and Co., Inc. Instrument Products Div. Wilmington 98, Delaware	DTA TGA	Robert L. Stone Co. 3316 Westhill Dr. Austin 4, Texas	DTA TGA
Eberbach Corp. P. O. Box 1024 Ann Arbor, Michigan	DTA	Technical Equipment Co. 917 Acoma St. Denver 4, Colorado	DTA TGA

APPENDIX II

Calibration Data

A. Thermocouple e.m.f.'s

The values tabulated on the following pages are taken from National Bureau of Standards Circular 561 by way of Leeds and Northrup Company Bulletin 077989, Issue 2.

A.1. CHROMEL VS ALUMEL

Thermal e.m.f. in millivolts compared to a reference junction at 0.0°C.

°C	0	1	2	3	4	5	6	7	8	9
0	0.00	0.04	0.08	0.12	0.16	0.20	0.24	0.28	0.32	0.36
10	0.40	0.44	0.48	0.52	0.56	0.60	0.64	0.68	0.72	0.76
20	0.80	0.84	0.88	0.92	0.96	1.00	1.04	1.08	1.12	1.16
30	1.20	1.24	1.28	1.32	1.36	1.40	1.44	1.49	1.53	1.57
40	1.61	1.65	1.69	1.73	1.77	1.81	1.85	1.90	1.94	1.98
50	2.02	2.06	2.10	2.14	2.18	2.23	2.27	2.31	2.35	2.39
60	2.43	2.47	2.51	2.56	2.60	2.64	2.68	2.72	2.76	2.80
70	2.85	2.89	2.93	2.97	3.01	3.05	3.10	3.14	3.18	3.22
80	3.26	3.30	3.35	3.39	3.43	3.47	3.51	3.56	3.60	3.64
90	3.68	3.72	3.76	3.81	3.85	3.89	3.93	3.97	4.01	4.06
100	4.10	4.14	4.18	4.22	4.26	4.31	4.35	4.39	4.43	4.47
110	4.51	4 55	4.60	4.64	4.68	4.72	4.76	4.80	4.84	4.88
120	4.92	4.96	5.01	5.05	5.09	5.13	5.17	5.21	5.25	5.29
130	5.33	5.37	5.41	5.45	5.49	5.53	5.57	5.61	5.65	5.69
140	5.73	5.77	5.81	5.85	5.89	5.93	5.97	6.01	6.05	6.09
150	6.13	6.17	6.21	6.25	6.29	6.33	6.37	6.41	6.45	6.49
160	6.53	6.57	6.61	6.65	6.69	6.73	6.77	6.81	6.85	6.89
170	6.93	6.97	7.01	7.05	7.09	7.13	7.17	7.21	7.25	7.29
180	7.33	7.37	7.41	7.45	7.49	7.53	7.57	7.61	7.65	7.69
190	7.73	7.77	7.81	7.85	7.89	7.93	7.97	8.01	8.05	8.09
200	8.13	8.17	8.21	8.25	8.29	8.33	8.37	8.41	8.46	8.50
210	8.54	8.58	8.62	8.66	8.70	8.74	8.78	8.82	8.86	8.90
220	8.94	8.98	9.02	9.06	9.10	9.14	9.18	9.22	9.26	9.30
230	9.34	9.38	9.42	9.46	9.50	9.54	9.59	9.63	9.67	9.71
240	9.75	9.79	9.83	9.87	9.91	9.95	9.99	10.03	10.07	10.11
250	10.16	10.20	10.24	10.28	10.32	10.36	10.40	10.44	10.48	10.52
260	10.57	10.61	10.65	10.69	10.73	10.77	10.81	10.85	10.89	10.93
270	10.98	11.02	11.06	11.10	11.14	11.18	11.22	11.26	11.30	11.34
280	11.39	11.43	11.47	11.51	11.55	11.59	11.63	11.67	11.72	11.76
290	11.80	11.84	11.88	11.92	11.96	12.01	12.05	12.09	12.13	12.17
300	12.21	12.25	12.29	12.34	12.38	12.42	12.46	12.50	12.54	12.58
310	12.63	12.67	12.71	12.75	12.79	12.83	12.88	12.92	12.96	13.00
320	13.04	13.08	13.12	13.17	13.21	13.25	13.29	13.33	13.37	13.42
330	13.46	13.50	13.54	13.58	13.62	13.67	13.71	13.75	13.79	13.83
340	13.88	13.92	13.96	14.00	14.04	14.09	14.13	14.17	14.21	14.25
350	14.29	14.34	14.38	14.42	14.46	14.50	14.55	14.59	14.63	14.67
360	14.71	14.76	14.80	14.84	14.88	14.92	14.97	15.01	15.05	15.09
370	15.13	15.18	15.22	15.26	15.30	15.34	15.39	15.43	15.47	15.51
380	15.55	15.60	15.64	15.68	15.72	15.76	15.81	15.85	15.89	15.93
390	15.98	16.02	16.06	16.10	16.14	16.19	16.23	16.27	16.31	16.36
400	16.40	16.44	16.48	16.52	16.57	16.61	16.65	16.69	16.74	16.78
410	16.82	16.86	16.91	16.95	16.99	17.03	17.07	17.12	17.16	17.20
420	17.24	17.29	17.33	17.37	17.41	17.46	17.50	17.54	17.58	17.62
430	17.67	17.71	17.75	17.79	17.84	17.88	17.92	17.96	18.01	18.05
440	18.09	18.13	18.17	18.22	18.26	18.30	18.34	18.39	18.43	18.47
450	18.51	18.56	18.60	18.64	18.68	18.73	18.77	18.81	18.85	18.90
460	18.94	18.98	19.02	19.07	19.11	19.15	19.19	19.24	19.28	19.32
470	19.36	19.41	19.45	19.49	19.54	19.58	19.62	19.66	19.71	19.75
480	19.79	19.84	19.88	19.92	19.96	20.01	20.05	20.09	20.13	20.18
490	20.22	20.26	20.31	20.35	20.39	20.43	20.48	20.52	20.56	20.60
500	20.65	20.69	20.73	20.77	20.82	20.86	20.90	20.94	20.99	21.03
510	21.07	21.11	21.16	21.20	21.24	21.28	21.32	21.37	21.41	21.45
520	21.50	21.54	21.58	21.63	21.67	21.71	21.75	21.80	21.84	21.88
530	21.92	21.97	22.01	22.05	22.09	22.14	22.18	22.22	22.26	22.31
540	22.35	22.39	22.43	22.48	22.52	22.56	22.61	22.65	22.69	22.73
550	22.78	22.82	22.86	22.90	22.95	22.99	23.03	23.07	23.12	23.16
560	23.20	23.25	23.29	23.33	23.38	23.42	23.46	23.50	23.54	23.59
570	23.63	23.67	23.72	23.76	23.80	23.84	23.89	23.93	23.97	24.01
580	24.06	24.10	24.14	24.18	24.23	24.27	24.31	24.36	24.40	24.44
590	24.49	24.53	24.57	24.61	24.65	24.70	24.74	24.78	24.83	24.87

A.1. CHROMEL vs ALUMEL (*Cont.*)

°C	0	1	2	3	4	5	6	7	8	9
600	24.91	24.95	25.00	25.04	25.08	25.12	25.17	25.21	25.25	25.29
610	25.34	25.38	25.42	25.47	25.51	25.55	25.59	25.64	25.68	25.72
620	25.76	25.81	25.85	25.89	25.93	25.98	26.02	26.06	26.10	26.15
630	26.19	26.23	26.27	26.32	26.36	26.40	26.44	26.48	26.53	26.57
640	26.61	26.65	26.70	26.74	26.78	26.82	26.86	26.91	26.95	26.99
650	27.03	27.07	27.12	27.16	27.20	27.24	27.28	27.33	27.37	27.41
660	27.45	27.49	27.54	27.58	27.62	27.66	27.71	27.75	27.79	27.83
670	27.87	27.92	27.96	28.00	28.04	28.08	28.13	28.17	28.21	28.25
680	28.29	28.34	28.38	28.42	28.46	28.50	28.55	28.59	28.63	28.67
690	28.72	28.76	28.80	28.84	28.88	28.93	28.97	29.01	29.05	29.10
700	29.14	29.18	29.22	29.26	29.30	29.35	29.39	29.43	29.47	29.52
710	29.56	29.60	29.64	29.68	29.72	29.77	29.81	29.85	29.89	29.93
720	29.97	30.02	30.06	30.10	30.14	30.18	30.23	30.27	30.31	30.35
730	30.39	30.44	30.48	30.52	30.56	30.60	30.65	30.69	30.73	30.77
740	30.81	30.85	30.90	30.94	30.98	31.02	31.06	31.10	31.15	31.19
750	31.23	31.27	31.31	31.35	31.40	31.44	31.48	31.52	31.56	31.60
760	31.65	31.69	31.73	31.77	31.81	31.85	31.90	31.94	31.98	32.02
770	32.06	32.10	32.15	32.19	32.23	32.27	32.31	32.35	32.39	32.43
780	32.48	32.52	32.56	32.60	32.64	32.68	32.72	32.76	32.81	32.85
790	32.89	32.93	32.97	33.01	33.05	33.09	33.13	33.18	33.22	33.26
800	33.30	33.34	33.38	33.42	33.46	33.50	33.54	33.59	33.63	33.67
810	33.71	33.75	33.79	33.83	33.87	33.91	33.95	33.99	34.04	34.08
820	34.12	34.16	34.20	34.24	34.28	34.32	34.36	34.40	34.44	34.48
830	34.53	34.57	34.61	34.65	34.69	34.73	34.77	34.81	34.85	34.89
840	34.93	34.97	35.02	35.06	35.10	35.14	35.18	35.22	35.26	35.30
850	35.34	35.38	35.42	35.46	35.50	35.54	35.58	35.63	35.67	35.71
860	35.75	35.79	35.83	35.87	35.91	35.95	35.99	36.03	36.07	36.11
870	36.15	36.19	36.23	36.27	36.31	36.35	36.39	36.43	36.47	36.51
880	36.55	36.59	36.63	36.67	36.72	36.76	36.80	36.84	36.88	36.92
890	36.96	37.00	37.04	37.08	37.12	37.16	37.20	37.24	37.28	37.32
900	37.36	37.40	37.44	37.48	37.52	37.56	37.60	37.64	37.68	37.72
910	37.76	37.80	37.84	37.88	37.92	37.96	38.00	38.04	38.08	38.12
920	38.16	38.20	38.24	38.28	38.32	38.36	38.40	38.44	38.48	38.52
930	38.56	38.60	38.64	38.68	38.72	38.76	38.80	38.84	38.88	38.92
940	38.95	38.99	39.03	39.07	39.11	39.15	39.19	39.23	39.27	39.31
950	39.35	39.39	39.43	39.47	39.51	39.55	39.59	39.63	39.67	39.71
960	39.75	39.79	39.83	39.86	39.90	39.94	39.98	40.02	40.06	40.10
970	40.14	40.18	40.22	40.26	40.30	40.34	40.38	40.41	40.45	40.49
980	40.53	40.57	40.61	40.65	40.69	40.73	40.77	40.81	40.85	40.89
990	40.92	40.96	41.00	41.04	41.08	41.12	41.16	41.20	41.24	41.28
1000	41.31	41.35	41.39	41.43	41.47	41.51	41.55	41.59	41.63	41.67
1010	41.70	41.74	41.78	41.82	41.86	41.90	41.94	41.98	42.02	42.05
1020	42.09	42.13	42.17	42.21	42.25	42.29	42.33	42.36	42.40	42.44
1030	42.48	42.52	42.56	42.60	42.63	42.67	42.71	42.75	42.79	42.83
1040	42.87	42.90	42.94	42.98	43.02	43.06	43.10	43.14	43.17	43.21
1050	43.25	43.29	43.33	43.37	43.41	43.44	43.48	43.52	43.56	43.60
1060	43.63	43.67	43.71	43.75	43.79	43.83	43.87	43.90	43.94	43.98
1070	44.02	44.06	44.10	44.13	44.17	44.21	44.25	44.29	44.33	44.36
1080	44.40	44.44	44.48	44.52	44.55	44.59	44.63	44.67	44.71	44.74
1090	44.78	44.82	44.86	44.90	44.93	44.97	45.01	45.05	45.09	45.12
1100	45.16	45.20	45.24	45.27	45.31	45.35	45.39	45.43	45.46	45.50
1110	45.54	45.58	45.62	45.65	45.69	45.73	45.77	45.80	45.84	45.88
1120	45.92	45.96	45.99	46.03	46.07	46.11	46.14	46.18	46.22	46.26
1130	46.29	46.33	46.37	46.41	46.44	46.48	46.52	46.56	46.59	46.63
1140	46.67	46.70	46.74	46.78	46.82	46.85	46.89	46.93	46.97	47.00
1150	47.04	47.08	47.12	47.15	47.19	47.23	47.26	47.30	47.34	47.38
1160	47.41	47.45	47.49	47.52	47.56	47.60	47.63	47.67	47.71	47.75
1170	47.78	47.82	47.86	47.89	47.93	47.97	48.00	48.04	48.08	48.12
1180	48.15	48.19	48.23	48.26	48.30	48.34	48.37	48.41	48.45	48.48
1190	48.52	48.56	48.59	48.63	48.67	48.70	48.74	48.78	48.81	48.85

A.1. CHROMEL vs ALUMEL (*Cont.*)

•C	0	1	2	3	4	5	6	7	8	9
1200	**48.89**	**48.92**	**48.96**	**49.00**	**49.03**	49.07	49.11	49.14	49.18	49.22
1210	49.25	49.29	49.32	49.36	49.40	49.43	49.47	49.51	49.54	49.58
1220	49.62	49.65	49.69	49.72	49.76	49.80	49.83	49.87	49.90	49.94
1230	49.98	50.01	50.05	50.08	50.12	50.16	50.19	50.23	50.26	50.30
1240	50.34	50.37	50.41	50.44	50.48	50.52	50.55	50.59	50.62	50.66
1250	**50.69**	**50.73**	**50.77**	**50.80**	**50.84**	50.87	50.91	50.94	50.98	51.02
1260	51.05	51.09	51.12	51:16	51.19	51.23	51.27	51.30	51.34	51.37
1270	51.41	51.44	51.48	51.51	51.55	51.58	51.62	51.66	51.69	51.73
1280	51.76	51.80	51.83	51.87	51.90	51.94	51.97	52.01	52.04	52.08
1290	52.11	52.15	52.18	52.22	52.25	52.29	52.32	52.36	52.39	52.43
1300	**52.46**	**52.50**	**52.53**	**52.57**	**52.60**	52.64	52.67	52.71	52.74	52.78
1310	52.81	52.85	52.88	52.92	52.95	52.99	53.02	53.06	53.09	53.13
1320	53.16	53.20	53.23	53.27	53.30	53.34	53.37	53.41	53.44	53.47
1330	53.51	53.54	53.58	53.61	53.65	53.68	53.72	53.75	53.79	53.82
1340	53.85	53.89	53.92	53.96	53.99	54.03	54.06	54.10	54.13	54.16
1350	**54.20**	**54.23**	**54.27**	**54.30**	**54.34**	54.37	54.40	54.44	54.47	54.51
1360	54.54	54.57	54.61	54.64	54.68	54.71	54.74	54.78	54.81	54.85
1370	54.88	54.91								

A.2. Iron vs Constantan

Thermal e.m.f. in millivolts compared to a reference junction at 0.0°C.

°C	0	1	2	3	4	5	6	7	8	9
-190	-7.66	-7.69	-7.71	-7.73	-7.76	-7.78				
-180	-7.40	-7.43	-7.46	-7.49	-7.51	-7.54	-7.56	-7.59	-7.61	-7.64
-170	-7.12	-7.15	-7.18	-7.21	-7.24	-7.27	-7.30	-7.32	-7.35	-7.38
-160	-6.82	-6.85	-6.88	-6.91	-6.94	-6.97	-7.00	-7.03	-7.06	-7.09
-150	-6.50	-6.53	-6.56	-6.60	-6.63	-6.66	-6.69	-6.72	-6.76	-6.79
-140	-6.16	-6.19	-6.22	-6.26	-6.29	-6.33	-6.36	-6.40	-6.43	-6.46
-130	-5.80	-5.84	-5.87	-5.91	-5.94	-5.98	-6.01	-6.05	-6.08	-6.12
-120	-5.42	-5.46	-5.50	-5.54	-5.58	-5.61	-5.65	-5.69	-5.72	-5.76
-110	-5.03	-5.07	-5.11	-5.15	-5.19	-5.23	-5.27	-5.31	-5.35	-5.38
-100	-4.63	-4.67	-4.71	-4.75	-4.79	-4.83	-4.87	-4.91	-4.95	-4.99
-90	-4.21	-4.25	-4.30	-4.34	-4.38	-4.42	-4.46	-4.50	-4.55	-4.59
-80	-3.78	-3.82	-3.87	-3.91	-3.96	-4.00	-4.04	-4.08	-4.13	-4.17
-70	-3.34	-3.38	-3.43	-3.47	-3.52	-3.56	-3.60	-3.65	-3.69	-3.74
-60	-2.89	-2.94	-2.98	-3.03	-3.07	-3.12	-3.16	-3.21	-3.25	-3.30
-50	-2.43	-2.48	-2.52	-2.57	-2.62	-2.66	-2.71	-2.75	-2.80	-2.84
-40	-1.96	-2.01	-2.06	-2.10	-2.15	-2.20	-2.24	-2.29	-2.34	-2.38
-30	-1.48	-1.53	-1.58	-1.63	-1.67	-1.72	-1.77	-1.82	-1.87	-1.91
-20	-1.00	-1.04	-1.09	-1.14	-1.19	-1.24	-1.29	-1.34	-1.39	-1.43
-10	-0.50	-0.55	-0.60	-0.65	-0.70	-0.75	-0.80	-0.85	-0.90	-0.95
(-)0	0.00	-0.05	-0.10	-0.15	-0.20	-0.25	-0.30	-0.35	-0.40	-0.45
(+)0	0.00	0.05	0.10	0.15	0.20	0.25	0.30	0.35	0.40	0.45
10	0.50	0.56	0.61	0.66	0.71	0.76	0.81	0.86	0.91	0.97
20	1.02	1.07	1.12	1.17	1.22	1.28	1.33	1.38	1.43	1.48
30	1.54	1.59	1.64	1.69	1.74	1.80	1.85	1.90	1.95	2.00
40	2.06	2.11	2.16	2.22	2.27	2.32	2.37	2.42	2.48	2.53
50	2.58	2.64	2.69	2.74	2.80	2.85	2.90	2.96	3.01	3.06
60	3.11	3.17	3.22	3.27	3.33	3.38	3.43	3.49	3.54	3.60
70	3.65	3.70	3.76	3.81	3.86	3.92	3.97	4.02	4.08	4.13
80	4.19	4.24	4.29	4.35	4.40	4.46	4.51	4.56	4.62	4.67
90	4.73	4.78	4.83	4.89	4.94	5.00	5.05	5.10	5.16	5.21
100	5.27	5.32	5.38	5.43	5.48	5.54	5.59	5.65	5.70	5.76
110	5.81	5.86	5.92	5.97	6.03	6.08	6.14	6.19	6.25	6.30
120	6.36	6.41	6.47	6.52	6.58	6.63	6.68	6.74	6.79	6.85
130	6.90	6.96	7.01	7.07	7.12	7.18	7.23	7.29	7.34	7.40
140	7.45	7.51	7.56	7.62	7.67	7.73	7.78	7.84	7.89	7.95
150	8.00	8.06	8.12	8.17	8.23	8.28	8.34	8.39	8.45	8.50
160	8.56	8.61	8.67	8.72	8.78	8.84	8.89	8.95	9.00	9.06
170	9.11	9.17	9.22	9.28	9.33	9.39	9.44	9.50	9.56	9.61
180	9.67	9.72	9.78	9.83	9.89	9.95	10.00	10.06	10.11	10.17
190	10.22	10.28	10.34	10.39	10.45	10.50	10.56	10.61	10.67	10.72
200	10.78	10.84	10.89	10.95	11.00	11.06	11.12	11.17	11.23	11.28
210	11.34	11.39	11.45	11.50	11.56	11.62	11.67	11.73	11.78	11.84
220	11.89	11.95	12.00	12.06	12.12	12.17	12.23	12.28	12.34	12.39
230	12.45	12.50	12.56	12.62	12.67	12.73	12.78	12.84	12.89	12.95
240	13.01	13.06	13.12	13.17	13.23	13.28	13.34	13.40	13.45	13.51
250	13.56	13.62	13.67	13.73	13.78	13.84	13.89	13.95	14.00	14.06
260	14.12	14.17	14.23	14.28	14.34	14.39	14.45	14.50	14.56	14.61
270	14.67	14.72	14.78	14.83	14.89	14.94	15.00	15.06	15.11	15.17
280	15.22	15.28	15.33	15.39	15.44	15.50	15.55	15.61	15.66	15.72
290	15.77	15.83	15.88	15.94	16.00	16.05	16.11	16.16	16.22	16.27
300	16.33	16.38	16.44	16.49	16.55	16.60	16.66	16.71	16.77	16.82
310	16.88	16.93	16.99	17.04	17.10	17.15	17.21	17.26	17.32	17.37
320	17.43	17.48	17.54	17.60	17.65	17.71	17.76	17.82	17.87	17.93
330	17.98	18.04	18.09	18.15	18.20	18.26	18.32	18.37	18.43	18.48
340	18.54	18.59	18.65	18.70	18.76	18.81	18.87	18.92	18.98	19.03
350	19.09	19.14	19.20	19.26	19.31	19.37	19.42	19.48	19.53	19.59
360	19.64	19.70	19.75	19.81	19.86	19.92	19.97	20.03	20.08	20.14
370	20.20	20.25	20.31	20.36	20.42	20.47	20.53	20.58	20.64	20.69
380	20.75	20.80	20.86	20.91	20.97	21.02	21.08	21.13	21.19	21.24
390	21.30	21.35	21.41	21.46	21.52	21.57	21.63	21.68	21.74	21.79

A.2. IRON VS CONSTANTAN (*Cont.*)

°C	0	1	2	3	4	5	6	7	8	9
400	21.85	21.90	21.96	22.02	22.07	22.13	22.18	22.24	22.29	22.35
410	22.40	22.46	22.51	22.57	22.62	22.68	22.73	22.79	22.84	22.90
420	22.95	23.01	23.06	23.12	23.17	23.23	23.28	23.34	23.39	23.45
430	23.50	23.56	23.61	23.67	23.72	23.78	23.83	23.89	23.94	24.00
440	24.06	24.11	24.17	24.22	24.28	24.33	24.39	24.44	24.50	24.55
450	24.61	24.66	24.72	24.77	24.83	24.88	24.94	25.00	25.05	25.11
460	25.16	25.22	25.27	25.33	25.38	25.44	25.49	25.55	25.60	25.66
470	25.72	25.77	25.83	25.88	25.94	25.99	26.05	26.10	26.16	26.22
480	26.27	26.33	26.38	26.44	26.49	26.55	26.61	26.66	26.72	26.77
490	26.83	26.89	26.94	27.00	27.05	27.11	27.17	27.22	27.28	27.33
500	27.39	27.45	27.50	27.56	27.61	27.67	27.73	27.78	27.84	27.90
510	27.95	28.01	28.07	28.12	28.18	28.23	28.29	28.35	28.40	28.46
520	28.52	28.57	28.63	28.69	28.74	28.80	28.86	28.91	28.97	29.02
530	29.08	29.14	29.20	29.25	29.31	29.37	29.42	29.48	29.54	29.59
540	29.65	29.71	29.76	29.82	29.88	29.94	29.99	30.05	30.11	30.16
550	30.22	30.28	30.34	30.39	30.45	30.51	30.57	30.62	30.68	30.74
560	30.80	30.85	30.91	30.97	31.02	31.08	31.14	31.20	31.26	31.31
570	31.37	31.43	31.49	31.54	31.60	31.66	31.72	31.78	31.83	31.89
580	31.95	32.01	32.06	32.12	32.18	32.24	32.30	32.36	32.41	32.47
590	32.53	32.59	32.65	32.71	32.76	32.82	32.88	32.94	33.00	33.06
600	33.11	33.17	33.23	33.29	33.35	33.41	33.46	33.52	33.58	33.64
610	33.70	33.76	33.82	33.88	33.94	33.99	34.05	34.11	34.17	34.23
620	34.29	34.35	34.41	34.47	34.53	34.58	34.64	34.70	34.76	34.82
630	34.88	34.94	35.00	35.06	35.12	35.18	35.24	35.30	35.36	35.42
640	35.48	35.54	35.60	35.66	35.72	35.78	35.84	35.90	35.96	36.02
650	36.08	36.14	36.20	36.26	36.32	36.38	36.44	36.50	36.56	36.62
660	36.69	36.75	36.81	36.87	36.93	36.99	37.05	37.11	37.18	37.24
670	37.30	37.36	37.42	37.48	37.54	37.60	37.66	37.73	37.79	37.85
680	37.91	37.97	38.04	38.10	38.16	38.22	38.28	38.34	38.41	38.47
690	38.53	38.59	38.66	38.72	38.78	38.84	38.90	38.97	39.03	39.09
700	39.15	39.22	39.28	39.34	39.40	39.47	39.53	39.59	39.65	39.72
710	39.78	39.84	39.91	39.97	40.03	40.10	40.16	40.22	40.28	40.35
720	40.41	40.48	40.54	40.60	40.66	40.73	40.79	40.86	40.92	40.98
730	41.05	41.11	41.17	41.24	41.30	41.36	41.43	41.49	41.56	41.62
740	41.68	41.75	41.81	41.87	41.94	42.00	42.07	42.13	42.19	42.26
750	42.32	42.38	42.45	42.51	42.58	42.64	42.70	42.77	42.83	42.90
760	42.96	43.02	43.09	43.15	43.22	43.28	43.35	43.41	43.48	43.54
770	43.60	43.67	43.73	43.80	43.86	43.92	43.99	44.05	44.12	44.18
780	44.25	44.31	44.38	44.44	44.50	44.57	44.63	44.70	44.76	44.82
790	44.89	44.95	45.02	45.08	45.15	45.21	45.28	45.34	45.40	45.47
800	45.53	45.60	45.66	45.72	45.79	45.85	45.92	45.98	46.05	46.11
810	46.18	46.24	46.30	46.37	46.43	46.50	46.56	46.62	46.69	46.75
820	46.82	46.88	46.94	47.01	47.07	47.14	47.20	47.27	47.33	47.39
830	47.46	47.52	47.58	47.65	47.71	47.78	47.84	47.90	47.97	48.03
840	48.09	48.16	48.22	48.28	48.35	48.41	48.48	48.54	48.60	48.66
850	48.73	48.79	48.85	48.92	48.98	49.04	49.10	49.17	49.23	49.29
860	49.36	49.42	49.48	49.54	49.61	49.67	49.73	49.79	49.86	49.92
870	49.98	50.04								

A.3. PLATINUM VS PLATINUM–10% RHODIUM

Thermal e.m.f. in millivolts compared to a reference junction at 0.0°C.

°C	0	1	2	3	4	5	6	7	8	9
0	0.000	0.005	0.011	0.016	0.022	0.028	0.033	0.039	0.044	0.050
10	.056	.061	.067	.073	.078	.084	.090	.096	.102	.107
20	.113	.119	.125	.131	.137	.143	.149	.155	.161	.167
30	.173	.179	.185	.191	.198	.204	.210	.216	.222	.229
40	.235	.241	.247	.254	.260	.266	.273	.279	.286	.292
50	.299	.305	.312	.318	.325	.331	.338	.344	.351	.357
60	.364	.371	.377	.384	.391	.397	.404	.411	.418	.425
70	.431	.438	.445	.452	.459	.466	.473	.479	.486	.493
80	.500	.507	.514	.521	.528	.535	.543	.550	.557	.564
90	.571	.578	.585	.593	.600	.607	.614	.621	.629	.636
100	.643	.651	.658	.665	.673	680	.687	.694	.702	.709
110	.717	.724	.732	.739	.747	.754	.762	.769	.777	.784
120	.792	.800	.807	.815	.823	.830	.838	.845	.853	.861
130	.869	.876	.884	.892	.900	.907	.915	.923	.931	.939
140	.946	.954	.962	.970	.978	.986	.994	1.002	1.009	1.017
150	1.025	1.033	1.041	1.049	1.057	1.065	1.073	1.081	1.089	1.097
160	1.106	1.114	1.122	1.130	1.138	1.146	1.154	1.162	1.170	1.179
170	1.187	1.195	1.203	1.211	1.220	1.228	1.236	1.244	1.253	1.261
180	1.269	1.277	1.286	1.294	1.302	1.311	1.319	1.327	1.336	1.344
190	1.352	1.361	1.369	1.377	1.386	1.394	1.403	1.411	1.419	1.428
200	1.436	1.445	1.453	1.462	1.470	1.479	1.487	1.496	1.504	1.513
210	1.521	1.530	1.538	1.547	1.555	1.564	1.573	1.581	1.590	1.598
220	1.607	1.615	1.624	1.633	1.641	1.650	1.659	1.667	1.676	1.685
230	1.693	1.702	1.710	1.719	1.728	1.736	1.745	1.754	1.763	1.771
240	1.780	1.789	1.798	1.806	1.815	1.824	1.833	1.841	1.850	1.859
250	1.868	1.877	1.885	1.894	1.903	1.912	1.921	1.930	1.938	1.947
260	1.956	1.965	1.974	1.983	1.992	2.001	2.009	2.018	2.027	2.036
270	2.045	2.054	2.063	2.072	2.081	2.090	2.099	2.108	2.117	2.126
280	2.135	2.144	2.153	2.162	2.171	2.180	2.189	2.198	2.207	2.216
290	2.225	2.234	2.243	2.252	2.261	2.271	2.280	2.289	2.298	2.307
300	2.316	2.325	2.334	2.343	2.353	2.362	2.371	2.380	2.389	2.398
310	2.408	2.417	2.426	2.435	2.444	2.453	2.463	2.472	2.481	2.490
320	2.499	2.509	2.518	2.527	2.536	2.546	2.555	2.564	2.573	2.583
330	2.592	2.601	2.610	2.620	2.629	2.638	2.648	2.657	2.666	2.676
340	2.685	2.694	2.704	2.713	2.722	2.731	2.741	2.750	2.760	2.769
350	2.778	2.788	2.797	2.806	2.816	2.825	2.834	2.844	2.853	2.863
360	2.872	2.881	2.891	2.900	2.910	2.919	2.929	2.938	2.947	2.957
370	2.966	2.976	2.985	2.995	3.004	3.014	3.023	3.032	3.042	3.051
380	3.061	3.070	3.080	3.089	3.099	3.108	3.118	3.127	3.137	3.146
390	3.156	3.165	3.175	3.184	3.194	3.203	3.213	3.222	3.232	3.241
400	3.251	3.261	3.270	3.280	3.289	3.299	3.308	3.318	3.327	3.337
410	3.347	3.356	3.366	3.375	3.385	3.394	3.404	3.414	3.423	3.433
420	3.442	3.452	3.462	3.471	3.481	3.490	3.500	3.510	3.519	3.529
430	3.539	3.548	3.558	3.567	3.577	3.587	3.596	3.606	3.616	3.625
440	3.635	3.645	3.654	3.664	3.674	3.683	3.693	3.703	3.712	3.722
450	3.732	3.741	3.751	3.761	3.771	3.780	3.790	3.800	3.809	3.819
460	3.829	3.839	3.848	3.858	3.868	3.878	3.887	3.897	3.907	3.917
470	3.926	3.936	3.946	3.956	3.965	3.975	3.985	3.995	4.004	4.014
480	4.024	4.034	4.044	4.053	4.063	4.073	4.083	4.093	4.103	4.112
490	4.122	4.132	4.142	4.152	4.162	4.171	4.181	4.191	4.201	4.211
500	4.221	4.230	4.240	4.250	4.260	4.270	4.280	4.290	4.300	4.310
510	4.319	4.329	4.339	4.349	4.359	4.369	4.379	4.389	4.399	4.409
520	4.419	4.428	4.438	4.448	4.458	4.468	4.478	4.488	4.498	4.508
530	4.518	4.528	4.538	4.548	4.558	4.568	4.578	4.588	4.598	4.608
540	4.618	4.628	4.638	4.648	4.658	4.668	4.678	4.688	4.698	4.708
550	4.718	4.728	4.738	4.748	4.758	4.768	4.778	4.788	4.798	4.808
560	4.818	4.828	4.839	4.849	4.859	4.869	4.879	4.889	4.899	4.909
570	4.919	4.929	4.939	4.950	4.960	4.970	4.980	4.990	5.000	5.010
580	5.020	5.031	5.041	5.051	5.061	5.071	5.081	5.091	5.102	5.112
590	5.122	5.132	5.142	5.152	5.163	5.173	5.183	5.193	5.203	5.214

A.3. Platinum vs Platinum—10% Rhodium (*Cont.*)

°C	0	1	2	3	4	5	6	7	8	9
600	5.224	5.234	5.244	5.254	5.265	5.275	5.285	5.295	5.306	5.316
610	5.326	5.336	5.346	5.357	5.367	5.377	5.388	5.398	5.408	5.418
620	5.429	5.439	5.449	5.459	5.470	5.480	5.490	5.501	5.511	5.521
630	5.532	5.542	5.552	5.563	5.573	5.583	5.593	5.604	5.614	5.624
640	5.635	5.645	5.655	5.666	5.676	5.686	5.697	5.707	5.717	5.728
650	5.738	5.748	5.759	5.769	5.779	5.790	5.800	5.811	5.821	5.831
660	5.842	5.852	5.862	5.873	5.883	5.894	5.904	5.914	5.925	5.935
670	5.946	5.956	5.967	5.977	5.987	5.998	6.008	6.019	6.029	6.040
680	6.050	6.060	6.071	6.081	6.092	6.102	6.113	6.123	6.134	6.144
690	6.155	6.165	6.176	6.186	6.197	6.207	6.218	6.228	6.239	6.249
700	6.260	6.270	6.281	6.291	6.302	6.312	6.323	6.333	6.344	6.355
710	6.365	6.376	6.386	6.397	6.407	6.418	6.429	6.439	6.450	6.460
720	6.471	6.481	6.492	6.503	6.513	6.524	6.534	6.545	6.556	6.566
730	6.577	6.588	6.598	6.609	6.619	6.630	6.641	6.651	6.662	6.673
740	6.683	6.694	6.705	6.715	6.726	6.737	6.747	6.758	6.769	6.779
750	6.790	6.801	6.811	6.822	6.833	6.844	6.854	6.865	6.876	6.886
760	6.897	6.908	6.919	6.929	6.940	6.951	6.962	6.972	6.983	6.994
770	7.005	7.015	7.026	7.037	7.047	7.058	7.069	7.080	7.091	7.102
780	7.112	7.123	7.134	7.145	7.156	7.166	7.177	7.188	7.199	7.210
790	7.220	7.231	7.242	7.253	7.264	7.275	7.286	7.296	7.307	7.318
800	7.329	7.340	7.351	7.362	7.372	7.383	7.394	7.405	7.416	7.427
810	7.438	7.449	7.460	7.470	7.481	7.492	7.503	7.514	7.525	7.536
820	7.547	7.558	7.569	7.580	7.591	7.602	7.613	7.623	7.634	7.645
830	7.656	7.667	7.678	7.689	7.700	7.711	7.722	7.733	7.744	7.755
840	7.766	7.777	7.788	7.799	7.810	7.821	7.832	7.843	7.854	7.865
850	7.876	7.887	7.898	7.910	7.921	7.932	7.943	7.954	7.965	7.976
860	7.987	7.998	8.009	8.020	8.031	8.042	8.053	8.064	8.076	8.087
870	8.098	8.109	8.120	8.131	8.142	8.153	8.164	8.176	8.187	8.198
880	8.209	8.220	8.231	8.242	8.254	8.265	8.276	8.287	8.298	8.309
890	8.320	8.332	8.343	8.354	8.365	8.376	8.388	8.399	8.410	8.421
900	8.432	8.444	8.455	8.466	8.477	8.488	8.500	8.511	8.522	8.533
910	8.545	8.556	8.567	8.578	8.590	8.601	8.612	8.623	8.635	8.646
920	8.657	8.668	8.680	8.691	8.702	8.714	8.725	8.736	8.747	8.759
930	8.770	8.781	8.793	8.804	8.815	8.827	8.838	8.849	8.861	8.872
940	8.883	8.895	8.906	8.917	8.929	8.940	8.951	8.963	8.974	8.986
950	8.997	9.008	9.020	9.031	9.042	9.054	9.065	9.077	9.088	9.099
960	9.111	9.122	9.134	9.145	9.157	9.168	9.179	9.191	9.202	9.214
970	9.225	9.236	9.248	9.260	9.271	9.282	9.294	9.305	9.317	9.328
980	9.340	9.351	9.363	9.374	9.386	9.397	9.409	9.420	9.432	9.443
990	9.455	9.466	9.478	9.489	9.501	9.512	9.524	9.535	9.547	9.559
1000	9.570	9.582	9.593	9.605	9.616	9.628	9.639	9.651	9.663	9.674
1010	9.686	9.697	9.709	9.720	9.732	9.744	9.755	9.767	9.779	9.790
1020	9.802	9.813	9.825	9.837	9.848	9.860	9.871	9.883	9.895	9.906
1030	9.918	9.930	9.941	9.953	9.965	9.976	9.988	10.000	10.011	10.023
1040	10.035	10.046	10.058	10.070	10.082	10.093	10.105	10.117	10.128	10.140
1050	10.152	10.163	10.175	10.187	10.199	10.210	10.222	10.234	10.246	10.257
1060	10.269	10.281	10.293	10.304	10.316	10.328	10.340	10.351	10.363	10.375
1070	10.387	10.399	10.410	10.422	10.434	10.446	10.458	10.469	10.481	10.493
1080	10.505	10.517	10.528	10.540	10.552	10.564	10.576	10.587	10.599	10.611
1090	10.623	10.635	10.647	10.658	10.670	10.682	10.694	10.706	10.718	10.729
1100	10.741	10.753	10.765	10.777	10.789	10.801	10.812	10.824	10.836	10.848
1110	10.860	10.872	10.884	10.896	10.907	10.919	10.931	10.943	10.955	10.967
1120	10.979	10.991	11.003	11.014	11.026	11.038	11.050	11.062	11.074	11.086
1130	11.098	11.110	11.122	11.133	11.145	11.157	11.169	11.181	11.193	11.205
1140	11.217	11.229	11.241	11.253	11.265	11.277	11.289	11.300	11.312	11.324
1150	11.336	11.348	11.360	11.372	11.384	11.396	11.408	11.420	11.432	11.444
1160	11.456	11.468	11.480	11.492	11.504	11.516	11.528	11.540	11.552	11.564
1170	11.575	11.587	11.599	11.611	11.623	11.635	11.647	11.659	11.671	11.683
1180	11.695	11.707	11.719	11.731	11.743	11.755	11.767	11.779	11.791	11.803
1190	11.815	11.827	11.839	11.851	11.863	11.875	11.887	11.899	11.911	11.923

A.3. PLATINUM VS PLATINUM—10% RHODIUM (*Cont.*)

°C	0	1	2	3	4	5	6	7	8	9
1200	11.935	11.947	11.959	11.971	11.983	11.995	12.007	12.019	12.031	12.043
1210	12.055	12.067	12.079	12.091	12.103	12.115	12.127	12.139	12.151	12.163
1220	12.175	12.187	12.200	12.212	12.224	12.236	12.248	12.260	12.272	12.284
1230	12.296	12.308	12.320	12.332	12.344	12.356	12.368	12.380	12.392	12.404
1240	12.416	12.428	12.440	12.452	12.464	12.476	12.488	12.500	12.512	12.524
1250	12.536	12.548	12.560	12.573	12.585	12.597	12.609	12.621	12.633	12.645
1260	12.657	12.669	12.681	12.693	12.705	12.717	12.729	12.741	12.753	12.765
1270	12.777	12.789	12.801	12.813	12.825	12.837	12.849	12.861	12.873	12.885
1280	12.897	12.909	12.921	12.933	12.945	12.957	12.969	12.981	12.993	13.005
1290	13.018	13.030	13.042	13.054	13.066	13.078	13.090	13.102	13.114	13.126
1300	13.138	13.150	13.162	13.174	13.186	13.198	13.210	13.222	13.234	13.246
1310	13.258	13.270	13.282	13.294	13.306	13.318	13.330	13.342	13.354	13.366
1320	13.378	13.390	13.402	13.414	13.426	13.438	13.450	13.462	13.474	13.486
1330	13.498	13.510	13.522	13.534	13.546	13.558	13.570	13.582	13.594	13.606
1340	13.618	13.630	13.642	13.654	13.666	13.678	13.690	13.702	13.714	13.726
1350	13.738	13.750	13.762	13.774	13.786	13.798	13.810	13.822	13.834	13.846
1360	13.858	13.870	13.882	13.894	13.906	13.918	13.930	13.942	13.954	13.966
1370	13.978	13.990	14.002	14.014	14.026	14.038	14.050	14.062	14.074	14.086
1380	14.098	14.110	14.122	14.133	14.145	14.157	14.169	14.181	14.193	14.205
1390	14.217	14.229	14.241	14.253	14.265	14.277	14.289	14.301	14.313	14.325
1400	14.337	14.349	14.361	14.373	14.385	14.397	14.409	14.421	14.433	14.445
1410	14.457	14.469	14.481	14.493	14.504	14.516	14.528	14.540	14.552	14.564
1420	14.576	14.588	14.600	14.612	14.624	14.636	14.648	14.660	14.672	14.684
1430	14.696	14.708	14.720	14.732	14.744	14.755	14.767	14.779	14.791	14.803
1440	14.815	14.827	14.839	14.851	14.863	14.875	14.887	14.899	14.911	14.923
1450	14.935	14.946	14.958	14.970	14.982	14.994	15.006	15.018	15.030	15.042
1460	15.054	15.066	15.078	15.090	15.102	15.113	15.125	15.137	15.149	15.161
1470	15.173	15.185	15.197	15.209	15.221	15.233	15.245	15.256	15.268	15.280
1480	15.292	15.304	15.316	15.328	15.340	15.352	15.364	15.376	15.387	15.399
1490	15.411	15.423	15.435	15.447	15.459	15.471	15.483	15.495	15.507	15.518
1500	15.530	15.542	15.554	15.566	15.578	15.590	15.602	15.614	15.625	15.637
1510	15.649	15.661	15.673	15.685	15.697	15.709	15.721	15.732	15.744	15.756
1520	15.768	15.780	15.792	15.804	15.816	15.827	15.839	15.851	15.863	15.875
1530	15.887	15.899	15.911	15.922	15.934	15.946	15.958	15.970	15.982	15.994
1540	16.006	16.017	16.029	16.041	16.053	16.065	16.077	16.089	16.100	16.112
1550	16.124	16.136	16.148	16.160	16.171	16.183	16.195	16.207	16.219	16.231
1560	16.243	16.254	16.266	16.278	16.290	16.302	16.314	16.325	16.337	16.349
1570	16.361	16.373	16.385	16.396	16.408	16.420	16.432	16.444	16.456	16.467
1580	16.479	16.491	16.503	16.515	16.527	16.538	16.550	16.562	16.574	16.586
1590	16.597	16.609	16.621	16.633	16.645	16.657	16.668	16.680	16.692	16.704
1600	16.716	16.727	16.739	16.751	16.763	16.775	16.786	16.798	16.810	16.822
1610	16.834	16.845	16.857	16.869	16.881	16.893	16.904	16.916	16.928	16.940
1620	16.952	16.963	16.975	16.987	16.999	17.010	17.022	17.034	17.046	17.058
1630	17.069	17.081	17.093	17.105	17.116	17.128	17.140	17.152	17.163	17.175
1640	17.187	17.199	17.211	17.222	17.234	17.246	17.258	17.269	17.281	17.293
1650	17.305	17.316	17.328	17.340	17.352	17.363	17.375	17.387	17.398	17.410
1660	17.422	17.434	17.446	17.457	17.469	17.481	17.492	17.504	17.516	17.528
1670	17.539	17.551	17.563	17.575	17.586	17.598	17.610	17.621	17.633	17.645
1680	17.657	17.668	17.680	17.692	17.704	17.715	17.727	17.739	17.750	17.762
1690	17.774	17.785	17.797	17.809	17.821	17.832	17.844	17.856	17.867	17.879
1700	17.891	17.902	17.914	17.926	17.938	17.949	17.961	17.973	17.984	17.996
1710	18.008	18.019	18.031	18.043	18.054	18.066	18.078	18.089	18.101	18.113
1720	18.124	18.136	18.148	18.159	18.171	18.183	18.194	18.206	18.218	18.229
1730	18.241	18.253	18.264	18.276	18.288	18.299	18.311	18.323	18.334	18.346
1740	18.358	18.369	18.381	18.393	18.404	18.416	18.427	18.439	18.451	18.462
1750	18.474	18.486	18.497	18.509	18.520	18.532	18.544	18.555	18.567	18.579
1760	18.590	18.602	18.613	18.625	18.637	18.648	18.660	18.672	18.683	18.695

A.4. COPPER VS CONSTANTAN

Thermal e.m.f. in millivolts compared to a reference junction at 0.0°C.

°C	0	1	2	3	4	5	6	7	8	9
-190	-5.379	-5.395	-5.411	....	....	....	....	....	....	....
-180	-5.205	-5.223	-5.241	-5.258	-5.276	-5.294	-5.311	-5.328	-5.345	-5.362
-170	-5.018	-5.037	-5.056	-5.075	-5.094	-5.113	-5.132	-5.150	-5.169	-5.187
-160	-4.817	-4.838	-4.858	-4.878	-4.899	-4.919	-4.939	-4.959	-4.978	-4.998
-150	-4.603	-4.625	-4.647	-4.669	-4.690	-4.712	-4.733	-4.754	-4.775	-4.796
-140	-4.377	-4.400	-4.423	-4.446	-4.469	-4.492	-4.514	-4.537	-4.559	-4.581
-130	-4.138	-4.162	-4.187	-4.211	-4.235	-4.259	-4.283	-4.307	-4.330	-4.354
-120	-3.887	-3.912	-3.938	-3.964	-3.989	-4.014	-4.039	-4.064	-4.089	-4.114
-110	-3.624	-3.651	-3.678	-3.704	-3.730	-3.757	-3.783	-3.809	-3.835	-3.861
-100	-3.349	-3.377	-3.405	-3.432	-3.460	-3.488	-3.515	-3.542	-3.570	-3.597
-90	-3.062	-3.091	-3.120	-3.149	-3.178	-3.207	-3.235	-3.264	-3.292	-3.320
-80	-2.764	-2.794	-2.824	-2.854	-2.884	-2.914	-2.944	-2.974	-3.003	-3.033
-70	-2.455	-2.486	-2.518	-2.549	-2.580	-2.611	-2.642	-2.672	-2.703	-2.733
-60	-2.135	-2.167	-2.200	-2.232	-2.264	-2.296	-2.328	-2.360	-2.392	-2.423
-50	-1.804	-1.838	-1.871	-1.905	-1.938	-1.971	-2.004	-2.037	-2.070	-2.103
-40	-1.463	-1.498	-1.532	-1.567	-1.601	-1.635	-1.669	-1.703	-1.737	-1.771
-30	-1.112	-1.148	-1.183	-1.218	-1.254	-1.289	-1.324	-1.359	-1.394	-1.429
-20	-0.751	-0.788	-0.824	-0.860	-0.897	-0.933	-0.969	-1.005	-1.041	-1.076
-10	-0.380	-0.417	-0.455	-0.492	-0.530	-0.567	-0.604	-0.641	-0.678	-0.714
(-)0	0.000	-0.038	-0.077	-0.115	-0.153	-0.191	-0.229	-0.267	-0.305	-0.343
(+)0	0.000	0.038	0.077	0.116	0.154	0.193	0.232	0.271	0.311	0.350
10	0.389	0.429	0.468	0.508	0.547	0.587	0.627	0.667	0.707	0.747
20	0.787	0.827	0.868	0.908	0.949	0.990	1.030	1.071	1.112	1.153
30	1.194	1.235	1.277	1.318	1.360	1.401	1.443	1.485	1.526	1.568
40	1.610	1.652	1.694	1.737	1.779	1.821	1.864	1.907	1.949	1.992
50	2.035	2.078	2.121	2.164	2.207	2.250	2.293	2.336	2.380	2.423
60	2.467	2.511	2.555	2.599	2.643	2.687	2.731	2.775	2.820	2.864
70	2.908	2.953	2.997	3.042	3.087	3.132	3.177	3.222	3.267	3.312
80	3.357	3.402	3.448	3.493	3.539	3.584	3.630	3.676	3.722	3.767
90	3.813	3.859	3.906	3.952	3.998	4.044	4.091	4.138	4.184	4.230
100	4.277	4.324	4.371	4.418	4.465	4.512	4.559	4.606	4.654	4.701
110	4.749	4.796	4.843	4.891	4.939	4.987	5.035	5.083	5.131	5.179
120	5.227	5.275	5.323	5.372	5.420	5.469	5.518	5.566	5.615	5.663
130	5.712	5.761	5.810	5.859	5.908	5.957	6.007	6.056	6.105	6.155
140	6.204	6.254	6.303	6.353	6.403	6.453	6.503	6.553	6.603	6.653
150	6.703	6.753	6.803	6.853	6.904	6.954	7.004	7.055	7.106	7.157
160	7.208	7.258	7.309	7.360	7.411	7.462	7.513	7.565	7.616	7.667
170	7.719	7.770	7.822	7.874	7.926	7.978	8.029	8.080	8.132	8.184
180	8.236	8.288	8.340	8.392	8.445	8.497	8.549	8.601	8.654	8.707
190	8.759	8.812	8.864	8.917	8.970	9.023	9.076	9.129	9.182	9.235
200	9.288	9.341	9.394	9.448	9.501	9.555	9.608	9.662	9.715	9.769
210	9.823	9.877	9.931	9.985	10.039	10.093	10.147	10.201	10.255	10.309
220	10.363	10.417	10.471	10.526	10.580	10.635	10.689	10.744	10.799	10.854
230	10.909	10.963	11.018	11.073	11.128	11.183	11.238	11.293	11.348	11.403
240	11.459	11.514	11.569	11.624	11.680	11.735	11.791	11.847	11.903	11.959
250	12.015	12.071	12.126	12.182	12.238	12.294	12.350	12.406	12.462	12.518
260	12.575	12.631	12.688	12.744	12.800	12.857	12.913	12.970	13.027	13.083
270	13.140	13.197	13.254	13.311	13.368	13.425	13.482	13.539	13.596	13.653
280	13.710	13.768	13.825	13.882	13.939	13.997	14.055	14.112	14.170	14.227
290	14.285	14.343	14.400	14.458	14.515	14.573	14.631	14.689	14.747	14.805
300	14.864	14.922	14.980	15.038	15.096	15.155	15.213	15.271	15.330	15.388
310	15.447	15.506	15.564	15.623	15.681	15.740	15.799	15.858	15.917	15.976
320	16.035	16.094	16.153	16.212	16.271	16.330	16.389	16.449	16.508	16.567
330	16.626	16.685	16.745	16.804	16.864	16.924	16.983	17.043	17.102	17.162
340	17.222	17.281	17.341	17.401	17.461	17.521	17.581	17.641	17.701	17.761
350	17.821	17.881	17.941	18.002	18.062	18.123	18.183	18.243	18.304	18.364
360	18.425	18.485	18.546	18.607	18.667	18.727	18.788	18.849	18.910	18.971
370	19.032	19.093	19.154	19.215	19.276	19.337	19.398	19.459	19.520	19.581
380	19.642	19.704	19.765	19.827	19.888	19.949	20.011	20.072	20.134	20.195
390	20.257	20.318	20.380	20.442	20.504	20.565	20.627	20.688	20.750	20.812

B. Heat Effects

As an aid in calibration, the materials listed may be used. The enthalpy values used were selected from Rossini (R31a), Kelley (K14a), handbook (L1a) and a tabulation already prepared by Bohon (B61). No decompositions have been included because the heat of reaction will be significantly dependent on the conditions of the experiment. Values at intervals along the temperature scale have been included because the observed thermal effect from a given quantity of heat varies with temperature. Some materials with large heat effects and some with small have been included.

Temperature	Material	Melting or inversion	Enthalpy change (cal./gm.)
64	Stearic acid	m	47.6
32.1	Ammonium nitrate	i	4.75
125.2	Ammonium nitrate	i	12.6
169.6	Ammonium nitrate	m	16.2
121.8	Benzoic acid	m	33.9
239	Potassium bifluoride	m	20.2
254	Lithium nitrate	m	88.4
273	Sodium nitrate	i	9.5
306.0	Sodium nitrate	m	41.1
327.4	Lead	m	5.89
412	Silver sulfate	i	6.1
440	Sodium molybdate	i	70.9
455	Silver chloride	m	22.0
583	Potassium sulfate	i	12.3
650	Manganous chloride	m	71.3
800	Sodium chloride	m	117
961	Silver	m	25.0
1069	Potassium sulfate	m	52.6

APPENDIX III

To assist the purchaser of an apparatus or accessories for thermogravimetric or differential thermal analysis the questions below are provided.
While there are no "book answers," the answers may still be found in the
book, i.e., for many questions there will be no general answer but the
discussion herein may suggest the best answer for the particular problem.
It is likely that no apparatus will answer the needs perfectly. At this point
a decision must be made as to whether to accept the closest approach or
to assemble an apparatus. This will probably be resolved by just one or
two of the questions that are of particular importance for the particular
problem.

The purchaser of thermogravimetric apparatus should also take note
of many of the questions suggested for differential thermal analysis, particularly if he is giving any thought to relating the data.

Differential Thermal Analysis

(a) Furnace Assembly
1. What range of sample sizes can be used?
2. Can dynamic atmospheres be used and effluent gases detected?
3. Can static controlled atmospheres be used?
4. What pressure ranges can be used?
5. Can dynamic water vapor be used?
6. Can sample holders be interchanged to accommodate different
   types of samples?
7. Is low-temperature operation possible?
8. Do phase transitions and melting of inorganic materials occur
   at the same temperatures at different heating rates?

9. Is the recorded temperature that of the sample, reference, block or other point? Can the point be chosen?

(b) Programming System

1. Is there a temperature vs. time record, either with ΔT or as part of the programmer?
2. Can the programmer reproduce the same curve on a reversible phase change for several cycles?
3. Can the programmer be made to reverse and repeat (cycle)?
4. Will the programmer and power supply drive furnaces of different wattages without extensive readjustment?

(c) Recording System

1. Can the recorder and amplifier produce (as a minimum requirement) a deflection to the edge of the chart with a ΔT of not more than 2°C without appreciable noise?
2. Can the recorder produce a record of ΔT of convenient length for examination over the chosen temperature range?
3. Can the recorder, without major adjustment, record ΔT vs. time to permit quantitative measurements?

Thermogravimetric Apparatus

1. Is the sample supported above or below the measuring system?
2. What provisions exist to prevent heating of the measuring system?
3. If the measuring system is a beam balance, would any inadvertent heating be symmetric?
4. Is there a way to compensate for buoyancy changes?
5. Can controlled atmospheres be used?
6. Can subambient and supraambient pressures be used?
7. Can corrosive atmospheres be used without damage to the measuring system?
8. Where is the temperature measured?
9. Will the furnace and sample holder design permit nearly uniform heating of the sample?

Author Index

Numbers in parentheses are reference citations and mean that an author's work is referred to although his name is not cited in the text. Numbers in italic show the page on which the complete reference is listed.

583

Subject Index

A

ABL-2056, 292
Absorption spectrometer, 449
Activation energy, 199, 205, 217
  by distortion of the lattice, 406
  calculated from rate of the reaction, 220
  lowered by providing another reaction mechanism, 406
Activation energies, physical significance, 217–220
Adjustable limit switch, 516
Agreement of data, 354
Alkaline earth oxides, 408–409
Alumina, thermal conductivity, 68
γ-alumina, 38
Ammeter, 519
Ammonium chloride, 174
Ammonium nitrate, 42, 43, 45
Ammonium perchlorate, 223–225, 242–244, 437, 438
Amplification, 115–7
Amplification, adjustable, fixed steps, 117
  electronic, 117
  optical, 116, 118
  thermopile, 115
Amplifiers, stabilized electronic, 117

Ankle bone, thermogram, 412
Apparatus design, 508–521
Apparatus for simultaneous determinations, 352
Apparent weight gain, 312
Array of hot and cold zones, 317
Arrhenius law, 157
Asymptotic reaction temperature, 91, 94
Atactic polypropylene, 194
Atmosphere, dynamic, 46
  influence of, 223
  nonaffecting, 149
  variation of, 169
Automatic balance, 456
Automatic recording vacuum microbalance, 329
Autotransformer, adjustable, 478–481, 511, 514
  motor-driven, 126

B

Balance, automatic lockup, 532, 533
  automatic recording, 324
  beam, 323
  corrosive gases, 322
  degassing, 321
  displacement measurement, 324, 333–4